PRINCIPLES OF STRATIGRAPHY

BY AMADEUS W. GRABAU

VOLUME TWO

DOVER PUBLICATIONS, INC.
NEW YORK   NEW YORK

Manufactured in the United States of America

Dover Publications, Inc.
180 Varick Street
New York 14, N. Y.

PRINCIPLES OF
STRATIGRAPHY

CHAPTER XIV.

ORIGINAL STRUCTURE AND LITHOGENESIS OF THE CONTINENTAL HYDROCLASTICS.

A very large, perhaps the largest, portion of the stratified clastics of the earth's crust consists of water-laid deposits, or hydroclastics. By this is not meant that they were deposited in standing water, though this is true of a large portion of them, but that water was influential in the making of the deposit. They therefore include river-laid clastics as well as those formed in the sea or in lakes.

Hydroclastic rocks may be divided into the following groups:

1. Stream or river-laid clastics (potamoclastics).
2. Lake or lacustrine clastics (limnoclastics).
3. The Delta—a transitional deposit.
4. Marine clastics (haloclastics).

Each of these will admit of a number of subdivisions. The potamoclastics and limnoclastics, together with the atmoclastics, anemoclastics, pyroclastics, and autoclastics belong to the continental or terrestrial type of clastics, as opposed to the marine or haloclastics. Seacoast deltas form the transition from the one to the other. The continental hydroclastics, together with the delta deposits, will be considered in this chapter; the marine hydroclastics being reserved for the next.

RIVER-LAID CLASTICS, OR POTAMOCLASTICS.

All along the river course, from near the head to the mouth, clastic deposits may be forming, their character and amount varying with the character of the stream and its environment. Under the latter, the kind of rock material and climate must be mentioned as all-important controlling factors. The amount of weathered rock material available for transport and final deposition is also of the greatest importance. We may consider the clastic river deposits under the following headings:

a. Alluvial fans.
b. Flood plains.
c. The playa—a temporary expanse of certain rivers.

Considering the classes of streams mentioned in Chapter III (p. 129), it may be noted that the deposits of consequents and insequents are essentially alike, those of overflow streams may be neglected as insignificant, but deposits of glacial streams, from their abundant supply, are of the greatest importance. Only the residual clays of subterranean streams need to be considered.

a. ALLUVIAL FANS. Wherever the débris-laden stream leaves its steep mountain bed and debouches upon the piedmont belt, or the floor of a large valley, it changes from a degrading stream, or one just at grade, to an aggrading stream, since the change in the angle of the river bed brings with it decreasing velocity of the current. In its steeper development the alluvial fan grades directly into the talus and other atmoclastic deposits with which, indeed, it forms a continuing sedimentary series, the river portion often being difficult to separate from the purely atmoclastic type.

Form and Extent of Modern Alluvial Fans. In extent alluvial fans vary from an area of only a few square feet to one covering thousands of square miles. Small alluvial fans are best described as semi-cones with a surface slope which may be as high as 20° or even 30°. As the fan increases in size its surface angle is lowered, until, in the very large deposits of this type, the surface seems almost to be horizontal. Small cones are seen to rise regularly toward the notch in the hills through which the river debouches, but in the very large alluvial fans there may result a confluence of many adjoining deposits, which will obliterate the effects of regularity. On all large fans, whether simple or confluent, erosion channels abound, for the streams building the deposits divide near the head of each fan into numerous distributaries, each of which, when not depositing, will be eroding. Thus a succession of contemporaneous erosion surfaces will result, and later beds will be deposited on the eroded surfaces of the older. In this manner the effect of a disconformity may be repeatedly produced within the depositional unit, and such apparent disconformities might lead to grave misinterpretations of the age and relationships of the adjoining beds. Should, by subsidence, the sea cover such an alluvial fan of great extent, a decided break would appear between the nonmarine and marine strata, the latter gradually encroaching by overlap upon the eroded surface of the old subaërial fan.

Among the large alluvial fans or dry deltas of modern times

may be mentioned that of the Merced in California, of the Garonne at the northern base of the Pyrenees, the delta of the Cooper River in the Lake district of South Australia, the great flood plain delta of the Huang-ho or Yellow River of China, and the similar but compound Indo-Gangetic delta plain of northern India.

The Merced River of California rises in the Sierra Nevadas and carries much waste down their steep western slopes. Reaching the broad open valley of California, which lies between the Sierra and the Coast range, it has built a fan which at present has a radius of about 40 miles. This consists of gravel near the mountain, and of fine silt at a distance. On account of the gentle slope of the surface, the water is turned readily from one channel into the other at the head of the fan.

"The many rivers issuing from the valleys of the Sierra Nevada and the Coast range upon the 'Valley of California' have formed an extensive plain, of which the Merced fan, . . . is only a part. The successive fans are so broad and flat that their slightly convex form can hardly be recognized without the aid of surveying instruments. Nearly all the streams run in shallow channels, but little beneath the gently sloping surface of the fans. The fans from the east and west meet in a broad, flat-floored trough." (Davis–18:*291*.)

River-made plains of this type are formed on both sides of the Alps. Those on the south have begun to cut valleys into the old deposits, while those on the north have cut to a depth of 1,000 feet, leaving the former plain as a series of ridges. The river Po flows eastward between the broad plain built by the rivers from the high Alps on the north, and the narrower one built by the streams from the lower Apennines. Where it enters the Adriatic Sea the Po builds a normal delta.

While the material of this river plain is typically a subaërial deposit, intercalated marine beds are not wanting. They have been reported from the Venetian region where they represent periodic encroachment of the sea. (Penck–41.)

One of the most extensive of modern dry deltas is that of Cooper Creek in the Lake district of South Australia. Its area is more than twice that of the Nile delta, its length being nearly 185 miles and its width over 170 miles. The water in the river, however, is abundant only after strong rains, the various distributaries being changeable canals on the surface of the delta. (Petermann–43.)

Even larger than the Cooper Creek alluvial fan is that of the Huang-ho or Yellow River of China. Its head is about 300 miles from the present shore, and has an elevation of only 400 feet above sea-level. It has thus an average fall of $1\frac{1}{3}$ feet per mile, a slope so gentle that it is imperceptible. Along the coast the fan extends from near Pekin southward for about 400 miles to where it joins the great plains of the Yang-tse-kiang, being interrupted, however, by the mountainous province of Shantung.

Owing to the very gentle slope of the fan the overflow at its head and the corresponding diversion of a distributary will result in the inundation of vast areas. The mouth of the river has been shifted more than 200 miles north or south, such shiftings having been numerous during Chinese history. "The flood of 1887 covered an area estimated at 50,000 square miles, immensely fertile and swarming with villages. The number of people drowned was at least a million and a greater loss followed from famine and disease caused by the flood." (Davis–18:290.) Flood plain fans of this type thus furnish excellent examples of the manner of destruction and burial by river silts of terrestrial organisms, and they further illustrate how peat deposits in swamps may be buried to be converted in the course of time into coals. The material carried by the Yellow River is mostly fine silt derived from the loess in the interior, which from its color gives the name to the river. The fineness of the material accounts in part at least for its very gentle slope, for it can be carried to great distances before it settles out.

Growing steadily but slowly seaward it is, of course, inevitable that marginal marine deposits should be enclosed in the growing fan. Very slight depression of the land would cause a partial flooding by the sea, with accompanying marine deposits. In its seaward growth the great delta has annexed the former rocky island, which is now the Province of Shantung.

The Indo-Gangetic alluvial plain is an example of a river plain formed of many confluent dry deltas and carried forward by the two great rivers of northern India—the Indus on the west and the Ganges, with the tributary Brahmaputra, on the east. Numerous small streams feed these rivers from the south slope of the Himalayas, carrying an abundance of coarse and fine débris. (Oldham–40.) The great alluvial plain extends over an area of about 300,000 square miles, and comprises the richest and most populous portion of India. It varies in width from 90 to nearly 300 miles, and entirely separates the lower peninsula of India from the Himalayas to the north. It rises 924 feet above the sea in its highest portion, and the deepest boring has located these deposits at a depth of nearly a thousand feet below the present sea-level. This is at

Lucknow, which lies approximately midway between the Indus and the Ganges headwaters and about 370 feet above sea-level. It abounds in gravels and conglomerates near the sloping borders, but lutaceous or clayey deposits, more or less arenaceous, prevail over much of the plain, especially near the center, with only subordinate deposits of sand, gravel, and conglomerates. Beds of blown sand of great thickness are found in some regions. Pebbles are scarce at a distance of more than twenty or thirty miles from the enclosing hills. Shells of river and marsh molluscs are occasionally found, and calcareous concretions and nodules of irregular shape, locally known as *kankar*, are frequent. "The more massive forms are a variety of calcareous tufa, which sometimes forms thick beds in the alluvium and frequently fills cracks in the alluvial deposits, or in older rocks." (Oldham–40:*437*.) Calcareous tufas also form conglomerates in the stream beds by cementing pebbles derived from the hills. In the clays along the borders and in the shoals of the Jumna River a great variety of vertebrate remains has been found, including elephant, hippopotamus, ox, horse, antelope, crocodile, and various fish. Borings in other regions revealed the presence of peat, forming extensive beds to a depth of 20 to 30 feet below the surface, while a layer of stiff blue clay 15 feet in thickness was found 10 feet below the surface at Calcutta. Clay and variegated sand with calcareous concretions, mica and small pebbles alternated to a depth of 120 feet, below which a quicksand was found. At 152 feet this became dark and coarse of grain and intermixed with red water-worn nodules of hydrated iron. At 159 feet a stiff clay was found which, at 163 feet, became friable and contained much vegetable and ferruginous matter. Lower still fine and coarse sands alternating with clays occur, while at 340 feet a ruminant bone was found, and pieces of tortoise shell at still greater depth. Three hundred and ninety-two feet below the surface pieces of coal, such as are found in the mountain streams, and fragments of decayed wood were found in the sand, while below 400 feet sand and shingle of fragments of primary rocks abounded. The borings also showed wood, remains of terrestrial mammals, fluviatile reptiles, and fresh-water molluscs. No traces of marine fossils have been found. The presence of earthy limestones in these deposits is of especial interest, because it shows that limestones do not necessarily indicate lacustrine or marine conditions. As already noted, in northern Mexico and other tropical regions of America, a superficial crust of white lime, often free from foreign material, is formed. This material, called *tepetate*, has been dissolved from the limestones of the surrounding region, transported in solution by the streams, and then redeposited by evaporation. (Hill and Vaughan–30:256.)

Basins Filled by River-Washed Waste. There are many examples of great basins surrounded by mountains and filled to a certain extent by the waste washed from the mountains. The larger of these basins are generally formed by tectonic movements, the process being a downwarping. An example of such a valley holding a "waste lake" is the upper Arkansas valley, back of the Front Range of the Rocky Mountains. As the basin was forming by warping, the rivers deposited their load on its floor, while at the same time the outlet of the Royal Gorge was being cut through the Front Range. The plains of waste within the basin slope forward from the mountainsides, but they have been only slightly dissected so far. Another excellent example is found in the Vale of Kashmir, enclosed by the front and middle ranges of the Himalayas in northwest India. In area this vale equals that of the Connecticut, being elliptical in form, a hundred miles long from southeast to northwest, and forty or fifty miles broad. It is formed by a downwarping between two lofty mountain ranges, which, for the most part, have very steep sides. The floor of the valley is deeply filled with river-laid waste, coarse near the mountains, but free from pebbles at the center. Its depth is measured probably by thousands of feet, while its surface elevation is more than 5,000 feet above sea-level. Across this plain meanders the Jhelam River, which escapes by a deep gorge through the enclosing mountains. Southern Europe furnishes another good example of a waste-floored basin in the oval plain of Hungary, which has a diameter of about 200 miles. Gravelly, sandy and loamy materials brought by the rivers from the enclosing mountains have formed this plain, which rises slightly toward the mountains, where it is formed of gravels, while the level center is a fine silt plain, resembling an abandoned lake bottom. The Danube and its tributaries meander through it and escape by the deep gorge of the Iron Gate cut through the Transylvanian Alps.

A somewhat similar basin lies in southwestern Wyoming, within the embrace of a series of mountain ranges, the Wasatch on the west, the Uinta on the south, and the Wind River Ranges on the north and east. The Green River flows through this basin and escapes by a deep canyon through the Uinta Mountains. The original deep filling of waste material has now been extensively trenched by the rivers and converted into a dissected upland, with valleys cut into the old waste deposit, in some cases a thousand feet deep. Other waste basins of this kind are found in Spain, Italy, and elsewhere.

In arid regions the basins often have an inward drainage and are filled by the combined atmoclastic creep and the river wash. Fans with their heads rising 500 feet or more above their bases and extending 10 or 15 miles outward characterize such basins. The water of the stream evaporates or sinks into the ground before the center of the basin is reached. When such fans become confluent they form huge waste plains of relatively steep grade, filling the valleys and partly burying the mountain slopes. In Utah, Nevada, and Arizona depressions of great depth have thus been wholly filled, while the waste mantle backs up 2,000 or 3,000 feet on the mountain flanks.

"A great part of Persia consists of large basins enclosed by mountains and without outlet to the sea. Long waste slopes stretch forward 5 or 10 miles with a descent of 1,000 or 2,000 feet, stony near the mountain flanks, and gradually becoming finer-textured and more nearly level. The central depressions are absolute deserts of drifting sands, with occasional saline lakes or marshes.

"Central Asia repeats the same conditions on a still larger scale. The basin of eastern Turkestan includes many half buried ranges in its central part. It is quite possible that some ranges are completely covered with waste. Many rivers flowing from the mountain rim wither on their way toward the chief central depression; only the largest river (Tarim) reaches it, there spreading out in Lob (Lake) Nor. The chief settlements are near the border of the basin, where the larger rivers come out from the mountains." (Davis–18 :*311*.)

The deposits of these regions must be considered as in part at least of purely atmoclastic and anemoclastic origin.

RIVER FLOOD PLAINS. River flood plains vary enormously in extent as well as in the character of the material. Streams with relatively steeply sloping beds may have stony flood plains, if they are abundantly supplied with coarse detritus from the head and sides. The flood plain of the Saco in the Intervale is covered with rounded cobbles and boulders, these often forming a regular cobblestone pavement. The stream is a rushing one, and in flood carries away all the finer material. A large part of the boulders and cobbles is formed of the granite of which this part of the White Mountain region is composed, but a part of the material at least is derived by the rehandling of flood-plain deposits formed during the preceding flooded stage period controlled by the melting ice of the glacial period.

Flood plains of streams of less velocity are made up of fine materials left by the river when it overflows its banks. As most of the deposit is formed near the river the banks on either side are higher than the surface of the plain away from it, there being thus a gentle slope away from the river. In this way the natural levees of the Mississippi are built, which rise considerably above the level of the "back swamps" on either side. Here the slope away from the river east or west is 5 or 10 feet to the mile, while the general southward slope of the entire flood plain is under half a foot to the mile.

A striking example of a flood plain is afforded by that of the Nile, which flows from a well-watered region through a desert country without receiving a tributary for a thousand miles, except a few small wet weather streams. Entrenched beneath the desert uplands this flood plain holds its own for a length of 500 miles, and maintains a width of from 5 to 15 miles, broadening on the delta to over 100 miles. The annual inundation of the flood plain is caused by the northward movement of the belt of equatorial rains in summer. The flood begins in June and usually rises 25 feet or more at Cairo in the late summer or early autumn. The annual addition of the river silt causes a slow rising of the entire flood plain estimated to amount to $4\frac{1}{2}$ inches a century.

This region furnishes an instructive example of widely varying contemporaneous deposits within the same general area. On the one hand occur the drifting, cross-bedded, well rounded and pure quartz sands of the desert, and, on the other, the extremely fine, well-stratified muds of the river flood plain. Both enclose the remains of organisms or of structures built by man, but there is an essential difference between the remains found in each deposit. Aside from ruins of human habitations and other works of man, only occasional remains of animals which were adapted to a dry climate are preserved in the desert sands. These, on the whole, will be rare because burial is often a slow process, and the bones of the dead creatures will crumble unless quickly covered. On the flood plain, on the other hand, aquatic organisms abound, giving a totally different faunal as well as floral association. According to the rash doctrine of the persistence of lithologic units, recently advocated by some geologists, such contemporaneous deposits would be interpreted as of different ages.

From the nature of deposits on river flood plains, perfect and often very fine stratification is to be expected. This may be considered as characteristic of typical flood plains. "The plains of the Po and of the Ganges and the great fan of the Huang-ho are very largely composed of fine sediments; the proportion of fine to coarse materials in the extensive deposits of these rivers seems to be greater than it is in many of the so-called lake beds of the west [of North America]." (Davis–19:*361-362*.)

River flood plains consisting of fine material are especially adapted for receiving the transit impression of organisms as well as sun-cracks, rain-drop impressions, etc. Indeed, almost the only known modern examples of such structures commonly referred to seashore origin are found on river flood plains or on the surfaces of the playas.

Another feature characterizing many river flood plains is the levelness of their surfaces, which argues well for the close approximation to horizontality of their strata. Many minor irregularities

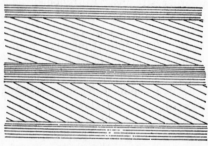

Fig. 123. Torrential type of cross-bedding; seen in modern torrential deposits. (After Hobbs.)

will, of course, be found, such as shallow channels, filled by later deposits and other evidence of contemporaneous erosion.

Cross-Bedding of Torrential Sediments. Whenever sands and gravels are spread by torrential floods, diagonal or cross-bedding on a large scale will result. Between the nearly horizontal layers of finer sands or gravels occur beds inclined at a nearly uniform and relatively large angle with the enclosing layers. Successive cross-bedded strata will have their beds slope in the same direction, which is that of the stream producing them. Such a type of cross-bedding is wholly inconsistent with the theory of wave formation or of currents in a body of water. It has been observed in modern torrential deposits (Hobbs–31:*291*), and is a characteristic feature of many ancient sandstones and conglomerates, the torrential origin of which it indicates (Fig. 123). It is not an infrequent structure in the torrential deposits of the terminal moraine on Long Island. (See further, Chapter XVII.)

Thickness and Composition of River Deposits. The thickness of river deposits is practically unlimited, and depends on the source of supply of material and the depth of the valley in which it is deposited. Where downwarping of a piedmont belt occurs, so as to form a geosyncline, the thickness of the formation may become enormous. Torrential deposits in Calabria, Italy, have been found 1,500 feet or more in thickness and including boulders of many petrographic types, often exceeding a foot in diameter. The Alhambra formation of Spain is at least 1,000 feet thick and consists mainly of river deposited pebbles distinctly water worn and varying in size from a fraction of an inch to six inches or more in length. Some of the partly dissected, but still unconsolidated torrential deposits fringing the Front Range of the Rocky Mountain region contain boulders many feet in diameter. Some torrential deposits may be entirely composed of rounded boulders with only enough sand and fine gravel to fill the interstices. Portions of the Old Red sandstone of Scotland furnish splendid examples of fossil boulder beds of this kind.

The Siwalik formation of India furnishes an excellent example of a sub-recent fluviatile deposit of great thickness. It skirts the southern border of the Himalayas, forming the Siwalik Hills. The strata have been uplifted by the latest movement in this region and exposed by erosion. The thickness of the formation is upward of 15,000 feet, and, except at the base, where it is characterized by passage beds from the underlying marine Sirmur group, it is of non-marine origin throughout. In age it is said to range from Miocenic to Quaternary, though most of it belongs to the Pliocenic. In this formation "sandstone immensely predominates . . . and is of a very persistent type from end to end of the region and from top to bottom of the series. Its commonest form is indistinguishable from the rock of corresponding age known as Mollasse in the Alps, and is of a clear pepper and salt gray, sharp and fine in grain, generally soft, and in very massive beds. The whole Middle and Lower Siwaliks are formed of this rock, with occasional thick beds of red clay and very rare thin, discontinuous bands and nodules of earthy limestone, the sandstone itself being sometimes calcareous and thus cemented into hard nodular masses. . . . In the Upper Siwaliks conglomerates prevail largely; they are often made up of coarsest shingle, precisely like that in the beds of the great Himalayan torrents. Brown clays occur often with the conglomerate, and sometimes almost entirely replace it. This clay, even when tilted to the vertical, is indistinguishable in hand specimens from that of the recent plains deposit; and no doubt it was formed in a similar manner, as alluvium. The sandstone, too, of this zone is exactly like the sand forming the banks of the great rivers, but in a more or less consolidated condition." (Medlicott and Blanford–38 :*524.*) The fossils of this formation are of fresh water or of terrestrial types exclusively, and they, as well as the nature of the deposit, point the continental origin of this formation. "The mountain torrents are now in many cases engaged in laying down great banks of shingle at the margin of the plains, just like the Siwalik conglomerates; and the thick sandstones and sandy clays of the Tertiary series are of just the same type of form and composition as the actual deposits of the great rivers." (Medlicott and Blanford.)

In the Salt Range of the Punjab these alternating gray and greenish sandstones and the red and light brownish orange clays "are from seventy to a hundred and twenty feet in thickness, being very frequently about a hundred feet each, but some zones are much thicker." (Wynne–62 :*108.*)

Depth of Compound Continental Deposits. The great amount of material which may accumulate in deserts as the product of combined creep, torrential and eolian deposit is seen from a well boring near Ashkabad, Turkestan (Walther–57 :*105*), which penetrated sands, clays and gravels to a depth of 666 meters without finding rock bottom. No organic remains were found, and the character of the material is similar to that of the surface deposits of the Transcaspian desert, from which it is inferred that this entire mass of over 2,000 feet of sediment accumulated under climatic and topographic conditions similar to those now prevailing.

Chatter or Percussion Marks. A characteristic feature of many boulder or cobblestone deposits of modern time as well as of former periods is the presence of numerous crescentic chatter or percussion marks on the finer grained and well-rounded pebbles, especially porphyries, quartzites, and the like. These have much the form and size of impressions made by the end of a finger nail in soft clay, and are due to the violent impact of one rounded pebble or boulder upon another. Such marks are plentifully produced by the impact, one upon another of the hard, fine-grained pebbles used for grinding in the revolving cylinders of cement mills and other works.

Organic Remains in Torrential Deposits. On the whole, organic remains will be few or absent in coarse torrential deposits. Even tough masses of wood will be shattered and completely annihilated. As a result, such deposits will be free from organic remains, though, of course, with increasing fineness of the sediment the possibility of the preservation of such remains increases. Since in semi-arid regions violent floods arise abruptly, sweeping down the previously almost dry river beds, and converting them in a few minutes into raging torrents, it is apparent that organisms may be surprised and suddenly overwhelmed and their remains entombed in the resulting deposits of the flood. We need only recall such disasters as that which recently befell a transcontinental railroad where the sudden flooding of a previously dry wadi swept away a trestle and its load of cars, these with their luckless passengers being buried in the sand and silt of the lower course of the stream. The many unrecorded entombments of cattle and other creatures by just such sudden floods would, if known, form adequate illustrations of the origin of many fossiliferous sandstones of the past.

One of the chief causes of the destruction of animal life on plains of subaërial deposition is found in the periodic droughts affecting these regions. The geologic effects of such droughts have been noted in many tropical countries, especially along the west coast of Africa, in India, and in South America. Darwin (17) has described the "gran seco" or great drought which occurred between the years 1827 and 1830, when, in the northern part of the province of Buenos Ayres (South America) and the southern part of St. Fé, vast numbers of birds and animals perished, the vegetation withered and died, and the brooks became dry, until finally the whole country was turned into a dusty, waterless waste. Darwin writes: "A man told me that the deer used to come into his courtyard to the well, which he had been obliged to dig to supply his own family with water; and that the partridges had hardly strength to fly away when pursued. The lowest estimation of the loss of cattle in the province of Buenos Ayres alone was taken at one million head. A proprietor at San Pedro had previously to these years 20,000 cattle, at the end not one remained.

"I was informed by an eye-witness that the cattle in herds of thousands rushed into the Paraña, and being exhausted by hunger they were unable to crawl up the muddy banks and thus were drowned. . . . Without doubt several hundred thousand animals thus perished in the river: their bodies when putrid were seen floating down the stream; and many in all probability were deposited in the estuary of the Plata. All the small rivers became highly saline, and this caused the death of vast numbers in particular spots; for when an animal drinks of such water it does not recover. . . . Subsequently to the drought of 1827 to '32 a very rainy season followed which caused great floods. Hence it is almost certain that some thousands of the skeletons were buried by the deposits of the very next year." Darwin adds very pertinently,

"What would be the opinion of a geologist, viewing such an enormous collection of bones, of all kinds of animals and of all ages,
thus embedded in one thick earthy mass? Would he not attribute
it to a flood having swept over the surface of the land, rather than
to the common order of things?" (Darwin–17, *Chapter vii.*)
These droughts are of frequent occurrence and seem to show an
approximate periodicity of about fifteen years.

Distances to Which Material May Be Carried by Rivers. Wade
(55), in his study of the distribution of the gravels derived from
the hills of igneous rock facing the western border of the Red
Sea, comes to some interesting conclusions regarding the distance
to which pebbles may be transported by subaërial agencies. On the
eastern side of these ranges the fragments have traveled only a
short distance, lying still in the plains at the foot of the hills. On
the western side of the Red Sea ranges the gravels appear to have
been carried along the main wadis and old lines of drainage often to
great distances. "The pebbles have traveled in more or less westerly
directions down the wadis, into the important north-and-south wadi
which continues the line of the Nile north from Quena. They are
abundant for some distance north and south of Quena. Thence
they have been carried northward down the Nile Valley. . . .
The most interesting occurrences of the rocks, which the Survey
geologists say 'could only come from the Red Sea' are at Heluan,
a few miles south of Cairo . . . and in the Delta itself, where
they were found in the Royal Society's boring at Zagazig. Thus
these rocks have been river-borne for at least 400 miles." (Wade–
55:*244.*) The age of these gravels is Pleistocenic.

Extensive deposits of apparently river-borne pebbles are found
in many older formations. In the Trias of England they have been
found 300 miles from their source. The Pottsville conglomerate
series of eastern North America extends northwestward for a distance of 400 miles or more, the pebbles of the series throughout being derived from the Appalachians on the southeast.

Purity and Rounding of Fluviatile Deposits. On the whole, the
material of a subaërial fan is very heterogeneous, but by prolonged
reworking and the sorting action of running water a considerable
assortment into kinds as well as sizes of grain may be effected.
In dry climates the disintegration of granitic rocks is not accompanied by extensive decomposition. Fresh feldspar crystals will
remain, and these may be rounded by wind attrition. (Wade–55.)
In moister climates, on the other hand, feldspar will decay, forming
kaolin or laterite, and by deflation or by flotation these products of
finer grain will be swept away.

Form of River Pebbles. Rudolf Hoernes (32) has recently insisted upon the distinctive characters possessed by the pebbles subject to prolonged river and wave transport. According to him, river-borne pebbles are always flat, and more or less wedge-shaped, owing to the fact that the current merely shoves the coarser material along its bottom. Marine and lacustrine pebbles, on the other hand, are rounded or roller-shaped, because the waves tend to roll the material.

Eduard Suess in 1862, in describing the fluviatile Belvedere gravels of the Vienna district, says, in effect (53 :*64, 65*) : "A comparison of a considerable quantity of such pebbles shows that they conform more or less to a single typical form, being almost without exception sharpened to a wedge-shaped form on one side. This form distinguishes shoved pebbles from rolled pebbles; it is produced by the pushing along, over the bottom, of the rock fragments by the current of the stream. Rolled pebbles, such as are moved to and fro by the surf on the shore, never have the wedge-shaped form, but a uniformly oval or cylindrical ground form." According to J. Lorenz von Liburnau (37 :*95, 96*) the flat river pebbles suffer chiefly a horizontal rotation, so that the top and bottom of the pebbles are rubbed against the overlying and underlying ones, while at the same time the edges are worn off, the result being a mass of flat, worn cakes with smooth, rounded edges.

In contradistinction to these observations and deductions, Penck emphatically insists upon the rolling of pebbles on the stream-bed as the chief method of river transport. Such rolling may affect scattered pebbles or the entire mass, in which case the entire sediment on the river bottom is in motion, the individual pebbles rolling and striking against one another, with the result that rounded pebbles are produced. In portions of the Rhine bed, such a mass three meters in depth is thus moved along. (Penck–41 :*284.*)

It is extremely doubtful if the distinctions made by Suess and Hoernes can be considered of more than local applicability. The character of the rock which has furnished the material is probably of much greater significance, as pointed out by Walther. Thus, on the shores of Lake Michigan, where the bed rock is a uniform grained limestone, the pebbles are chiefly of a rounded or roller-shaped character, while on Lake Erie, where the cliffs are of shale, flat gravel predominates, except where glacial deposits have formed a local source of supply. Again, on a relatively steep shore, where wave-work is pronounced, as on the northern Massachusetts coast, the pebbles are well rounded through rolling, while on a shallow coast, where the wash of the waves rushes up and down the beach as a sheet flood, the pebbles are more often merely moved backward and forward without much overturning, or, again, the pebbles are scarcely moved, but polished and worn by the sand carried back and forth across them.

Pebbles of glacial stream deposits are always rounded, since in such deposits only the more massive rocks escape destruction. The pebbles and coarser rocks of the White Mountain streams are all well rounded, this being especially well shown in the flood plain of the Saco River at Intervale. Destruction of all the weaker type of rocks by prolonged river transport is also imminent, and this is especially the case on large river flood plains or deltas. Prolonged exposure of granitic or other coarse-grained igneous rocks results in their disintegration, and thus by a process of assorting, the pebbles may be reduced to a few fundamental lithologic types, such as quartz, porphyry, etc. There are many older quartz conglomerates with well-rounded pebbles, but free from fossils, which appear to represent extreme cases of concentration. The Millstone grit, the Pottsville conglomerate, and the Shawangunk and other conglomerates are almost wholly composed of quartz pebbles. In many cases these quartz pebbles are derived from vein quartz, but in other cases they are probably a highly indurated quartzite in which the individual grains have become obliterated.

It is difficult to understand how extensive conglomerates, sometimes many hundreds or even a thousand feet in thickness, and composed almost entirely of quartz pebbles embedded in quartz sand, can have originated. If the material of the pebbles is *vein* quartz, an enormous destruction of rock is indicated, since veins form only a small portion of the rock mass carrying them. If the material of the pebbles is an older quartzite, the problem is less difficult. Again, in some cases the pure quartz pebble conglomerates may be formed of the reworked gravels derived from the destruction of older conglomerates. Thus the pebbles of the "yellow gravel" of the coastal plain may be the product of the destruction of the formerly much more extensive Pottsville conglomerate. In this connection it is interesting to record that some of these pebbles are fossiliferous, carrying corals of Siluric age. This may represent a silicified limestone, the silica thus being of secondary origin. Whether any such origin may be postulated for a considerable portion of the quartz pebbles is doubtful.

From our present knowledge of the subject, it seems that no constant differences can be ascertained between river and shore pebbles, both may be round or flat, and both may be well worn or subangular, and form part of a mass of a very uniform lithic character, or one composed of a heterogeneous aggregate. On the whole, destruction of all but the resistant quartz seems more assured on the flood plain of large rivers than on the seashore; and certainly the wide transport of such material is more readily effected by streams.

The sorting action of streams on sands has already been discussed. (Chapter V, p. 252.)

Overlap Relations of River Deposits. In a growing subaërial river delta, the later formed portions will progressively overlap the earlier formed parts, coming to rest upon the basement beds, beyond the margin of the older beds of the delta. Since, however, this can be recognized only as an overlap of formations of definite chronologic value, and not an overlap of continuous beds, this subject is better discussed after the simpler type of marine overlap has been described. The general theoretical relationship is expressed by the following diagram (Fig. 124), from which it will be seen that the principal overlap is away from the source of supply. There may, of course, be a slight headward overlap due to aggrada-

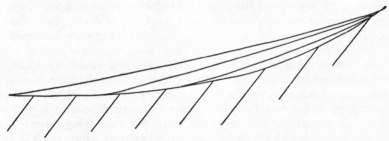

Fig. 124. Diagram showing normal non-marine progressive overlap, each later stratum resting upon the old land surface beyond the edge of the preceding one. A slight headward overlap is also indicated.

tion of the upper part of the river channels as the grade is lowered. This, as a rule, will be slight and local as compared with the overlap at the other end, though it is not to be denied that at times such a headward overlap may be considerable.

Flood Plains of Glacial Streams. These are of exceptional character owing to the abundant supply of detritus as well as water from the melting ice. As already pointed out in Chapter III, p. 136, such streams when overloaded will form extensive deposits in their valleys, aggrading these to a considerable depth. Subsequent change in the character of the stream, either from diminution of supply, from increase in the amount of water by sudden melting, or from a general uplift of the region, will cause the rivers to entrench themselves in the old flood plains, leaving the remnants as terraces on either side of the valley. Nearly all the streams coming from the glaciated region have such terraces, which mark the greater deposition in periods preceding the present one. Examples of deposits of this type now forming are seen in the valleys of the streams coming from the Alaskan and other glaciers.

River and Flood Plain Deposits from Continental Ice-Sheets. Several types of such deposits are recognized and are noteworthy on account of their peculiarity; among these are: 1. the torrential moraine, or kame; 2. the frontal, or apron plain; 3. the esker; and, 4. the glacial sand plain, or temporary lake delta. The essential characters of each are as follows:

1. *Torrential moraine or kame deposits.* These are irregular hills of semi-stratified sands and gravels, all of the pebbles being water worn. The material was derived from the ice and was dumped by the rivers in front of the ice-sheet. These deposits are commonly of irregular shape, being more or less confluent cones of débris, and often complicated by the formation of kettle holes from the melting of included ice blocks, as in normal moraines. The topography of such a deposit, when extensive, is often a series of knobs and basins.

2. *The frontal or apron plain.* This is also a subaërial deposit and consists of the material carried forward from the glacial moraine by streams, and spread as a veneer or mantle over the older formations in front of the ice. Where it is spread over a coastal plain, it is generally of uniform thickness, this decreasing from the source outward. The material also becomes finer away from the source of supply. Kettle holes may occur, but they are less frequent than in the kame moraine. Cross channels made by the streams from the ice are not uncommon features. Typical examples of such apron plains are found south of the moraine on Cape Cod, and in similar relations to the moraines on Nantucket, Martha's Vineyard, and Long Island. In the Cape Cod sections of this apron plain facetted pebbles or dreikanter have been found in place, indicating wind activity and further proving the subaërial origin of this deposit. Such wind work may locally modify the deposit, substituting wind cross-bedding for the horizontal bedding given to them by the water.

Marine fossils may be locally embedded in such deposits if they are formed near the shore, and when a partial subsidence is succeeded by further deposition by streams from the ice. A fine example is shown by the fossiliferous layers of Sankaty Head on Nantucket, which, however, lie really within the kame-moraine area rather than in the present apron plain. It is probable, however, that the fossiliferous beds themselves belong to an earlier apron plain, for it is known that the Wisconsin ice sheet advanced over this deposit and built its moraine and apron plain further south. (Wilson–60:*13*.)

3. *The esker.* (Swedish *os,* pl. *osars.*) This term is applied to long, narrow ridges of sand and gravel with steeply sloping sides and often a sinuous outline. The summit of the esker is generally a narrow, flat space between the sloping sides, the cross-section being very nearly a triangular one. The eskers of the last glacial period run in general parallel with the direction of the ice movement and while occurring largely perhaps in the north and south valleys, along which the main drainage lines from the ice discharged, they are not confined to these, but often pass indifferently over hills and through valleys. In height they rarely exceed 100 feet, but in length they may be followed for tens or in rare cases even hundreds of miles. Their best development in this country is in New England, while Scandinavia and Finland furnish some of the best illustrations in the Old World.

Eskers may be formed in various ways, such as by filling of gorges in the ice, by accumulation of débris in englacial tunnels and by aggradation of their bed by sub-glacial streams. (Grabau–23.) This last is the most characteristic method of formation. Streams originating under the ice are enclosed in a tunnel and, being under an enormous hydrostatic pressure, will fill this tunnel after the manner of the water in a city main. It may thus be forced upward and will discharge at a level much above that of its upper courses, if it is located in a valley sloping against the ice mass, as is so often the case.

Flowing uphill, such a stream will tend to erode the roof of its tunnel, and simultaneously to aggrade its bottom in the higher (upstream) parts. As the stream rises in the ice by roof erosion, the floor is more and more aggraded until this filling all along the line has reached the level of the outlet, or risen slightly above it. Melting removes the supporting walls on either side of this aggraded river-bed, when the sides will slump, giving the characteristic lateral slopes and the triangular cross-section to the esker. At points where the original deposit is narrow, so much material will be involved in the slumping to give the proper angle of repose that the surface of the esker will be actually lowered. Thus irregularities in height in the esker are readily accounted for. (Woodworth–61.)

4. *Glacial sand plains.* Whenever the ice holds up a temporary body of water between its front or sides and the margins of
the valley or basin in which it lies, opportunity for the formation of
glacial deltas or sand plains is given. These may be formed around
the margins of the lake by streams coming from the land, when
they partake of the true delta to be described beyond. Such deltas
have been recorded from glacial lakes in New Jersey and elsewhere. The marginal sand plains of the Upper Hudson Valley
were deposited in lakes bordering the ice sheet which occupied
the center of that valley. Sand plains formed at the front of the ice
of material carried by streams from the ice abound in New England, especially in eastern Massachusetts, where they have been
fully described.* A characteristic feature of these sand plains is
their correspondence in height to the elevation of the outlet, which
determined the level of the temporary lake. Not infrequently a
number of successive sand plains is formed corresponding to a succession of lake levels determined by progressive uncovering of lower
outlets. In New England these plains are generally highest in the
southern portions of the old northward sloping valleys and become
progressively lower toward the north. In Lake Bouvé, an extinct
glacial lake in the Boston Basin, eight series of such sand plains are
known, each series lower than the preceding one on the south.
(Grabau–23:*580.*) A special example of rather striking character
is seen in the sand plains of Wellfleet, Eastham, and Truro on Cape
Cod, which were deposited in a lake held in an embayment in the
eastern ice lobe, and dammed in part by the terminal moraine of
that ice lobe, across which the discharge of the waters occurred.
In this case the highest series of plains lies between the two lower
series. By the melting of the ice these plains were left without any
immediately surrounding land barrier, as isolated sand masses running northward into the ocean from the eastern end of the terminal
moraine. (Grabau–24; Wilson–60:*52-66, pls. 34, 36, 37, 38.*) In
form the isolated sand plain, revealed on the melting of the ice
and the drainage of the temporary lake, consists of a *surface slope*
which is gently forward from the center of origin; a steeper *frontal
or delta slope,* joining the surface slope abruptly, and having a
lobate or scalloped outline, and a still steeper *back slope* often with
concavities between sharp cusps. This latter surface is due to
slumping after the supporting ice front against which the delta was
built had melted away. Its slope, therefore, represents the angle
of repose of the material under the conditions of formation. The
gentle surface slope represents the subaërial part of the delta, while

* See papers by Crosby, Grabau, Clapp, etc., cited in Chapter III.

the lobate front is the slope of the front of the original delta where the oblique frontal layers or fore-set beds were added. The lobation is due to the division of the stream into a number of spreading fingers or distributaries, each of which builds its own portion of the delta forward. In section it will be seen that the greatest part of the sand plain is composed of the sloping fore-set beds, which are inclined at an angle of 20 or more degrees. The upper ends of the fore-set beds are abruptly truncated, and on these truncated edges rest the coarser, nearly horizontal, top-set beds which constitute the subaërial part of the delta. The foot of the fore-set beds generally rests upon a thin series of bottom-set beds of finest material, often of clay or rock flour. All the beds are well stratified and the pebbles are, as a rule, well rounded.

Consolidated Sand Plains. Sand plains of Pleistocenic age have, in some cases, become consolidated so as to form a rock mass of more or less induration. This is especially the case where many of the pebbles are of limestone, when partial solution and redeposition of the lime in the interstices will occur. A typical example of such a consolidated deposit is seen on the banks of the lower Niagara River, near the railroad station at Lewiston, New York. Here steep fore-set beds are seen dipping at an average angle of 15-20 degrees toward the south. The beds are sufficiently well cemented to form a vertical wall, though the material can be broken into its component pebbles by blows of a hammer. The deposit, which is perhaps 30 or 40 feet thick, appears to have formed in a body of water held up against the front of the Niagara escarpment by an ice lobe lying a short distance to the north. Streams from this ice lobe supplied the pebbles and sand which built up the delta.

This deposit is sufficiently consolidated to resist ordinary erosion, and river, lacustrine, or even marine sediments could be formed over it without disturbing it. Indeed, since the formation of this deposit this region is believed to have been invaded by the sea by way of the Hudson, Lake Champlain, and the St. Lawrence, but this was not of sufficient duration to permit the formation of extensive marine deposits. It is easy to see, however, that these steeply inclined delta beds of coarse material, followed by marine sediments, such as would have been formed had the sea stood here longer, and this in turn by lacustrine deposits, such as would be formed if the present lake should expand, would give a complex succession of formations, the history of which would be decipherable only with considerable difficulty.

The Nagelfluh of Salzburg. (Crammer–13:*325-334.*) The city of Salzburg in the Austrian province of the same name and close

to the Bavarian border furnishes a remarkable example of a consolidated conglomerate or pebble rock of the type described. This
goes by the name of Nagelfluh, from the fact that where the relatively small pebbles have fallen out of the matrix a depression
like that made by the head of a nail is seen. This rock appears
in several large erosion remnants within the city; one of them,
the Mönchsberg, rises with perpendicular walls (partly artificial)
and is pierced by a tunnel through which one of the city streets is
carried. Other remnants are the neighboring Rainberg, and the
more distant hill of Hellbrunn. All of these are evidently part of a
once continuous conglomerate bed, which has since been dismembered by erosion. The cohesion of the material is such that old
crypts hollowed in this rock and used in the third century as places
of secret worship are still in a practically unchanged condition.

The walls show inclined bedding which indicates the delta character of these deposits (Penck–42:*161-166*). According to the
opinion of Penck, Crammer, and others, the sand and pebbles were
washed into a lake which occupied the Salzburg basin during
post-glacial time. The fact that the Nagelfluh rests upon a glacial
moraine, as determined by excavations and observations on natural
and artificial exposures, seems to indicate that this deposit is of
post-glacial age, though other observers have held that the age
of the deposit might be greater, perhaps late Tertiary.

Nagelfluh of similar character, but probably of greater age, is
found in a number of localities in South Germany and elsewhere.
In some cases, as in Munich, it is used extensively for building
purposes. It is, of course, not necessarily true that all conglomerates of this type are of non-marine origin, though most of them
probably are river deposits.

PLAYAS OR TAKYRS AND SALINAS. In the low, flat-bottomed
depressions of undrained desert basins the rivers at times of flood
will spread out into extensive shallow lakes of temporary existence.
In the Great Basin region of western North America one such
temporary lake reaches a length of about 100 miles by a breadth of
12 to 15 miles, but with the water scarcely more than a few inches
deep. Here the fine silt of the river is deposited, gradually subsiding as the shallow lake evaporates. After complete evaporation a
smooth, hard-baked surface remains, marked by sun-cracks and
the tracks of animals which visited the spot before complete hardening of the mud had occurred. Raindrop impressions likewise remain on such a surface. In structure the material is beautifully
and finely stratified, as may be seen on the sides of the sun-crack
rifts. This constitutes the *playa* of the American deserts (Mexico

and the southern United States), the *takyr* or *schala* of Asia, or the *sebcha* of Africa. Russell has described a number of such temporary playa lakes from the western United States (49:50). He finds them a characteristic feature of the greater part of the valleys of Nevada, the largest being in the Black Rock Desert in the northwestern part of the state. It forms during the winter months and reaches an area of from 450 to 500 square miles, but is seldom over a few inches in depth. Often after storms it is a vast sheet of liquid mud, a characteristic of many playa lakes. In a few hours or a few days the water of the lake may all evaporate, leaving a hard, dry and absolutely barren surface, cracked in all directions as the surface contracts in drying. "The lake beds then have a striking resemblance to tesselated pavements of cream-colored marble, and soon become so hard that they ring beneath the hoof-beats of a galloping horse, but retain scarcely a trace of his foot-prints." Around the margin of the lakes is a belt of plain with desert vegetation, the transition to which is formed by a marshy tract which in summer is marked by an abundant efflorescence of salts.

Mechanical analysis has shown that the material of the playa may be 100 per cent. clay, and that laterally it will gradually pass through the addition of sands into the surrounding eolian deposits. In limestone regions where siliceous rocks are wanting the material of the playa will be largely lime mud, and this may be the origin of some of the finely bedded, sun-cracked calcilutytes of the American Siluric, where the percentage of lime and magnesium carbonates is seventy or less.

If the playa lake exists for some time it may become stocked with certain forms of organisms, especially types whose eggs or larvæ can be transported by wind or by birds. The small crustaceans Estheria, Daphnia, and Cypris are characteristic of desert lakes, the first having been found in ponds which are dry for eleven successive months. (Fischer, quoted by Walther–57:94.) When, as is frequently the case, salts are present in the sediment, these effloresce on the surface, and from their hygroscopic character keep the surface of the playa sufficiently moist to prevent the removal by the wind of the accumulated material, and further to catch all dust particles carried across the surface by the winds. Thus the surface of the playa becomes dusted over with a fine coating of sand or dust, this process being repeated as the salts rise to the surface of the newly added layer. Where salt is present in great abundance a moist, slippery surface with incrustations of salt results, thus forming *salinas*. When wet, their surface is impassable, but when dry a crust of hard salt of dazzling whiteness characterizes the salina.   As already noted, the thickness which such a salt deposit may reach is practically limited only by the depth of the basin and the supply of the salt.

The deeply cleft surface of the dry playa is not infrequently buried by the wandering sands of the desert, while the rifts between the polygonal blocks are filled with wind-blown material, or the mud of the next succeeding inundation, and so preserved. This is made possible by the rapidity with which the playa surface becomes flooded, a case being on record where a lake 10 to 15 kilometers wide and of immeasurable length, though only from an inch and a half to a foot in depth, came into existence in twenty minutes. (Obrutschew, quoted by Walther–57:*110*.)   It must, however, be noted that the dried surface of the playa is not infrequently softened on being wetted, and that from swelling and flowage of the mud the cracks may be closed again before they are filled.   In this manner many mud-cracked surfaces are again obliterated. From preliminary experiments, Barrell concludes (2:*531-532*) that "a mud-cracked loam or silty clay, even when the sand particles are imperceptible to the fingers, is an unfavorable material for the preservation of its detailed surface features, . . . Upon being wet by rain the rapid swelling and disintegration of the surface stratum would turn the surface of such a deposit into a creamy mud. . . ." On the other hand, "a pure clay, slowly subsiding from quiet waters, and wet sufficiently long to become compact upon drying, would retain its mud cracks upon rewetting, either by rain previous to flooding or by the flood waters themselves." When the newly deposited layer is a very thin one it will curl up like shavings on drying and these clay shavings will be blown into the sand dunes, where, upon subsequent softening, they will be compressed into clay lentils or pebbles, and so become a constituent part of an otherwise pure sandstone.

PRESERVATION OF FOOTPRINTS, ETC., IN SUBAËRIAL DEPOSITS. Of the greatest significance is the relative ease with which tracks of animals are preserved in desert deposits.   The scarcity of rain permits their almost indefinite retention on suitable surfaces without being buried.   In the Sahara desert tracks of camels made in 1877 were still perfectly recognizable in 1892 (Foureau–21:*175*), the interval of fifteen years having altered them but little.   Wherever (Walther–57:*88*) a temporary accumulation of water after a desert rain attracts the varied desert fauna, or allows animals living on the border of the desert to make extended excursions into the flooded regions, their footprints will be left upon the impressionable surface of mud, remaining after such an inundation.   These will in time be covered by the shifting sands of the desert and a relief mold will be produced by the covering sands. Such a relief impression will be more readily preserved than the original impression, which may be destroyed by the softening of the clay surface of the playa. A single extensive inundation by heavy rains of a desert surface may permit a wide horizontal migration across this surface of animals which never before and never after entered this region. Thus their tracks may be widely preserved in a single horizon in a desert formation, like those of Cheirotherium in the Upper Buntsandstein (Walther–57:*88*), even though the animal lived during a much longer time period. Repeated floodings, annually or at intervals of many years, will permit the formation of successive track-bearing layers, by animals living on the border of the desert. This mode of preservation certainly accords best with the characters of the tracks found in such formations as the Newark sandstone of the eastern United States, whereas the frequent assumption that the successive track-bearing beds were made between tides and buried by the sediment brought in by the returning tide does not allow for the obliterating effect of the tide, an argument equally applicable to stream-laid deposits upon the fresh tracks. (Voigt–54:*166.*)

The conditions favoring the preservation of footprints in desert regions militate against the preservation of the animals themselves. For, unless the body is buried at once, it is sure to fall a prey to the desert carnivora, while sun and wind will complete the destruction of what remains. This explains the scarcity of remains of the animals in the strata which contain their footprints.

Other Structural Characters. Ripple marks and rill marks, though usually regarded as typical only of marine formations, are equally, if not more, characteristic of the non-marine deposits. Their discussion is, however, deferred until hydroclastic sediments have been more fully discussed.

NORMAL PALUDAL AND LACUSTRINE CLASTIC DEPOSITS.

Clastic deposits in swamps (paludal clastics) are of relatively little importance except when associated with vegetal deposits. These latter are by far the most important, the clastics being subordinate and confined to the sediments carried in by wet weather streams and rains, or the dust settling out of the air.

Deposits in ponds and lakes, on the other hand, *i. e.*, in water bodies free or nearly so from growing vegetation, are of more significance, since they add a decided individualistic note to the terrestrial hydroclastic series with which they are commonly associated. It is true that many of their most pronounced characteristics are due to peculiarities in the composition of their waters which will give rise to deposits of special chemical character, such as have been discussed in preceding chapters. In other respects, again, the nature of the sediment is not very different from that of the ocean, except in so far as the absence of the tides, the difference in composition and specific gravity of the water and the difference in size of the water body influence such deposition. The last falls practically out of consideration in lakes of great size, such as the American Great Lakes.

The clastic sediment of lakes is chiefly derived from two sources, that resulting from the erosion of its shores by waves, and that brought in by the tributary streams. Erosion is very marked, especially in the larger lakes, such as Erie, Ontario, Huron, etc., and the product is distributed along the shore as shingle, or heaped up into storm terraces, as on Lake Michigan. Coarse material is seldom carried far out into the lake, but accumulates along the shores, where it is subject to constant wave attack. The finer sand and mud, however, resulting from such wave attack are carried out from shore and slowly settle all over the lake bottom and sides. This also happens to some of the fine slime brought in by streams, but this tends for the most part to sink to the lake bottom. The coarsest of the river-borne sediments will build up a delta at the shore, but the finer mud, which is held in intimate suspension in the stream water, is carried beyond this point. Its presence in the stream water renders that water heavier, and it will, therefore, not mingle with the lighter warm water of the surface of the lake, but will sink to the deeper, cooler and denser strata. Thus a mud-laden stream passing into a lake will become submerged, often passing along the lake bottom, and occasionally forming a channel there, bounded by submerged mud banks on either side. The force of the current will finally be dissipated in the deeper waters of the lake and the sediment will slowly sink to the bottom, forming horizontal and well-stratified layers of mudrock, free from irregularity of bedding and of uniformly fine grain. Mingled with sediments of this type are the muds which were held suspended for a time in the upper waters and which settled all over the lake bottom.

With the seasonal variation in the strength of the streams there must be a corresponding variation in the grain of the sediment.

Thus when the current is powerful and surcharged with sediment slightly coarser material may be carried to the lake bottom than is the case during the period of lessened river activity. A series of annual layers is thus formed which in any given case may serve to measure the length of time required for the formation of the deposit. This method has been applied by Berkey (8) for the determination of the time required for the deposition of finely bedded clays.

DELTAS.

Deltas are the terminal deposits of rivers, and, as such, have an intimate association with the continental clastics. It is true, of course, that a part of the delta of the seacoast is of submarine origin, and its discussion therefore falls more essentially under the heading of marine clastics. Still, deltas are peculiar features of relatively limited distribution, and in no way represent normal marine conditions. Indeed, a part of the delta is always typically non-marine, and the place of the delta is therefore intermediate between true continental and marine clastics. Moreover, deltas are common in lakes, these belonging, of course, entirely to the continental division of the hydroclastics.

A typical delta may be taken as one that is built into a body of standing water, the level of which is essentially a permanent one. Subsequent drainage of the water body may expose the delta as we have seen, but all such changes bring the delta-building process to an end. On the whole, deltas are more abundant on lakes than on the seashore, partly because lakes are not subject to tidal currents and fluctuation of level, but partly also because wave activity on the sea coast is greater. Fluctuation in level due to tides does not necessarily militate against delta building, as is shown by the Indus delta, which is built where the tidal range is 10 feet, while that of the Ganges is built into a sea having a tidal range of 16 feet. Where wave action is strong, however, and especially where long shore transport of material is pronounced, delta building is restricted. Deltas are thus the triumph of river deposition over wave and current destruction, and their location and extent will be determined by the relative importance of the opposing processes. As examples of typical existing deltas on the sea coast may be named that of the Nile, on the Mediterranean; of the Po, on the Adriatic; the confluent deltas of the Rhine and Meuse; and that of the Ems, on the North Sea; the deltas of the Lena and of the Mackenzie, on the open Arctic Ocean; those of the Ganges, Brah-

maputra and the Indus, on the Indian Ocean; of the Niger and the
Orinoco, on the Atlantic Ocean; and the Mississippi delta on the
Gulf of Mexico. Of the numerous deltas on the protected waters
of Europe and Asia may be mentioned that of the Danube on the
Black Sea, the Volga on the Caspian, and those of the Oxus (Amu-
darja) and the Jaxartes (Syr-darja) on the Aral Sea.

Form and Rate of Growth of Deltas. The form of the deltas
varies greatly from the typical triangular outline resembling the
Greek letter delta (Δ) characteristic of the Nile delta (the type
of deltas; Fig. 125) to the long, narrow estuarine filling of the
Mackenzie mouth, on the one hand, and the very broad, but short,
cuspate delta of the Tiber, or the still narrower strip-like or stunted
delta formed by the Cavonne on the Gulf of Taranto, southern Italy,

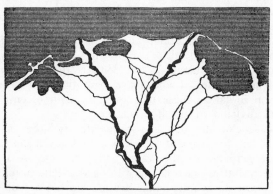

FIG. 125. The Nile Delta.

on the other. The mouth of the delta-building river may advance
singly (unilobate) without dividing into distributaries, as is nearly
the case with the Ebro on the northeast coast of Spain, or it may
be multilobate with the distributaries pushing each its own narrow
lobe forward, which may even become a finger-like extension, as
in the remarkable Mississippi delta. If the distributaries are numerous, they may form a network of streams, as on the Nile delta,
which advances by a continuous, more or less scalloped front.

In size the deltas of the present day vary from an insignificant
deposit at the mouth of a small stream to areas covering many
thousands of square miles, as in the deltas of the Nile, the Lena,
and the Mississippi. Confluent deltas of several streams occur,
making irregular deposits with many lagoons, as in the Rhine-
Meuse-Ems delta; while deltas building on a coast with many

islands may gradually annex these to the land by enclosing them in the growing delta. The hilly province of Shantung has thus been enclosed in the great delta of the Huang-ho, and a number of small islands have been included in the delta of the Aspropotamos in western Greece.

The rate of growth of deltas varies greatly and is often considerable. Thus the Jaxartes increased by 13¾ square miles between 1847 and 1900. (Andrussow–1 :49.) The delta of the Rhone is said to have lengthened more than 26 kilometers since 400 B. C. The southwest pass of the Mississippi delta grew, according to Captain Talcot, 104 meters in length in 1838, the south pass 85 meters, the northeast and southeast passes each 40 meters, and the pass à l'Outre 92 meters, giving an average of 80 meters per year for each pass. While this holds for the year in question, it is not possible to consider that such an increase occurs in all years. Indeed, often one year destroys what is built in the preceding year. The Po delta has increased between the years 1200-1600 at an average rate of 25 meters per year, but from 1600 to 1804 its rate of increase was 70 meters per annum. One of the most rapidly growing deltas is that of the Terek, on the Caspian. Within a period of 30 years the water has been pushed back 15 kilometers by the growth of the delta, which increased thus at the rate of half a kilometer per year. The other extreme is shown by the delta of the Danube, which at one of its mouths is not over 4 meters per year, though somewhat more rapid at another. The average increase of the Nile is about 4 meters per year, while the delta of the Tiber is estimated to increase at the low rate of 1 meter per year. According to Pumpelly, the Huang-ho has increased on the average at a rate of 30 meters per year between B. C. 220 and A. D. 1730.

Thickness or Depth of Deltas. (Credner–14.) The depth of delta deposits on modern sea coasts varies greatly, but is, on the whole, comparatively slight. Thus the mud of the Nile delta is not over 10 or 15 meters thick. It rests on loose sea sand. The delta deposits of the Rhine have a thickness of 60 meters, those of the Rhone over 100 meters. In the Po the depth averages 122 meters, though near Venice 172.5 meters were penetrated without reaching bottom. The delta deposits of the Ganges and Brahmaputra rest on older sediments and average only 20 meters in thickness. The actual delta deposits of the Mississippi range from 9.5 to 16 meters near New Orleans, increasing to 30 meters at the head of the passes, beyond which the thickness rapidly increases. They rest throughout on a stiff blue clay of earlier age. The Rhone delta in Lake Geneva has a thickness of 180 to 275 meters and a length of nearly two English miles.

Delta Slopes. The surface of the delta has always a gentle slope, this being steeper in the smaller deltas than in the larger ones, and steeper also in the deltas of coarse material than in those of fine silts. The frontal slope of the delta is, as a rule, much steeper, being sometimes as high as 25° or 30°, or in some cases even 35° in the small deltas of Pleistocenic and modern lakes. In the larger deltas, especially those on the sea coast, the frontal slope is much gentler. The strata of the Rhone delta in Lake Geneva are so slightly inclined that they almost take on a horizontal attitude. The total thickness of this delta, 180 to 275 meters, is distributed over nearly 2 miles. The frontal slope is 1 to 18. A much gentler slope is seen in the delta of the same stream in the Mediterranean, where the rate is 1 in 160, the depth increasing from 4 to 40 fathoms in the distance of 6 or 7 miles from the mouth of the stream.

Deltas of small lakes often show a steeper inclination for the older coarser beds than for the finer younger ones. Thus the delta of the Aar in the Lake of Brienz shows near the shore an inclination of the beds amounting to 30 degrees. About 300 meters from the shore the grade has decreased to 20 degrees, while at the extreme margin of the present delta, 1,100 to 1,200 meters from the shore, the beds are nearly horizontal. The delta of the Dundelbach in the southwest angle of the little Lake of Lungern in Switzerland shows coarse beds near the margin, sloping at an angle of 35 degrees, while the younger layers have a very gentle slope only.

The Bird-foot Delta of the Mississippi. The lower part of the Mississippi delta has a remarkable form, distinguishing it from all other modern deltas. From Forts Jackson and St. Philip onward for a distance of nearly 25 miles the river is confined in a narrow channel or "neck" which finally divides at the "Head of the Passes" into three divergent channels, or passes, each bordered by low banks of stiff clay and forming a structure resembling a bird's foot. One of these passes, the Pass à l'Outre, divides again into the North Pass and the Northeast Pass. The other two, the South Pass and the Southwest Pass, continue, as single narrow fingers, the latter for nearly 20 miles. Some distance above the head of the passes a similar channel, the Main Pass, extends northward, and still farther up a group of small channels diverges from the neck. The material composing the banks of the neck and the passes is wholly unlike ordinary river silt, though in general a thin superficial layer of this occurs. Primarily, however, the banks consist of a stiff blue clay not unlike the stiff "Port Hudson clays" (Hilgard–29) which underlie the whole delta. Such mud is brought to the surface in a series of mud volcanoes or mud-lumps which, from time to time, arise on the delta surface. These are believed by Hilgard to be formed of the fine mud brought down by the river and precipitated outside of the delta by flocculation. Over this liquid mud are spread the river sediments, the weight of which and that of the growing marshes and their pressure upon the mud

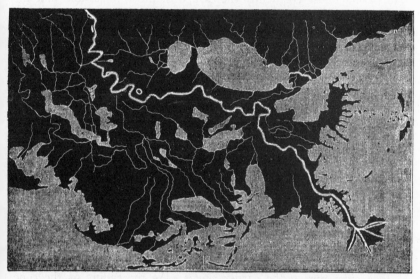

Fig. 126. The Mississippi Delta. At the "bird foot" the passes are from right to left: North Pass, Northeast Pass (these two unite to form the Pass à l'Outre), South Pass, Southwest Pass. The Northeast Pass has a small southern branch, the Southeast Pass (not shown), while another group of channels, diverges from the "neck" about five miles above the "head of the passes."

layers result in local upheavals and formation of mud lumps or craters, as long ago suggested by Lyell. Rod soundings in such a crater have reached a depth of 24 feet, but no solid bottom. The mud flow from these craters varies with the stages of the river, becoming much more lively in times of flood, when great masses of water, or of silt brought down by the river, press upon the layer of liquid mud. Hilgard believes that the banks of the neck and the passes are formed of the disintegrated and redeposited mud from such mud lumps, and that when a mud lump arises in the channel, as has recently occurred, a division is likely to take place. Hilgard testifies to the tough, resistant character of this clay, which when wet is almost inerodable by pure water. (29.)

Structure and Composition of the Delta. Theoretically the delta consists of bottom-set, fore-set, and top-set beds. These are all well developed in the small deltas formed in Pleistocenic time in temporary ice-dammed lakes and now open to examination after the draining of these lakes. In the deltas on the sea coast, however, one or the other of these beds is often absent, or two may merge, this being most frequently the case with the fore-set and bottom-set beds.

The fore-set beds of small or young deltas are generally steeply inclined, as already noted. This is especially the case when the supply of detritus is large. As the delta increases in size the later fore-set beds become more flattened and bend over at the bottom into the horizontal bottom-set beds. The upper ends of the fore-set beds, on the other hand, show more or less of erosion and across their truncated edges are deposited the top-set beds. There may, of course, be at times a bending over of the top-set beds into the fore-set, but in the young delta the contact is more or less sharp. In the larger deltas of fine material, on the other hand, the top-set beds may be more or less continuous with the fore-set, and, indeed, the two may imperceptibly grade into each other, without even a change in angle.

The top-set beds of small deltas consist of the coarser material laid down in nearly horizontal beds. If we assume that the normal delta begins as a subaqueous detrital cone or semi-cone growing in circumference, it is apparent that fore-set and bottom-set beds alone exist during the earlier stages. As the radius of the cone increases, its summit is invariably truncated by the waves and by the stream itself, which carries the detritus out to the front of the cone. Thus a level plane is formed partly by non-deposition and partly by contemporaneous erosion truncating the fore-set beds. Its surface will be to some extent below water level, the depth depending on the strength of the wave activity. Upon this plane will be deposited the top-set series which the current can no longer carry to the edge of the growing delta. The top-set series will continue to grow in thickness and extent as the delta grows, and its landward part will begin to emerge and become subaërial. The extent to which this subaërial part of the top-set series will grow is determined by the strength of the river and the slope which it can control. In smaller deltas the frontal angle of the delta is also the junction between top-set and fore-set beds and marks the extent of sub-mergence of the delta. In larger deltas the top-set beds go deeper.

Examination of deltas permanently or temporarily laid dry shows that the structure is by no means a uniform or simple one throughout. Thus the delta of the Dundelbach, laid open to observation by the partial drying of the Lake of Lungern into which it was built, showed striking variation. Near its head it consists of beds of coarse and fine gravel, sloping at an angle of about 35 degrees. Large, flat rock fragments rest with their surfaces on the inclined gravel layers, and a bed of compressed bituminous woods and leaves, six inches in thickness, is interbedded with these gravels in one part of the section. In general, the successive inclined layers are only a few inches thick; and this thickness does not increase toward the lower end in the coarser layers. In the fine mud layers, however, there is an increase in thickness downward before the layers bend over horizontally at the bottom. These finer textured layers rest gently against the steeper, coarser ones, filling especially the angle between the steeper layers and the flat lake bottom.

The numerous (20 or more) well borings made into the confluent deltas of the Po, Etch, and Brenta, in the region about Venice, have revealed the fact that the structure of the delta is an extremely heterogeneous one. While the beds are, in general, horizontal, with only minor undulations, the succession is scarcely the same in any two of the bore holes. This proves that the beds of the delta form a succession of lenticular masses, of very limited extent. Only two sandy layers, carrying water, have proved in any way constant; all other layers quickly wedge out laterally. (See the combination of profiles given by Credner–14: *pl. I, Fig. 9*.) The successive layers comprise brown clays alternating with yellowish sands with lignites and occasionally layers containing marine organisms. The series includes several beds with molluscan remains. Marine molluscs, especially Cardiacea, abound in the higher fossiliferous layers, while in the deeper beds only occurs the intermingling with these of fresh-water types. In some wells lignites with associated land snails, such as Succinea, Pupa, Helix, etc., were found. Vegetable material occurs at four successive horizons in the Po delta down to a depth of 100 meters. The material is the same as that now forming marshlands on the coast of the Adriatic. This and the occurrence of the land snails in the lower beds would suggest subsidence since delta-building began here. The borings near Venice show that about one-third of the material making up the upper sixty meters of the delta ground consists of lignite and peat.

Quite a different picture from this is presented by the mud

deposits of the Nile. At low water these are visible in the steep banks which then rise 8 to 10 meters above water level. The hardened Nile mud forms a series of horizontal beds varying in thickness from a few inches to several feet, and looks more like an ancient stratified series than like a modern deposit. The material of the Nile mud is a more or less uniformly fine-grained one, the size of the grains varying from 1/13 to 1/100 mm., rarely reaching 1/10 mm. in size. It is a unique deposit probably not paralleled by any other modern one on the face of the earth. An analysis of the mud (Clarke–12:481) gave:

SiO_2	45.10
Al_2O_3	15.95
Fe_2O_3	13.25
MgO	2.64
CaO	4.85
K_2O	1.95
Na_2O	0.85
SO_3	0.34
H_2O	15.54
	100.47

The remarkable fact about this mud is its high iron and low organic content, though some analysts have found the finely divided organic matter as high as 5.53 per cent. or even 7.9 per cent. Some analyses show an admixture of barium carbonate over wide areas.

In other deltas the organic material is pronounced. The abundant admixture of leaves and more or less lignitized wood in some deltas has already been noted. In the Po delta it occurs in four successive horizons. In the Ganges delta such deposits are found between 9 and 15 meters in depth, together with carbonized trunks of trees characteristic of the region, such as *Heritiera littoralis,* which abounds in the lower part of Bengal. In the lower Mississippi delta driftwood is common, the logs being at times united into floating rafts. Not infrequently erect trunks are found among these, with their roots spreading in all directions, as if while growing there they were submerged by a subsidence. The Mackenzie River delta likewise contains an abundance of carbonized driftwood, and this is true of many other deltas.

More striking, however, in some ways is the abundance of finely divided vegetable matter in some deltas. Thus the mud of the Vistula (Weichsel) loses, according to G. Bischof (9) 23.3 per cent. on ignition, most of this being organic material. The clay of the Vistula delta in the Bay of Danzig is so rich in organic material that it has a deep black color, and is locally known as pitch, "pech." The bearing of this fact on the origin of some black shales will be considered later.

Organisms of the Delta. Marine organisms are not uncommon in sea-coast deltas, but they are, as a rule, distributed in certain layers only. Lyell has explained the occurrences of marine molluscs in extensive beds between the fresh water layers of the delta as due to wave work, which casts masses of shells upon the growing delta surface. In some parts of the Rhone delta marine and fresh water shells alternate in the deposit. This is explained by Lyell as probably due to the alternating occupancy of lagoons and channels on the growing delta by salt or by fresh water, according as the prevailing wind or other causes may ordain. As already noted, the delta of the Po also contains fresh water organisms associated with marine shells, but only in the lower beds, while upward the shell deposits become purely marine. Foraminiferal shells often abound in modern deltas. Thus the Mississippi mud was found to contain an abundance of marine Polygastrica and Phytolitharia as well as fresh water Polythalamia. Phytolitharia also abound in the mud of the Nile. Indeed, the range of foraminiferal shell material in the Nile mud is from 4.6 to 10 per cent., while the Ganges carries as high as 12.4 or even 25 per cent. of foraminiferal material.

Other animal remains have been found, but are less abundant. Remains of arthropods occur in the Po delta sometimes in close association with the lignites. Remains of river animals also abound in modern deltas, as shown by the presence of turtles and crocodile remains in the delta deposits of the Ganges and the Zambesi. Terrestrial vertebrate remains have likewise been found in these deltas, among them bones of recent antelope, buffalo, lion, hippopotamus, and other mammals.

Gaseous Emanations of Deltas. The gradual decomposition of the organisms in the delta deposits gives rise to gaseous emanations which either escape through artificial borings in the delta or find natural passageways through the mud, building up craters as in the mud-lumps of the Mississippi delta. The numerous borings in the delta of the Po have furnished an abundance of inflammable gas, the use of which for illuminating purposes has actually been attempted. Sulphuretted hydrogen is also developed, especially where sea water comes in contact with the decaying vegetable matter, as noted in the case of marine marshes (see *ante,* page 493). In the mud-lumps of the Mississippi delta, the volume of gas emitted is between 1/20 and 1/30 that of the mud flow from these craters. The gas is probably not instrumental in these mud eruptions, but merely an accompaniment of the same.

Cementation of Delta Deposits. The delta deposits may be compacted merely by pressure, or the component particles may be bound together by the introduction of a cement. The Rhone delta contains much sandstone, the grains of quartz being bound by a calcareous cement, due to the abundance of lime in the stream. The presence of numerous limestone pebbles in glacial deltas also becomes a source of lime which is redeposited among the pebbles and cements them. Such an example is found in the partly consolidated gravels of the Pleistocenic delta in the Ontario basin near Lewiston, and a still more extensive one in the Nagelfluh delta of the Salzburg region already referred to. Cementation by infiltrated iron oxides also occurs.

Deposits of lime are especially abundant in deltas of arid regions, such as the Volga, the Indus, the Nile, and the Colorado. Extensive deposits of massive travertine and caliche have been formed in Arizona and New Mexico. Such deposits are, however, also found where the river water is high in lime content, as in the Rhine delta and in the Rhone delta already mentioned. In the latter case the approach to a semi-arid climate over the delta in the mediterranean is a further factor aiding deposition of lime. The silt of the Rhine delta in the Lake of Constance contains 30.76% of $CaCO_3$, 1.24% $MgCO_3$, and 5.20% $FeCO_3$. The other principal constituents are SiO_2 50.14%, Al_2O_3 4.77%, Fe_2O_3 2.69%, and small quantities of the oxides of manganese, magnesium, calcium, potassium, and sodium.

Modification of the Delta Surfaces. The chief modifications suffered by the delta are wave and wind erosion, and the formation of deposits over the surface of the delta. Wind erosion affects the surface of the delta, while wave erosion occurs around the margin of the delta when the force of the river no longer is able to continue construction. It is common on a sinking coast, as is shown by the encroachment of the sea on the deltas bordering the North Sea. Wave erosion may also become effective when delta-building has practically come to an end owing to the decrease of supply incident to development of low relief with old age. In such a case the sea may gradually encroach on the delta and plane away the upper layers, until the remaining remnant of the delta is wholly submerged, when normal marine sediments may succeed. In all such cases there is commonly found a fringing belt of dunes at the outer margin of the delta, as in the case of the Rhine delta. Such dunes may also be formed where building is still in progress, as in the Rhone delta, where dunes are formed between the two principal mouths of the stream. Other eolian deposits may form on the delta, such as dust brought from a distance and wind-arranged material from the surface of the delta itself. Additional river deposits in the form of natural levees may be built by the overflowing river, which leaves much of its material near the bank, which is thus raised above the surface of the delta on either side. The floor of the channel may also be raised by aggradation, and the river thus flows at a level much higher than that of the surrounding country. Where the levees are artificially raised the river bed may come to occupy a position far above the normal level of the delta or flood plain. Thus the channel of the Po has been elevated in this manner to such an extent that it is said to rise above the tops of the houses in the town of Ferrara (Le Conte–36:26). Where the sea temporarily floods part of the delta, deposits of salt may occur, as in the Rann of Cutch and other low-lying delta districts. The Nile delta is likewise characterized by saline deposits along the coast, due to evaporation of the sea water which at intervals floods the surface. Over these salt beds sand dunes are seen to wander. Deposits of vegetal material in swamps further characterize many delta surfaces. Such deposits may be marine marsh deposits or fresh water swamp deposits, or both. Salt and gypsum deposits are not uncommon on the lower part of the deltas in arid climates.

Relation of Delta Building to Crustal Movements. From the known relations of rivers to delta building it would appear that periods of strong river activities are also, as a rule, periods of pronounced delta formation, while, conversely, periods of diminished river work will be, on the whole, periods of slow and comparatively limited delta building. In general, youthful ungraded conditions of a land with corresponding high relief favor delta building, while mature or graded conditions characteristic of regions of low relief are correspondingly unfavorable to delta building. There are, however, modifying circumstances which may, to a certain extent, reverse these results, but as a general working proposition they may be confidently accepted. Furthermore, conditions of youth and high relief with active river work are productive of an abundance of coarse waste, which will result in the outward and upward building of deltas with strongly contrasted slopes in fore-set and top-set beds, while the finer waste supplied in lesser quantities by a region of relative maturity will tend to build outward deltas of gently inclined layers and, on the whole, of uniformity of slopes or confluence of top-set, fore-set, and bottom-set beds. In youthful regions of much waste supply the subaërial part of the delta will become a prominent feature, while the reverse will be true in regions past maturity and of slight supply of waste. It is thus readily conceivable that periods of intensive and extensive delta building may alternate in the earth's history with periods during which deltas are of relatively insignificant extent and the size and number of deltas in one period afford no criterion by which those of another may be measured.

Effect of subsidence. While the effect of stationary sea-level will be the rapid outward building of the delta, with pronounced development of the fore-set beds, slow subsidence will result in the extensive development of top-set beds and a restriction in the building of the fore-set beds. If the subsidence is periodic and interrupted, the sea will temporarily encroach on the delta, and the terrestrial top-set beds will be covered by a layer of marine sediments. Continued deposition by the rivers will, however, crowd back the sea, and renewed building of top-set beds will occur. In this manner intercalated marine layers will be formed between the terrestrial deposits. Such layers are found in modern deltas as already noted, and they are also common in older delta deposits, where they are generally taken as indicating the marine origin of the entire formation. That they have no such value is clearly shown by their relation to the continental beds in modern delta deposits. If subsidence were slow and more or less regular, continued deposition by rivers would tend to keep the sea out altogether, and a thick deposit of top-set beds of terrestrial origin would result. Such deposits of considerable thickness are found to characterize the larger modern deltas, which thus appear to occupy sites of continued subsidence. Similar conditions prevailed over the sites of delta deposits of Mesozoic and Palæozoic time, resulting in the formation of continental deposits of great thickness.

Subsidence of such a rate as to be in excess of the building power of the streams will put an end to the process of building the deltas and result in their final submergence. This has been brought about in a number of cases where former deltas and parts of deltas are now below sea-level. In earlier geologic periods such complete submergence has resulted in the burial of the delta deposit beneath a marine series of greater or less thickness. Credner (14) and others have, indeed, held that any subsidence is detrimental to the process of delta building, and that such stuctures are found only on rising or at least stationary coasts. That subsidence has, however, played a part in the formation of modern deltas is shown by the presence in most of them of terrestrial remains and peat layers, etc., which now lie at a considerable depth beneath sea-level (Fig. 127).

Effect of elevation. Slight elevation of the delta area results in the destruction by erosion of the top-set series in the upper parts of the delta, and the carrying forward of the material to be added to the subaqueous fore-set series. The zone over which continental deposition takes place will also advance seaward, and thus terrestrial sediments will come to rest on marine deposits. Where the inclination of the fore-set beds is very gentle these terrestrial beds may come to rest upon them with practically no change in dip. Cessation of elevation or reversal of movement and the resumption of normal delta building will result in the deposition of a new terrestrial series on top of the erosion plane, and a new marine series on top of the terrestrial series nearer the sea. A hiatus and disconformable relationship will thus appear between the two members of the terrestrial part of the delta, and this disconformity will be re-

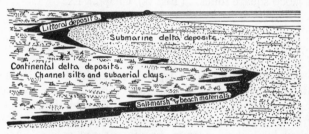

Fig. 127. Diagrammatic section of a seashore delta, showing the relation of continental and submarine deposits in a region of fluctuating sea-level. (After Barrell.)

placed seaward by a terrestrial layer interpolated between two marine series. If the delta front is comparatively steep it may, of course, happen that the uplift carries the erosion to the top of the delta front, beyond which deposition will be submarine. In a very large delta slow rising will result in the slow seaward migration of the zones of erosion and the zone of terrestrial deposition, the lowering of the upper part of the delta by erosion progressing steadily, while at the same time the zone of terrestrial deposition extends farther and farther outward. (Barrell–6.)

Deltas Merging into Desert Deposits. A remarkable combination of a river delta with desert deposits, on the one hand, and marine deposits, on the other, is shown by the Colorado on the Arizona-California and Lower California boundary. This delta was originally built into the Gulf of California, the head of which was by it completely severed from the main part of this funnel sea. The cut-off portion dried out completely under the influence of the drying westerlies, leaving the arid Coahuila basin north of the delta, the central portion of which is 300 feet below sea-level; while southward the delta enters the present head of the California Gulf. Occasionally a northwest distributary of the Colorado, the New River, carries water into the basin, which in the past has filled to overflowing, a fresh water lake being thus formed. The drying up of this left saline deposits upon the lacustrine beds, and these, together with the eolian and occasional river deposits, form a complicated series of sediments succeeding the former marine deposits of the region, all of these changes being brought about without any change in the sea-level. A moderate subsidence or a partial destruction of the delta would let the sea in again, and thus marine deposits would once more succeed the complicated terrestrial series. The area thus affected is somewhere in the neighborhood of 5,000 square miles. (Fig. 69, Chapter IX.)

COLORS OF CONTINENTAL CLASTICS.

The color of clastic rocks depends to a very large degree upon the states of oxidation of its iron content, and the absence or abundance of carbon. A low state of oxidation gives colors ranging from green to blue, while the higher states of oxidation are marked by yellow, orange, brown, or red colors. According to the carbon content, the color may vary from white, when no carbon is present, through various shades of gray to black. Abundant carbon in the strata will prevent oxidation of the iron and will reduce the higher oxides to the lower. Lack of carbon favors high oxidation.

Sediments deposited on land or in very shallow waters are especially subject to oxidation, unless there is an abundance of organic matter present to prevent such oxidation. In moist or pluvial climates with a moderate amount of vegetation, the soil is apt to be bluish from the prevention of a high degree of oxidation by the vegetation. This is especially true where the vegetation is intimately associated with the soil. The manner in which this is accomplished on the western side of Nicaragua has already been referred to (p. 36). Where black soils are formed, as on swampy surfaces, especially on low alluvial plains or peneplains, oxidation is likewise prevented. The same thing is true of delta deposits rich in carbon. Where, however, vegetation is extremely luxuriant it may prevent the saturation of the soil with moisture through transpiration and likewise prevent a satisfactory commingling of the vegetation with the soil. In such cases oxidation may proceed without hindrance, as in the case of the eastern slopes of Nicaragua, where red soil from 3 to 10 meters deep underlies the dense vegetation.

In seasons of dryness, when the amount of vegetation is small, the iron of the sediments of deltas and alluvial fans may become thoroughly oxidized. Where dryness prevails for most of the year, and where vegetation is as a result scanty, such oxidation may be especially favored. Thus semiarid or even desert regions would furnish the best conditions for such oxidation. On river flood plains there is always sufficient moisture to result in the formation of hydroxides of iron, and hence the colors of such deposits will range from yellows to ocher and brown. It is only under conditions of intense heat that dehydration will result with a consequent change in color toward the reds. Such change of color may, however, take place as the result of aging of the deposit, as pointed out by Crosby. In such a case dehydration is virtually spontaneous, and " . . . the color of the deposit, so far as it is due to ferric oxide, is, other things being equal, a function of its geological age." "In other words," says Crosby further, "the color naturally tends with the lapse of time to change from yellow to red; and, although this tendency exists independently of the temperature, it is undoubtedly greatly favored by a warm climate." (15.)

Barrell (4:*288*) holds that "a still more potent cause exists . . . in the dehydration effected by the great increase in pressure and moderate rise in temperature which takes place upon the burial of the material to some thousands of feet beneath later accumulations." Under such pressure the tendency would be for the oxide to give up its water with corresponding reduction in volume (see *ante,* p. 177), just as shales are formed by the giving off of about one-half the combined water by the silicate of alumina, and this at temperatures probably often far below boiling point.

It is, of course, necessary that organic matter should be absent from such a deposit, for its presence would prevent oxidation in the first place. It is not necessary that the absolute amount of iron should be very large to affect the color of the deposit. The brilliant red Vernon shales of the eastern New York Siluric carry only 2.25 per cent. of ferric iron and 0.75 per cent. of ferrous iron (Miller–39). The chief desideratum is that the iron should be in an extremely fine state of subdivision and intimately disseminated or diffused through the mud or dust deposits. This fine division and diffusion of the iron have been noted by Dawson for the red

Mississippic beds of Nova Scotia, where the iron has "the aspect of a chemical precipitate rather than of a substance triturated mechanically" (20:25). The same thing has been noted by Hilgard with regard to the red tropical soils, where the percentage of ferric oxide is by no means markedly high, but where the oxide is very finely diffused throughout the mass.

Finely diffused oxide of iron, but in the state of ferric hydrate, is the coloring agent of the yellow loess of China. The total amount of ferric oxide in American loess ranges from 2.50 per cent to 3.74 per cent., and in one case to 5.22 per cent., while a limited amount of FeO (from 0.12 to 1.02%) is also present, but organic carbon is very slight, ranging from 0.09 to 0.19 per cent. Dehydration of the iron with age, especially after burial, would result in the formation of fine-grained red deposits, in every respect similar to the Vernon red shales.

The red Vernon shales, like red shales and sandstones frequently, are associated with salt and gypsum deposits. This is an indication of arid conditions during the deposition of the muds from which these shales are formed. Salt and gypsum deposits of the present time are associated with gray and bluish-gray muds and it is only by subsequent oxidation and dehydration that the red color is produced.

One of the essentials in the production of red rocks by such subsequent oxidation and dehydration appears to be the virtual absence of organic matter which would prevent oxidation. Where the ground water level is high organic matter will accumulate and oxidation is prevented. But where the sands and muds are exposed to circulating air in dry seasons, with a low ground water level, more or less complete oxidation of the iron will take place. Such a condition is found in delta deposits of arid regions, as, for example, the Nile delta, in which organic matter seems to be of very small amount, while the iron content is comparatively high. It is probable that the Nile mud on aging would take on a red color.

There is, however, another factor which may affect the change in color, and that is the lime carbonate content of the deposit. This is high in many delta deposits of arid regions and its presence may prevent the production of a red color by the formation of complex silicates of lime, iron, and alumina. According to Ries (47:6, 11) a buff or cream color is produced if clay containing three times as much lime as iron or more is burned into bricks. Magnesia has the same coloring effect on the burned ware as lime, while alkalies tend to turn the iron red into a brown. As the Rhine delta in the Lake of Constance has nearly 12 times as much lime carbonate as iron oxide, it would not produce red bricks, and it is not improbable that the lime would have the same effect in preventing the formation of a red color with age.

Alternation of Red Beds with Those of Other Colors. This is a feature often found in older formations and has also been observed in modern continental hydroclastics. Huntington (34:364) has described such deposits of pinkish or reddish sandy clays and sands alternating with whitish or greenish clays from the uplifted and dissected Pleistocenic deposits of the basin of Seyistan in eastern Persia. These layers are well shown in cliffs from 400 to 600 feet high, exposed by recent erosion. The red beds are continuous and, while preserving their general aspect for many miles, they vary greatly in detail. Wedging out layers of sand or even gravel occur, slight erosion disconformities, occasional ripple marks, worm-casts and rain-drops are not uncommon, and the uniform oxidation of these beds indicates long exposure to the air under conditions of aridity. This is further shown by the condition of the modern delta deposits of the region, of which the subaërial part is well drained and aërated and everywhere of a light brown color. On the shores of the modern Lake of Seyistan, where the clayey beds are saturated with water and subject to successive floodings, the brown colors are replaced by light colored soils with black bands. The margin of the present lake supports a dense growth of reeds and the clay deposits on its bottom are greenish and white. The greenish and whitish beds of the dissected older deposits correspond to these lake sediments. They represent subaqueous deposits formed during the greater extent of the lake, and in continuity and uniformity, as well as color, they contrast strongly with the pink and red beds formed during the contraction of the lake as subaërial sediments.

Alternating red and white layers of this type are characteristic of the Moencopie formation of northern Arizona and southern Utah, a deposit of Permic age. The absence of fossils and the general close correspondence between these beds and the series exposed in the dissected basin of Seyistan have led Huntington to the conclusion that both have a similar origin.

Alternations of gray and green sandstones with red clays are well shown in the Middle Siwalik group, a late Tertiary deposit exposed in the foothills of the Himalayas. As previously noted, this formation represents a fluviatile deposit, of the type now forming over the Indo-Gangetic plain. A corresponding Devonic example is seen in the Catskill formation of eastern New York and Pennsylvania, where, through a thickness of perhaps 5,000 feet, there is a constant alternation of red shales and greenish sand-stones. The physical characteristics of the deposit and the absence of marine and presence of land and fresh water organisms show that this series was formed under fluviatile conditions similar to those of the Siwalik.

Lateral variation in color is also a frequent feature of older deposits and can be explained by the contemporaneous beds now forming in the Seyistan basin, where the oxidized subaërial deposits merge laterally into the unoxidized subaqueous or lacustrine ones. The fossiliferous Permic limestones and shales of Kansas may be traced southward into red sandstone and shales of the same age in Oklahoma, the latter being practically unfossiliferous. These red clays may be in part the residual clays from dissolved limestones (Beede–7) and in part of clastic origin. Their high state of oxidation suggests widespread subaërial deposition under sufficiently arid conditions to permit the free influence of the atmosphere. Lateral variation of a more irregular character is shown in some Mesozoic clays, such as the Potomac group of the Atlantic coast, and the Cretacic Atlantosaurus or Como beds of Wyoming, and in the Tertiary beds of the Wind River and Big-horn basins and elsewhere. In the Wasatch and Wind River clays analyses have shown the iron content to be as follows (Sin-clair and Granger–52:*115*):

Horizon	Phase	Total Iron calculated as Fe_2O_3 %	Total Iron	
			FeO %	Fe_2O_3 %
1. Mottled (red and blue) clay, Wind River..............	red	8.16	0.19	7.91
	blue	6.67	0.38	6.24
2. Blue clay, Wasatch	blue	3.34	0.52	2.77
3. Red clay, Wasatch, same locality	red	4.82	0.58	4.18

Sinclair and Granger comment on these analyses as follows: "In all the samples examined, the *total iron* in the red clays is in excess of that present in the blue by 1.48 per cent. to 1.49 per cent. The amount of *ferrous iron* in the blue Wasatch clay is less than that present in the red, while in the mottled Wind River clay it is slightly greater in the blue than in the red phase, but in neither case does it seem possible to ascribe the blue color to ferrous oxide, as this substance is far exceeded in amount by *ferric iron,* evidently occurring in the blue clay in some other form than ferric oxide (hematite), perhaps as a hydrous silicate. In the Wasatch clay the red contains 1.41% more Fe_2O_3 than the blue; in the Wind River clay Fe_2O_3 in the red phase is 1.67% greater than in the blue. If this excess of iron is present in the form of hematite, as the red color seems to show, it is possible that the remaining iron in the red clay may be in the same form as in the blue (a hydrous silicate?) and that the blue color has been masked by the red pigment."

"The results of analysis seem to show that the blue color has not been derived from the red by reduction of the iron as ordinarily understood. The red color may have been derived from the blue by conversion of the hypothetical silicate into carbonate by meteoric waters, and the subsequent oxidation of these salts, or by the introduction of iron compounds in solution and their concentration and oxidation possibly under drier climatic conditions than existed during the deposition of the blue clays. We favor the latter alternative and regard the coloration of the clays as a phenomenon controlled by conditions active during the deposition of each individual stratum (red or blue, as the case may be), and not by subsequent or secondary changes. Under the arid conditions which exist at present over most of the Wind River and Bighorn basins, the blue clays show no tendency to weather red. The layer of weathered mud-cracked clay on the surface of bad land slopes cut in the blue clays is yellow from the hydrous oxide, limonite." (52:*115, 116.*)

Original Red Color of Sediments. Whatever the case above mentioned shows, it must not be overlooked that some sediments when deposited already have a decidedly red color, or that this may be acquired before burial. Soils washed from regions of extensive laterite formation will be deposited as red sediments either on land or in the sea. Such sediments may be carried great distances from regions where they are formed to regions where their production is prohibited by the local climatic conditions. Russell held that the red sands of the Newark system were deposited with a coating of red iron oxide formed during decomposition. This conclusion may, however, be questioned.

Desert sands not infrequently have their grains coated with a thin deposit of iron oxide which often gives the sands a brilliant color, as in the case of the carmine sands of the Nefud desert of northern Arabia. The source (57:25) of the iron is believed to be in the sand itself, as shown by analysis, the coating having formed under the influence of the sun's heat, as the desert varnish forms on the larger pebbles and boulders. This latter, however, is subject to destruction owing to the size of the fragments, for Walther has observed that after a heavy rain this brown coating is quickly removed by the impact of the rock masses. In like manner a coating of iron oxide on sand grains subject to wind transport must be destroyed, and this probably accounts for the almost uniform white or golden color of desert sands. The absence of such a coating, then, on the pebbles of ancient desert gravels need not be surprising, and the yellow or white color of gravel and coarse sand beds intercalated between red deposits may not necessarily indicate great climatic differences, but may result rather from the destruction of the color coat in the coarser material.

EXAMPLES OF OLDER CONTINENTAL HYDRO-CLASTICS.

Examples of fluviatile and lacustrine deposits have been recognized in nearly all geological horizons, from the pre-Cambric to the present. Not all stratigraphers agree in regarding the formations enumerated below as of unequivocally non-marine origin, but the more obviously fluviatile and glacial formations are recognized as such by most recent students of the subject.

Cenozoic or Tertiary Examples.

Among the Tertiary deposits of the Great Plains regions of the western United States are many beds showing stratification, but composed in large part of alternate pebble and sand beds, with cross-bedding structure well marked. These have commonly been classed as "lake deposits," but, as Davis (19:345) has shown, these are more likely deposits made by running water, and represent outwash plains or alluvial fans, formed by the streams from the mountains. Some of these deposits, as in the case of the Vermillion Creek beds in Wyoming, consist near the mountains from which they have been derived of excessively coarse conglomerates between 3,000 and 4,000 feet thick, nearly structureless, lines of stratification being rarely perceived "The blocks of which the conglomerate is chiefly formed range from the size of a pea to masses with a weight of several tons . . ." (King–35:369.) At some distance from the mountains the beds consist of coarse red sand-stones interbedded with clays and arenaceous marls. In the Arapa-hoe and Denver formations of Colorado, basal conglomerates from 50 to 200 feet in thickness are succeeded by arenaceous clays, and these, in turn, are followed by 400 feet of eruptive débris, above which are again conglomerates and sands derived from the moun-tains. Cross-bedding and wedging out of layers are common, show-ing a considerable current. In some of the beds "tree stumps in erect position with roots in mud layers and broken trunks in sand or gravel . . ." occur (Cross–16:*168*) and contemporaneous lava flows are interbedded with the sediments.

In these deposits the remains of terrestrial vertebrates are fre-quently abundant, while fresh water animals are found only where temporary bodies of water existed. Associated with typical atmo-clastic are lacustrine deposits, often rich in remains of fish or other fresh water animals, and eolian deposits (anemoclastics). Not infrequently the atmoclastics extend out covering either lacus-trine or eolian deposits.

The Eocenic and Oligocenic deposits of the Wind River and Bighorn basins in Wyoming have already been referred to. These deposits consist of clays and sands often well banded and alternat-ing red and bluish in color, of arkose sands, and of conglomerates and occasional fine tuffs or pyrolutytes. They contain land and river vertebrates, such as crocodiles, turtles, garpike, Eohippus, Heptodon, Lambdotherium, etc., and shells of Unio. Microscopic as well as macroscopic study of the deposits has shown that they are derived from the crystalline or other rocks of the enclosing mountains, and their character and mode of occurrence show that they were either wind or river transported. In the coarser sand-stones and arkoses of the Wind River and Bridger (?) beds, Archæan granites and Palæozoic quartzites are readily recognizable. "The well-rounded gravels, found in some of the arkoses, point with equal certainty to running water as the transporting agent, while fluviatile deposition is shown by the frequent channels filled with coarse sandstone which cut irregularly across the finer clays, by the frequent interstratification of sandstone lenses with the clays and by the presence in the latter of fish, crocodiles, and turtles, and occasional beds of Unios. Local swamps are indicated by lignites in the blue clays and sandstones, but never in the red clays."

Sometimes change in climate or steepening of grade is indi-cated by coarsening of sediments . . . "for instance, the coarse, frequently cross-bedded arkose forming the lower member of the so-called Bridger of the Beaver Divide appears to represent a series of conjoined alluvial fans spreading out over the banded clays of the Wind River, but it is not possible to say whether the gravels and sands were transported by torrential streams under a dry climate or by streams whose carrying capacity had been increased by uplift." (Sinclair and Granger–52:*113*.) The freshness of the feldspars indicates that they had not been leached by carbonated waters, such as might be expected to occur if they were deposited in a region of high humidity. This also suggests that they have not been derived from the parent rock by ordinary weathering processes, but rather by temperature changes, which shatter the minerals without affecting their freshness. Altogether, the deposits suggest dry, not necessarily arid, climate, with rapid changes of temperature and rapid transportation for short distances and burial beyond the reach of carbonated waters.

The clays of the Wasatch and Wind River deposits are commonly banded, alternating beds of red and blue-green clay or of red with mottled clay occurring. "The red clays are frequently streaked with blue-green color along joint cracks or are traversed by anastomosing green lines along what may have been the courses of roots. The beds are lenticular in shape, varying from a few inches in thickness, with little horizontal extent, to strata from 18 inches to 50 feet in thickness, traceable sometimes for several hundred yards to a mile or more. . . . Lignite is never found in the red clays, but may be present in the blue. . . ." The fossils found in the red beds are always fragmentary, "the more resistant parts, such as jaws and teeth, predominating. In the blue and mottled clays associated skeletons . . . of Coryphodon were found." (Sinclair and Granger–52:*114, 115*.) The microscope has not revealed any essential difference between the variously colored clays.

Sinclair and Granger ascribe the color banding to the alternation of moist and dry climatic conditions, though no evidence of excessive aridity has been found; the fauna of the red and blue bands being the same. "The clays cannot owe their color to different sources of supply, for they are microscopically the same and the alternation of color bands is too regular and of too frequent recurrence to permit this inference. The red clay cannot represent upland oxidized wash, for waters swift enough to carry the bone fragments found in the clay would also transport rock fragments of some size, and these are not found." The blue clays of the Wasatch are sometimes lignitic and often afford associated skeletal remains, and this suggests that they were formed during cycles of more abundant rainfall, when the surface of the intermontane basin was prevented from drying out rapidly. The red clays, however, appear to have been formed "during the drier cycles, when the carbonaceous matter of decaying plants was completely oxidized, concentration and oxidation of iron compounds occurred, and animal bones exposed at the surface were weathered and broken before entombment." Conditions of this kind seem to have been widespread, as shown by similar color banding in the Wasatch in other localities.

In the Wasatch formation along the contacts of red and blue beds or in many of the red beds themselves great numbers of fragmentary jaws and scattered teeth of vertebrates have been found. The clays appear to represent the deposits on the dry basin floor over which the bones of these creatures were scattered and weathered before being buried. In the blue clays associated skeletons are common. These are the remains of animals which were either drowned and rapidly covered beneath fluviatile sediments or were mired in the soft clays. The teeth found in the Wind River area usually have the roots worn away and only the harder enamel-covered crowns are preserved. The Unio beds of the Wasatch are always of limited extent and seem to be confined to the blue clays. The lignite layers in these clays are usually mere dirt bands, but some in the Wind River basin have considerable thickness (52:*117*).

The Oligocenic beds of this region contain limestone deposits associated with wind-laid volcanic tuffs. These limestones, which are found near the top of the series, are a spring deposit forming sheets of tufaceous limestone, or layers of white nodular masses, calcareous without, but containing more or less silica within. Worn quartz, feldspar, and pink granite pebbles are sometimes found in the limestone, which is also partly replaced by silica in the form of opal or chalcedony. No fossils have been found in the limestone, which appears to have been formed under relatively dry climatic conditions.

These Tertiary deposits on the eastern slopes of the Rockies have thus all the characteristics of deposits formed under semiarid conditions. These conditions prevail to-day in this region under the influence of the westerly winds, which, on crossing the Coast Range, where they leave most of their moisture, become still drier on crossing the Rockies. Greater elevation of the mountain ranges would probably increase the aridity of the intermont basins in this region and so reëstablish the conditions of Tertiary time.

Hobbs (31) has recently described a typical torrential formation of great thickness from southern Spain. This ranges in age from Miocenic to the present. Its material is derived from the crystallines of the Sierra Nevada, from the northern flanks of which it extends for twenty-five miles, and locally from the Triassic dolomite of the Sierra Haraña (Alhambra formation). The formation, approaching a thousand feet in thickness, is a conglomerate near the mountains with pebbles varying "from a fraction of an inch to six inches or more in length." Within the various stream valleys local peculiarities of rock material exist, corresponding to the peculiarities of the rocks in the respective headwater branches of these streams. At a distance from the mountains fine material prevails, much of it of a loess-like character, indicating wind and playa-lake deposition. Floated plant material, such as roots and brushes, appear to be characteristic of some of the finer deposits. These torrential deposits seem to be intimately related to the semiarid conditions of the interior of Spain, caused by the monsoon winds. These winds blow northward from the Mediterranean in summer, crossing the Sierra Nevada and leaving much of their moisture on the southern slopes. Descending the northern slopes they are relatively drying winds and so permit the formation of these periodic torrential deposits.

Similar torrential deposits of great thickness and ranging in age from late Tertiary to the present are described from southern Italy (31 :*290*). A marked cross-bedding structure, already referred to (Fig. 123), so similar to what is commonly found in ancient sandstones, is characteristic of many of these deposits. The Siwalik formation of India has already been cited as a subaërial deposit of similar character and age. It is of great interest in that it reaches the enormous thickness of 15,000 feet. Here also belongs in part the Mollasse of the Alps. This is a complex series of light-colored sandstones and conglomerates with occasional limestones, found in the Alpine forelands, in the south of Germany and in Switzerland. The lower part of the Mollasse is of Oligocenic age and begins as a marine series. In southern Germany this reaches in places a thickness of 600 meters (Bavaria) and is followed by an immense series of fresh water sands and conglomerates approaching a thousand meters in thickness. This series shows in part brackish water and in part fluviatile and lacustrine conditions. The brackish water phase contains Cyrena, Cerithium, Cytherea, etc., and the fresh water Limnæus, etc. Numerous leaves and other remains of land plants (Cinnamomum, Juglans, Quercus, Betula, Rhamnus, etc.) are found locally, forming what is known as "Blättermollasse" and forming occasional beds of brown coal, which is extensively exploited in the Bavarian fore-Alps. Red sediments forming the "red Mollasse" are frequent in the upper non-marine part of the Oligocenic Mollasse, especially in Switzerland, but occur also in upper Swabia. The red beds are generally followed by conglomerates with pebbles ranging in size from that of an egg to that of a man's head and locally kown as Nagelfluh. These in places reach a great thickness. Away from the Alps the material becomes finer. The Miocenic Mollasse succeeding this often begins with calcareous beds to a large extent formed of the shells of the land snail, *Helix rugulosa* (Rugulosa limestones). This is followed by a series of loose sands, glauconitic sandstones and conglomerates (Nagelfluh) several hundred meters thick in the southern part of the region. The lower part of this series is again purely marine, but the upper part is once more brackish and non-marine, beds containing *Cardium sociale,* Melanopsis, etc., marking the brackish portion; sands with Paludina, Unio, and Chara fruits, marking the lacustrine and fluviatile. These series constitute the Middle Mollasse. The highest beds finally forming the Upper Mollasse of Upper Miocenic age are again wholly non-marine. They consist of sands, clays, marls, occasional thin beds of brown coal, local volcanic tuffs and especially non-marine limestones. These so-called Sylvana limestones consist of the shells of the land snails *Helix sylvana* and *H. inflexa,* of those of the pond and river snails Planorbis, Limnæus, etc. Bones of the mastodon also occur. Other beds contain an abundance of the shells of the river and lake molluscs, Unio, Anodonta, Limnæus, Melania, Melanopsis, etc. Local deposits of thin marly limestones with plant (maple, poplar, etc.) and insect remains also occur, as in the celebrated deposit of Öningen on the Lake of Constance (Bodensee) and local deposits like those of the Steinheim basin with its sands filled with Planorbis, Helix, and land vertebrates. Remains of terrestrial vertebrates abound in all of these deposits.

Since the axis of the Alps is parallel to the direction of the rain-bringing winds, both sides receive an abundant rainfall, though within the mountains are dry valleys. The extensive formation of the Mollasse, partly of subaërial origin on the northern side of the Alps, suggests a different condition during Tertiary times, so as to result in a more arid condition on the north, or, at any rate, in conditions which would favor the formation of extensive alluvial fans.

MESOZOIC EXAMPLES OF CONTINENTAL HYDROCLASTICS.

The Potomac Formation of the Atlantic coast of North America represents a series of delta and flood plain deposits comparable to those of the Huang-ho and the Indo-Gangetic plain. Extensive torrential deposits are absent here, the series being composed mainly of sands and clays. The series goes back to late Jurassic or early Comanchic time, and comprises four main divisions, the Patuxent, Arundel, Patapsco, and Raritan. The organic remains in these deposits are chiefly land plants, while the remains of a land fauna have also been found. No marine organisms are known except in the upper part of the series, the Magothy formation of New Jersey, which, however, also contains land plants. Above this series lie sands and clays with an Upper Cretacic marine fauna. These deposits were spread upon a broad coastal belt by rivers coming from the region of Palæozoic and older strata on the northwest, where peneplanation was in progress. The sea margin at this time must have been some distance farther to the east than the present coast. The rivers were numerous and more or less evenly spaced, so as to produce a continuous series of confluent deltas which extended from Massachusetts to the Gulf of Mexico. Landward the subdivisions of this series are separated by erosion disconformities, marking periodic upwarpings, but seaward they become thicker, and the disconformities probably disappear. Somewhere east of the present coast line these deposits probably pass into a continuous marine series, now submerged.

The fluviatile origin of these deposits is suggested by the discontinuity of the strata, beds and lenses of clay and gravel occurring in sand and vice versa. Many of the clays are strongly variegated in color, the state of oxidation of the iron varying both horizontally and vertically, while concentrated segregations of the iron also occur. Such variable conditions for oxidation exist on river flood plains, but not in lakes or on the sea bottom. The abundant plant remains, which by their character show little transportation, as well as the absence of marine, brackish or even lacustrine organisms, strongly indicate fluviatile conditions, as do also the bones of dinosaurs, turtles, and crocodiles.

The Arundel formation appears to have been deposited within stream valleys eroded in the Patuxent, and in this formation gypsum has been found. This suggests greater aridity during the period of deposition of this formation than during the time the more widely spread sands and clays of the other divisions accumulated. In the Raritan formation feldspathic sands occur, further suggesting an increase in aridity, while lignitic quartz sands alternating with highly oxidized sands testify to a variety of conditions. Some of the quartz sands show the characteristics of dune deposits. Upward the occurrence of lignites with Teredo borings marks the beginning of marine invasion, the river building processes being overcome by the invading forces of the sea. (See further, Barrell–6.)

The Red Beds of North America. The Red Beds of the Rocky Mountain region and the similar red sandstones of the Newark formation of the eastern United States are now generally recognized as subaërial deposits, in part of fluviatile and in part of eolian origin, with subordinate lacustrine and rarely estuarine conditions. The source of the western red beds was the old Palæocordilleran chain of mountains formed at the end of the Palæozoic, and extending northwestward from Arizona to northern California. On the Pacific side of this chain marine Triassic and Jurassic beds were forming, while east of the range a series of alluvial fans accumulated, these being now in part represented by the Red beds. Their highly oxidized character indicates that accumulation was under semi-arid climatic conditions, such as would prevail with a westerly wind sweeping over a mountain chain of sufficient height to deprive it of most of its moisture. That vegetation, nevertheless, existed in some parts of the mountain slopes is shown by the abundance of the petrified woods preserved in these deposits, into which they were probably carried by torrential streams. According to Williston and Case (59) the upper Red beds, from Lander, Wyoming, on the north to New Mexico, Kansas, and Texas, on the south, range from five hundred to possibly a thousand feet in thickness and are "barren or almost barren measures characterized by light colors of the sandstone, often of eolian origin, and more or less interspersed or capped with massive beds of gypsum." It may be added, however, that some authors still hold to the marine theory of origin of these beds. (See, especially, Henning–28.)

Vertebrate fossils of Triassic (Keuper) age are reported from all along the line of outcrop, chiefly comprising phytosaurs and labyrinthodonts, closely agreeing with species from the European Keuper. Some of the lower Red beds of the southern and western region are of Permic age, and indicate the earlier commencement of this type of sedimentation.

Triassic Red Beds of Eastern North America and of Europe. The Newark series is likewise best regarded as forming local remnants of a combination of widespread alluvial fans, river flood plain, and eolian deposits, derived from the Appalachians to the west and built out toward the east on the low coastal plain, or into depressions, and under conditions of semi-aridity which permitted pronounced oxidation of the sediments. The beds themselves abound in shrinkage cracks, raindrop impressions and animal footprints. Fish remains and shells of Estheria are found in inter-calated black shales, and terrestrial plant remains are not uncommon in some sections. Much feldspar occurs and this together with the oxidation of the iron compounds indicates the relative aridity of the climate. Intrusive sheets and lava flows characterize the northern development, and coal beds the southern. Barrell and Kümmel have brought forward evidence in the sediments that a part of the material in Connecticut and in New Jersey was derived from the east as well as from the west. They therefore consider the deposits as formed in large basins bounded by faults, rather than accumulations on a coastal plain surface. Until recently the Triassic deposits of eastern North America were interpreted as estuarine accumulations (Russell–48; Chamberlin and Salisbury–11), but the detailed study of the physical characters of the rocks has developed the evidence which shows them to be continental deposits (Barrell–5). Similarly the corresponding Triassic deposits of northern and western Europe, the New Red sandstone of England and the Bunter Sandstein and Keuper of Germany had been regarded as estuarine, tidal, or lake deposits (Reade–46), but their subaërial origin, as sediments deposited by rivers chiefly from the mountains of that period on the south and west, is being more generally recognized. On the Continent the material was chiefly derived from the old Vindelician mountain range which existed where now is the valley of the Danube and separated the Alpine Triassic sea from the North German lowlands. According to Bräuhäuser (Fraas–22:*513*) the pebbles of the Lower Bunter sandstein of Schramberg are not worn by rolling, but the pebbles of the conglomerate forming the base of the Middle Bunter are well rounded and their size decreases from southeast to northwest. The material is derived from the crystallines and from the Rothliegende of the Permic. Wind-cut facetted pebbles also occur, but they have been more or less worn by subsequent reworking. Walther (58:*79*) speaks of middle and eastern Europe in Lower Triassic time as a huge desert area supplied with variable detritus by streams from the mountains on the south and west, and covered by endless dunes, interspersed with ponds, and once at least by a large relict sea. Clastic material accumulated to a depth of 400 to 600 meters, after which the sea invaded the region from the east and the marine Muschelkalk was deposited. An earlier temporary and partial invasion of the sea is suggested by fossiliferous horizons. The Keuper marks a return to continental sedimentation, which in Switzerland, France, and England was uninterrupted. At the beginning widespread sandstones (Schilfsandstein) were formed, these being interpreted as flood plain and delta deposits. (Fraas–22:*516*). The upper sandstone (Stubensandstein) has been interpreted as probably in part a fluviatile and in part an eolian formation, the sandstones representing an accumulation on a flat piedmont area at the foot of the actively eroded Vindelician mountain chain. The extensive variegated clays of the Keuper have been regarded by Lang and others as marine sediments, but Philippi (44:*463*), Fraas (22:*517*), and Walther (58) consider them rather as aërial sediments especially of eolian origin, representing a sort of loess-like accumulation. This interpretation is suggested by the manner of occurrence in these sediments of the skeletons of phytosaurians, aëtosaurians, land turtles, and labyrinthodonts, with occasional dinosaurs, all lacking evidence of transport or destruction by aquatic animals such as might be expected if the remains were carried into the sea. The prevailing color of these sediments is red except where they were subsequently reworked by water, and here a gray color predominates.

PALÆOZOIC DELTA DEPOSITS.

These are numerous, especially in North America, where a whole series has been determined. Thus the entire Coal Measure series and Permic of eastern North America chiefly consist of river deposits with only occasional incursions of the sea. The Pottsville conglomerate at the base of the series is an especially good example. It was deposited from two centers, one in east central Pennsylvania, the other in southern Virginia. From these points outward the beds progressively overlap away from the source of supply, and apparently upon an old land surface, there being in these sections no marine equivalents. The Pocono sandstone is a similar deposit, and between it and the Pottsville lies the Mauch Chunk red shale, a deposit of river flood plain and eolian origin during a period of relative aridity (Barrell–3). Still earlier in the Devonic a similar deposit, the Catskill, was formed progressively replacing a marine formation (Chemung) westward (Grabau–25). The Oneonta (Portage) sandstone of New York and the upper Hamilton or Ashokan formation is interpreted as of the same character. Still earlier in the Devonic the Esopus grit represents the characters of a sea-level delta built westward by a stream debouching near northern Pennsylvania. The Gaspé sandstone of eastern Canada likewise represents a Devonic dry delta deposit. Still earlier in the Siluric and Ordovicic similar dry deltas were built to the northwest by streams from an old Appalachian continent, these deposits sometimes replacing marine sediments westward, at others building out upon a dry land or, in one case at least, a desert area. (Grabau–27).

A remarkable feature of these deposits is the repeated succession upon light colored pebble deposits, with evidence of torrential origin, of finer red sediments with characters suggesting flood plain and eolian origin. Such are in the Ordovicic the light Bald Eagle conglomerate followed by the red Juniata shales, in the Siluric the Shawangunk conglomerate followed by the red Longwood shales, in the Devonic the Hamilton and Oneonta sands followed by the Catskill red beds, in the Mississippic the Pocono conglomerate and sandstone followed by the red Mauch Chunk shale. This succession seems to indicate conditions which permitted easterly winds to sweep across a more or less elevated land mass (Appalachia), where they were deprived of much of their moisture, thus creating semi-arid conditions on the west of this land mass. Moderate aridity, with periodic torrential rainfalls and swollen streams

FIG. 128. Hypothetical section of Appalachia in Palæozoic time to show the possible arrangement of the winds, and the corresponding deposits.

forming alluvial fans of pebbles, seems to have existed repeatedly, but in each case was followed by drier conditions such as would be produced by a renewed elevation of the land, and the consequent deposition in the lee of the land mass of highly oxidized sands and dust as river flood plain and eolian formations, which are now seen in the red beds. The conditions favoring such deposition are illustrated in the preceding diagram (Fig. 128).

Deposits of a similar character are found in the Old Red sandstone of western Europe, and the Siluric deposits of the north of England and the south of Scotland also show much evidence of deltaic origin.

One of the most striking examples of a seashore delta of Upper Devonic age seems to be represented in the black shale of Ohio, Michigan, and western New York. To be sure this has also been interpreted as a deep sea deposit, but its peculiarities all point to a delta-like origin, represented to a certain degree by the modern deposits at the mouth of the Mississippi. The abundance of spores of rhizocarp-like plants, represented to-day by fresh water plants, the presence of tree trunks, and especially the thinning away eastward and southward, and their interpolation between normal shallow water marine sediments, all point to the delta origin of these shales.

NOTE:—For a full discussion of the Early Palæozoic delta deposits of Eastern North America, see Grabau, 27.

BIBLIOGRAPHY XIV.

1. ANDRUSSOW, N. 1893. Physical Exploration of the Black Sea. Geographical Journal, Vol. I, pp. 49–51.
2. BARRELL, JOSEPH. 1906. Relative Geological Importance of Continental, Littoral and Marine Sedimentation, Journal of Geology, Vol. XIV, pp. 336–354; 430–457; 524–568.
3. BARRELL, JOSEPH. 1907. Origin and Significance of the Mauch Chunk Shale. Bulletin of the Geological Society of America, Vol. XVIII, pp. 449–476, pls. 49–52.
4. BARRELL, J. 1908. Relations between Climate and Terrestrial Deposits. Journal of Geology, Vol. XVI, pp. 159–190; 255–295; 363–384.
5. BARRELL, J. 1911. Central Connecticut in the Geologic Past. Proceedings and Collections of the Wyoming Historical and Geological Society, Vol. XII, pp. 1–30.
6. BARRELL, J. 1912. Criteria for the Recognition of Ancient Delta Deposits. Bulletin of the Geological Society of America, Vol. XXIII, pp. 377–446.
7. BEEDE, J. W. 1912. Origin of the Sediments and Coloring Matter of the Red Beds of Oklahoma. Science, N. S., Vol. XXXV, pp. 348–350.
8. BERKEY, C. P. 1905. Laminated Interglacial Clays of Grantsburg, Wisconsin. With chronological deductions. Journal of Geology, Vol. XIII, pp. 35–44.
9. BISCHOFF, GUSTAV. 1863. Lehrbuch der chemischen und physischen Geologie, 2nd edition, Vol. I. English: Elements of Chemical and Physical Geology, edited and in part translated by G. H. Paul, London, Cavendish Society, 1859, 3 vols.
10. BLAKE, W. P. 1901. The Caliche of Southern Arizona. Abstract. Engineering and Mining Journal, Vol. LXXII, pp. 601–602.
11. CHAMBERLIN, T. C., and SALISBURY, R. D. 1906. Geology. Vol. III. New York, Henry Holt & Co.
12. CLARKE, F. W. 1911. The Data of Geochemistry. 2nd edition. Bulletin United States Geological Survey, No. 491.
13. CRAMMER, HANS. 1903. Das Alter, die Entstehung und Zerstörung der Salzburger Nagelfluh. Neues Jahrbuch für Mineralogie, u. s. w., Beilage Band XVI, pp. 325–334.
14. CREDNER, GEORG RUDOLF. 1878. Die Deltas, Ihre Morphologie, Geographische Verbreitung und Entstehungs Bedingungen. Petermann's Geographische Mittheilungen Ergänzungsheft, No. 56, pp. 1–74, 3 Tafeln.

15. CROSBY, W. O. 1891. On the Contrast in Color of the Soils of High and Low Latitudes. American Geologist, Vol. VIII, pp. 72-82.

16. CROSS, WHITMAN. 1896. Geology of the Denver Basin in Colorado. Monograph U. S. Geological Survey, XXVII.

17. DARWIN, CHARLES. 1841. The Voyage of the Beagle.

18. DAVIS, W. M. 1898. Physical Geography. Ginn & Co.

19. DAVIS, W. M. 1900. The Fresh-water Tertiary Formations of the Rocky Mountain Region. Proceedings of the American Academy of Arts and Sciences, Vol. XXXV, pp. 345-373.

20. DAWSON, J. W. 1848. On the Coloring Matter of Red Sandstone and of Grayish and White Beds Associated with Them. Quarterly Journal of the Geological Society of London, Vol. V, pp. 25-26.

21. FOUREAU, F. 1893. Au Sahara, Reviewed in Petermann's Geographische Mittheilungen, Bd. XLVII, Litteraturbericht, p. 175, 1897.

22. FRAAS, E. 1911. Geologische und Palæontologische Beiträge aus dem Triasgebiet von Schwaben und Franken seit 1907. Geologische Rundschau, Band II, pp. 511-520 (with literature).

23. GRABAU, A. W. 1894. Lake Bouvé, an Extinct Glacial Lake in the Boston Basin. Occasional Papers of the Boston Society of Natural History, Vol. IV, pt. 3, pp. 564-600.

24. GRABAU, A. W. 1897. The Sand Plains of Truro Wellfleet and Eastham, Cape Cod. Science, N. S., Vol. V, pp. 334-335, 361.

25. GRABAU, A. W. 1906. Types of Sedimentary Overlap. Bulletin of the Geological Society of America, Vol. XVII, pp. 567-636.

26. GRABAU, A. W. 1910 Continental Formations of the North American Palæozoic. Compte Rendu du XIᵐᵉ Congrès Géologique International, pp. 997-1003.

27. GRABAU, A. W. 1913. Early Palæozoic Delta Deposits of North America. Bulletin of the Geological Society of America, Vol. XXIV, No. 3, pp. 399-528.

28. HENNING, KARL L. 1913. Die Red Beds. Ein Beitrag zur Geschichte der bunten Sansteine. Geologische Rundschau, Bd. IV, Heft 4, pp. 228-244.

29. HILGARD, E. W. 1912. A New Development in the Mississippi Delta. Popular Science Monthly, Vol. LXXX, pp. 237-245, Map.

30. HILL, ROBERT T., and VAUGHAN, T. WAYLAND. 1898. Geology of the Edwards Plateau and Rio Grande Plain Adjacent to Austin and San Antonio, Texas, with references to the occurrence of underground waters. 18th Annual Report, United States Geological Survey, pt. II, pp. 194-322.

31. HOBBS, W. H. 1906. Guadix Formation of Granada, Spain. Bulletin of the Geological Society of America, Vol. XVII, pp. 285-294.

32. HOERNES, RUDOLF. 1911. Gerölle und Geschiebe. Verhandlungen der kaiserlich-königlichen geologischen Reichsanstalt, Bericht vom 30ten Sept., 1911, No. 12, pp. 42 et seq.

33. HUNTINGTON, ELLSWORTH. 1907. The Pulse of Asia. Houghton, Mifflin Co.

34. HUNTINGTON, E. 1907. Some Characters of the Glacial Period in Non-glaciated Regions. Bulletin of the Geological Society of America, Vol. XVIII, pp. 351-388, pls. 31-39.

35. KING, CLARENCE. 1878. Systematic Geology. United States Geological Exploration of the Fortieth Parallel. Vol. I.

36. LE CONTE, JOSEPH. 1896. Elements of Geology, 4th ed. D. Appleton & Co., New York

37. LIBURNAU, J. LORENZ VON. 1888. Die geologischen Verhältnisse von Grund und Boden.

38. MEDLICOTT, HENRY B., and BLANFORD, W. T. 1879. Manual of the Geology of India, pt. II.

39. MILLER, W. J. 1910. Origin of the Color in the Vernon Shale. New York State Museum Bulletin 140, pp. 150–156.

40. OLDHAM, R. D. 1893. Manual of the Geology of India, 2nd edition, Calcutta.

41. PENCK, ALBRECHT. 1894. Morphologie der Erdoberfläche, Vol. I.

42. PENCK, ALBRECHT, and BRÜCKNER, E. 1902. Die Alpen im Eiszeit-Alter.

43. PETERMANN, A. 1867. Ein Flussdelta im Inneren von Australien und die neuesten Entdeckungen von Warburton und den deutschen Missionären Walder, Kramer und Meissel, 1866 and 1867. Petermann's Geographische Mittheilungen, pp. 437–447.

44. PHILIPPI, EMIL. 1901. Ueber die Bildungsweise der Buntgefärbten klastischen Gesteine der continentalen Trias. Centralblatt für Mineralogie, Geologie und Paläontologie, pp. 463–469.

45. PHILLIPS, J. A. 1881. On the Constitution of Grits and Sandstones. Quarterly Journal of the Geological Society of London, Vol. XXXVII, pp. 6–27.

46. READE, T. MELLARD. 1889. The New Red Sandstone and the Physiography of the Triassic Period. The Naturalist, April, 1889, pp. 108–111.

47. RIES, HEINRICH. 1910. Clays and Shales of Michigan. Geological Survey of Michigan, Vol. VIII, pt. I, pp. 1–67.

48. RUSSELL, ISRAEL C. 1878. The Physical History of the Triassic Formation of New Jersey and the Connecticut Valley. Annals of the New York Academy of Sciences, Vol. I, No. 8, pp. 220–254.

49. RUSSELL, I. C. 1895. Present and Extinct Lakes of Nevada. National Geographic Monograph No. 4, American Book Co.

50. RUSSELL, I. C. 1897. Lakes of North America. Macmillan & Co.

51. RUSSELL, I. C. 1899. Subaërial Decay of Rocks and Origin of the Red Color of Certain Formations. Bulletin 52, U. S. Geological Survey.

52. SINCLAIR, W. J., and GRANGER, WALTER. 1911. Eocene and Oligocene of the Wind River and Big Horn Basins. American Museum of Natural History, Bulletin, Vol. XXX, pp. 83–117, pls. IV–IX.

53. SUESS, E. 1882. Der Boden der Stadt Wien.

54. VOIGT, F. S. 1836. Weitere Nachrichten über die Hessberger Thierfährten. Neues Jahrbuch für Mineralogie, u. s. w. 1836, pp. 166–174.

55. WADE, ARTHUR. 1911. Observations on the Eastern Desert of Egypt. Quarterly Journal of the Geological Society of London, Vol. LXVII, pp. 238–262, pls. 13–16.

56. WALTHER, J. 1893–94. Einleitung in die Geologie als Historische Wissenschaft.

57. WALTHER, J. 1900. Das Gesetz der Wüstenbildung in gegenwart und Vorzeit. Ed. I (Ed. II, 1912).

58. WALTHER, J. 1910. Die Bunte Sandwüste. Lehrbuch der Geologie von Deutschland. Kapitel 13, pp. 79–82. Die Keuperzeit—ibid., Kapitel 15, pp. 87–90.

59. WILLISTON, SAMUEL W., and CASE, E. C. 1912. The Permo-carboniferous of Northern New Mexico. Journal of Geology, Vol. XX, pp. 3–12.
60. WILSON, J. HOWARD. 1906. The Glacial History of Nantucket and Cape Cod, Chapter IV; Columbia University Press, Geological Series, Vol. I.
61. WOODWORTH, J. B. Some Typical Eskers of Southern New England. Boston Society of Natural History Proceedings, Vol. XXVI, pp. 197–220.
62. WYNNE, A. B. 1878. The Geology of the Salt Range in Punjab Memoirs Geological Survey of India, Vol. XIV, p. 608.

CHAPTER XV.

STRUCTURAL CHARACTERS AND LITHOGENESIS OF THE MARINE HYDROCLASTICS.

Marine hydroclastics are accumulating in nearly every portion of the ocean to-day, and their fossil representatives are among the most widespread of the geological formations. They are most abundantly developed in the littoral portion of the seas, including the epicontinental seas, but also occur in the abyssal regions. In general, we may classify the material with reference to its source, either as terrigenous or land-derived, or as oceanic or derived from purely marine deposits. The latter group is essentially limited to the regions around coral reefs or other organic deposits, and so has a marked uniformity of petrographic character. Viewed as a whole, marine clastics are nearly always well stratified, and they are as a rule fossiliferous. Indeed, it may be seriously questioned if marine clastics are ever wholly free from organic remains, though for considerable distances off certain shores organisms may be so rare as to escape detection. Thus Kindle (54) reports dredging off the coast of Alaska for a hundred miles or more along the shore, without finding any organic remains whatever. This of course does not prove their absence, but only indicates their scarcity, and indeed at another point of the same coast organisms were abundant. Moreover, such dredging affects only the surface layers of the sea floor, and does not prove the absence of remains in somewhat deeper layers.

It is perfectly well known that marine organisms migrate with the seasons, and that at a certain locality, where life was abundant during one season, it is almost entirely absent in another, the organisms having migrated into deeper water. What is true of seasons is also true of longer periods, some regions formerly well stocked with organisms being barren for years at a time, after which a return of the fauna takes place. Such migration up and down the ocean floor is often determined by factors difficult to ascertain. In the Alaskan case it may be due to the abundance of cold water carried in from the land by the melting of the glaciers, which, as shown by Tarr (92), has recently become very marked through changes which also caused an advance of the glaciers in certain localities. Portions of the glaciers hitherto protected by débris or otherwise have been suffering ablation during July and early August at a rate sufficient to lower the ice surface four inches a day.

While marine fossils are as a rule a reliable indication of the marine origin of a given series of clastics, this is the case only when the fossils are generally distributed throughout the mass, or when there is no other positive indication of a non-marine origin. As has already been shown, eolian limestones composed almost wholly of marine organisms are forming at the present time, and have formed in the past. Fossils weathering out from a marine series may be incorporated in the next overlying continental formation, as in the case of the Eocenic and other fossils of the rocks forming the floor of the Libyan desert, which are included in the overlying desert sands. Marine organic remains may be carried inland by winds, by birds or in some other manner, and thus become incorporated in terrestrial formations. Finally, deposits of terrestrial character may be at intervals submerged by a momentary encroachment of the sea, as in the case of the Po, the Rhine and other deltas, with the result that intercalated marine sediments are formed. Or, again, the sea may invade a large territory previously the theater of terrestrial deposition, and by reworking the upper layers of the continental deposits, or in some cases the entire mass, may impress upon it locally a marine character. This has been the case with the St. Peter sandstone, largely an eolian formation; with the upper part of the Sylvania sandstone of similar origin; with the Dakota and apparently also with the Potsdam sandstone, which, in many sections, still shows characters pointing to torrential or eolian origin of a considerable portion of the rock.

It should of course also be emphasized that the reverse is likely to hold, namely, that absence of marine fossils is not an absolute indication of the non-marine character of a formation, though absence over a very large area may probably be taken as a fairly certain guide. The physical characters of the rocks and their relationships must be taken into careful consideration. Among the negative characters of marine clastics are: the absence of mud cracks, rain prints, footprint impressions, rill marks, etc., though all of these *may* occur in the shore zone.

SUBDIVISIONS OF THE AREAS OF MARINE DEPOSITION. TYPES OF MARINE DEPOSITS.

The following districts and zones or regions of deposition of clastic material may be recognized in the sea:

1. *The Littoral District,* or that ranging from the shore to the edge of the continental shelf, that portion of mediterraneans corresponding to this, and the whole of the bottoms of epicontinental seas. Deposits formed here are "littoral deposits," and they are among the most varied of their kind. The littoral district is divisible into the shore zone between tides and the permanently submerged shallow water or *neritic* zone * (*Flachsee*), extending to the isobath of 200 meters.

2. *The Bathyal District* (Renevier) is that district lying between the outer limit of the neritic zone, *i. e.,* the 200-meter line, and approximately the isobath of 900, or, in round numbers, 1,000 meters. It represents the steep slope from the edge of the continental shelf to the point of decreasing angle of slope. This comprises only the upper portion of Penck's aktic region, which extends to the mean sphere level of 2,400 meters below sea-level (see Chapter I). (Fig. 1, p. 8.)

3. *The Deep Sea or Abyssal District.* This, according to Penck and others, begins at the 2,400-meter line, but so far as deposition is concerned begins practically at the 1,000-meter isobath.

A general classification of oceanic sediments, including all types, was made by Murray and Renard (62: *186*), as follows:

Murray and Renard's Classification of Marine Deposits.

1. **Deep-sea** deposits beyond **100** fathoms.	Red clay Radiolarian ooze Diatom ooze Globigerina ooze Pteropod ooze Blue mud Red mud Volcanic mud Coral mud	I. Pelagic deposits formed in deep water removed from land
2. Shallow-water deposits between low-water mark and 100 fathoms	Sand, gravels, muds, etc.	II. Terrigenous deposits formed in deep and shallow water, mostly close to land
3. Littoral deposits between high and low-water marks.	Sands, gravels, muds, etc.	

* Haug (43:*86*) and others have shown a tendency to use neritic in the sense in which littoral is here used, restricting that term to the shore zone or intercotidal region. The use here advocated seems the most serviceable.

Otto Krümmel (55 : *152*) has made a threefold division of marine sediments, modifying the classification of Murray and Renard as follows:

Krümmel's Classification of Marine Deposits.

I. LITTORAL OR NEAR LAND DEPOSITS.

1. Strand or shore deposits.
2. Shelf (shallow water) deposits:
    Each comprises boulder, gravel, sand, and mud deposits, which according to their source are clastic, volcanic, biogenic, chemical (halmyrogenic) and glacial.

II. HEMIPELAGIC OR DEEP SEA TERRIGENOUS DEPOSITS.

1. Blue and red mud (including volcanic mud).
2. Greensand and green mud.
3. Lime sand and lime mud:
    (Subdivisions as under littoral.)

III. EUPELAGIC DEPOSITS DISTANT FROM LAND.

A. Epilophic deposits (formed on the submarine ridges and swells).
    (a) Calcareous deep sea ooze.
        1. Globigerina ooze.
        2. Pteropod ooze
    (b) Siliceous deep sea ooze.
        3. Diatomaceous ooze.
B. Abyssal deposits:
        4. Deep sea red clay
        5. Radiolarian ooze

Since diatomaceous oozes have been found at depths of 5,000-6,000 meters, and Globigerina ooze is sometimes found in depths greater than that where red clay accumulates, the subdivisions of the Eupelagic deposits as given by Krümmel are hardly satisfactory (Philippi–69). Andrée (4) suggests dividing Krümmel's Group III into calcareous and noncalcareous (siliceous), the former comprising Globigerina ooze, with Pteropod ooze as a facies, the latter diatomaceous ooze and the deep-sea red clay with the radiolarian ooze as a facies of the latter. This entire class, with the exception of the red clay, has been discussed under organic deposits or biogenics (Chapter X).

The distinction between areas of deposition and types of deposits must be clearly kept in mind. The former, as we have seen, comprise (1) the littoral district, with its two zones, (a) the shore and (b) the neritic zones; (2) the bathyal district and (3) the abyssal district. Oceanic deposits must be classified first as to their origin and next as to their mode of occurrence. Thus we may make the following classification, taking oceanic deposits as a whole:

A New Classification of Marine Deposits.

I MARINE HYDROGENICS (HALMYROGENIC deposits) or chemical precipitates from the sea water.   (These have been fully discussed in Chapter IX.)

II MARINE BIOGENICS or organic deposits of marine origin
 A *Benthonic* or living on sea bottom
  1 *Littoral*—originating in littoral district
   a *Shore zone*
    (1) autochthonous or growing *in situ*
    (2) allochthonous or cast up from deeper water
   b *Neritic or shallow water zone*
    (1) autochthonous—growing *in situ*
    (2) allochthonous—transported, usually from shore zone
  2 *Bathyal*
    (1) autochthonous
    (2) allochthonous—transported, usually from littoral zone
  3 *Abyssal*
    (1) autochthonous
    (2) allochthonous—transported from the littoral or bathyal regions
 B *Pelagic* or living in the open ocean and its extension into the shore indentations, either as plankton or nekton.   (See Chapter XXVII.) These may settle in the Littoral, Bathyal or Abyssal districts, remaining either in place, or more or less rearranged or worked over, especially in shallow water whence they may be cast on shore and even blown inland.

III MARINE CLASTICS.   Fragmental material worn off by or in the sea
 A *Hydroclastics*—worn off or rearranged by the sea waves or currents
  1 *Terrigenous* or land-derived
   a from continent including continental islands
   b from oceanic islands exclusive of coral reefs, and other organic deposits
  2 *Thalassigenous;* or sea-derived
   a organic lime sand and mud derived from coral reefs, from nullipore reefs, shell deposits, etc.
   b derived from halmyrogenic or chemical deposits.   Clastic material derived by destruction by waves of chemical deposits formed by the sea (not known).   Chemically formed marine oölites when worn by waves may come under this head
 B *Bioclastics:* rock material broken up by marine organisms
  Marine bioclastics.   These may, according to the source from which the material was originally derived, be classed as
  1 *Terrigenous*, from continents and islands
  2 *Thalassigenous*, from coral reefs, etc.

IV MARINE DERELICTS, or stragglers from other realms.   These may be deposited in the Littoral, Bathyal or Abyssal districts
 A *Land-derived*, either from continents or islands
  1 *Terrestrial*, derived from the land

a   *Organic:* land plants or animals floating out to sea or rafted seaward (as under b) and deposited in the Littoral, Bathyal or Abyssal districts. (Microörganisms blown out to sea with the dust would also be classed here.)

b   *Inorganic:* rocks, sand, gravel, etc., rafted from land and deposited in the Littoral, Bathyal or Abyssal districts. According to the method of transport we have:

(1)   *plant rafted:* rocks, etc., held by roots of floating trees etc.
(2)   *animal rafted:* stones in stomachs of modern sharks, and seals, and of Jurassic Mystriosaurus and Plesiosaurus as well as in the stomachs of many land animals which may float out to sea
(3)   *ice rafted:* by icebergs and floating ice cakes
(4)   *wind rafted:* wind-blown dust or sand, and volcanic material brought from the land
(5)   *ship rafted:* substances carried out by ships or man-made rafts and cast overboard or deposited on the foundering of the ship
(6)   carried into the sea by slipping or gliding

2   *Aquatic:* derived from the rivers and estuaries. This would comprise chiefly river animals and plants which have been carried out to sea

3   Derived from adjacent higher zone by gliding or thrusting

B   *Atmospherically derived*

Since the chief atmogenic solids, *snow* and *hail*, have only a temporary existence, deposits from this source may be neglected. Rare cases of *organisms*, such as seabirds, which spend most of their lives in the air, might perhaps be included here, but they may as well be classed with terrestrial derelicts

C   *Meteoric—of Extratelluric origin*

Here belong the cosmic dust and the meteorites

D   *Of Subcrustal Origin*

This includes volcanic eruptions beneath the sea and on the coast, so that both pyrogenics and pyroclastics flow or are projected into the sea. The direct pyroclastics merge of course into the wind-transported pyroclastics

DISCUSSION OF THE MARINE CLASTICS.

In the following pages the clastic deposits will be discussed with reference to the regions in which they are deposited. Lacustrine clastics will be repeatedly used for parallel illustrations.

THE LITTORAL DISTRICT AND ITS DEPOSITS.

The term *littoral zone* is frequently restricted to the part between high and low-water mark, *i. e.*, the shore, while the term neritic has recently come into use for that portion between low water and the edge of the continental shelf. The term *littoral dis-*

trict is, however, best applied to all that part of the sea above the deep-sea portion, *i. e.,* approximately above the hundred-fathom line. This is in conformity with usage of the term in bionomics (Ortmann–63 : 5), where the littoral fauna and flora are those occupying the sea bottom within the illuminated region. It is in this sense that the term littoral will be used throughout this book, while the *littoral zone* or the zone between high and low water will be referred to as the shore.

Littoral deposits are found between the edge of the continental shelf and the high-water edge of the shore. In the shore zone they grade imperceptibly into continental deposits, through the zone of the *strand,* while at the outermost margin of the littoral district they grade into abyssal deposits. Around the margins of oceanic islands the littoral belt is of greater or less width, according to the slope of the submerged portion of the island.

It is within the littoral district as here defined that by far the largest proportion of clastic material is deposited. It is here also that the bulk of the hydrogenic and the biogenic deposits of the sea is formed.

The Shore Zone (Inter Co-tidal Zone; Littoral Zone in Restricted Sense).

The separation of the shore zone, or that portion between high and low-water mark, from the portion of the littoral district never uncovered, is of very little significance from the lithogenetic point of view, however much its import biologically. For, although this zone is the focus of the destructive activity of the waves, their work is not limited to this portion. It is known that wave work is very effective at a depth of thirty feet, while at sixty it has still an influence upon the bottom deposits. In fact on a gently sloping coast, the destructive work of the waves is found in the deeper water away from the shore, rather than in the shore zone. Neither has the shore a distinctive type of sediment; not even the pebbly sediment is confined to it, but occurs also at a distance from shore; nor are sands, muds or even organic deposits excluded from the shore, the sands and muds being often more characteristic than the pebbles. As for organisms, only stationary or attached types discriminate between the shore and the permanently submerged zone, and among these certain ones do not make an absolute distinction. The shore zone is, however, of significance in this respect, that characters typical of continental deposits, such as mud cracks, rain-prints, footprints, etc., can be impressed upon the exposed sediments, and preserved under favorable circumstances.

Since the magnitude of tides varies with the moon's phases, the exact limit of the shore zone is never fixed. During spring tides the zone encroaches upon the strand, that indefinite zone just above high water, while the ebb succeeding will lay bare portions of the zone generally submerged. On lakes the shore zone practically disappears (it would be wrong, however, to say that there is no littoral district on the lakes) unless the seiche is to be considered as equivalent to the tides.

Facies of the Shore Zone. The shore zone may represent one or more of a variety of facies, or types of material, none of which can be considered as strictly confined to it. The most typical facies of the shore zone are: 1, the rocky cliff facies; 2, the bouldery facies; 3, the gravelly facies; 4, the sand facies; 5, the mud flat facies, and 6, the organic facies. Each of these facies has its distinct physical and organic characters.

1. *Rocky cliff facies.*

This is most significant from the point of view of bionomics, as will be more fully discussed in a later chapter. Erosion is active here, and coarse fragments are broken from the cliff and accumulate as a submarine talus and boulder pavement. Where rock accumulation takes place, a rudaceous phase will be found next to the cliff, the material of the rock fragments being that of the cliff from which they are derived. Since in such cases the rock fragments broken from the cliff may fall into water sufficiently deep to prevent much attrition of the fragments. the resultant rudyte may be a breccia, the fragments being in the main angular. Examples of such cliff rudytes are found in the St. Croix formation of the Dalles region of the Wisconsin River, and in the Lake Superior sandstone of Marquette, Michigan. Some of these may of course be old, subaërial talus slopes reworked by the transgressing sea. This appears to be the case with the basal Mid-Devonic limestones (Dundee) of Michigan and western Ontario. (See Chapter XIII.)

2. *Bouldery facies.*

Where a rock cliff fronts the waves, the fragments broken from the cliff by the frost and by the sea are generally ground into pebbles, sand and mud, unless the water at the foot of the cliff is sufficiently deep to render the force of the waves ineffective. Thus boulders will seldom accumulate in such numbers as to make a boulder beach at the foot of a cliff, since the destruction of the cliff proceeds with sufficient slowness to allow the reduction of most of the fragments to pebbles or smaller particles. If, however, the sea eats into a morainal or other bouldery deposit, as is the case of many portions of the New England and Long Island coast of the North Atlantic, a heavy boulder beach arranged in the form of a pavement by the close approximation of the boulders through wave and shore-ice work will result. In like manner, when the sea encroaches upon an old subaërial talus heap, a boulder beach may be formed, the waves being able to round off and arrange the boulders, but not to destroy them. The boulders themselves become a natural barrier, against which the waves beat themselves to pieces without accomplishing much erosional work. Where the tides are exceptionally high, as in the Bay of Fundy, the boulders broken from the cliffs by the frost and insolation will be rolled and worn at high tide, but the power of the waves is too small, and the time during which the boulders are subject to their influence too short, to produce any other results. Here the accumulation of boulders is really to be compared with a subaërial talus, which is periodically, but for a short time only, exposed to wave activity. On the whole, boulder beaches other than those due to erosion of drift deposits are of comparatively rare occurrence, and the same thing may be said of ancient marine boulder beds. It is doubtful if many such existed, most of the boulder beds of former geologic epochs being probably of continental origin. That boulders of even moderate size may for a long time remain entirely unmoved by the waves is shown on the east coast of Scotland, where the boulders and ledges are covered by living Acmæa or by extensive growth of sea weeds. Even delicate sea anemones are found attached to these boulders, often in such a position that a slight movement of the boulders would grind them to pieces. In other cases the boulders and pebbles are encrusted by a growth of Lithothamnion or Melobesia. It sometimes happens that in certain zones, or areas, the waves are able to move the boulders, with the result that there they are entirely bare of either vegetation or animal covering.

3. Gravel facies.

By far the greater part of the present shore lines of the world is sandy or gravelly, the former predominating. Gravelly beaches or

beaches of cobbles or shingles are chiefly characteristic of steeply
sloping and exposed rocky shores, where the finer product of erosion is carried by the undertow to deeper water, the coarser alone
remaining. The character of the pebbles will of course partake of
that of the cliff from which they are formed, those derived from
the more easily shattered rock, as well as the most difficult to grind
to powder, predominating. Thus on the north shore of Massachusetts felsite pebbles predominate, on Lake Michigan limestone pebbles, and on the shore of Lake Erie flat shale pebbles. These pebbles are often piled up into extensive terraces, especially after heavy
storms. These terraces may show on section a rude and irregular
bedding, but the regular cross-bedding (torrential type) found in
many old conglomerates was not formed in this manner.

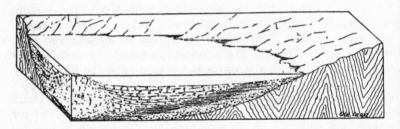

Fig. 129.   Diagram illustrating the deposits in the littoral district of the sea.
At the shore gravelly and sandy facies occur, these shading off
seaward into lutaceous, and, finally, calcareous sediments. The
latter are derived from the coral reef C. R., *i. e.*, they are thalassigenous, while the others are terrigenous. The overlapping of
the formations is also shown.

Organic remains in pebble beds. On the beach, where the pebbles undergo much movement, most organic remains, such as shells,
bones, etc., are rapidly destroyed. Nevertheless, they are occasionally preserved, as is shown by the occurrence of worn shell
fragments even in the high gravel terraces.

That organic remains are common in older boulder and pebble
beds has been the experience of many geologists, though some of
the so-called conglomerate beds are due to causes other than those
active on sea beaches. A comparatively modern example of a pebble
and sand beach now abandoned by a slight elevation of the coast
is found in eastern Scotland. Near Goldspie on the Moray Firth,
the lower of the elevated beach lines abounds in entire shells of
Acmæa and other shore forms, as well as in worn fragments of
this and other shells. Boulders up to the size of six inches or more,

and well worn, are found in this beach. Other examples no doubt occur in other sections of this coast and elsewhere.

Boulder beds of Tertiary age are not uncommon. In the Miocenic of the Vienna Basin, some of the best preserved pelecypod and gastropod shells are found in a boulder bed with pebbles up to six inches or more in diameter, and well rounded. The Cretacic boulder beds of South Germany and of Sweden are other examples. In the former well-worn boulders up to several feet in diameter constitute the deposit, while among them abound fragments and entire individuals of brachiopods, pelecypods and other organisms often in a remarkable state of preservation. In the Dresden region pothole-like hollows are found in the old porphyries with a depth of 20 feet or more, and these are filled with a coarse boulder conglomerate of Cretacic age, the individual boulders often a foot or more in diameter, and well worn. Among these boulders sponges, oysters and other organisms occur in abundance. In Scania and elsewhere an Upper Cretacic conglomerate of pebbles and boulders worn or angular contains Belemnites and other fossils of that period, many of them showing no wear. One of the most striking examples of such a conglomerate is found on the present eastern coast of Sutherland, North Scotland, near the village of Helmsdale. The formation occurs as a coastal strip, largely eroded by the present sea, and forming a series of low-lying skerries exposed at low water. The age of the formation is Jurassic, but it is almost wholly composed of large and small fragments of Caithness flags (Lower Old Red sandstone), some of the fragments reaching the astonishing length of 20 feet or more. The larger fragments lie in irregular positions, their stratification planes dipping in all directions, and they resemble in every respect the fragments now found at the foot of the cliffs of these flags on the exposed Caithness coast. Among the fragments and firmly embedded in the conglomerate and breccia matrix are worn heads of coral (*Isastrea*), shells, Belemnites and other Jurassic organisms. Many of the smaller organisms have apparently escaped all wear.

4. *Sandy facies.*

Sand is by far the most typical material of the shore zone, on lakes as well as on the seashore. To a large extent the sand consists of quartz grains, since this is the least destructible constituent of rocks. In regions of purely calcareous sources of sand, as in the Bermudas, and on many coral reef islands, the sand is largely or wholly composed of grains of calcium carbonate, with or without magnesium.

As Shaler has pointed out, the sand of the seashore is compacted into a resistant mass by the films of water which separate the grains and which are held in position by capillary attraction. Whoever has walked on wet beach sand has noted the difference in firmness between the wet and dry sands, the former often constituting a hard, level floor. On such a surface the force of the waves is spent; the sands will retain their original angular character, since the dividing film of water acts as a cushion, which prevents the mutual attrition of the grains. Thus the grains of beach sand are normally angular and with fresh surfaces, and this type of sand should be looked for in normal marine sandstones. (Shaler–88.) Shaler cites as an example of marine sands protected in this manner from wearing, the sand of northern Florida . . . "which has traveled southward from the region beyond Cape Hatteras" . . . and which "is not more rounded than much which is in the inner or landward dunes of the coast within sound of the ocean waves." (88:*151*.)

When, through drying, the binding films of water are destroyed, the sands become loosened and are then readily shifted about by the wind, accompanied by mutual attrition of the grains. Here, then, no permanent structural features are formed. Both rill and ripple marks left on the retreat of the tide are either obliterated by the wind or washed away by the returning tide, owing to the noncoherency of the material. An exception to this seems to be the wave mark on a very gently sloping sand beach, and the hollows excavated behind pebbles or shells by the return of the wave on such a beach. Examples of these are known from the Upper Medina sandstone in western New York, and in other formations. (Fairchild–32.)

Marine arkoses. Accumulation of feldspathic sands on the sea coast and their incorporation in marine strata are effected under a peculiar combination of circumstances such as exist to-day in the Gulf of California, as described by McGee (57). The granitoid rocks of this region are subject to disintegration under the arid climatic conditions, due to the interception of the Westerlies by the coast ranges. Decomposition is practically absent, the disintegrated material being transported by sheet floods. These result from exceptional thunderstorms, accompanied by sudden and extensive precipitation. Part of the material is carried into the Gulf and there assorted by the waves, the coarsest and cleanest material being deposited at the salients of the coast, while in the reëntrants much finely comminuted material is deposited with the coarse quartz and feldspar. Quartz-feldspar-mica sandstones are thus produced under conditions permitting the entombment of marine organisms.

Sorting of sands and gravels by waves. The conditions under which waves accomplish sorting of sands and gravels according to size and material are given by Bailey Willis (105: *481*) as the following:

(a)   Vigorous wave action, accompanied by strong undertow.
(b)   Prolonged transportation in consequence of deep water and continuous currents.
(c)   Moderate volume of sediments.

On the other hand, the conditions under which sorting is **not or but slightly** accomplished are, according to Willis:

(a')   Feeble or diffused wave action.
(b')   Concentrated deposition.
(c')   Excessive volume of sediment.

In general, with a given amount of loose materials to work upon, the waves will accomplish sorting in proportion to their strength and the strength of the undertow. The finest material will be carried out farthest, while only the coarsest material will be left behind. Where the material is all of one kind, as, for example, quartz sand, the sorting will be entirely according to size, while variation in the mineralogical character of the material may lead to a sorting, according to the specific gravity as well. Thus quartz sands may be entirely washed free from mica and clay particles, while garnet and magnetite, two characteristic accompaniments of sands derived from many igneous or metamorphic rocks, will segregate through the washing out of all quartz grains.

This sorting according to size and specific gravity is best accomplished if, in addition to the strong wave movement which stirs up the sediment, strong currents exist which can transport the material for long distances. The smallest and lightest material may thus be carried much farther away from the point where the coarsest is dropped, the separation being thus most pronounced. In this respect the separation by currents will be analogous to the separation of sediments by wind. A water current of a given velocity is equaled in carrying power only by a wind current of 28 times that velocity (Udden–99: *319*), but wind currents exceeding average ocean currents in velocity by very much more than that are characteristic of many regions, especially in the upper atmosphere. Thus material projected or carried into the air stands a much better chance of sorting than does material in the sea. Moreover, material dropped by one air current may be picked up again by another, while sands dropping in deeper water below the reach of the currents are more likely to be left undisturbed by them.

If the amount of supply of detritus is great, sorting will be impeded. Flocculation, or the gathering together of particles, will occur, the coarser carrying down with them the finer. Flocculation is less marked in wind-transported material, where the load is always much less per unit of bulk of the carrier than in most waters, and for this reason also the sorting by wind is more pronounced than that by water. Udden thinks that under ordinary circumstances this difference is nearer 1 to 100,000 than 1 to 1,000. (99:*328*.) The slope of the sea bottom (Willis–105:*484*) is also a determining factor in the transportation of material by marine currents. Where the slope is a gentle one, sand may be carried for 200 miles or more, as on the Atlantic coast of the United States, where the continental plateau is covered with sands to its outer rim. The transporting current here is the undertow, assisted by tides. Since, however, the force of the undertow is largely determined by the strength of the waves, it follows that in circumscribed and very shallow seas no such extensive transportation is possible. Where the slope is a steep one, as on the west coast of South America, the force of the undertow is dissipated, though pebbles and sand will more readily move down the slope. As a rule, the distance to which sands are transported in such a case is limited.

Organic remains in marine and lacustrine sands. These are generally common, especially in the sea, though areas free from such remains are known, as in the case of the Alaskan coast, already cited. Such absence is, however, due to purely local causes. Even in the beach sands organic remains abound. Everywhere along our coasts shells in numbers, and crustacean and echinoderm tests to a lesser degree are buried in the sands of the beach, and in those just below the low-water line. In the neritic zone animal life of all kinds abounds on the sandy bottoms (see Chapter XXVIII). Abandoned shores of lakes and of the sea also are rich in organic remains. The higher beaches of the late Pleistocenic stages of the Great Lakes contain numerous shells of fresh-water mollusca, and so do the sands of the old shore lines of Niagara and other rivers. So abundant are shells and other organisms in the sands of the modern sea coast that their entire absence from older sandstones must be looked upon as indicative of conditions of deposition other than normal. It is begging the question to assume the subsequent removal of such remains either by solution or otherwise, for even though percolating waters should dissolve away the shells a mold or impression of the same will remain, which no agent short of metamorphism can obliterate, and that not always. The abundance of organic remains in sandstones of all kinds and colors and of all ages shows that there are no inherent characteristics in sand which prevent the preservation of such remains. In practically all cases when organic remains or their impressions are wanting in sandstones, we have a right to assume that they were not present at the time of formation of the deposit. Such absence suggests a subaërial rather than subaqueous origin for the deposit, and as such it should be considered unless other unmistakable characteristics point to a subaqueous (marine or lacustrine) origin. (For application to basal beds see Pumpelly–75 :*217.*)

5. *Muddy facies.*

This generally occurs in intimate association with an organic facies in the shore zone. Where sands accumulate in sheltered marginal lagoons, plants (eel grass) and animals commonly contribute their remains to enrich and color the mud. Salt marshes are the normal successors of the mud flat, the organic element here being in the ascendency. (See *ante,* Chapter XI.) The purely inorganic structures of such a mud flat are, in addition to stratification, the mud cracks, rain prints and rill marks, and the tracks and trails of animals frequenting the shore. During very high spring tides extensive portions of a very flat shore may be covered with a layer of mud, which on the retreat of the tide may become marked by mud cracks and footprint impressions. Since such areas will be uncovered for a fortnight, the clay may become sufficiently hardened to permit the permanent preservation of the mud cracks. It must, however, be borne in mind that when the mud deposit made by one inundation is comparatively thin, as is apt to be the case, this layer will on drying curl up into shaving-like masses and be blown away by the wind. While under exceptional conditions the mud cracks, rill marks and tracks formed in the shore zone may be preserved, such preservation is far from being characteristic.

Flocculation and the conditions of mud deposits. The formation of mud deposits at the mouths of great rivers emptying in the sea, as in the case of the Mississippi, is favored by the presence of the salt in the sea water. Flocculation, or the drawing together of particles, takes place much more extensively in salt than in fresh water, and as a result such particles will sink more quickly in sea water than in lakes. Experiments (Brewer–11 : *168*) have shown that clay which had been in suspension in fresh water for thirty

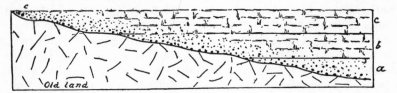

FIG. 130. Diagram showing the lateral shading off of the clastic sands and pebbles into calcareous deposits without intervening muddy phase. The successive formations *a, b,* and *c* change shoreward into arenytes. An apparently continuous sand bed; *a-c* is thus produced resting upon the old land surface.

months had not settled out as clearly as the same clay from a solution of common salt in less than thirty minutes. These results have, however, been questioned by Wheeler (103), who gives the accompanying table, showing the rate of settlement in the two media:

Table Showing Rate of Settlement of Solid Matter in Fresh and Salt Water.

No.	No. of grains to a lineal inch	Material	Time taken to settle				Water clear				Ft. per minute	Remarks
			Fresh		Salt		Fresh		Salt			
			m.	sec.	m.	sec.	h.	m.	h.	m.		
1	5	Small pebbles..........	0	1	...	...	...	...	...	...	0.50	Water not discolored
	10	Small pebbles..........	0	1½	...	...	...	...	...	...	0.42	do
	20	Coarse sand...........	0	2¼	...	...	...	...	...	...	0.21	do
	20-60	Coarse sand...........	0	4	...	...	...	...	...	...	0.13	do
2	100	Sand..................	0	10	...	...	...	...	...	...	5.04	do
3	200	Sand..................	0	25	...	...	...	...	...	...	2.40	do
4	....	Whiting...............	12	0	...	...	0	30	...	...	....	do
5	....	Plaster of Paris........	5	0	...	...	0	10	...	...	....	do
6	300	Warp Trent...........	0	43	0	45	0	1	0	1	1.20	Water scarcely discolored
7	1,400	(Fine warp, Dutch river).	12	0	15	0	3	30	22	0	0.70	Water turbid
8	500	Silt, salt marsh........	2	0	2	0	0	6	0	9	0.42	do
9	1,000	Warp marsh...........	8	0	9	0	1	0	0	33	....	do
10	2,000	(Alluvium, Boston Dock)	33	0	28	0	7	0	1	30	0.11	do
11	600	(Alluvium, River Parrett)	4	0	2	40	0	15	0	18	0.22	do
12	1,500	Tilbury Basin..........	18	0	18	0	10	0	9	0	0.46	do
13	1,600	Brick clay.............	17	0	15	0	1	30	1	0	0.40	do
14	1,440	Boulder clay...........	24	0	0	22	0	43	0	30	0.35	do

The phenomena of flocculation have been attributed to chemical reaction, but seem to find a better explanation in the forces of attraction or tension existing among the fine particles of a solid in suspension. These forces are modified by the existence of the salt in the solution. (Whitney–104; Clarke–20.) According to the experiments of G. Bodländer (10), the sodium chloride of the sea water is not so important in this respect, other salts, especially magnesium chloride, being more active. Carbon dioxide, which abounds in sea water, also rapidly clears it of suspended clay particles, but temperature changes seem to be of little significance in this respect. (Krümmel–55: *152-214*.) Even in sea water, however, the finest particles do not settle out completely after several weeks of rest.

Terrigenous muds extend from the shore to abyssal depths. They will be more fully considered under the neritic zone.

6. *Organic facies.*

This consists of the eel grass and peat marsh areas of the sea coast and of the rush and swamp borders of lakes and ponds. The characteristics of these have been fully described in previous chapters, and need not be dwelt upon here at length. Extensive mussel beds such as are forming in many places on our sea coast may also be classed here, though these are as a rule intimately associated with the muddy facies of the flats. Shallow-water coral and Lithothamnion growths are other examples of this facies, which belongs with the lithogenic rather than the lithoclastic division.

Subaqueous Solifluction.

The movement or gliding of rock material when saturated with water, which under subaërial conditions is called solifluction (see Chapter XIII), also takes place under subaqueous conditions. Arnold Heim proposed to distinguish this mode of movement as subsolifluction (*47:141*). Such movements have occurred in many regions of the world, both on lakes and on the seashore, but only a few cases have been fully investigated. Among these are the glidings which in 1875 and again in 1877 affected the village of Horgen on the Lake of Zurich (Switzerland), and the one which took place in the village of Zug on the Zuger See in the Canton of Zug (Zoug), north central Switzerland. Both of these were described by Professor Albert Heim and others in special publications, and summarized by Arnold Heim in 1908 (*47: 136*).

The village of Horgen is situated on the southern shore of the Lake of Zurich. The shore, which is here composed of the sandstones and marls of the Mollasse, was covered originally by sand, gravel and clay in the upper part, and this, near the shore, was underlain by soft muds, which extended lakeward, covering the rocks to the center of the lake. On the ground thus underlain with soft mud rests a part of the railroad, which skirts the southwestern shore of the lake (Zürichseebahn), the Horgen station being built close to the shore. A sea wall was built and the surface raised a slight amount (0.4 to 0.6 meter) by filling-in, but prior to this a number of buildings and a stone-cutting yard were removed, so that on the whole the excess of loading was slight. On February 9, 1875, when the filling in was nearly complete, the new sea wall and the filled area suddenly sank for a length of 135 meters, the lake along the line of the railroad reaching a depth of 7 meters. The examination showed that a part of the bottom layer of soft mud had slid lakeward, so that the more resistant overlying sand and gravel beds came to rest upon the rock surface. The gliding continued until the mud layers had completely bared the rock slopes for a distance of nearly 300 meters lakeward. The most pronounced of these glidings occurred on June 12, 1875, this, however, affecting mainly the sublacustrine mud layers. By filling in a part of the sunken area and carrying the railroad line farther inland, the construction was completed and the line opened for traffic September 20, 1875. The following day was one of heavy rains, and on the morning of the 22nd fissures began to open in the made land, the new wall began to crack, and suddenly a part of the wall, 85 meters long, and the station lands and tracks to a width of 23 meters sank beneath the inrushing lake waters. Just before noon a second subsidence took place, a third one followed early in the afternoon, and others followed on the 23rd and 24th of September. The total area which thus disappeared beneath the water of the lake had a length of 204 meters and a width of 48 meters, with an area of 6,560 square meters. Subsequent glidings occurred in October and November.

The gliding began on the steeper slopes at a distance from shore, and was then transferred shoreward. The first effect of the gliding of February 9 was the lowering of the outer slope from 31 per cent. to 27 per cent., but the gliding of June 12 caused the complete baring of the rock for a distance of 150 meters or more, and a change of grade back to 30 per cent. or 31 per cent., and even a higher one farther lakeward. This became even more pronounced in the glidings of September and later. The total extent of the glidings was 450 meters, and the material was carried out to a depth of 125 meters. The affected part of the coast extended from Horgen to Käpfnach, a distance of 1.5 km. The material was spread over the lake bottom, raising it from 1 to 3 meters. In October, 1877, another small portion (the Sustplatz) subsided (*Frankfurter Zeitung,* Beilage zu No. 304, 1877), showing that movements are not ended. More recent glidings if they occurred have not come to our notice.

The village of Zug has a similar record. As early as 1435, on March 4th, 26 houses on the "Niederen Gasse," in the old part of the village, slipped into the lake, 60 persons perishing at the time. In 1593 the level of the lake was lowered by drainage, and further subsidences occurred. On July 5, 1887, three successive portions of the shore fell into the lake, submerging more than 20 houses. The material which slid into the sea consisted of sandy mud, a delta built by the Lorze when the lake stood at its higher level. A broad stream of mud flowed into the sea, 300 meters from the point of fracture, to a depth of 23 meters, under the lake level, and then continued outward to a distance of about 1,020 meters from shore and a depth of 45 meters below lake level as a broad mud flow 150 to 250 meters wide and from 1 to 4 meters high. The gliding began in the lakeward region, and migrated landward, as in the case of headward-growing streams. The remarkable fact here is that the average grade of the surface along which the gliding has taken place from the break to the end of the mud stream, a distance of 1,020 meters, was only 4.4 per cent. The earlier, smaller movement extended for only about 500 meters into the lake and over a grade of 6 per cent. The same rule thus seems to hold for the subaquatic as for the subaërial solifluction, namely, *the larger the moving mass the smaller the average slope on which it moves.*

Many similar though less instructive glidings have taken place on the Swiss lakes, among them those of Montreux-Veytaux on Lake Geneva (Schardt–85; 86). Nathorst has also described similar subaquatic glidings in Sweden.

In 1895 or thereabouts movements of this type occurred at Odessa, where several buildings slid into the Black Sea. The distance to which this mass was carried is unknown, but it was on a much larger scale than that at Zug.

Submarine glidings of this type are probably common, but no measurements are made of them. Such glidings are often indicated on the steeper slopes by the breaking of the cables. In no case, however, have the magnitude and extent of the glidings been ascertained, though dislocations by faulting are known (see page 890).

It is of course evident that material thus sliding down a submarine surface must be piled up to some extent in the deeper areas where it comes to rest. As the result of such gliding the strata must suffer much deformation, especially if they are at all consolidated. Such deformations have all the characters of orogenic disturbances due to lateral pressure, and indeed it has been suggested that some extensive mountain folds and overthrusts may have originated in this manner. These deformations will be more fully discussed in Chapter XX.

Accessory Features of Subaqueous Gliding. Among the accessory features produced by subaqueous and especially submarine solifluctions, we may mention in addition to the deformations already noted, and to be more fully discussed in a later chapter, the following phenomena :

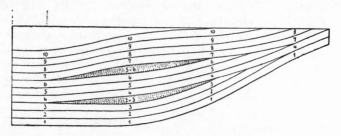

Fig. 131.   Diagram illustrating the changes in stratification due to subaquatic gliding. In the shore section strata are eliminated, while farther out duplication occurs.   (After Heim.)

1. Increase of the strata in the lower regions where the shore material is carried by gliding, and where strata are thus repeated by the superposition of portions of the same strata upon one another. 2. Reduction of the number of strata in the zone affected by the gliding where the ends of the strata are thus removed, and on the deposition of subsequent beds a local disconformable relation is produced with hiatus signifying no appreciable time interval. 3. Superposition of older on younger beds. Thus at Zug, the mass which slid into the sea was more than 99 per cent. formed during the former high-water period of the lake, and came to rest by gliding upon the deposits formed since the present water level was established (Fig. 131). 4. Displacement of facies. Thus at Zug gravel and even coarse blocks were carried by gliding into the region where they would otherwise be absent. In submarine solifluction shore sediments may be carried out to the neritic belt, or the latter into abyssal regions. A shore breccia may thus come to lie among off-shore marine sediments. 5. Destruction of life. The benthonic and to

some extent also the pelagic life will be destroyed by such glidings and the distribution of the fauna will be altered. Such a case has been noted in connection with the rock slide at Elm. Such disturbance might result in the sudden destruction of the entire benthonic fauna, young and old alike, all stages being found together. Above the mass of material which caused this destruction may come a stratum carrying only remains of planktonic organisms without sedentary benthos, which would return only after a while. (Heim–47 : *157*.)

The Permanently Submerged or Neritic Zone (Flachsee, Shallow Water or Thalassal Zone).

This zone extends from the low-water line of the shore zone, a somewhat variable line, to the edge of the continental shelf. Several provinces of more or less importance may be recognized, chief of which are:

    1. The estuary.
    2. The marginal lagoon.
    3. Epicontinental seas and mediterraneans.
    4. The ocean littoral.

    1. *The Estuary.* This is the point of meeting place of the terrestrial and marine realms. It receives on the one hand the sediments and other material brought by the rivers from the land, and on the other it admits the waters of the sea, which for a time at least modify the character of the deposit. Alternately the waters of the land and of the sea predominate, as a result of which the deposits formed in the estuary will have characteristics typical of both. As a good example, we may consider the estuary of the La Plata in South America. This has a length of 125 miles, and receives the water of the Paraña and Uruguay rivers. The currents of these rivers thus come into periodic contention with the tides from the Atlantic. (Willis–105 :*491.*) Where the power of the tidal wave balances that of the rivers, no current exists, a condition which may continue for hours. (Revy–81 : *29, 30.*) Here at from 10 to 20 miles above the mouth of the estuary, the material held in suspension is dropped, as a result of which submerged banks are forming, which eventually grow into islands. The current during both flood and ebb tide is swifter in the deep channels than in shallow portions of the estuary, hence deposits made during flood tide will be more copious over the shallows than in the deeper channels,

which latter are also more subject to scour during the ebb tide. The shallows thus become tide flats, which later are raised rush-grown islands, thus restricting the water within narrow channels. The original length of the La Plata was 325 miles, but about two-thirds of this has been filled up in the manner described. Where material of different sizes is brought by the rivers into the estuary the coarser will be dropped when the current is first checked by the rising tide, the finer following when the checking is complete. During the scouring of the bottom at ebb tide much of the fine material may be carried away again. (Willis–105: *492*.)

The floor of the Hudson has in many places been built up by mud deposits to such an extent that extensive mud flats are laid

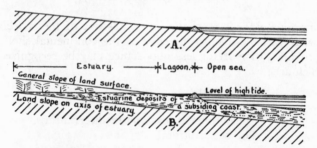

Fig. 132. Diagram illustrating the relationship between subsidence and the growth of estuarine deposits. A, bar and lagoon (barachois) on a young coast; B, estuarine deposits covered by transgressing sea on subsiding coast. The bar and lagoon rest on terrestrial deposits and not on the old crystalline base. (After Barrell.)

bare at low tide, a hundred or more miles above its mouth, while the channel over much of this distance is comparatively shallow. The rock bottom of the Hudson, on the other hand, is, in places, as in the Highlands, more than 600 feet below tide level. It is proper to note, however, that a part of the filling of this channel is probably glacial, only the upper hundred feet on the average being river silt.

The estuary of the Severn (Sollas–89) may serve as another example. The tidal channel of this river is notorious for its mud. "At high tide it is filled with a sea of turbid water, thick and opaque with tawny-colored sediment; as the tide ebbs a broad expanse of shining mud flats is revealed fringing the coast; but so like is the water to the mud that, seen from a distance, it is often hard to tell where the sea ends and the shore begins. It is the same with its tributaries, the Wye, the Usk, Ely and Rhymney on the Welsh side, the Avon, Yeo, Parrot and others on the English coast." (Sollas–89:611.)

The origin of this mud has been a subject of much dispute. In part no doubt it is supplied by the rivers which have a catchment basin of 9,193 square miles (English), but much is also produced by the waves washing the shores of the estuary. The water in the tidal portion of the Severn Channel flows up and down twice daily at the rate of from 6 to 12 miles an hour, a velocity much greater than that required to move along large boulders of rocks. As a result scouring of the channel occurs in many places. The development of the currents has been described by Mr. W. R. Browne (13): "In ordinary tidal channels such as the Avon below Bristol, the course of events during an ebb seems to be as follows. At first the slope of the surface is exceedingly small (in the Avon it was about 1½ feet in 7¼ miles), and, while the velocity at the surface is considerable, it diminishes rapidly from thence downward, and at some distance from the bottom becomes *nil*. This continues for about two-thirds of the ebb, the surface velocity increasing up to a certain point, and then becoming nearly constant. During all this time not only is no scour going on at the bottom, but, if the waters be muddy, an actual deposition of silt is taking place. At this time, after about two-thirds of the ebb, the water has fallen about three-quarters of its total height, the slope of its surface has considerably increased, and the conditions approximate to those of an ordinary river. The bottom layers of the water then spring suddenly into motion, the surface velocity diminishes steadily as the tidal waters disappear, until it assumes the normal rate of the low-water flow. During this period a scour of the bottom is of course going on; but, as this velocity is not much higher than in the subsequent period of low-water flow, the rate of scour will not be much greater; and the actual scour will be insufficient to compensate for the amount of deposit from the tidal waters which has taken place, not only during the period of high water, but also during the first two-thirds of the ebb. It must follow, therefore, that the scouring effect of the tide is little or nothing, and the observed incapacity of tidal flows to sweep away the silt they have deposited is amply and satisfactorily explained."

Sollas thinks that eventually much of the silt will find its way out to sea, owing to the constant outward pressure of the normal river current. As a part of the material is carried seaward from the constant mass moved back and forth, new material is supplied by the rivers.

The material of this estuarine mud consists of "a variable quantity of fine, argillaceous granules, small, angular fragments of color-less transparent quartz containing numerous minute included cavi-ties, a few similar fragments of flint, siliceous fragments of a glauconite green color, minute crystals of quartz of the ordinary form, minute prisms of tourmaline highly dichroic and similar in form to macroscopic prisms of schorl, and minute rhombohedra of calcite." Materials of organic origin also occur, such as coccoliths and rarely coccospheres, both of the ordinary cyatholith type so common in adjacent seas and in the Atlantic ooze; further, For-aminifera, including Miliola, Textularia, several species, *Nonionina crassula, Polystomella umbilicata,* Rotalia sp., Spirillina sp., etc., more rarely spicules of Alcyonaria, fragments of echinoderm skele-tons and minute spines; and triradiate spicules of calcisponges, probably Sycandra. "Most of the Foraminifera are quite empty, glassy and transparent; but some contain a brownish, soft granu-lar material; and in one instance a small Rotaline form was ob-served partially replaced by pyrites." (*90:614.*) The siliceous or-ganic remains comprise chiefly sponge spicules, very rarely Radi-laria, and a variable quantity of diatoms. The remains of other organisms found in the mud are all of marine types, though they occur on the banks of rivers at a great distance from a truly marine area.

In the muds of the rivers above the limit of tidal influence, only spicules of fresh-water sponges and diatoms were found (*Spongilla fluviatilis*), foraminifera and other marine organisms being absent. Nor were any of these organisms derived from the Mesozoic strata through which these rivers flow. The organic remains of the modern, as well as the older, muds of the Severn estuary were ap-parently all derived from the Bristol Channel, which is the further enlargement of the Severn estuary and along the shores of which from 10 to 15 miles west of the Severn estuary marine life abounds. The older alluvial deposits of the Severn estuary have a maximum thickness of about 50 feet. These comprise in descending order:

Zone 1. Upper clay
{
a More sandy zone 5 to 7 feet
b More argillaceous zone, with disseminated vegetable matter 7 to 8 feet ±
}
Upper peat, 1 to 2 feet 6 inches

Zone 2. Lower clay
Lower peat, 1 to 4 feet

Zone 3. Sands and mud
Gravel
Triassic sandstones

The gravel contains glacial pebbles and rolled boulders up to a cubic foot in size. It is not always present. The mud is a marine or tidal deposit like the blue clay which replaces it elsewhere, and from which it differs chiefly in being nearly or quite free from clay. There seems to be a gradual transition from coarse at the bottom to fine at the top. Some of the sands contain fragments of a bryozoan, and many chips of pelecypod shells, including a small Avicula. Foraminifera, spines of echinoderms and sponge spicules also occur. In a section through Caldicot Marsh near Portskewet, fifty feet deep, a bed of marl was encountered 10 feet above the base, which contained a mixture of fresh and brackish water shells, such as Limnæa, Planorbis, *Scrobicularia piperata* and *Cardium edule*. Diatoms are common in it, and also remains of Chara. A similar bed occurs near Cardiff, about 19 miles farther south. It occurs at the same depth. Altogether the beds of zone 3 represent a normal estuarine deposit, with a fauna and flora both brackish and fresh.

The lower part of zone 2 has remains of forest trees associated with it. It is covered by blue clay with Foraminifera and other marine organic remains, indicating a subsidence. The upper Peat bed, sometimes the only one, "consists of various plant remains, including leaves and roots of yellow flags and spores and mycelia of fungi, while its upper surface is strewn with trunks and branches of trees, oak, fir, and birch being the chief. The fir still retains its bark, and the heartwood, when cut, is often found to have preserved its original color. Some of the wood has been bored by some kind of beetle." (90:*621*.) The peat is very pure, though containing occasional sand grains, Foraminifera or sponge spicules. It often contains an abundance of spherules of iron pyrites, and sometimes the vegetable cells are filled with it, these occupying the place of the departed protoplasm within the resistant cell walls. The origin of this pyrite is similar to that of coast marshes or swamps in general. When the salt water comes in contact with the decaying vegetable matter a series of reactions occurs, which will end in the formation of iron pyrites. The upper clay contains Foraminifera, sponge spicules and other marine organisms, besides disseminated vegetal material.

2. *The Marginal Lagoon or Barachois*. These names are applied to the water bodies cut off from the main portion of the sea by the formation of barrier beaches. So long as the lagoon is not filled in by silt and organic deposits, it belongs to the neritic zone of the littoral district. The process by which it is converted into

tidal flats and marshes has already been sketched. (See Chapter XI.) It need only be noted here that the deposits accumulating in the lagoon are the finer sands and muds brought by the tidal currents, and the sands blown across from the beach. Though stratification may be well marked in these lagoon deposits, the evidence of agitation by waves or currents is slight. Cross-bedding structure is not characteristic of such deposits, but ripple marks, of the oscillation type, i. e., symmetrical, sharp crests with broad, rounded troughs, may be formed. A characteristic feature of these deposits is the presence of the eel grass leaves which penetrate the strata in a vertical direction, having been instrumental in the precipitation around them of the suspended material, through a checking of the velocity of the current. In the last-formed deposits of the lagoons organic matter will predominate and peat beds—the coal of the future—mark the transition through the shore zone to terrestrial conditions. Of older deposits of this type the Lowville limestone has already been cited. This is a formation of fine lime mud deposited around vertical stems or branches of a marine organism, probably not a plant, however. Thus the resulting calcilutyte is penetrated by numerous vertical tubules, now largely occupied by crystalline calcite, and producing on the bedding planes the so-called bird's-eye structure which gave the formation its original name.

3. *Epicontinental Seas and Mediterraneans.* Those portions of the littoral district which extend into the land as arms or partly enclosed embayments of no great depth, without being estuaries of great rivers, are of considerable importance to the stratigrapher, since epicontinental seas of this type were very characteristic of many geologic epochs. Their chief significance is, however, a faunal one, since sedimentation, except in special cases, does not differ much from that upon the continental shelf. Nearly landlocked epicontinental seas within pluvial districts, such as Hudson Bay or the Baltic Sea, do not differ appreciably from the littoral belt of the open ocean, but where such enclosed seas occur in arid climates the greater density and increased salinity of their waters will influence perceptibly not only the fauna and flora, but also the deposits. If the intracontinental sea of the arid or semiarid climate is a mediterranean, i. e., if its center extends to depths much greater than its outlet, the peculiarities of the deposits will be emphasized. The Black Sea forms an instructive example of the conditions found in an almost completely enclosed water body of great depth in a semiarid region. According to Andrussow (5; 21:200), the superficial

water layer, of about 125 fathoms, has a less salinity and density than the deeper water, being largely renewed by the fresh water of the drainage. The heavier lower water is derived from the Mediterranean by way of the richly saline Marmora and Ægean seas, requiring about 1,700 years for its renewal. Vertical currents are slight on account of the greater density of the deeper water, and hence these lower waters have not sufficient oxygen to support animal life. Sulphuretted hydrogen is separated out, probably through the agency of sulphobacteria, in the deeper water; beginning at 100 fathoms, with 33 c.c. of H_2S per 100 liters of water until, at 500 fathoms, 570 c.c. of H_2S per 100 liters of the water are separated. Below this the increase is less rapid. As the H_2S increases, the sulphates of the water decrease, and carbonates and FeS are separated out.

The sediments of the Black Sea comprise sandy detritus to a depth of 20 fathoms, below which occurs gray, blue, sticky mud rich in *Modiola phaseolina* to the 100-fathom line. In the great depths occurs a very fine, sticky, black mud with rich separation of FeS, abundant remains of planktonic diatoms, and shells of young pelecypods, which have descended to this depth on completion of their early pelagic existence (mero-planktonic stage). Besides the black is a dark-blue mud with less FeS, but a richer separation of $CaCO_3$ in minute grains, this lime often constituting thin banks, while pelagic diatoms are likewise abundant. Clarke (21 : 201) has suggested the possible origin of some of the Upper Devonic black shales of New York (Portage) under similar conditions, but this is a much mooted question. Pompeckj (71 : 43 et seq) has interpreted the black *Posidonia bronni* shales of the Jurassic of Regensburg, Bavaria, as deposits of this type. It is, however, difficult to understand how such a region can furnish conditions for the perfect preservation of the saurians of that period, so that in some cases even the skin of the animals is intact.

4. *The Ocean Littoral, or the Neritic Zone.* This is the most widely distributed littoral belt at the present time. Its deposits vary considerably, according to distance from shore, depth of water and relation to currents. In general a seaward gradation in the texture of the material from coarse to fine is observable, sands being found near shore (though often extending out for great distances), while muds are formed further offshore and in specially protected places. In the Arabian Sea muds are carried from 700 to 800 miles from land, owing to the nature of the ocean currents. Calcareous accumulations are typical of this region, especially those formed around coral reefs. These have been fully described above.

DEPOSITS OF THE BATHYAL DISTRICT.

On the whole the deposits of this region, which nominally lie between 200 and 900 meters or between 100 and 500 fathoms, are continuous with those of the neritic zone on the one hand, and with those of the abyssal on the other. The following deposits seem to be most characteristic of this district, though extending into both of the adjoining ones:

Table Showing Kinds and Distribution of Bathyal Deposits.

	Clastic deposits	Mean depth		Area covered in square miles
		in fathoms	in meters	
1	Blue mud.....................	1,411	2,397	14,500,000
2	Red mud.....................	623	1,140	100,000
3	Green mud...................	513	920	850,000
4	Green sand..................	449	821	
5	Volcanic mud................	1,033	1,889	600,000
6	Volcanic sand...............	243	444	
7	Coral mud...................	740	1,353	2,556,800
8	Coral sand..................	176	322	

The table on page 669, taken from Clarke's Data of Geochemistry (20b:489), gives the analysis of the terrigenous and volcanic muds and the green sands: 1, Blue mud dried at 110° (Brazier); 2, red mud dried at 100° (Hornung); 3, green mud dried at 110° (Brazier); 4, green sand dried at 110° (Brazier); 5, volcanic mud dried at 110° (Brazier).

Three types of land-derived muds are found in the modern sea away from the shore. These are the blue, the red and green muds.

The Blue or Slate-Colored Mud. This is the most widely distributed, extending, according to Murray and Renard, over an area of 14,500,000 square miles. It covers the floors of the shallow sea to the edge of the continental shelf, as well as the floor of the entire polar sea. The greatest depth at which it was observed by the *Challenger* was 5,120 meters. In the Gulf of Naples it begins at a depth of 15 meters, where in contact with the sea water it gen-

TABLE OF ANALYSES OF MUDS OF TERRIGENOUS AND VOLCANIC ORIGIN.

	(1) Blue mud	(2) Red mud	(3) Green mud	(4) Green sand	(5) Volcanic mud
Ignition..........	5.60	6.02	3.30	9.10	6.22
SiO_2..............	64.20	31.66	31.27	29.70	34.12
Al_2O_3	13.55	9.21	4.08	3.25	9.22
Fe_2O_3	8.38	4.52	12.72	5.05	15.46
MnO_2.............	......	......	......	......	trace
CaO.............	2.51	25.68	0.30	0.22	1.44
MgO.............	0.25	2.07	0.12	0.13	0.22
Na_2O.............	......	1.63	......	......	......
K_2O	......	1.33	......	......	......
$CaCO_3$...........	2.94	......	46.36	49.46	32.22
$Ca_3P_2O_8$	1.39	......	0.70	trace	trace
$CaSO_4$...........	0.42	......	0.58	1.07	0.27
$MgCO_3$	0.76	......	0.57	2.02	0.83
SO_3..............	......	0.27	......	......	......
CO_2..............	......	17.13	......	......	......
Cl................	......	2.46	......	......	......
Total........	100.00	101.98	100.00	100.00	100.00
Less O = Cl....		0.87			
		101.11			

erally has a red or brown color, due to iron oxide or hydrate, and when dried its color is gray or brown from the oxidation of its contained iron sulphides. Pure clay often constitutes only a small proportion of this mud (though ranging from 16 to 97 per cent.), and the lime content may be as high as 35 per cent. Quartz is a characteristic constituent. This is the type of mud which has in the past given rise to most of the marine shales and slates.

The Red Mud. This is much more restricted in its distribution than either the blue or green. It is found opposite the mouths of tropical rivers, such as the Amazon and the Yang-tze-Kiang, and is derived from the red laterite or residual soil of the tropical countries. Its percentage of pure clay varies from 28 to 68, and its lime content varies from 6 to 60 per cent.; glauconite is absent, but quartz is characteristic. The red mud closely resembles the red mud of the deep sea, which has, however, a different origin, being probably in large part the product of decay of volcanic material which has settled to this depth. Muds of this kind may easily preserve an abundance of shells and other remains of marine organisms. Since they are formed opposite the mouths of great rivers, which may sweep terrestrial organisms into the sea, such remains may also be expected in these deposits.

The Green Mud. This ranges in depth from 180 to 2,300 meters (99 to 1,250 + fathoms), and may contain as much as 56 per cent. of lime. In shallower depths this green mud passes into greensands. The percentage of clay in the green mud varies from 24 to 48. Glauconite is one of the chief constituents of both the greensands and green muds.

Greensand. This is essentially the mineral glauconite, an impure hydrous silicate of iron and potassium. Clarke states that, "according to the best analyses, glauconite probably has when pure the composition represented by the formula $Fe''' KSi_2O_6$ aq., in which some iron is replaced by aluminum, and other bases partly replace K." This is forming in the present ocean near the "mud line" around continental shores. It is never pure, but contaminated by alteration products and other substances, and hence its composition varies widely. In the present ocean it is chiefly formed on the interior of foraminiferal shells, and it is believed that the decomposing organic matter in these shells is responsible for its formation. According to Murray and Renard (62:*383*), the shell is partly filled with fine silt or mud, and upon this the organic matter will act. "Through intervention of the sulphates contained in the sea water, the iron of the mud is converted into sulphide, which oxidizes later to ferric hydroxide. At the same time alumina is removed from the sediments by solution, and colloidal silica is liberated. The latter reacts upon the ferric hydroxide in presence of potassium salts extracted from adjacent minerals, and so glauconite is produced." (Clarke–20b:*402.*) The constant association of the glauconite shells with the débris of rocks in which potassium-bearing minerals such as orthoclase and muscovite occur seems to sustain this view of Murray and Renard of the origin of glauconite.

Glauconite may, however, form under other conditions than those now obtaining in the glauconite region of the present oceans. L. Cayeux (15) has shown that in certain instances glauconite has formed subsequent to the consolidation of the rocks in which it occurs. Cayeux shows that this mineral can also form without the intervention of organisms.

While glauconite of the present sea and in the sedimentary rocks is crystalline (monoclinic, La Croix), having a definite cleavage, though not crystal form, the mineral caladonite of nearly identical composition is earthy in texture and never granular. This is a decomposition product of augite in various basaltic rocks, and may be identical with glauconite (Clarke). Another mineral of similar appearance is greenalite, found in the iron-bearing rocks of the Mesabi range of Minnesota. It is free from potassium, the iron being practically all in the ferrous state (Leith–56: *240*), while in glauconite, where potassium is an essential constituent, the iron is mainly in the ferric state. Cayeux has also observed that glauconite is frequently present in arable soils, in all conditions from perfect freshness to complete alteration into limonite, to which Clarke remarks that the formation of the species is perhaps "one of the modes by which potassium is withdrawn from its solution in the ground water." (20b:*494.*) "Probably, in all their occurrences," says Clarke, "the final reaction is the same, namely, the absorption of potassium and soluble silica by colloidal ferric hydroxide. In the ocean these materials are prepared by the action of decaying animal matter upon ferruginous clays and fragments of potassium-bearing silicates. In the sedimentary rocks, where glauconite appears as a late product, the action of percolating waters upon the hydroxide would account for its formation. In igneous rocks the hydroxide is derived from augite, or perhaps from olivine, and percolating waters again come into play. Thus the various productions of glauconite and caladonite become the results of a single process, which is exactly equivalent to that in which potassium compounds are taken up by clays." (20b:*494.*)

Greensands are found in nearly all formations from the Cambric to the present, and often constitute a predominant element of the formation, as in the Cretacic Greensands of England and America. Analyses of the mineral from different horizons show on the whole a close correspondence in composition, there being, however, a steadily decreasing percentage of potash from the older to the more recent. In the table on page 672, the average composition of various glauconites is given: (a) from the Lower Ordovicic of Minnesota, (b) from the Cretacic Greensands of Wooburn, Antrim, Ireland, (c) from the Cretacic Greensand marls of Hanover County, Virginia, (d) modern oceanic glauconite, mean of four analyses from *Challenger* dredgings (analyses b, c, d quoted from Clarke–20b: *494*).

The mechanical composition of typical greensand marls (Navesink) of the Cretacic of New Jersey has been determined by Prather (73: *162*; 74) to be as follows:

Fine clay (settling out of suspension in water in the course of from 1 to 24 hours), 14.41 per cent.; sand, almost wholly composed of pure glauconite, pyrite, shell fragments and Foraminifera (set-

Table of Analyses of Glauconite from Various Horizons.

	(a) Ordovicic	(b) Cretacic Ireland	(c) Cretacic Virginia	(d) Modern oceanic
SiO_2	48.18	40.00	51.56	53.61
Al_2O_3	6.97	13.00	6.62	9.56
Fe_2O_3	......	16.81	15.16	21.46
FeO	27.08	10.17	8.33	1.58
MnO	......	......	......	trace
MgO	......	1.97	0.95	2.87
CaO	......	1.97	0.62	1.39
Na_2O	1.25	2.16	1.84	0.42
K_2O	7.40	8.21	4.15	3.49
H_2O	8.75	6.19	10.32	5.96
Total...............	99.63	100.48	99.55	100.34

tling out of suspension in water in five minutes or less), 85.59 per cent. A sample from a lower bed of the same formation (Navesink) gave clay as above 8.18 per cent.; sand, composed about equally of pure glauconite and of rounded grains of quartz, with some mica, 91.82 per cent.

Many grains of glauconite represent internal molds of foraminiferal shells, though frequently further enlargement of these molds, after the solution of the shell, produces irregular glauconite nodules. W. B. Clark (17 : *238*; 18) believes that the New Jersey glauconites were formed in much the same manner as the modern glauconites of the ocean, but Prather (74 : *509*) points out some objections to this interpretation, and cites evidence of shallow-water conditions during the accumulation of these glauconite sands. He finds that the casts of Foraminifera are the exception. The greensand grains of the Lower Ordovicic dolomites of Minnesota are regarded by Hall and Sardeson (42 : *186*) as having their origin "in the chemical conditions of the mingled mineral matters of the including rocks. . . ." and not in the chemical changes within foraminiferal shells. (See Hunt–49 : *303*; 50 : *196*, *309*; 51 : *257*.) Though modern glauconite deposits are chiefly confined to depths at or for some distance below the 100-fathom line, the frequent association of this mineral with typical littoral deposits, and in formations containing a littoral fauna, indicates that in the past it may have formed in shallower water sufficiently removed from the shore to prevent excessive detrital deposition.

The secondary origin, through erosion of older greensand deposits and redeposition of the material in shallow water, must also be considered. Such deposits are forming at the present time by the erosion of the Cretacic greensands of the Atlantic coastal plain. Andrée (3:381) holds that this may have been the origin of greensand lenses in the Neocomien sandstones of northwest Germany (Teutoburger Wald, especially the Oswing). The lower Cenomanien deposits of greensands (Essener Greensand) of northwestern Germany are other examples of such deposits formed near shore, passing laterally near Mons into a shore conglomerate with rich fauna.

Greensand is to-day found sporadically on the shallow ocean floor under the Gulf Stream in depths of only a few hundred meters. (Pourtales–72:397.)

The decomposition of glauconite produces, according to L. Cayeux, ferric hydroxide and pyrite, but other alteration products may also result. Thus the bright-red "Redbank" sands of the New Jersey Cretacic seem to owe their color to the decomposition of the glauconite mingled with the quartz grains of the deposit. This decomposition may be due to the more porous character of these sands, but that it was not produced under present climatic conditions is shown by the bright-red tints which indicate a prolonged period of subjection to dehydrating agencies.

Deposits on Lee Banks and on the Edge of the Continental Shelf.

Where ocean currents carrying fine silt pass from shoals to deep water, the checking of the current resulting causes a deposition of more or less of the silt. (Willis–105:497.) Thus on the lee of a submerged ridge a bank of silt will form, the structure of which is probably that of the delta, the successive additions being at a comparatively steep angle. The Gulf Stream crosses several shoals or submerged terraces, and deposits of the type mentioned are formed in the lee of these. "The steepest slope of the Gulf of Mexico from the 100th to the 2,000th-fathom line is in the position of a lee-bank northwest of the Yucatan plateau. . . . The Blake plateau, over which the Gulf Stream sweeps north of the Bahamas, is clean, hard limestone, but a lee-bank of mud and ooze is forming on its short, steep slope into deep water." (105:497.)

A similar type of deposit is forming on the edge of the continental plateau off the Atlantic coast of North America. The plateau or shelf itself is covered with shore-derived arenaceous deposits. Dredgings from these were examined by Bailey Willis, who states that they "are indeed finer near the eastern edge, yet are distinctly granular and incoherent."

The black muds of the Ordovicic with their world-wide distribution of graptolites seem to offer an older illustration of this type of sedimentation. The graptolites are often arranged so as to indicate current action, and it appears that these muds (Deep Kill, Norman's Kill, Utica) were distributed by these currents and deposited on the ocean floor under their pathway.

ABYSSAL DEPOSITS.

In the abyssal district of the ocean, beyond the one thousand-meter line, current-borne detrital material is relatively unimportant. Terrestrial material borne by currents is not unknown, however, as in the case of the deep-sea vegetal deposits already referred to. Even rock waste is carried by currents to realms of greater depths where these are not far from shore, while terrestrial material carried by floating icebergs or rocks held by the roots of floating trees or sea weeds may come to be deposited at any depth. Among other deposits of the littoral district which pass over into the abyssal, greensand has already been noted, as extending to a depth of 700 fathoms. The characteristic deposits of this district, exclusive of the marine derelicts, may be divided, according to their origin, into the pelagic and the terrigenous. To these must be added the meteoric or extra-terrestrial materials, and the subcrustal or volcanic.

Abyssal Deposits of Pelagic Origin.

Pelagic deposits are those which have descended to the bottom from the pelagic district of the ocean, i. e., the upper hundred-fathom layer of water of the open ocean. They comprise chiefly the shells and skeletal parts of pelagic animals and plants, such as Foraminifera, radiolaria, pteropods, ostracods and diatoms, the shells and other hard parts of pelagic molluscs, and the skeletal parts of fish, especially the teeth of selachians, and, further, the ear bones of whales, and other hard parts of this as well as other pelagic vertebrates. The young stages of organisms, such as molluscs, brachiopods and echinoderms, may also be included in these deposits. The former group may be termed the holopelagic group, since it comprises organisms permanently at home in the pelagic district, while the latter may be termed the meropelagic group, comprising types at home in the pelagic district during part of their lives only.

Foraminifera, ostracods and pteropod shells are calcareous, and these form the chief source of the lime deposits of the deep sea. Foraminiferal oozes of the modern sea generally abound in the shells of Globigerina, hence the term Globigerina ooze is applied to them. It should be emphasized, however, that the Foraminifera of this ooze are pelagic species, *i. e.,* types which float in the pelagic district of the open ocean. This point is often overlooked in interpreting former foraminiferal oozes as deep-sea deposits. Thus it has been shown repeatedly that the Foraminifera of the chalk are largely of littoral types with only such pelagic additions as might be expected from the fact that the pelagic district really overlaps the littoral. Nevertheless the chalk is commonly compared with the modern Globigerina ooze, and referred to abyssal deposits, whereas the Foraminifera composing it point rather to a littoral origin.

The great purity of deep-sea oozes of pelagic origin is due to the fact that the amount of terrigenous material settling here is relatively slight. Thus in tropical seas, in depths of 600 fathoms or less, pelagic shells of carbonate of lime often constitute 80 per cent. to 90 per cent. of the deposit. With increasing depth, however, the percentage of carbonate of lime decreases, though the surface conditions are the same. Thus at 2,000 fathoms the lime is less than 60 per cent., at 2,400 fathoms 30 per cent. and at 2,600 fathoms 10 per cent. (Chamberlin and Salisbury–16: *382*), while below this lime is generally absent. The most rapid falling off of the percentage of lime carbonate is below 2,200 fathoms, while between 2,400 and 2,600 fathoms the floor of the ocean is covered with red clay. The explanation generally given for this decrease in the percentage of carbonate of lime is the greater power of solution of the deeper waters, owing either to the great pressure under which it exists or to the abundance of CO_2 in it derived from emanations from the sea floor, or to both causes. (For other factors influencing this, see Philippi–69.) The red clay of the deeps has been regarded as the insoluble residue left on solution of these shells, a not unlikely source for at least a part of this deposit.

Radiolaria and diatom shells are siliceous, and often constitute extensive deposits in the modern oceans. Diatoms are, however, not confined to salt water, but occur in fresh water as well. Extensive beds of diatoms are known in various older deposits both marine and lacustrine. Characteristic examples are found in the coastal plain strata of eastern North America, where a single bed underlying the city of Richmond, Virginia, has a thickness of 18 feet. Beds of fossil Radiolaria of considerable thickness are also known from older deposits, the most famous being the "Barbadoes earth" and the "Tripolite," though this name is often applied to diatomaceous or other siliceous earths.

Abyssal Deposits of Terrigenous Origin.

Among these may first be noted the terrigenous matter carried to great distances by the currents, especially opposite the mouths of great rivers. Thus terrigenous deposits are carried out for a thousand miles opposite the mouth of the Amazon. The fine coral mud, found around oceanic coral islands, often making the water milky for miles, may settle to the more moderate depths of the abyssal region around these islands. Characteristic deep-sea deposits of continental origin are the blue, green and red clays already referred to, the greensand in the upper portion and the deposits of drift logs and leaves, such as were dredged by the *Blake* and the *Albatross* in the Caribbean and off the west coast of America. The most abundant deep-sea deposits of terrestrial origin are volcanic ejectamenta, especially the finer volcanic ashes which are spread far and wide by wind currents and eventually settle on sea and land alike. Even fragments of pumice, dropped on the surface of the ocean and floated until they become waterlogged, are characteristic of deep-sea deposits. Volcanic glass and lapilli are likewise found in the deep-sea deposits, some of these probably originating from submarine volcanoes. It is believed that much of the red clay which covers the deeper ocean floor is a result of the decomposition of such volcanic material. This floating volcanic débris is often classed as pelagic, but it is evident that it has nothing in common with the true pelagic material. It may for convenience be classed as pseudo-pelagic, in which class also may be included the leaves, tree trunks, etc., which have floated out from the land (pseudoplankton) and come to rest on the bottom of the deep sea. All of these are strictly terrestrial, only the holopelagic and meropelagic types being truly marine.

The Red Clay.

The red clay of the deep sea is distributed over an area aggregating 51,500,000 square miles, and occurs in depths below 2,400 to

2,600 fathoms. It contains much volcanic débris, besides the bones of mammals, zeolitic crystals and spherules of extra-terrestrial origin. As already noted, the solution of the pelagic shells in deeper water liberates a minute quantity of such red clay, but a considerable part also appears to be derived by decomposition of volcanic dust. The clay is generally rich in Radiolaria; indeed these have been regarded as forming merely a phase of the red clay deposit of the deep sea, they seldom if ever occurring quite pure.

Analyses of Deep-Sea Deposits.

The following analyses quoted from Clarke (20a–436) give (a) the composition of the red clay from 23 analyses. Others have given a carbonate of lime content as high as 60 per cent. Added to this are analyses of (b) radiolarian ooze, (c) diatom ooze, (d) Globigerina ooze, average of 21 analyses, (e) Globigerina ooze very high in carbonate, and (f) pteropod ooze. All samples dried at 110°. Soluble and insoluble portions in analyses a, b and d are not separated in the table.

Table of Analyses of Deep-Sea Deposits.

	a Red clay	b Radio- larian ooze	c Diatom ooze	d Globi- gerina ooze	e Globi- gerina ooze	f Ptero- pod ooze
Ignition......	4.50	7.41	5.30	7.90	1.40	2.00
SiO$_2$.........	62.10	56.02	67.92	31.71	1.36	3.65
Al$_2$O$_3$	16.06	10.52	0.55	11.10	0.65	0.80
Fe$_2$O$_3$	11.83	14.99	0.39	7.03	0.60	3.06
MnO$_2$	0.55	3.23	.....	trace	.....	.....
CaO.........	0.28	0.39	.....	0.41	.....	.....
MgO.........	0.50	0.25	.....	0.12	.....	.....
CaCO$_3$.......	0.92	3.89	19.29	37.51	92.54	82.66
Ca$_3$P$_2$O$_8$......	0.19	1.39	0.41	2.80	0.90	2.44
CaSO$_4$.......	0.37	0.41	0.29	0.29	0.19	0.73
MgCO$_3$......	2.70	1.50	1.13	1.13	0.87	0.76
Insoluble*....	.....	.....	4.72	.....	1.49	3.90
	100.00	100.00	100.00	100.00	100.00	100.00

* Contains silica, alumina, and ferric oxide not separated.

Older Deposits That Have Been Considered of Deep-sea Origin.

The question, Are there any deep-sea deposits among the sediments in the older geological series, has been variously answered in the past. Sir John Murray held that abyssal sediments were not represented among the known sediments, except perhaps in such instances as the radiolarian ooze of Barbados. Chalk has in the past frequently been cited as an example of a deep-sea deposit of Cretacic time, and this opinion is still defended by some. (Supan– 91 : *855.*) There seems to be, however, a growing recognition of the fact that this formation is of comparatively shallow-water origin, the organisms composing it being benthonic rather than pelagic.

Many older radiolarian cherts or radiolarites have been referred to deep-sea origin. Their almost constant interpolation between beds of shallow-water origin has, however, thrown doubt upon this interpretation. Of comparatively deep-water origin are believed to have been the massive limestones of the Trias of the eastern Alps and of some of the Jurassic deposits of the Alpine region. This applies especially to the Aptychus beds of the Upper Jurassic, some of which seem to have no other remains than the opercula of ammonite shells, the so-called Aptychi. These opercula are believed to have sunk to the bottom on the death and decay of the pelagic ammonite, while the shell continued to float and eventually was deposited in other sediments of generally shallower water origin.

Whether these deposits will eventually prove to have such an origin, or whether they, too, may not be of shallow-water origin must for the present remain undecided.

In North America the black muds of the Upper Devonic have been regarded as of deep-water origin (Clarke–21), but formed under conditions similar to those obtaining in the Black Sea. The same origin has been suggested by Pompeckj (71) for the dark Liassic shales with saurian remains found in Württemberg and in England. In both cases, however, the deposits may with equal if not greater certainty be classed as of shallow-water origin.

Concretions of the Deep Sea.

Concretions are a characteristic feature of the deep sea. Though not clastic, they may be noted here for the sake of completeness. Foremost among these are manganese concretions, which are widely distributed on the abyssal ocean floor. Sometimes they occur in heaps of small grains or lumps. They range in depth to over 8,000 meters, being especially abundant in the Pacific. They are, however, also found in shallow water, as in the case of the deposits formed in Loch Fyne in Scotland. (Buchanan.) The mineral is generally the hydrous oxide, and, according to Murray, is a product of disintegration of the volcanic rocks found so abundantly in these deeper waters. The manganese and iron derived from the volcanics are at first in the form of carbonate, after which they become altered to the oxide. The concretions commonly contain fragments of pumice or lapilli or a bone or other organic structure as a nucleus. (See also Chapter IX.) Besides the manganese concretions there are concretions of other minerals, of which barium is one.

Cosmic Deposits in the Deep Sea.

Fine particles with a metallic interior often magnetic are found in the deeper water deposits. These have been interpreted as cosmic dust, the product of meteoric showers. Chamberlin and Salisbury (16: *381-2*) state that the number of meteorites which enter the atmosphere daily has been estimated at from 15,000,000 to 20,-000,000, and that if on the average each weighs 10 grains (a high estimate), the total amount of extra-terrestrial matter reaching the earth yearly would be 5,000 to 7,000 tons, of which about three-fourths on the average would fall into the sea. At this rate it would take some fifty billion years to cover the sea bottom with a layer one foot in thickness.

Submarine Volcanic Deposits.

Deposits formed on the floor of the ocean by submarine volcanic eruptions probably constitute an important part of the deep-sea deposits. Not all of the widely distributed volcanic material, however, found in the deep sea is the product of submarine volcanic eruptions; a large part of the pumice, lapilli and volcanic glass and dust is derived from terrestrial volcanoes, and is carried to the deep sea by flotation on the surface of the ocean, or as wind-borne dust, or as both. The Hawaiian Islands represent the result of prolonged submarine volcanic eruptions, and the accumulation of the material in the vicinity, until they rose to the present height of the sea-level. For the general subject of submarine eruptions, see Thoulet (94). (See also Chapter XXII.)

INTERRUPTIONS OF MARINE SEDIMENTATION.

It is generally assumed that deposition in the deep sea is relatively constant and not subject to interruptions of any but accidental character. Under this latter may be classed the appearance of submarine volcanoes, which will act in a twofold manner by disturbing the waters of the bottom of the sea and creating currents which will stir up and sweep away sediment previously accumulated, and, second, by forming a new series of deposits, as well as creating new slopes and regions of deposition. Seismic disturbances likewise cause interruptions of sedimentation and rearrangement of sediments.

In the lesser depths of the ocean, however, the currents of the surface will to a certain extent also affect the bottom sediment. This is partly due to their ability to sweep away loose material even in considerable depths and partly to their influence in preventing sedimentation. As already noted in Chapter V in narrow passages, the currents may be effective at considerable depths. Agassiz states "that the bottom of the Gulf Stream along the Blake plateau is swept clean of slime and ooze, and is nearly barren of animal life." (1: 259.) This effect is felt to a depth of 1,281 meters. According to Verrill, the floor of the ocean beneath the Gulf Stream in depths of 150 to 600 meters, and at a distance of 100 to 200 km. from land, is covered with fine sand, mostly quartz, some feldspar, mica and magnetite, fragments of shells, etc., coral and rhizopods. Fine mud is absent and is even scarce in depths of 1,000 meters, having apparently been carried away by the Gulf Stream. A current of more than 7 mm. per second at the bottom can stir up and move shell particles of 0.12 mm. or less in diameter and be quite effective in transporting mud particles. Currents of 3 mm. per second can carry along Globigerina ooze. Measurements on the Gulf Stream have shown a velocity of about 31 mm. per second at a depth of 910 m. west of the Bermudas. In 1,100 m. depth, however, no measurable velocity was shown.

As already noted (Chapter V), the passages between the several islands of the Canary group have their bottoms kept clean by the tidal currents rushing through them. These currents are effective to a depth of 2,000 meters. On the submarine banks in the neighborhood of these islands the denuding effect of the tidal currents is felt to considerable depths. On the Seine bank only hard rock bottom was found in depths of less than 200 meters. In greater depths, down to 964 meters, only coarse sand was found. Only in the depths exceeding 1,500 and 2,000 meters is an accumulation of the fine Globigerina ooze possible.

In the passes between the islands of the Indian Archipelago, the *Siboga* expedition found mostly "hard bottom," the sounding instruments bringing up only broken-off rock fragments, or impressions of a rock bottom. In exceptional cases coarse sand was found. Since these depths extend to 1,500 meters, it is probable that we have here a prevention of sedimentation by the removal of the particles before they reach the bottom, rather than any effect of eroding work of the current at such depth. (Weber–101 : *187*.) Compensatory currents, such as those formed in the Roman Mediterranean by greater evaporation, also affect sedimentation. In the case mentioned the Gibraltar current flows in at the surface, while a deeper current passes out beneath, affecting the lower 30 meters of the water in the pass. Currents due to melting ice also affect sedimentation. The diatoms of the Antarctic region settle only north of the region of drift ice (Philippi). In addition to the oceanic and the tidal currents, the upward currents, which bring the colder water of the depths to the surface, are effective agents in modifying deposition. All such currents are further effective in determining the facies of the sediment, and abrupt changes from one to another type of sediment may often be due to them.

It thus appears that sedimentation on the sea bottom is unequal in extent and that the surface of more elevated ridges, or areas subject to current scour, may remain free from sediment, while this is accumulating all around. Cases of interruption of the continuity of sediments referable to such causes are not unknown from the older rocks. A good example is found in the Upper Siluric beds of the Helderberg Mountains in eastern New York. Near the city of Kingston a submarine ridge of folded and eroded sandstones of Mid-Ordovicic age projected above the general bottom of the late Siluric sea, and was kept free from the deposits accumulating all around it. Thus the Rosendale waterlimes and the Wilbur limestone are wanting over the Kingston ridge, but present all around at a distance of a few miles. Only the upper part of the Cobleskill limestone is deposited upon the ridge, which became buried in the deposits accumulating around it, to which, however, the ridge itself did not contribute any material. These deposits, however, accumulated in shallow water, as lime muds derived by the erosion of a not too distant limestone shore. The shallow water is indicated by the abundance of mud cracks at several levels. The absence of the Credneria beds and of the carinata-quader (sandstone) in the vicinity of Dresden (Plauenscher Grund) has also been referred to the existence of elevated ridges and cliffs in the Cretacic sea in that vicinity, on which coarse boulders formed the only loose material, while around were accumulating finer sediments. (Petrascheck–65 : 26 et seq., Fig. 45.)

It further appears that interruption of sedimentation and even contemporaneous erosion are processes which may be active in the moderate depths of the ocean, especially between depths of 200 and 900 meters, i. e., in the bathyal zone of the sea. Such an interruption may give rise to a distinct hiatus, as well as a variation in thickness of sediments. It is not improbable that some of the breaks in the geological series referred to subaërial erosions and the formation of disconformities may be due to the processes outlined above. That such is frequently the case may perhaps be questioned, though much emphasis is laid upon it by some stratigraphers and students of Palæogeography. (Bailey Willis–106; 107.)

The numerous breaks in the Alpine Jurassic limestone series have been regarded by Neumayr and others as examples of discontinuous deposition without the occurrence of periods of dry land and erosion. Currents are believed to have been the disturbing agent. From the Rhætic upward irregularities in the distribution of the sediment are of increasing frequency and extent; these are partly due to variations in the sea-level, partly to tectonic movements of the suboceanic floor, and partly to the periodic want of material for sedimentation (Diener). In part these breaks may also be due to oceanic or tidal currents. (Andrée–3.)

Stratigraphic gaps are numerous in the geological formations of North America, but it remains still to be determined which of these, if any, are due to contemporaneous erosion, or to prevention of deposition by currents, etc. Some of the gaps in the Ordovicic limestones of the Appalachians may be explained in this manner. When the great limestone series of the Palæozoic of western North America are more fully investigated, evidences of such intraformational gaps may be found.

PERSISTENCE AND VARIATION IN THICKNESS OF MARINE STRATA.

One of the familiar phenomena confronting the field geologist is the enormous variation in the thickness of strata when traced from point to point. For this variation several explanations are available. In the first place, it often happens that a given series of great thickness is in other regions represented by only a fraction of the formation, this being due to the occurrence of a constantly widening hiatus between the adjacent formations. Thus it appears that the Lower Ordovicic series of eastern North America is represented by some 2,500 feet of limestones in central Pennsylvania, while only about 400 feet are found in the Mohawk Valley of New York. This diminished series, however, represents only the lowest part of the Pennsylvania deposits, the entire middle and upper part being absent. Upon these beds rests a series of limestone 2,500 feet thick and representing the Middle Ordovicic, but this again is represented by less than 100 feet in the Mohawk Valley. This time, however, it is the upper part of the Middle Ordovicic which is present. Thus the gap in the Mohawk Valley cuts out all but the lowest of the Lower Ordovicic and all but the highest of the Middle Ordovicic. Southward the gap becomes less by the appearance of higher members of the subjacent and lower members of the superjacent series. This is perhaps the most frequently applicable explanation of the differences in thickness of marine formations of similar lithologic character. In the next place, there is variation in thickness due to variation in character of the sediment. Formations of different lithic composition may show great variation in thickness due to original difference in deposition. Thus a sandy series is likely to be much thicker than a shale series into which it passes and which was formed during the same period. Again, sediments of two kinds from separate sources may overlap, and so one may thin away as the other thickens. This is especially the case where continental sediments overlap a marine series of the same age or vice versa. The Catskill and Chemung series of the Upper Devonic of the eastern United States is a case in point. The Catskill continental beds are thick in the east, but die away westward, while beneath the thinning cover of this series the marine Chemung increases progressively from nothing in the east until it alone fills the interval in western New York. But even the marine series may overlap in this manner. Thus the Black shales of Portage time are thickest in Ohio, and wedge out eastward in New York and Pennsylvania. Their place is taken by the sandy Portage beds which have their source in the east and grow thinner toward the west.

The third cause of differences in thickness is local variation in the regions of sedimentation. A relatively shallow and stationary area of the sea bottom may experience little sedimentation, while a slowly subsiding area may receive a great supply of sediment of essentially similar character. The Moscow shale of the Middle Devonic of western New York is a good example of this. In the Genesee Valley region its thickness is about 250 feet, while on Lake

Erie it is only 17 feet. Still further west in Canada the thickness increases again to over a hundred feet. The 17 feet of shales in the Lake Erie section apparently represent the 250 feet of the eastern section, but owing to lack of accumulation, probably because the water remained shallow and currents were active, the amount of deposit was slight. That this shallow area seems to have formed a barrier between the eastern and western faunas is indicated by their diversity.

In contradistinction to this marked variation is the persistence in thickness of the underlying Encrinal or Morse Creek * limestone. This bed is only about 2 feet thick, but it has been traced almost continuously from western Ontario (Thedford) to the Genesee Valley, a distance of over 200 miles, and throughout the extent it retains its lithic character, thickness and uniformity of organic content. (Grabau–39.)

COMPREHENSIVE FORMATIONS.

Under this title may be grouped deposits which apparently without break continued over long periods of time. That such exist has frequently been observed, though many apparent lithic units have been found to consist of several members separated by disconformities. The Hunton limestone of Oklahoma was formerly believed to be a unit, extending without break from the Niagaran to the Oriskanian. It is now known to consist of at least four distinct and disconformable members separated by great time gaps (Reeds–80). The Durness limestone of northern Scotland, believed to range from Lower Cambric to Ordovicic, is now known to consist of a basal member of Lower Cambric age, separated by a hiatus and disconformity from the Lower Ordovicic, the Middle and Upper Cambric being wanting. (Grabau–40.) That such comprehensive formations occur, nevertheless, is shown by the deposits on the floor of the modern deep sea, where teeth of Tertiary sharks (Carcharodon) occur side by side with remains of organisms now living. Here sedimentation is so slow that the time interval since the Tertiary, when these sharks died, has not been sufficient to completely bury their teeth.

So far, however, no such comprehensive sediments are known from the older geological formations, though a commingling of organisms of various geological horizons is not uncommon. This

---

* The "Encrinal Limestone" of western New York is not the same as the Tichenor of central New York.

may be due to a weathering out of the fossils of an older formation and their incorporation in the deposits of a later one, as in the case of the Ordovicic fossils included in the base of the overlying Mississippic black shale in Tennessee, or again fossils of an older formation may be washed out along the shore and incorporated in the new deposit. Thus Miocenic oyster shells on the Atlantic coast serve as a basis for attachment of modern oysters, and are buried with these in the modern deposits.

BIBLIOGRAPHY XV.

1. AGASSIZ, ALEXANDER. 1888. Three Cruises of the Blake, Vol. I. Houghton, Mifflin & Co.
2. ALLEN, H. S. 1901. The Settlement of Solid Matter in Fresh and Salt Water. Nature, Vol. LXIV, pp. 279–280. London.
3. ANDRÉE, KARL. 1901. Ueber Stetige und Unterbrochene Meeressedimentation, ihre Ursachen, sowie ueber deren Bedeutung für die Stratigraphie. Neues Jahrbuch für Mineralogie, etc. Beilage Bd. XXV, pp. 366–421.
4. ANDRÉE, K. 1912. Ueber Sedimentbildung am Meeresboden, 1ter Teil. Geologische Rundschau, Bd. III, pp. 324–360 (with extended bibliography).
5. ANDRUSSOW, N. 1897. La Mer Noire. Guide des Excursions du VIIme Congrès Géologique International, No. 29.
6. BARUS, CARL. 1889. Subsidence of Fine Solid Particles in Liquids. American Journal of Science, 3rd series, Vol. XXXVII, pp. 122–129.
7. BEHRENS, J. H. 1873. Ueber die Untersuchung der Grundproben (der Pommerania-Expedition 1871 in die Ostsee). 1. Jahresberichte des Committee's für Wissenschaftliche Untersuchungen der deutschen Meere in Kiel, pp. 57–63. Berlin.
8. BIGELOW, H. B. 1905. The Shoal-water Deposits of the Bermuda Banks. Proceedings of the American Academy of Arts and Sciences, Vol. XL, pp. 559–592.
9. BLAKE, J. F. 1903. On the Original Form of Sedimentary Deposits. Geological Magazine, N. S., Dec. IV, Vol. X, pp. 12–18, 78–80.
10. BODLÄNDER, G. 1893. Versuche ueber Suspension. Neues Jahrbuch für Mineralogie, etc., Vol. II, pp. 147–168.
11. BREWER, W. H. 1883. On the Subsidence of Particles in Liquids. Memoirs of the National Academy of Sciences, Vol. II, pp. 163–175.
12. BREWER, W. H. 1885. On the Suspension and Sedimentation of Clays. American Journal of Sciences, 3rd series, Vol. XXIX, pp. 1–5.
13. BROWNE, WALTER R. 1881. The Relative Value of Tidal and Upland Waters in Maintaining Rivers, Estuaries and Harbors. Proceedings of Institute of Civil Engineers, Vol. LXVI, pp. 1–68 (including extended discussion).
14. BUCHANAN, J. Y. 1891. On the Composition of Some Deep-sea Deposits from the Mediterranean. Royal Society of Edinburgh, Proceedings, Vol. XVIII, pp. 131–138.
15. CAYEUX, L. 1897. Contributions à l'étude micrographique des terrains sédimentaires. Mémoires Société géologique du Nord. Tome IV, part 2, pp. 163–184.

16. CHAMBERLIN, T. C., and SALISBURY, R. D. 1906. Geology, Vol. Ï. Henry Holt, New York.

17. CLARK, WILLIAM B. 1893. A Preliminary Report on the Cretaceous and Tertiary Formations of New Jersey. Geological Survey of New Jersey, Annual Report, Vol. II, pp. 169–239, pls. IV–VI.

18. CLARK, W. B. 1894. Origin and Classification of the Greensands of New Jersey. Journal of Geology, Vol. II, pp. 161–177.

19. CLARKE, F. W. 1907. The Composition of the Red Clay. Journal of Geology, Vol. XV, pp. 783–789.

20. CLARKE, F. W. 1908–1911. The Data of Geochemistry. U. S. Geological Survey (a), Bulletin 330, (b), 2nd edition, 491.

21. CLARKE, JOHN M. 1903. The Naples Fauna, part II. Memoir. N. Y. State Museum of Natural History, VI.

22. COLE, G. A. J., and CROOK, T. 1910. On Rock Specimens, Dredged from the Floor of the Atlantic off the Coast of Ireland, and Their Bearing on Submarine Geology. Memoirs of the Geological Survey of Ireland. 34 pp., 9 figs., 1 map.

23. COLLET, L. W. 1908. Les Depôts marins. Paris. 8ᵛᵒ, 325 pages.

24. COLLET, L. W., and LEE, G. W. 1906. Sur la Composition chemique de la Glauconie. Compte Rendu 142, pp. 999–1001.

25. COLLET, L. W., and LEE, G. W. 1906. Recherches sur la Glauconie. Proceedings of the Royal Society of Edinburgh, Vol. XXVI, pt. IV, pp. 238–278.

26. CORNISH, VAUGHN. 1898. Sea-beaches and Sandbanks. Geographical Journal, Vol. XI, pp. 528–543, 628–657.

27. CORNISH, V. 1898. On the Distribution of Detritus by the Sea. Report of the 67th Meeting of the British Association held at Toronto, 1897, p. 716.

28. DAUBRÉE, A. 1894. Deep-sea Deposits. A review of the Challenger Expedition. (Translated from "Journal des Savants," Dec., 1892, pp. 733–743, Jan., 1893, pp. 37–54.) Annual Report Smithsonian Institution for 1893, pp. 545–566.

29. DELESSE, A. 1871. Lithologie des Mers de France et des Mers principales du Globe. E. Lacroix, Paris.

30. DURHAM, W. 1878. Suspension of Clay in Water. Proceedings of the Royal Physical Society of Edinburgh, Vol. IV, pp. 46–50.

31. EHRENBERG, C. G. 1872. Mikrogeologische Studien als Zusammenfassung seiner Beobachtungen des kleinsten Lebens der Meeres-Tiefgründe aller Zonen und dessen geologischer Einfluss. Monatsberichte der königlichen Akademie der Wissenschaften. Berlin, pp. 265–322.

32. FAIRCHILD, H. L. 1901. Beach Structure in the Medina Sandstone. American Geologist, Vol. XXXVIII, pp. 9–14, 3 pls.

33. FENNEMAN, N. M. 1902. Development of the Profile of Equilibrium of the Subaqueous Shore Terrace. Journal of Geology, Vol. X, pp. 1–32.

34. FORBES, EDWARD. 1844. On the Light Thrown on Geology by Submarine Researches. Edinburgh New Philosophical Journal, Vol. XXXVI, p. 318.

35. FORCHHAMMER, G. 1841. Geognostische Studien am Meeresufer. Neues Jahrbuch für Mineralogie, u. s. w., pp. 1–38, taf. III.

36. FUCHS, TH. 1883. Welche Ablagerungen haben wir als Tiefseebildungen zu betrachten? Neues Jahrbuch für Mineralogie, u. s. w. Beilage Bd. II, 1883, pp. 487–584.

37. GEBBING, J. 1909. Chemische Untersuchungen von Meeresboden-,

Meerwasser- und Luftproben der Deutschen Südpolarexpedition. "Deutsche Südpolarexpedition, 1901–1903", VII, Heft II, pp. 77–234.

38. GLINKA, K. 1896. Der Glauconit, seine Entstehung, sein chemischer Bestand und die Art und Weise seiner Verwitterung. Publication de l'Institut agronomique de novo-Alexandria. St. Petersburg.

39. GRABAU, A. W. 1898. Faunas of the Hamilton Group of Eighteen Mile Creek and Vicinity. 16th Annual Report, N. Y. State Geologist, pp. 231–239.

40. GRABAU, A. W. 1910. Ueber die Einteilung des Nordamerikanischen Silurs. Compte Rendu du XIme Congrès Géologique International, pp. 971–995.

41. GÜMBEL, C. W. VON. 1888. Die Mineralogisch-Geologische Beschaffenheit der auf der Forschungsreise S. M. S. *Gazelle* gesammelten Meeresgrund-Ablagerungen. In "Die Forschungsreise S. M. S. *Gazelle* in den Jahren 1874 bis '76," II. Physik und Chemie, pp. 69–116. Berlin.

42. HALL, CHRISTOPHER W., and SARDESON, F. W. 1895. The Magnesian Series of the Northwestern States. Geological Society of America Bulletin, Vol. VI, pp. 167–198.

43. HAUG, ÉMILE. 1907. Traité de Géologie, Tome I.

44. HAZEN, ALLEN. 1904. On Sedimentation. Transactions of the American Society of Civil Engineers, Vol. LXIII, pp. 45–88.

45. HEIM, ALBERT; CULMANN; GRÄNICHER, G.; HELLWAG, W.; LANG, FR., MOSER, R. 1876. Bericht und Expertengutachen ueber die im Februar und September, 1875, in Horgen Vorgekammenen Rutschungen (mit 3 Tafeln). Zurich, 1876. (A copy of this now rare publication is in the Geological Library of Columbia University.)

46. HEIM, ALBERT; MOSER, R.; BURKLI; ZIEGLER, and others, 1888. Die Katastrophe von Zug, 5 Juli, 1887 (mit 5 Tafeln). Gutachten der Experten, herausgegeben auf Veranlassung der Behörden von Zug. Verlag von Hofer und Burger, Zurich, 1888.

47. HEIM, ARNOLD. 1908. Ueber Rezente und Fossile Subaquatische Rutschungen und deren Lithologische Bedeutung. Neues Jahrbuch für Mineralogie, etc., 1908, II, pp. 136–157, 2 figs., pl. 13.

48. HEIM, F. 1911. In W. Brennecke. Ozeanographische Arbeiten der deutschen Antarktischen Expeditionen. Annalen der Hydrographie, etc., Vol. XXXIX, pp. 350–353, 464–471, taf. 25, pp. 642–647.

49. HUNT, T. STERRY. 1878. Chemical and Geological Essays.

50. HUNT, T. S. 1891. Mineral Physiology and Physiography.

51. HUNT, T. S. 1892. Systematic Mineralogy.

52. JOLY, J. 1900. The Inner Mechanism of Sedimentation. Report of the British Association for the Advancement of Science, p. 732.

53. JOLY, J. 1902. *Ibid.* Proc. R. Dublin Soc., N. S., Vol. IX, pp. 325–332.

54. KINDLE, E. M. 1911. Cross-bedding and Absence of Fossils Considered as Criteria of Continental Deposits. American Journal of Science, Vol. XXXII, pp. 225–230.

55. KRÜMMEL, OTTO. 1907. Handbuch der Ozeanographie, Bd. I, 2nd ed.

56. LEITH, C. K. 1903. The Mesabi Iron-bearing District of Minnesota. Monograph U. S. Geological Survey, XLIII, 316 pp., 33 plates.

57. McGEE, W. J. 1896. The Formation of Arkose. Science, N. S., Vol. IV, pp. 962–963.

58. MURRAY, JOHN. 1900. Description of Marine Deposits on the Cable Route between Bermuda, Turk's Island and Jamaica. Proceedings of the Royal Society of Edinburgh, Vol. XXII, pp. 409–429.

59. MURRAY, JOHN. 1909. On the Depth and Marine Deposits of the Indian Ocean, with Descriptions of the Deposit-Samples, Collected by J. Stanley Gardiner in 1905. (The Percy Sladen Trust Expedition to the Indian Ocean in 1905.) Transactions of the Linnæan Society, Vol. XIII, 3, pp. 355–396, pls. 22–24. London.

60. MURRAY, JOHN, and LEE, G. V. 1909. The Depth and Marine Deposits of the Pacific. Memoirs of the Museum of Comparative Zoölogy at Harvard College, Vol. XXXVIII, 169 pp.

61. MURRAY, JOHN, and PHILIPPI, E. 1908. Die Grundproben der "Deutschen Tiefsee-Expedition," Bd. X der Wissenschaftlichen Ergebnisseder "Deutschen Tiefsee-Expedition 1898–1899" auf dem Dampfer *Valdivia*, pp. 67–206, taf. XVI–XXII, 2 maps. Jena.

62. MURRAY, JOHN and RENARD, A. F. 1891. Deep Sea Deposits. In "Report on the Scientific Results of the Voyage of H. M. S. *Challenger* during the years 1873–1876." London. (Reviewed *in extenso* by K. Futterer in Neues Jahrbuch für Mineralogie, u. s. w., 1893, Bd. II, pp. 281–320.)

63. ORTMANN, ARNOLD E. 1894. Anmerkung über Littoral Jenaische Denkschrift, Vol. VIII, p. 5. Anmerkung.

64. OWENS, J. S. 1911. Experiments on the Settlement of Solids in Water. Geographical Journal, Vol. XXVII, pp. 59–79.

65. PETRASHECK. 1894. Studien über Facienbildung im Gebiete der sächsischen Kreideformation. Leipziger Inaugural Dissertation.

66. PHILIPPI, E. 1908. Ueber das Problem der Schichtung und ueber Schichtbildung am Boden der heutigen Meere. Zeitschrift der deutschen geologischen Gesellschaft, Vol. LXI, pp. 346–377.

67. PHILIPPI, E 1908. Zwei Proben vom antarktischen Eisrand. Centralblatt für Mineralogie, pp. 356–357.

68. PHILIPPI, E. 1909. Ueber Schichtbildung am Boden der heutigen und vorweltlichen Meere. Internationale Revue der gesammten Hydrobiologie und Hydrographie, Vol. II, p. 9.

69. PHILIPPI, E. 1910. Die Grundproben der deutschen Südpolar-Expedition 1901–1903. "Deutsche Südpolar Expedition," Vol. II, Heft 6, pp. 411–416.

70. PHILIPPI, E. 1910. Ueber Sandablagerungen am Boden, der küstenfernen Tiefsee. Compte Rendu, 9me Congrès International de Géographie, Genève 1908, t. II, pp. 426–432.

71. POMPECKJ, JOSEF F. 1901. Die Jura Ablagerungen zwischen Regensburg und Regenstauf. Geognostische Jahreshefte, Bd. XIV, pp. 43 et seq.

72. POURTALÈS, L. F. VON. 1870. Der Boden des Golfstroms und der atlantischen Küste Nordamerikas. Petermann's Geographische Mittheilungen, Bd. XVI, pp. 393–398.

73. PRATHER, JOHN K. 1905. The Atlantic Highlands Section of the New Jersey Cretacic. American Geologist, Vol. XXXVI, pp. 162–178, 3 pls.

74. PRATHER, J. K. 1905. Glauconite. Journal of Geology, Vol. XIII, pp. 509–513.

75. PUMPELLY, R. 1891. The Relation of Secular Rock Disintegration to Certain Transitional Crystalline Schists. Bulletin of the Geological Society of America, Vol. II, pp. 209–224.

76. QUINCKE, G. 1901. The Clearing of Turbid Solutions. Report of the British Association for the Advancement of Science. Glasgow.

77. QUINCKE, G. 1904. Ueber die Klärung trüber Lösungen. Verhandlungen des Naturhistorisch-Medizinischen Vereins. Heidelberg, N. F., Bd. VII, pp. 97–104.

78. RAMANN, E. 1906. Einteilung und Benennung der Schlammablagerungen. Zeitschrift der deutschen geologischen Gesellschaft, Bd. LVIII, Monatsberichte, pp. 174–183.

79. RAMSAY, W. 1876. On the Influence of Various Substances in Accelerating the Precipitation of Clay Suspended in Water. Quarterly Journal of the Geological Society of London, Vol. XXXII, pp. 129–133.

80. REEDS, CHESTER A. 1911. The Hunton Formation of Oklahoma. American Journal of Science, 4th series, Vol. XXXII, pp. 250–268.

81. REVY, J. J. Hydraulics of Great Rivers.

82. ROBERTSON, D. 1874. Note on the Precipitation of Clay in Fresh and Salt Water. Transactions of the Glasgow Geological Society, Vol. IV, pp. 257–259.

83. ROBSON, H. 1904. Abysmal Deposits. Nature, Vol. LXIX, p. 297.

84. RUTOT, A. 1883. Les Phénomènes de la Sédimentation Marine étudiés dans leurs rapports avec la Stratigraphie Régionale. Bulletin du Musée royal d'Histoire naturelle de Belgique, Vol. II, pp. 41–83.

85. SCHARDT, H. 1892. Notice sur l'effondrement du Quai du Trait du Baye, etc. Bulletin de la Société Vaudoise des Sciences Naturelles. 28, No. 109.

86. SCHARDT, H. 1893. L'effondrement du Quai du Trait de Baye à Montreux survenu le 19 Mai, 1891. Bulletin de la Société Vaudoise des ingénieurs et des architects.

87. SCHUCHT, F. 1904. Das Wasser und seine Sedimente im Flutgebiete der Elbe. Jahrbuch der königlich-preussischen geologischen Landesanstalt, XXV, pp. 431–465.

88. SHALER, NATHANIEL S. 1895. Beaches and Tidal Marshes of the Atlantic Coast, National Geographic Monographs, No. 5, pp. 137–168. American Book Company.

89. SOLLAS, W. J. 1883. The Estuaries of the Severn and Its Tributaries; an Inquiry into the Nature and Origin of Their Tidal Sediment and Alluvial Flats. Quarterly Journal of the Geological Society of London, Vol. XXXIX, pp. 611–626.

89a. SORBY, HENRY C. 1908. On the Application of Quantitative Methods to the Study of the Structure and History of Rocks. Quarterly Journal of the Geological Society of London, Vol. LXIV, pp. 171–233, pls. xiv–xviii.

90. SPRING, W. 1900. La Floculation des Mileux Troublés. Recueil des travaux chimiques des Pays-Bas, Vol. XIX, pp. 222–294.

91. SUPAN, ALEXANDER. 1911. Grundzüge der physische Erdkunde. 5te Auflage, Leipzig, Veit & Co.

92. TARR, RALPH S. 1907. Recent Advance of Glaciers in Yakutat Bay Region, Alaska. Bulletin of the Geological Society of America, Vol. XVIII, pp. 257–286.

93. THOULET, J. 1900. Fixation des argiles en suspension dans l'eau par les corps poreux. Comptes Rendus, des Séances de l'Académie des Sciences, Paris. 130, p. 1639.

94. THOULET, J. 1903. Les volcans sous-marins. Revue des Deux Mondes. 73 année, 5ème période, t. XIII, livre 3, 1, II, pp. 611–624.

95. THOULET, J. 1906. Le calcaire et l'argile dans les fonds marins. Comptes Rendus, des Séances de l'Académie des Sciences, Paris. 142, pp. 738–739.

96. THOULET, J. 1908. Étude comparée des fonds marins anciens et actuels. Annales des Mines, 10 series, t. XIII, p. 236.

97. THOULET, J. 1910. Instructions pratiques pour l'établissement d'une carte bathymétrique-lithologique sous-marine. Bulletin de l'Institut Océanographique de Monaco, Nr. 169.

97a. THOULET, J. 1911. Carte bathy-lithologique de la côte du Golfe du Lion entre l'embonchure de la. Têt et Gruissan. Comptes Rendus des Séances de l'Académie des Sciences, Paris: 152, pp. 1037–1038.

98. TORNQUIST, AL. 1909. Ueber die Wanderung von Blöcken und Sand am ost-preussischen Ostseestrand. Schriften der physisch-ökonomischen Gesellschaft, pp. 79–88, taf. I, II.

99. UDDEN, J. A. 1894. Erosion, Transportation and Sedimentation Performed by the Atmosphere. Journal of Geology, Vol. II, pp. 318–331.

100. VERNON-HARCOURT, L. F. 1900. Experimental Investigations on the Action of Seawater in Accelerating the Deposit of River-silt and the Formation of Deltas. Minutes of the Proceedings of the Institute of Civil Engineers, Vol. CXLII, pp. 272–287. London.

101. WEBER, M. 1900. Die niederländische "Siboga" Expedition zur Untersuchung der Marinen Fauna und Flora des Indischen Archipels. Petermann's Geographische Mittheilungen, Vol. XLVI, p. 187.

102. WEULE, K. 1896. Zum Problem der Sedimentbildung. Annalen der Hydrographie, Bd. XXIV, pp. 402–413.

103. WHEELER, W. H. 1902. The Sea Coast. New York, Longmans, Green & Co.

104. WHITNEY, MILTON. 1892. Some Physical Properties of Soils. United States Department of Agriculture, Bulletin No. 4.

105. WILLIS, BAILEY. 1893. Conditions of Sedimentary Deposition. Journal of Geology, Vol. I, pp. 476–520.

106. WILLIS, B. 1910. Principles of Palæogeography. Science N. S., Vol. XXXIII, Feb. 18, 1910, pp. 246–251.

107. WILLIS, B. 1911. The Influence of Marine Currents on Deposition in Continental Seas. Abstract, Science, N. S., Vol. XXXIII, pp. 313–314.

108. WORTH, R. H. 1899. The Bottom-deposits of the English Channel from the Eddystone to Start Point, near the Thirty-fathom Line. Transactions of the Devonshire Association for the Advancement of Science, Vol. XXXI, pp. 356–375.

CHAPTER XVI.

CHARACTERS AND LITHOGENESIS OF THE BIOCLASTIC ROCKS.

Bioclastic rocks consist of fragments of older rocks which have been broken by the mechanical activities of organisms. Among these man is the most active, and he is undoubtedly the greatest producer of bioclastic rocks. To distinguish this type the name of artificial clastics is applied to it, and as examples concrete and other artificial stone may be mentioned. These need not be more fully discussed, though their variety is great and their characters manifold.

There are also other organisms which in a more or less effective way render rocks clastic and so furnish the material from which new rocks may be formed. Chief among these are the great herds of vertebrates of the plains and steppes and the even larger animals of former geological periods.

Pechuel-Loesche (7 : 823) describes the destruction of the land surface through the immense herds of cattle which he had witnessed in Herero land, German Southwest Africa. He says in effect: "In extensive manner these animals aid in the leveling of many land areas. As the dryness increases, the herds of grazing cattle become more numerous around the last of the sparsely distributed water bodies. Thousands and tens of thousands of the large and the small animals overrun for miles the surrounding country for days, weeks and months. Through countless hoofbeats the ground is loosened, and so furnishes enormous masses of dust, while at the same time all inequalities are trampled down and destroyed. The inclined surfaces would be furrowed by numerous rain-water gullies, if these were not constantly destroyed by the hoofs of the roaming animals, and if it were not for the fact that the rain water is constantly guided along the paths formed by the animals going to and from the water in long lines ranged one behind the other. Furthermore, the cover of dust prevents to an astonishing degree the penetration of the short, heavy downpour of rain into the deeper strata."

Where herds abound, the surface of the country is a comparatively level plain, but where herds are absent, as in the regions between Karibib, the Otyipatura and the Erongo, infested by the Hottentot robber hordes, the country is much dissected by rain-water streams.

Passarge thinks that it is not too much to attribute to the destructive force of the great herds of vertebrates in semiarid regions the principal rôle in the lowering of great regions and the production of gently inclined plains free from river furrows, with remnants of higher monadnocks such as the Inselberge of the Kalahari (Passarge–6 : *130-131*).

What is true of the modern herds of vertebrates must have been equally true of the great herds of mammals of Tertiary time, and

FIG. 133.   White ants' nests of earth in Matto Grosso, on the plains of the upper Paraguay.   (After Branner.)

perhaps to an even greater extent of the gigantic saurians of the Mesozoic.   Certain it is that by their activities these creatures have furnished an immense supply of material to the winds, which would carry it to other regions and deposit it as new sediment.   Burrowing mammals such as the prairie dog, rabbit, mole, badger, woodchuck, gopher and ground squirrel are also very active in tunneling the upper layers of the soil and in transferring material from below to the surface.   The beaver may also be mentioned in this connection as a destructive as well as a constructive agent.

The manner in which fish, feeding on corals and nullipores, produce fine coral sand and mud has already been noted.   In like manner crustacea are known to be active in breaking up the skeletons of echinoderms and other organisms, thus producing lime sand. Sponges and algæ riddle shells and even rocks, forming winding passageways, which render these masses more liable to destruction by waves and other agencies.   Similarly certain mollusca, Pholas,

Saxicava, etc., bore into solid rocks or into heavy shells, thus aiding in the destruction of the mass. To a certain extent this is also true of some echini.

Earthworms are active agents in loosening and rearranging the soil particles, and to a certain extent in destroying the rock masses. According to Darwin, in many places over 50,000 earthworms are at work in a single acre of soil. The amount of material which they transport to the surface each year was estimated by Darwin to be over 18 tons per acre. (4.) The lugworms or lobworms, crawling through the sands along the shore, are similarly active in

Fig. 134. Mound of white ants in the laterite region of Africa. (After Branner.)

working over the soil. They leave behind casts of sand, and the amount of soil they work over has been estimated to be sometimes as much as 3,147 tons per acre. (Davison–5: *491*.) Ants and termites are also important agents in the rearrangement of the soils, especially in tropical regions, where, according to Branner, they "are vastly more important as geologic agents than the earthworms of temperate regions." (1: *152*; 2; 3.) In Brazil the ants excavate chambers and galleries, which radiate and anastomose in every direction, and into these they carry great quantities of leaves. The mounds resulting from these excavations are often from 15 to 30 meters long, from 3 to 6 meters across and from one-third to over one meter high, and contain tons of earth. In the forests the mounds are sometimes 14 feet high (4½ meters), and from 10 to 30 feet (3 to 9 meters) in basal diameter. They are often so close together that their bases touch each other. Branner has estimated (3 : 469) that in an area of 10,000 square meters on which 53 mounds occurred the amount of earth brought up by ants and built into mounds would cover the area with a layer 22.25 centimeters in thickness.

The termites' nests rise to 3½ meters in height, and may be 3 meters in basal diameter. They, too, are often closely set, those along the upper Paraguay being not over 3 meters apart. (Fig. 133.)

A comparison of the work of earthworms and ants gave the following result (Branner–3 : 493). Total weight of earth brought to the surface in 100 years over 1 hectare (10,000 square meters) :

By worms in England (Darwin–4), 2,598,500 kilograms.

By ants in Brazil (Branner–3), 3,226,250 kilograms.

The work of ants on the soil and subsoil is summarized by Branner as follows (3 : 494) :

Directly :

1. "By their habits of making underground excavations that radiate from a central nucleus and often aggregate several miles in length.

2. "By opening the soil to the atmospheric air and gases.

3. "By bringing to the surface large quantities of soil and sub-soil.

4. "By introducing into their subterranean excavations large quantities of organic matter, which must yield acids that affect the soil and the subjacent rocks.

5. "By using these excavations for habitations and the production of gases that attack the soil and its contained minerals."

Indirectly.

6. "By the periodic passage and circulation of meteoric waters through their extensive tunnels.

7. "By affecting the availability of the soil for agricultural purposes.

8. "By affecting the habitability of the land by man.

9. "By the destruction of crops.

10. "By the consumption (by the termites) of dead plants and of timbers and lumber used in houses and for the manufacture of furniture, machinery, etc."

In temperate regions ants are less active, though, according to Shaler, they transfer annually half a centimeter of material from the subsoil to the surface, in certain fields in Massachusetts. (8.)

Plants also are destroyers of rocks, though their work is normally very slow. Lichens growing on smooth rock surfaces will eventually roughen them by appropriating some of the material. Roots of higher plants often penetrate into the rock, especially limestones, to an astonishing extent. In sandstones they have been found to penetrate several meters. Growing saplings in fissures tend to disrupt the rock masses. Finally bacteria abound in the upper soil layers (2½ millions have been estimated in a cubic centimeter of soil in the surface layers), and these are active agents in modifying the soil.

It thus appears that the work of organisms is by no means a negligible factor, and will in the course of time produce important results. Of these organisms man is of course the most important, and it is not going too far to say that on the whole he is the most powerful geological agent at work in modifying the surface of the land.

BIBLIOGRAPHY XVI.

1. BRANNER, JOHN C. 1896. Decomposition of Rocks in Brazil. Bulletin of the Geological Society of America, Vol. VII, pp. 255–314.
2. BRANNER, J. C. 1900. Ants as Geological Agents in the Tropics. Journal of Geology, Vol. VIII, pp. 151–153.
3. BRANNER, J. C. 1910. Geologic Work of Ants in Tropical America Bulletin of the Geological Society of America, Vol. XXI, pp. 449–496.
4. DARWIN, CHARLES. 1883. The Formation of Vegetable Mould. D. Appleton & Co., New York, pp. 1–313.
5. DAVISON, CHARLES. 1891. Work Done by Lobworms. Geological Magazine, 3d Ser., Vol. VIII., pp. 489–493.
6. PASSARGE, SIEGFRIED. 1911. Die pfannenförmigen Hohlformer der südafrikanischen Steppen. Petermann's Mittheilungen LVII, pt. ii, pp. 130–135.
7. PECHUEL–LOESCHE. 1884. Das Ausland.
8. SHALER, NATHANIEL S. 1892. Effects of Animals and Plants on Soils. In "The Origin and Nature of Soils," U. S. Geological Survey, 12th Annual Report, pt. I, pp. 219–345 (268–287).

CHAPTER XVII.

SUMMARY OF ORIGINAL FEATURES OF CLASTIC ROCKS.

We may now summarize the various structural features of clastic rocks which were formed at the time these rocks were deposited and which therefore serve as guides in the determination of the mode of origin of the rocks possessing them. In dealing with each feature separately it will be possible to indicate the extent to which it is characteristic of one or the other of the types of clastic rocks so far discussed.

We may treat these characters under the following headings:

1. Stratification.
2. Cross-bedding.
3. Beach cusps.
4. Wave marks.
5. Rill marks.
6. Mud cracks (sun cracks or desiccation fissures).
7. Clay galls.
8. Clay boulders and pebbles.
9. Rain prints.
10. Ripple marks.
11. Impressions made by animals in transit.
12. Application of these structures in determining position of strata.
13. Rounding and sorting of sand grains, and wearing of pebbles.
14. Characteristics of inclusions in sand grains.
15. Organic remains.
16. Concretions (partly secondary).
17. Secretions (secondary).

Nearly all of these structural characters have been generally considered as preëminently if not exclusively characteristic of marine or lacustrine hydroclastics. From the foregoing discussion, however, it will appear that many of them are far from being the exclusive features of these types of deposits. In fact, it may be said that, with the exception of the beach cusps, the wave marks and the clay pebbles, they are characteristic of subaërial deposits, while some of them, such as cross-bedding, desiccation fissures, rain prints and footprints, are almost exclusively confined to the formations other than marine or lacustrine. The most pronounced of the characters enumerated, stratification, is also of frequent occurrence in the endogenetic formations.

Concretions are only occasionally original structures, being for the most part secondary. Secretions are always of secondary character, but they are included here for the sake of comparison with concretions which belong here in part.

1. STRATIFICATION. In its broadest sense (Walther–23 :620 *et seq.*) stratification is the arrangement of rock masses in layers or strata, each one of which was at one time the latest deposit, and the top of each stratum was successively the top of the lithosphere at that point. Stratification thus defined occurs in all rocks, which are deposited in successive layers. Thus a series of lava-flows will show stratification, each flow representing a distinct stratum. These volcanic strata are often steeply inclined, as is also the case in clastic strata along the margins of coral reefs or in the alluvial fan or talus heap.

Among the pyrogenic rocks stratification is produced where lava streams of different composition succeed each other, or where streams of the same composition are separated by an interval, during which the surface of the earlier one either hardened or became altered to some extent, or again was covered by a layer of clastic material, before the second flow occurred. Atmogenic snow ice or glacial ice becomes stratified when the succeeding deposits of snow are separated by intervals during which the older layer solidified or was covered by a thin layer of dust or by other clastic material. False stratification is often produced in this rock by the formation of shearing planes, along which some of the subglacial detritus is carried up into the ice. Hydrogenic and biogenic rocks may also be stratified, this being brought about by cessation of deposition, by change in the material, through interposition of clastics, or by alternation in deposition of different classes of endogenetic materials. Examples of this are shown in the alternation of layers of gypsum and salt, or in the intercalation of layers of potash and other salts between the beds of ordinary rock salt. The numerous intercalated silt layers of the salt deposits of the Bitter Lakes of Suez further serve as an illustration. While stratification is thus not confined to the clastic rocks, it finds its most typical expression in this group. All clastic deposits may be stratified, this stratification being due to change in material, to change from one type of clastic to another, or to alternation of clastic with endogenetic deposits. The most typical development of stratification is in the water-laid clastics (hydroclastics), and especially in those laid down in standing water. Before considering the various kinds of stratification, however, we must first have a clear conception of the meaning of the term stratum.

Definition of Stratum. The current definitions of the term stratum vary greatly, as will be seen from the following quotations: (a) "A layer of rock; a portion of a rock mass which has so much homogeneity and is so separated from the rock that lies over and under it that it has a character of its own." (Century Dictionary.) (b) "The term stratum is sometimes applied to one layer and sometimes to all the consecutive layers of the same sort of

Fig. 135. A mass of stratified rocks bounded by joint faces and isolated by erosion. The strata are inclined but appear horizontal in one section.

Fig. 136. Stratified chalk penetrated by pipes of sand and gravel. Kent, England. (Prestwich.)

rock." (Chamberlin and Salisbury, Geology–1 : *464.*) (c) *"Strata* or *Beds* are layers of rock varying from an inch or less up to many feet in thickness. A stratum may be made up of numerous laminæ, if the nature of the sediment and the mode of deposit have favored the production of this structure . . . [it] . . . may be one of a series of similar beds in the same mass of rock, as where a thick sandstone includes many individual strata, varying considerably in their respective thicknesses; or it may be complete and distinct in itself, as where a band of limestone or iron stone runs through the heart of a series of shales."

"The smallest subdivisions of the Geological Record are laminæ, a number of which may make a stratum, seam or bed. As a rule, a stratum is distinguishable by lithological rather than palæontological features." (Geikie–Textbook, 4th ed.–1 : *635*; 2 : *860.*)

(d) "In the description of a formation the term *stratum* (from the Latin for bed, *strata* in the plural) is used for each section of the formation that consists throughout of approximately the same kind of rock material. Thus, if shale, sandstone and limestone succeed one another in thick masses, each is an independent *stratum*. A stratum may consist of an indefinite number of *beds,* and a bed of numberless *layers*. But the distinction of layer and bed is not always obvious." (Dana–Manual, 5th ed.–*91*.)

(e) Schichten nennt man plattenförmige Lagen welche " . . . durch parallele Flächen begränzt werden, bei weiter Ausdehnung in der Regel, nur geringe Dicke besitzen, und das Product successiver Ubereinanderlagerung bilden." (Credner–Elemente, 8th ed.,–*25*.)

(f) "The material between two planes of stratification forms a *stratum* or *bed,* though if the deposit be very thin it is known as a *lamina,* and the planes are spoken of as *planes of lamination* (no hard and fast line can be drawn between strata and laminæ; several of the latter usually occur in the space of an inch)." (Marr–Principles of Stratigraphical Geology–*27*.)

From the foregoing definitions it will be seen that there is a considerable diversity of opinion regarding the value of the term stratum. We may gain a clearer concept if we consider it in the light of its origin. Continuous deposition under the same conditions will produce a deposit nearly uniform throughout, and of a thickness commensurate with the rate of deposition, the length of time and the coarseness of the material. A sudden change in conditions will bring about an abrupt change in the character of the material deposited. It may be coarser, or it may be finer in grain, or it may be of a wholly different composition. Variation in grain, or texture, unless an abrupt change occurs, is indicative of only minor changes in physical condition of the region. But variation in the composition of the material denotes a change of some magnitude. This being the case, a decided change in the composition of the material ought to be considered a change in strata, while a change in texture, unless it be a great one, should be considered as of minor value, and therefore should constitute a subdivision of the stratum into layers. The great changes in texture which may conveniently be regarded as of stratum value are those from one to the other of the three primary textural divisions of the clastic rocks, namely, lutaceous, arenaceous and rudaceous. Thus a rudyte following an arenyte may well be considered a distinct stratum. But the change from a fine arenyte to a coarse one or vice versa is better regarded as a change in layers. Where deposition is continuous, while increase in the force of the currents and increase in the coarseness of the deposit are progressive, an arenyte may gradually pass upward into a rudyte, whereupon the distinction of strata is a matter of judgment. In such cases the stratum of arenyte terminates with a layer of rudaceous arenyte where the arenaceous material still predominates, while the stratum of rudyte begins with a layer of arenaceous rudyte, in which the rudaceous material has become most prominent.

A change in composition is not always of sufficient magnitude to warrant separation into a new stratum. Thus a stratum of silicarenyte or pure quartz sandstone may have interbedded layers of ferruginous, argillaceous, calcareous or glauconite material, where this material is only of sufficient quantity to produce a variety of the sandstone. Where, however, a calcarenyte or a clay rock (argillutyte) succeeds to a silicarenyte, a new stratum is produced. Where deposition is continuous, but the supplied material changes in composition, a gradation from a pure silicarenyte to a pure calcarenyte may occur, without break of continuity. In this case, as in the case of the gradation in texture, the line of division between the two strata must be drawn on the relative preponderance of materials. The stratum of silicarenyte will terminate with a layer of calcareous silicarenyte, while the stratum of calcarenyte will begin with a layer of siliceous calcarenyte.

While gradations as here discussed are not of uncommon occurrence, in the more familiar type of stratification the strata abruptly succeed each other. Thus a stratum of limestone, clastic, organic or chemical and frequently composed of only one layer, may be intercalated between strata of shales. Again strata of limestones are separated by strata of carbonaceous clay or by sandstones, the separating strata in many cases being mere films. In such cases the stratum of clayey material is represented by only one lamina. Not infrequently strata of clastic limestones (calcarenytes) are separated by a thin stratum of organic limestone in a single layer, and generally containing an admixture of clayey matter. A decided change in color may readily serve as a basis for division into strata, since such change generally indicates a marked change in physical conditions during deposition. Thus a black shale succeeding a gray or bluish one marks a change in conditions of deposition. A change from a gray to a red sandstone likewise indicates physical changes from conditions preventing to those permitting extensive oxidation, as elsewhere discussed. Finally the occurrence or indications of decided physical breaks, such as erosion surfaces and disconformities, serves to separate distinct strata.

Types of Stratification. Walther (23:631) recognizes two kinds of stratification, *direct* and *indirect*. The former is produced when the changes in sedimentation produce differences in the strata, as when, for example, volcanic ashes are deposited upon a lava flow, or when fine clay deposits are succeeded by deposits of sands from a rising flood, or when in the deep sea, after continuous deposition of Globigerina ooze, a bionomic change brings about a deposition of diatomaceous oozes. Here each stratum corresponds to the physical change which brought about the change in deposition. When, however, a rearrangement of the sediment of the shallow sea occurs, owing to the agitation of this sediment by the waves, a secondary separation of materials results, which was not dependent on original changes in sedimentation. Thus a mixed sand may be assorted into layers, according to grain, or a pebbly deposit, charged originally with sand, may be separated into a stratum of conglomerate and one of sand. Again, a deposit of mixed foraminiferal and pteropodan shells may be separated into two strata, one of Foraminifera, the other of pteropods, on account of the difference in their specific gravities. The cases just cited constitute what Walther has termed *indirect stratification*. Sometimes it finds expression in layers, sometimes in strata. The remarkable alternation of pure limestone and calcareous clays in the Cincinnati series of the Ordovicic of Ohio, etc., has been explained in this manner as indirect stratification. The sharp assortment of the material, the abruptness of contact and freedom from gradations would seem to indicate that this interpretation is correct. (Perry–18.)

Stratification is often indicated only by the arrangement of pebbles, mica scales, or of fossils in interrupted horizontal lines, within a single stratum or even a single bed. The arrangement of the flints in the chalk suggests the stratification of this deposit, a single stratum appearing often of exceeding thickness, while the material is of uniform texture, thus exhibiting no lamination. The same thing is true of the *Lösspüppchen* or concretions of the loess, but in this case it is not always the stratification which is indicated by them, but lines of permeability, which have no direct relation to stratification. This may possibly be the case also in some flint layers of the chalk, as already suggested.

2. CROSS-BEDDING. This is most readily seen in clastics of an arenaceous texture, though rudytes sometimes show it on a large scale. It consists of an arrangement of the grains in diagonal layers with reference to the plains bounding the strata. Originally these laminæ may have been deposited at a considerable angle from the horizontal. Above and below, these oblique layers are bounded by the planes of stratification, and they are commonly truncated on

their upper surfaces. Successive beds may have their oblique laminæ inclined at different angles or in different directions, and horizontal layers may rest upon the truncated edges of inclined layers, thus simulating unconformity. This oblique lamination may range in magnitude from beds a millimeter or less in thickness to strata having a thickness of a hundred feet or more. In such a case the deposit was generally formed as a delta in a standing body of water, with strong currents flowing in and depositing the sands or pebbles on the growing delta front. Oblique beds formed in this manner are known as "fore-sets," and are generally truncated at the top by the currents, which deposit horizontal beds or "top-sets," generally of coarser material, upon the truncated upper edges. Basally the fore-set beds will either rest upon or directly merge into the bottom-set beds, which are made of finer material, mostly clay and silt. The angle of the fore-set beds generally decreases outward, the last fore-sets of a large delta being fine and less steeply inclined than the older ones (see *ante,* p. 610). Small deltas were formed in numerous localities toward the end of the last glacial epoch in standing bodies of water along the ice front. Their structure can readily be examined in many sand pits. Several types of cross-bedding may be distinguished.

a. *Delta Type.* This type of cross-bedding, already noted, consists essentially of a single bed of diagonal layers bounded below and above by nearly horizontal beds. It appears to be characteristic of deltas deposited in a standing body of water. Whether or not this type is also characteristic of deltas formed on the sea coast depends on the strength and magnitude of the tides. It is evident that only one series of fore-set beds will be formed in any given delta, and that relatively stationary conditions alone permit the formation of the delta. If, after the building of a delta in a lake, a rise in the water level should occur, a new delta might be built up over the old one, and thus the resulting formation would show two sets of diagonal beds, separated by horizontal beds, the top sets of the first and the bottom beds of the second. Such a superimposition of two deltas is, however, difficult to conceive of on a subsiding sea coast where subsidence is accompanied by transgression, and consequent transference of the zone of delta building.

b. *Cross-bedding of Torrential Deposits.* Superimposition of obliquely bedded strata is, however, eminently characteristic of torrential deposits. Each succeeding deposit will be characterized by fore-set and top-set beds, and the number of such superimposed strata is chiefly dependent on the frequency of recurrence of the torrents. The length of the fore-set bed formed by a river on dry land is of course much less than that of a delta fore-set. Most likely a greater length than six feet is rare, while probably by far the greater number fall below a foot in length. The angle which the fore-set beds make with the horizontal varies proportionately to the coarseness of the material, but in any given case it is approximately uniform. Moreover, the angle of the fore-sets of successive strata is as a rule similar and in the same direction, while the dividing top-set beds are parallel in the successive strata. Thus a section of a torrential deposit will show a succession of obliquely bedded strata, separated and bounded above and below by strata, which make a high angle with them, are parallel to each other, and originally represented the surface slope of the deposit. The inclinations of the laminæ of the successive cross-bedded strata are uniform, and the laminæ all slope in the same direction. This is the type of cross-bedding found in many ancient sandstones, and it seems to be highly improbable that any such structure could be produced by agents working on the sea coast. (Fig. 123.)

c. *Cross-bedding of Eolian Deposits.* Such regularity of cross-bedding as is found in both lacustrine and torrential deposits is, however, not characteristic of eolian deposits. In these the laminæ when oblique show no uniformity of slope or direction within either the same stratum or successive strata. Nor are the dividing laminæ parallel to each other. Cross-bedding of eolian deposits is brought about in the following manner: A sand dune in its structure shows a series of concentric shells of sand consisting of alternating coarse and fine layers. This is a feature characteristic, according to Forchhammer (9:7), of every dune of the Jutland coast, and inferentially of the majority if not of all sand dunes. Toward the side of the wind the dune layers have an angle of 5°, while on the lee side the angle is as high as 30°. The stratification is shown chiefly by the varying coarseness of the grains composing successive layers, this being determined by the variable strength of the winds, to which the dune owes its origin. If through a change of the conditions which built up the dune, *i. e.,* change in the force or the direction of the wind or in the amount of the sand supplied, or through other causes, the dune begins to migrate, a part of its basal portion may remain behind, as the truncated base of the dune, while upon this truncated surface a new dune may accumulate, which in turn will meet with the same fate, leaving its basal portion behind. Successive portions of this kind will eventually produce a bed of sand in which the cross-bedding is of extreme irregularity and inconstancy. (Fig. 137.) (Walther–22: 715 [*519*].) Huntington (15) has shown that a characteristic feature of such cross-bedding is the tangency of the layers at the base, while at the top erosion has sharply truncated them.

This type of cross-bedding is not infrequently met with in arenytes among the strata of all ages. The Medina sandstone (Siluric) of western New York affords some excellent examples of this type, and it is highly probable that the beds showing this structure were originally wind-laid deposits. Other excellent examples of such cross-bedding are shown in the Sylvania sandstone (Upper Siluric) of Ohio, Michigan and Canada (Figs. 119, 120) and in the White Cliff sandstones (Jurassic) of the Kanab Plateau and in the La Platte sandstone (Jurassic) of Utah. Calcarenytes, too, sometimes show this structure, as noted above, for the Junagarh limestone of India and for other modern deposits recognized as wind-laid. The cross-bedding of the Somersetshire oölite (Forest marble), referred to above (Fig. 121), appears also to be indicative of the eolian origin of this rock. Excellent exam-

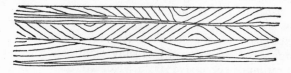

Fig. 137. Eolian cross-bedding as found in desert sands. (After Walther.)

ples of this type of bedding in a heavy-bedded, non-siliceous limestone (calarenyte) have been observed by the author in the cut through the Warsaw (Mississippic) limestone on the Missouri Pacific Railroad, south of St. Louis, Missouri. This is reproduced in Figs. 122a and b, on page 577. Compare, also, Figs. 138, 139.

Comparison of Types. A comparison of the three types of cross-bedding, *i. e.,* the delta, the torrential and the eolian, will show the distinctive character of each, namely: uniformly sloping fore-set beds in one series and generally on a large scale, for delta deposits; uniform fore-set beds of small size and in successive but similar series separated by horizontal deposits, for torrential deposits; and oblique beds, variable in angle and slope within the same and successive series commonly without horizontal dividing beds, for eolian deposits. While these types grade into each other where the deposits meet or overlap, it is not known that any one type of cross-bedding is produced by another agent. Thus the torrential type of cross-bedding cannot be readily conceived of as formed in the sea, and the same may be said of the eolian type. The bedding of a sand bar may perhaps show something analogous to the wind-formed cross-bedding, but conditions for the preservation of such are perhaps seldom realized. Gilbert has described the mode of formation of cross-bedding through the shifting of ripples on the

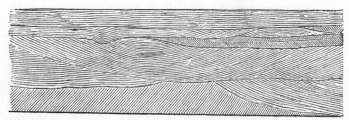

Fig. 138. Cross-bedding of the Eolian type (Orange sand or La Fayette Formation), Mississippi Central Railroad, Oxford, Miss. (After Hilgard.)

sea floor, due to a current accompanying oscillatory movements. He considers "that sediment may be added to a rippled surface without any disturbance of the pattern, but that there is usually a coincident gradual bodily shifting of the pattern in some direction."

Fig. 139. Ledges of sandstone near Colorado Springs, showing Eolian cross-bedding.

"The shifting of the ripple profile during the accumulation of the sediment makes the accumulation unequal on the two sides of the trough (figure 3), and, if the ratio of shifting to deposition exceeds a certain amount, there is deposition on only one side of the trough and erosion on the other." (Gilbert–12:*139, Figs. 3-4.*) In this case two sets of oblique planes are produced, one due to deposition, the other to erosion, the latter representing the progress of the profile of the troughs along certain tangents. The tangent planes are often nearly horizontal, in which case the cross-bedding would approach in appearance the torrential type. The absence of dividing strata would, however, readily distinguish it. Cross-bedding of this type has been observed by Gilbert in the Medina sandstone of western New York, and referred to wave work.

"When the waves from a new direction act on a surface already rippled, they produce a new pattern, which at first combines with the old one, but eventually obliterates it. The troughs of the new pattern are formed in part by excavation from ridges of the old, and the lamination associated with the old ridges is truncated, so that the new lamination is unconformable." (12: *140, Fig. 5.*) Several such unconformities may succeed each other, and Gilbert holds that the irregular cross-bedding of the Medina sandstone, referred to above as perhaps of eolian origin, was produced in this manner. It may be doubted, however, if ripples of a sufficient magnitude to produce such a structure are ever produced under water, and still more if when produced they are accompanied by such rapid deposition as the case would seem to require. For, as Gilbert has pointed out, the formation of large ripples requires great waves, and therefore broad and deep water bodies, and in such deposition of sands is not extensive. On the whole, the structure described conforms much more nearly to the observed structure of anemoclastic deposits. It may also be questioned if the ripple cross-bedding on a small scale may not with equal or perhaps greater facility be produced by the wind alone. It would seem that shifting wind ripples, which are sand dunes on a small scale, would produce the same structure that shifting sand dunes produce on a larger scale.

Strata which show the irregular type of cross-bedding must be carefully scrutinized for other evidence of eolian activity as well as for evidence of marine or fluviatile origin. The occurrence in the rock of scattered marine organisms is no conclusive evidence of the marine origin of the formation, unless it can be shown that the organisms in question lived where found or at least were carried there by currents of water and not by wind.

3. BEACH CUSPS. (Johnson–16.) Beach cusps are triangular ridges extending across the beach generally at right angles to the shore front. When most typically developed the beach cusp has the form of an isosceles triangle with its base parallel to the beach, but at its upper edge, and its apex near the water. The cusp may be broad, approaching in form an equilateral triangle, but more generally it is long, narrow and extremely acute, the sides sometimes

appearing almost parallel. "The cusps may constitute the serrate seaward side of a prominent beach ridge, or may occur as isolated gravel hillocks separated by fairly uniform spaces of smooth, sandy beach. They may be sharply differentiated from the rest of the beach, or may occur as gentle undulations of the same material as the beach proper, and so be scarcely discernible as independent features." "A cusp may rise from an inch or less to several feet above the general level of the beach. Many are relatively low and flat, others high and steep-sided. Sometimes the highest part is comparatively near the apex; at other times the highest part is far back, and from it a long, sloping ridge trails forward toward the water. As a rule, the cusps appear to point straight out toward the water—that is, the axis of the cusp is at right angles to the shore line—and neither side of a cusp is steeper than the other, except where oblique, wind-made waves have eroded one side only." (Johnson–16: *605-606*.) The material of the cusp varies from the finest sand to the coarsest cobblestone, there being no necessary relationship between the size of the cusp and the size of the material composing it. Gravel cusps are often found on sandy beaches, the cusps being always built of the coarser material of the beach. In size cusps vary from a length of 8 or 12 inches to 30 feet or more. The distance between cusps, measured from crest to crest, ranges on small ponds from less than a foot to two feet or more. On sea beaches they may be less than 10 feet apart, while those built by large storm waves may be 100 feet apart. The spacing is fairly regular, though in some cases there seems to be irregularity in spacing, as shown by Jefferson. (Johnson–16.) Compound cusps are also occasionally formed.

Various theories have been propounded to explain the origin of beach cusps; for a review of these the reader is referred to the paper by Johnson, where a reference to the bibliography is also found. Johnson's theory, and the one best supported by the facts, is, concisely stated, "that selective erosion by the swash develops from initial, irregular depressions in the beach, shallow troughs of approximately uniform breadth, whose ultimate size is proportional to the size of the waves, and determines the relative uniform spacing of the cusps, which develop on the intertrough elevations." (16: *620.*)

Fossil Beach Cusps. Beach cusps on old shore lines are known especially from the Medina sandstone of western New York. They were described by Gilbert (12) as giant ripples, but, as suggested by Branner (3) and by Fairchild (7), they are undoubted examples of ancient beach cusps. The spacing of these cusps varies from

10 to 30 feet, and their height from 6 inches to 3 feet. Fairchild has found crests 80 feet apart, but it is not certain that all such structures are referable to cusps.

4. WAVE MARKS. On shallow coasts the advancing waves slide up onto the shore after breaking, forming the "swash." After the retreat of the wave, its furthermost advance is found to be marked by a fine, wavy line, corresponding in outline to that of the water's edge, and composed of fine particles of mica, fragments of seaweed, fine sand grains and other matter light enough to be carried along by the water. Numerous wave lines of this character may generally be seen on a shore of the type noted. In exceptional cases, as in the Medina sandstone of New York, these are finely preserved after the consolidation of the rock, appearing often as perfect as on the unconsolidated beach. (Fairchild–7.)

5. RILL MARKS. The water running off after each swash, or on the retreat of the tide, frequently cuts rills into the surface of the beach. These rills represent a river system in miniature, and generally consist of a number of small, quickly widening channels, which join a trunk channel at a very oblique angle, and which are in turn joined by other branches at an oblique angle.

A different type of rill marks is found where small streams debouch upon a flat, sandy or clayey plain. Here the waters of the stream will divide into innumerable fingers and fingerlets, the reverse of the river-system type. Thus before the water sinks into the ground or runs off, a series of channels, branching more and more in their lower courses, have been produced. These channels are reproductions on a small scale of the large channels spreading over the subaërial deltas at the debouchure of desert streams.

After the dying out of the streamlets which produced the rills, the conditions are generally favorable for the preservation of these in the hardening mud, and through covering by wind-drifted sand or flood deposits. On the shore conditions for the preservation of rill marks are less favorable, since the succeeding wave will generally destroy the marks left by the run-off preceding. Occasionally, however, such a preservation may occur. In either case, the filling mud or sand will on hardening show the relief of the original rill, reproducing the minutest channel as a raised ridge. These relief structures greatly resemble branching stems of plants and have sometimes been described as such. (Rogers, Lesquereux, Newberry.)

Water flowing down the beach is often checked locally by pebbles or shells lying partly buried on the beach. In such cases the water flowing down on either side of the obstruction will excavate

characteristic depressions, or the water falling over the obstruction
will gully the surface for a short distance below. Examples of
these are found in the Medina sandstone.

6. MUD-CRACKS, SUN-CRACKS OR DESICCATION FISSURES.
When lutaceous deposits are exposed by the retreat of the tide, or
by the shrinking or disappearance of a playa lake or a pond, or by
the uncovering of the flood-plain of a river, the drying which they
undergo will result in the formation of polygonally arranged cracks,
and a gentle concaving of the upper surfaces of the polygons thus
bounded. When the desiccated layers of mud are thin, they will
often curl up like wood shavings, and may be blown away by the
wind. When on reflooding of the surface or by the deposition of
wind-blown material, these cracks are filled in by deposits of the
same or different material, the polygons will remain more or less
perfectly outlined. This desiccation fissure, sun-crack, mud-crack,
prismatic, or paving block structure, as it is variously called, is
found not only in clayey rocks, but also in fine calcilutytes, like
those of the Helderberg mountains (Rondout waterlimes), the
Solnhofen beds (Marsh), the Cincinnati limestones (Perry–18), and
in many other lutaceous deposits. They testify to the exposure
of these deposits before they were solidified. (For a full discussion of this subject see Barrell–1.)

Playa Surface. Taking the areas of mud-crack formation in
the order of their magnitude, the playa surface would probably
stand first. Here the entire surface for hundreds of square miles
becomes mud-cracked, often to considerable depth, on the complete
drying up of the temporary playa lake. Here, too, the conditions
for the preservation are most favorable. Not only is the exposure
a long one, often the greater part of the year, or for many years,
and for much of the time to intense heat, but the chances of proper
burial are much greater. Wandering sand dunes may thus preserve
the record, dust deposits may fill the fissures, or, at the next flood,
sands or mud may be swept into them. In fact, the playa or takyr
seems to be the ideal surface for mud-crack record, and one is
tempted to refer most mud-cracked strata to such an origin. Certainly where fossil mud-cracks penetrate a formation to the depth
of ten feet, as is the case in the upper Shinarump (Jura-Triassic)
shales of Utah (Gilbert–11:9), it is difficult to believe that they
could be formed under other conditions than those permitting prolonged exposure such as is found only in the playas of the desert,
where ten years or more may elapse between rainfalls.

Permanent Lake Surface. Much less extensive, and of minor
significance, are the sun-cracked areas which come into existence

around permanent lake bodies as the result of periodic shrinking of the lake after a flooding of the adjacent lands. Such mud-cracked areas will be exposed for long periods of time and so resemble the flood plains of rivers. They at best, however, form but a narrow marginal belt around the lake and the beds characterized by them would grade laterally into fresh water lake beds in which remains of fresh water organisms are found. The mud cracks of the Tertiary lake beds of Florissant may be of this type.

River Flood Plains. Next in importance to the playa, and perhaps even rivaling it in extent, is the river flood plain. Here after a great flood extensive areas may be laid bare and be subjected to desiccation and cracking during the long period of exposure before the next flood. Since, in the lower reaches of rivers, the material spread out by the flood is of the nature of a fine silt, the conditions for the formation of the mud-cracks are fully satisfied. Here, too, preserval of the mud-crack record is readily accomplished by the filling of the fissures by the sediment of the next flood.

The mud-cracked flood plain deposit would differ from the playa deposit in the more frequent presence of carbonaceous material, since vegetation is an accompaniment of river courses, but, as a rule absent from the playa, or found only around the margin. Aquatic animals, too, should be more characteristic of the flood-plain than of the desert deposit, and would especially characterize the old stream channels dissecting the flood plain, and recognizable in the fossil state by the lines of coarser sediment—the filling of these channels—which traverse the finer deposits.

The Shore Zone. The shore zone between high and low water also may furnish conditions favorable for the formation of mud cracks. This is especially the case where, as in the Bay of Fundy, the tide recedes very far, and where large tracts remain exposed during the fortnightly interval between high spring tides. Along the margins of estuaries broad mud-flats are often exposed, an here shrinkage cracks may form between tides. The time of exposure of all but the highest parts of the shore zone, is, however, too short to allow of a sufficient hardening of the mud-cracked area to enable it to resist the softening and destroying effects of the returning tide. Moreover, in modern mud flats of this type, organisms exist in great numbers, so that we would expect to find mud-cracked rocks which are formed on the shore to be more or less fossiliferous.

On the whole, mud-cracks are much more characteristic of continental deposits, especially of the playa and flood plain, than of the seashore. Only under exceptional conditions can we expect the preservation of extensive mud-cracked surfaces of the sea-shore. Moreover, the formation of great littoral deposits must be accompanied by a subsidence of the sea-floor, and a consequent landward transgression of the seashore with its attendant phe-nomena. The migration of the shore zone would thus bring about a transference of the zone of mud-crack formation, so that we could hardly expect to find a thick marine formation with repeated horizons of mud-cracked layers unless we assumed that the subsi-dence was so gradual a one that deposition kept pace with it.

7. CLAY GALLS (THON-GALLEN). When the mud layers on the playa surface or on the river flood plain are very thin, drying will cause them to curl up into masses resembling shavings. Such curly mud shavings occur on river flood plains exposed to a hot sun, and they may also under favorable conditions be formed on the seashore, as in the case of the coast of the Red Sea (Walther–23:847). When thoroughly dry these shavings may be blown by the wind into neighboring sand dunes in which they become buried. Subsequent softening of the clay when the sand dune is saturated with water, as in the rainy seasons, will bring about a compression of the clay-shaving into a thin, flat pellet of clay which will lie embedded in the sand parallel to the stratification. Such clay pel-lets, called *Thon-gallen,* or clay galls, are common in sandstones of subaërial origin, especially in red sandstones. They may, indeed, be regarded as practically positive evidence of a subaërial origin of the rock containing them, though these rocks may be seashore dunes or formed far inland.

8. CLAY BOULDERS. Clay boulders formed of plastic clay rolled about by the waves are not uncommon occurrences on the sea-shore. They have been recorded by Walther (23:847) and by O. Fraas (10:277) from the coast of the Red Sea. On the coasts mentioned they represent the clay deposited during the previous high tide, which on exposure at low tide dries and breaks up into fragments. These are rolled into balls by the returning tide and incorporated in the later sediment, where they have the appearance of concretions. Examples of such structures seem to occur in the Devonic calcilutytes of Michigan, where rounded balls of a darker color are included in lighter bedded deposits of similar character.

The author has observed the formation of clay boulders on the coast of Scotland. Here fragments of glacial clays broken from the cliffs are rolled about by the waves and fashioned into pebbles and boulders of elongate but well-rounded outline. Where these are rolled over a pebble beach, the hard pebbles are pressed

into the clay ball which then assumes the appearance of a worn
conglomerate fragment. As such it may be embedded in the succeeding formation. Frass (10) records such boulders with shell
fragments for pebbles, from the Jurassic of Spitzbergen.

9. RAIN PRINTS. Partly dried clay surfaces and to some extent those of other lutaceous deposits, when exposed to a short,
sharp rain, will receive the impressions made by the striking rain
drops. When the rain drops strike obliquely a low rim around part
of the impression shows where the mud was displaced more
strongly, and therefore the side away from that from which the
rain slanted. Thus the more pronounced marking is always on the
obtuse side of the intersection of the surface and the path of the
rain drop. A replica in relief of this impression is found on the
under side of the layer of mud spread next above. This feature is
eminently characteristic of continental mud deposits, its preservation on the sea coast being a matter of doubtful probability. Impressions apparently of this character have, however, been re-

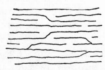

FIG. 140. Plan of Eolian ripple-marks in fine sand.
(After Walther.)

FIG. 141. Diagram showing direction of
currents and vortices in the formation
of ripple-marks. (After Darwin.)

ported from the marine (shallow water) limestones of the Cincinnati region. (Perry–18: *329, Fig. 1.*)

10. RIPPLE MARKS. These are rhythmic undulations or waves
of the sand due either to the motion of the air or of the water.
Two types of ripples are recognized: 1. Current ripples, formed
by the wind on the surface of sand dunes, etc., or by currents of
water in shallow basins; and 2. Oscillation ripples, formed by the
vortices of water in the sands at the bottoms of shallow stationary
water bodies.

"A current of water flowing over a bed of sand reacts on any
prominence of the bed. An eddy or vortex is created in the lee of
the prominence, and the return current of this vortex checks traveling particles, causing a growth of the prominence on its downstream side. At the same time the upstream side is eroded, and the
prominence thus travels downstream. It is a subaqueous dune. Its
upstream slope is long and gentle; its downstream slope is short and
steep." (Gilbert–12:*137.*) The natural mold of this type of ripple

will be difficult to distinguish from the original ripple, though the directions of the slopes will be reversed. A careful examination, however, will show that, whereas the surfaces of the normal current ripple are gently convex, those of the mold will be gently concave.

Oscillation ripples are produced . . . "by the to-and-fro motion of the water, occasioned by the passage of wind waves. During the passage of a wave each particle of water near the surface rises, moves forward, descends, and moves back, describing an orbit which is approximately circular. The orbital motion is communicated downward, with gradually diminishing amplitude. Unless the water is deep the orbits below the surface are ellipses, the longer axes being horizontal, and close to the bottom the ellipses are nearly flat, so that the water merely swings forward and back. It is in this oscillating current, periodically reversed, that the sand-ripples are formed. A prominence occasions vortices alternating on its two sides, and is thereby developed in a systematic way, with equal slopes and a sharp apex. There is a strong tendency to produce the mole laterally into a ridge, the space between ridges is definitely limited by the interference of vortices, and in time there results a regular pattern of parallel ridges equally spaced." (Gilbert–12.) In the center of the oscillation ripple a low sharp ridge is frequently found which on the mold is represented by a groove. (Van Hise–21 : 720.) See, further, the discussion by Darwin (6) of the movements and vortices involved in ripple formation (Fig. 141).

The amplitude of the water oscillations and their frequency control the size of the resulting ripples, as has been shown by experiment. The depth of the water has a direct bearing upon the amplitude of the wave and therefore upon the size of the ripple. No definite law has, however, been worked out as yet.

According to Siau, who studied the ripple-marks of the haven of St. Giles, on the English Channel, their crests are distant from 30-45 cm. at a depth of 20 meters, while their troughs are from 8-10 cm. below their crests, and contain heavier basaltic gravel. At greater depths their size diminishes. The greatest depth at which they were observed was 188 meters. (Hunt–14.)

In cross-section the oscillation ripple presents regular concavities divided by sharp ridges, and a faint central ridge in many cases. This type is distinguished from the mold of the current ripple chiefly by the asymmetry of the concavity of the latter, one side being shorter and steeper than the other in the mold of the current ripple. The central ridge when present is likewise a characteristic feature. A mold of the oscillation ripple would show gently rounded or convex ridges often with a groove on top, and separated by sharp depressions. This mold is distinguished from the normal current ripple mainly by its symmetry. In the desert, wind ripples of all dimensions and of great variety of form occur. They vary in width from 2 cm. or less to a meter or more. Sometimes they are sharp angled, at others round. They generally occur in long parallel series, often branching repeatedly, the branch running parallel to the main stem. (Walther–*22* : *523* [*179*].) (Figs. 140, 142.)

The width and height of the ripple-mark are dependent on the size of the grain of sand and the strength of the wind. Uniform currents will produce an elongation of the ripple which always extends at right angles to the direction of the wind. (Hunt–14.) In many respects the arrangement of wind ripples and of sand

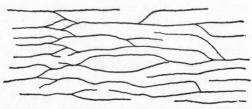

FIG. 142. Plan of Eolian ripple-marks in coarse desert sand. (After Walther.) (Compare with Fig. 140.)

dunes in deserts is very similar, the former being reduced replicas of the latter.

In the distribution of the material of the wind ripple, there appears also to be a distinctive character, in that the coarser material is found on the crest of the ripple, instead of in the trough, as in subaqueous ripples.

11. IMPRESSIONS OF ANIMALS AND PLANTS IN TRANSIT. Animals walking or crawling over a surface of mud or sand commonly leave characteristic impressions. Plants rafted along by the wind or waves, and medusæ floating and dragging their tentacles, also make characteristic markings, though these are not always readily determinable. All such markings are depressions, and they will be reproduced in relief on the under side of the next overlying stratum. Occasionally the burrows of certain animals will be marked by elevations or knobs. These structures will be discussed in their biological relations in the chapter on fossils, and they are mentioned here only to complete the survey of minor original features of sediments.

As to their occurrence, it may be repeated that footprints of terrestrial animals are best preserved in the clays of the desert playas, and the flood-plains of rivers, while those formed on the seashore are commonly obliterated again by the action of the returning tide and the waves. Tracks and burrows of worms, and trails of molluscs and crustacea, on the other hand, point more generally to a seashore or the borders of interior tideless seas, or, again, more rarely to river flood-plains.

12. APPLICATION OF THESE STRUCTURES IN DETERMINING POSITION OF STRATA. The importance of discriminating between the original structure as here described and its reproduction in reverse, in the overlying stratum, will be appreciated when it is considered that strata often stand vertical, and are even overturned. The determination of the upper and lower surfaces of the strata may be the only means for recognizing the superposition of the strata of a region. In all cases, the surface on which the structure (ripple-mark, impression, etc.) was originally made is the upper surface of the stratum, while the surface having a reverse reproduction of the structure (raised footprint, mold of ripple-mark, etc.) is the lower surface of that stratum.

13. ROUNDING AND SORTING OF SAND GRAINS AND WEARING OF PEBBLES. This subject has already been discussed in previous sections, but may be briefly summarized here. Sand grains under 0.1 mm. in diameter will not be rounded by wave action upon the coast, for they are held in suspension, and, moreover, capillarity provides the adjacent grains with a separating cushion of water which prevents mutual attrition. Larger grains may under favorable conditions be rounded by the waves. They are even better situated in this respect in river beds. The most efficient agent of all in the rounding of grains is the wind, as it it is also the most efficient sorting agent.

Pebbles are rounded largely by the action of running water and by waves. That the wind is able to do work in this direction is shown by the rounded pebbles of the Hamada or stony desert, where water activity is absent. It has been repeatedly asserted that there is a decided difference in form between pebbles of river bottoms and those of the shore. The former are said to be typically flat, from the fact that they are shoved along on the bottom of the stream, while the latter are rounded because they are rolled about by the waves. The reverse has also been held. Until more detailed observations on modern shores and river bottoms are made, no such general criterion can be accepted. As a matter of fact, flat pebbles abound on many shores where the material from which they are derived is a thin-bedded rock or tends to split into thin layers. Here the pebbles are shoved up the beach and dragged back, rolling being seldom seen. Pebbles formed from angular fragments, on the other hand, are rolled about on the beach. Thus it appears that the original form of the material is of more significance than the agent active in the rounding.

14. CHARACTERISTICS OF INCLUSIONS IN SAND GRAINS. In tracing the source of the quartz grains in sands and sandstones Mackie (17) has advocated the use of inclusions found in the quartz or their absence. He divides the inclusions into:

(1) *Regular inclusions,* of quartz, chlorite, muscovite, biotite, rutile, apatite, zircon, garnet, magnetite, titaniferous iron, etc. Characteristic of the quartz of schists.

(2) *Acicular,* or fine needle-like inclusions of doubtful mineral, capable of being subdivided according to arrangement of the needles. Characteristic of granites.

(3) *Irregular inclusions,* mostly fluid lacunæ with or without gas bubbles. Characteristic of granites, but more readily subject to disruption by changes in temperature or to crushing than the others, and, hence, diminishing in proportion with the age of the formation, and the repeated reworkings of the grains.

The absence of inclusions in quartz suggests vein quartz as the source, or the quartz of schists. After a determination of the inclusions in the quartz grains of the crystallines which might have furnished the sands of the Rothes Burn, and the determination of the percentage of feldspar, garnet, staurolite, mica, hornblende, chlorite and magnetite in the sands of this stream, together with the inclusions in the quartz grains, Mackie concludes that 23% of the sand was derived from granite, 57% from schist, and 20% from diorite. The matrix of the Lower Old Red conglomerate of Gollachy Mill was in like manner determined as derived 20% from granite, 77% from schist, and 3% from diorite and volcanics. In these analyses the feldspar was divided between the granite schist and diorite, the garnet, staurolite, mica, chlorite and the quartz with regular inclusions and without inclusions were referred to schists, while the hornblende and magnetite were referred to diorite. Analyses of the sand grains of successive members of both the lower and upper Old Red Sandstone showed that, during the process of erosion of the lands supplying the material of this formation in northern Scotland, different sand-supplying formations were uncovered, the first or highest of which supplying material for the oldest beds was non-granitic.

From the nature of the inclusions Berkey has been enabled to determine that the quartz grains of the St. Peter sandstone were derived from the gneisses and granites of the Canadian Old Land, and that the Sylvania sands were most probably derived from the older St. Peter sands, with which they agree in all respects.

15. ORGANIC REMAINS. Abundant remains of marine organisms are generally a good criterion for the marine origin of the strata containing them. There are, however, important exceptions to this. Thus the foraminiferal limestones of India and South Africa are formed as eolian deposits upon dry land, and often at a distance from the shore, though the remains themselves are all of marine types. Marine types may also be included in a terrestrial deposit as a result of derivation from older marine strata by weathering or erosion. Again shells of marine organisms may be carried inland by birds and other animals (including man) and become embedded in later deposits. Man-made shell heaps are generally recognizable by the presence in them of human implements as well as evidence of fire, but shells carried inland by birds are not readily recognizable as such. The occurrence of organisms of marine types in relict seas distant from the coast must be considered. This subject will be more fully discussed in a subsequent chapter.

Occasional intercalation of marine layers in delta formations otherwise of non-marine origin must also be noted here. Such intercalations have been used to prove the marine origin of an entire formation, the bulk of which is most probably of terrestrial origin.

Fresh water and terrestrial organisms when exclusively found in a formation indicate a continental origin. But such remains may be as characteristic of fluviatile as of lacustrine deposits and often more so. Thus the remains of land vertebrates and of plants in a formation indicate more commonly river, flood-plain, swamp, or, in the case of the vertebrates, steppe deposits, the remains being embedded in the river muds or covered by blown sands. Abundant remains of fresh water molluscs, Crustacea, etc., of Chara and other fresh water plants, indicate a lacustrine or paludal origin of the formation containing them.

Terrestrial organisms, especially plants, may also be carried out to sea and so become embedded in marine formations. The same thing is true of river-inhabiting fish, Crustacea, and Mollusca. The extent of such transportation is generally determinable, as shown by David White (24), by the degree of injury suffered by the perishable parts, such as bark, leaves, etc. Seeds and spores of river plants, such as the water ferns or rhizocarps, may also be carried out to sea and buried in normal marine sediments. Their occurrence, however, always suggests a river-borne origin for the mud in which they are found, as in the case of the Genesee and Portage muds of the Devonic in which occur the spore cases of the water fern Protosalvinia, mingled with marine organisms.

16. CONCRETIONS. Concretions are segregations of mineral matter which grow in size by addition externally, internally or interstitially. From the point of view of their origin and relationship to the enclosing rocks, two types may be distinguished: (1) those forming as contemporaneous accumulations, afterward buried by clastic or other strata, and (2) those forming within the strata after their deposition. This second group clearly belongs to the secondary structures of rocks.

Concretions of calcium carbonate, of barite, of manganese, and concretions composed of fragmental material cemented by phosphate of lime are among the first group, forming at the present time. The phosphate concretions are most characteristic of the shore zone, while the manganese concretions are common in the deep sea. The latter (Walther–23 : 701) are most abundant in the Pacific between 767 and 8,183 meters, and in the Indian and Antarctic Oceans between 2,926 and 4,754 meters depth. In the Atlantic Ocean they are found between 767 and 5,211 meters depth, chiefly in the neighborhood of volcanic islands.

These concretions commonly constitute the uppermost layer of the lithosphere in the deep sea, and they are gradually buried by the accumulation of fine muds. Not infrequently they constitute the foundation on which corals or other sedentary benthonic organisms gain a foothold, and such a concretion in moderately deep water may serve as the nucleus about which a coral reef is built up. Chemically formed oölites and pisolites should be mentioned under contemporaneous concretions. These have been fully discussed in a preceding chapter.

The secondarily formed concretions, or those growing within the strata, and therefore of later age, are represented by clay-stone concretions, so characteristic of shale and clay beds, and readily recognized as belonging to this secondary type by the fact that the stratification lines are seen to pass through them. Large examples of these are found in Devonic and later lutaceous deposits. They have not infrequently grown about fossils. Many of these also show the septarium structure as described below. The Lösspüppchen and "Lössmännchen," of the German loess, the "Marlekor" and "Näkkebröd" of similar Swedish deposits, the "Kankar" of India, and the clay iron stones of the British Carbonic shales are other examples of concretions of this type.

According to their method of growth concretions have been divided by Todd into four types (20):

1. Accretions.
2. Intercretions.
3. Excretions.
4. Incretions.

Accretions grow regularly and steadily from the center outward by successive additions of materials. This type of concre-

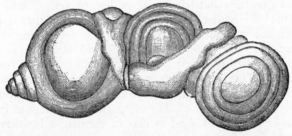

FIG. 143. Concretion (accretion) of clay stone, Connecticut Valley. (After Gratacap.)

tion will be solid from the center and if of subsequent growth will include or enmesh particles of the rock in which it forms without any considerable disturbance of it. The stratified structure may also be preserved in accretions, unless by crystallization a radiate structure is produced. Examples of this type are the remarkable concretions of the postglacial clays of the Connecticut Valley. (Sheldon–19.) (Fig. 143.)

The radial structure due to crystallization is well developed in the large spherical concretions of the Devonic black shales of Kettle Point,* Ontario, and of Michigan. From their fibrous structure they are not infrequently mistaken for petrified wood. (Daly–5.)

Intercretions grow by accretion on the exterior and by interstitial addition, causing a circumferential expansion and resultant cracking and wedging apart of the interior of the concretion. The cracks widen toward the center and are commonly filled by mineral

* So named from the resemblance of partly exposed concretions to inverted kettles.

matter, chiefly calcite, the accumulation of which helps to widen
and extend these internal fissures. Concretions of this type are
familiarly known as septaria, from the fact that when they have
been worn on the surface the veins sometimes weather in relief,
and thus produce a septate structure. Often, however, the veins are
depressed. These concretions are sometimes thought to be petrified turtles, and in many localities are known by the name of
"turtle stones." They are abundant in the Devonic shales of
eastern North America and in the Cretacic beds of the interior,
while the Jurassic of western Europe is famous for its remarkably
beautiful examples.

Excretions are centripetal concretions "consolidation progressing inward from the exterior." (Dana–*Manual, 4th ed.*—*98.*)
They are represented by nodular shells of sand cemented by iron
oxide, and generally filled by more or less unconsolidated sand or
contain other shells of cemented sand. Todd holds that normal accretions or intercretions of ferrous carbonate, on coming in contact
with waters charged with carbon dioxide and oxygen, will begin to
dissolve and a shell of ferric hydroxide will form on its surface by
precipitation. The iron carbonate of the portion of the concretion
within this shell will similarly be dissolved and reprecipitated as
ferric hydrate, a second shell thus being added on the interior of the
first. The impurities of sand or clay in the original concretion remain behind, in a loose condition. Thus while the actual thickening
of the shell is on the inside, and the growth, therefore, from without
inward, the molecular movement of the iron salts is from within
outward, *i. e.*, from the core of the original concretion to the inner
wall of the shell. When the process is completed a loose mass of
sand or other impurities alone remains behind, or, if the original concretion was free from impurities or nearly so, the resultant excre-
tion may be hollow. Excretions formed within ferruginous sandstones are often the cause of puzzling hollow cavities.

Incretions. These are cylindrical concretions with a hollow
core. Todd infers that these originate where the walls of a cavity,
like the cylindrical tube left by a decayed root in the sand or clay,
serve as the nucleus for deposition. The iron is drawn from the
surrounding material and moves inward to the center, where it
is added to the central cylinder, which grows in thickness outward
by the addition of successive shells on the exterior, until the surrounding matrix is depleted.

Minute concretions of this type are common in the loess. They
consist of carbonate of lime, and resemble clay pipe stems in size
and form.

17. SECRETIONS. Secretions are deposits formed on the walls of cavities in rocks, the first layer being the outer one of the secretion. A constant supply of material may bring about the filling of the cavity, as in veins and agate geodes, while the cutting off of the supply results in the production of hollow geodes, lined with crystals.

All secretions are secondary rock structures, and they are mentioned in this chapter merely for convenience in comparison with concretions. Of the latter, incretions and excretions are secondary structures, and the same is true largely if not wholly of intercretions. Accretions are, however, extensively represented by contemporary concretions, though many kinds of true accretions are also formed secondarily in strata of various kinds.

BIBLIOGRAPHY XVII.

1. BARRELL, JOSEPH. 1906. Relative Geological Importance of Continental, Littoral and Marine Sedimentation, Part III. Journal of Geology, Vol. XIV, pp. 524–568.
2. BERKEY, CHARLES P. 1906. Paleogeography of Saint Peter Time. Geological Society of America, Bulletin, Vol. XVII, pp. 229–250.
3. BRANNER, JOHN C. 1901. Origin of Ripple Marks. Journal of Geology, Vol. IX, pp. 535–536.
4. CANDOLLE, CASIMIR DE. 1883. Rides formús à la surface du sable déposé au fond de l'eau et autres phénomènes analogues. Archives des Sciences Physiques et Naturelle, Genève. No. 3, Tome IX, pp. 241–278.
5. DALY, REGINALD A. 1900. The Calcareous Concretions of Kettle Point, Lambton County, Ontario. Journal of Geology, Vol. VIII, pp. 135–150.
6. DARWIN, GEORGE H. 1883. On the Formation of Ripple Mark in Sand. Proceedings of the Royal Society of London, Vol. XXXVI, pp. 18–43.
7. FAIRCHILD, HERMAN L. 1901. Beach Structure in the Medina Sandstone. American Geologist, Vol. XXVIII, pp. 9–13, pls. II–IV.
8. FLEMING, J. A. 1902. Waves and Ripples in Water, Air and Æther. London.
9. FORCHHAMMER, G. 1841. Geognostische Studien am Meeresufer. Neues Jahrbuch für Mineralogie, etc., pp. 1–38, t. III.
9a. FOREL, F. A. 1883. Les Rides de Fond étudiús dans le lac Léman. Archives des Sciences Physiques et Naturelles, Genève, (3.) Tome X, pp. 39–72.
10. FRAAS, O. 1872. Heuglin's geologische Untersuchungen in Ost Spitzbergen. Petermanns geographische Mittheilungen, Bd. XVIII, pp. 275–277.
11. GILBERT, G. K. 1877. Report on the Geology of the Henry Mountains. United States Geographical and Geological Surveys of the Rocky Mountain Region.

12. GILBERT, G. K. 1899. Ripple Marks and Cross-bedding. Bulletin, of the Geological Society of America, Vol. X, pp. 135–139, pl. XIII 5 figs.

13. GRABAU, AMADEUS W. 1907. Types of Cross-bedding and Their Stratigraphic Significance. Science, N. S., Vol. XXV, pp. 295–296.

14. HUNT, A. R. 1882. On the Formation of Ripple Mark. Proceedings of the Royal Society of London, Vol. XXXIV, pp. 1–18.

15. HUNTINGTON, ELLSWORTH. 1907. Some Characteristics of the Glacial Period in Non-Glaciated Regions. Geological Society of America, Bulletin, Vol. XVIII, pp. 351–388, 9 pls., 16 figs.

16. JOHNSON, DOUGLAS W. 1910. Beach Cusps. Geological Society of America Bulletin, Vol. XXI, pp. 599–624 (with review of previous literature on Beach Cusps).

17. MACKIE, WILLIAM. 1897. The Sands and Sandstones of Eastern Moray. Edinburgh Geological Society Proceedings, Vol. VII, pp. 148–172.

18. PERRY, NELSON W. 1889. The Cincinnati Rocks. What was their Geological History? American Geologist, Vol. IV, pp. 326–336, 2 pls.

19. SHELDON, J. M. ARMS. 1900. Concretions from the Champlain Clays of the Connecticut Valley. Boston, 1900.

20. TODD, J. E. 1903. Concretions and Their Geological Effects. Bulletin of the Geological Society of America, Vol. XIV, pp. 353–360.

21. VAN HISE, CHARLES R. 1896. Principles of North American Pre-Cambrian Geology. U. S. Geological Survey, 16th Annual Report, Pt. I, pp. 581–872, pls. CVIII–CXVII.

22. WALTHER, JOHANNES. 1891. Die Denudation in der Wüste. Abhandlungen der königlich-kaiserlichen Gesellschaft der Wissenschaften. Mathematische-Physische Klasse, Bd. XVI, pp. 345–570 (1–225).

23. WALTHER, J. 1894. Die Auflagerungsflächen und die Entstehung der Schichtung, pp. 620–641, and other chapters in Einleitung in die Geologie als Historische Wissenschaft, 3 Teil. Lithogenesis der Gegenwart.

24. WHITE, DAVID. 1911. Value of Floral Evidence in Marine Strata as Indicative of Nearness to Shores. Geological Society of America Bulletin, Vol. XXII, pp. 221–227.

CHAPTER XVIII.

OVERLAP RELATIONS OF SEDIMENTARY FORMATIONS.

Overlap, or the extension of one formation beyond the other, is a structural feature of the greatest significance in stratigraphy. Two kinds of overlap may be recognized, the irregular and the regular or progressive. The irregular overlap of strata, resulting from sudden changes of physical conditions, is more of the nature of an accidental feature, and belongs rather to the general subject of unconformity of formations. While its recognition is of great importance in establishing the progress of events, it has not the stratigraphic significance of the other type.

PROGRESSIVE OVERLAP.

Under this term we include the regular overlapping of successive formations due either to a normal transgressive movement or to a regular regressive movement. According as we deal with marine or non-marine sediments we have (Grabau–3): (A) The *marine progressive* or (B) the *non-marine progressive* overlaps. The former are the more varied in type and will be discussed first.

A. MARINE PROGRESSIVE OVERLAP. We may distinguish two types of marine progressive overlap: 1. Normal *transgressive* overlap, due to a progressively encroaching sea; and, 2. *Regressive* or retreatal overlap, due to a progressively retreating sea. Generally a regressive movement is both preceded and followed by a transgressive movement, so that as a result of this compound progressive overlap a complex type of structure comes into existence.

The progress of deposition of the clastic sediments on a normal shelving seashore is controlled by two factors: namely, the rate of supply of material, and the rate and direction of change in the relative position of sea-bottom and sea-level. According to the variation of one or both, sedimentation will vary.

Three relations of land and sea may be recognized:

1. Subsiding land block or rising sea-level.
2. Stationary sea-level.
3. Rising land block or falling sea-level.

Each of these conditions is further complicated by variation in the rate of subsidence, or elevation, and the rate of supply of detrital material. In general, rising sea-level produces transgressive movements, except where the supply of detritus is excessive, when stationary or regressive movements are produced. Stationary and falling sea-level produce regressive movements.

I. Rising Sea-Level or Positive Diastrophic Movement.

A subsiding land block or rising sea-level may be either of local or of world-wide effect. Its cause may be diastrophic movements, or the gentle displacement of the water by the accumulation of sediment on the ocean floor. Such rising of the sea-level produces a continuous transgression of the sea upon the land, *i. e.*, a landward migration of the shore-line. The rate of migration, other things being equal, varies inversely as the steepness of the slope of the coast. Thus a slight depression of a very gentle shore will cause a great transgression of the sea, while even a considerable depression of a steep or vertical coast may produce little or no transgression. In the following discussions, the slope of the land surface affected by the transgression will be considered as a gentle one, such as is produced by a period of prolonged erosion of an old land surface.

Wilson (9:*118*; Rutot–7) has tabulated the possible relationship between the rate of depression of the land (rise of the sea-level) and the rate of supply of detritus, as follows:

Rate of Depression				Rate of supply of detritus
Uniform	⟵	⟦≷⟧	⟶ Uniform	
Variable	⟵	⟦≷⟧	⟶ Variable	

The simplest conditions are those in which the rate of depression and the rate of supply are both uniform. These alone will be considered; the variable conditions of either one, or of both factors, will produce corresponding variations of the norm to an almost unlimited degree.

With uniform rates of both subsidence and supply, three cases may be considered:

    a. Rate of depression is equal to the rate of supply of detritus.

    b. Rate of depression exceeds rate of supply.

    c. Rate of depression is exceeded by rate of supply.

The first case would result in the production of relatively stationary conditions, if the shore-line were bounded by a vertical face, when a uniform regular amount of detritus equaling the amount of subsidence would produce a constant depth of water. With a shelving shore, on the other hand, a uniform regular transgressive movement would occur, with a regular and uniform change in the character of the deposit at any given point. The second case will produce a rapid transgressional movement with a less normal succession of formations, while the third will produce either stationary or retreating coast-line, coupled with an increasing amount of subaërial deposition.

1. *Transgressive Movements.*

    a. *Rate of Depression Equals Rate of Supply.* Under these conditions a uniform and progressive overlapping of each later layer over all the preceding ones takes place. Each layer has a rudaceous or coarsely arenaceous texture at the shore, and grades seaward into finer arenaceous and ultimately lutaceous material. If the shore is composed of old crystalline rocks, the rudytes and arenytes resulting from their destruction will be largely siliceous, while the lutytes will be argillaceous and more or less micaceous. The coarse shoreward ends of the beds, when viewed in their *ensemble,* will appear as a single coarse bed resting upon the old land. From the consideration of its origin, however, it will be seen that no two portions of the bed along a line transverse to the seashore will be of the same age, each seaward portion will be younger than that lying next to it nearer the land. Thus the formation line, limiting the basal conglomerate or sandstone, will run diagonally upward through the planes of synchronous deposition. The basal bed is not generally a conglomerate, for where the sea transgresses upon an old land which has long been subject to subaërial disintegration a basal sandstone will be produced, since there is not coarse material enough to form pebbles. When decomposition has gone on for a long time prior to the transgression of the sea, and when the decomposed material is subjected to a

thorough sorting by the encroaching waters, a nearly pure silicarenyte may come to rest directly upon the eroded surface of the
crystalline old land. This is finely shown in the basal Palæozoic
contact in portions of the Front Range of the Rocky Mountains,
where a nearly pure quartz sandstone rests on an almost perfectly
even erosion surface of granite. (Crosby–2.) Where atmospheric
agencies have been sufficiently active to disintegrate a granite
surface, without, however, reducing the feldspar to clay, the basal
sandstone will be a feldspathic arenyte or arkose. Again examples
are known where decomposition has affected the underlying crystalline old land to a considerable extent, but where little sorting of
material was accomplished by the transgressing sea, so that the
basal bed is a highly argillaceous arenyte. The contact of this with
the underlying crystalline basement rock will in consequence not
be a sharp one, the crystalline rock grading through a decomposed
zone into the overlying sandstone. An example of this indefinite
type of contact is seen on Presque Isle near Marquette, Michigan,
where the Lake Superior sandstone passes downward into a rock
produced by the consolidation of the undisturbed disintegrated surface of the basal peridotite.

A consideration of the progressive landward migration of the
coarser deposits under uniform conditions will lead to the recognition that the changes in any given bed, from the shore seaward,
will be exactly duplicated by the changes in a given vertical section from the base upward.* For it will· be seen that the coarse
bed deposited directly upon the old sea-floor of crystalline rock is
succeeded upward by a somewhat finer bed, since the zone of deposition of the coarse material has, by the continuous subsidence,
migrated further landward. Thus, as shown in the annexed figure
(Fig. 144), the lowest coarse deposits of bed (a) which form the
shore zone of that bed are succeeded vertically by the finer deposits
of bed (b) made at a somewhat greater distance from the new
shore. At this new shore (of bed b) coarse deposits are accumulating, but they are beyond the belt of the former deposition of
coarse material. Again an advance of the shore to c transfers
the shore belt of coarse (rudaceous) deposition in the same direction and by the same amount. Consequently the belt of arenaceous
deposits of bed c is likewise transferred shoreward and comes to

---

* The variation in texture of deposits due to storms and the corresponding
change in the power of waves and currents discussed in a preceding chapter,
are here left out of consideration, since they will at best produce only minor
variations in the strata.   The present discussion deals with formations on a large
scale.

rest on the belt of rudaceous deposits of bed *b,* just as the arenaceous deposits of that bed come to rest on the rudaceous deposits of bed *a.* In like manner the lutaceous deposits of bed *c* come to rest on the arenaceous deposits of bed *b,* just as the lutaceous deposits of bed *b* come to rest on the arenaceous belt of bed *a.* Two sections, then, made at I and II, will show precisely the same succession in coarseness and kind of material from the bottom up, the only difference being that in section II the lutaceous bed is much thicker than in section I. Erosion, however, may remove so much of the lutaceous beds of section II as to equalize the amount in the two sections. It would, of course, be incorrect to consider each lithic unit in section I to be of the same age as the corresponding lithic unit in section II, for, although there is a similar lithic succession, bed *a,* and the lower portion of bed *b* are unrepresented in

Section I.   Section II.

FIG. 144. Diagram showing regular marine progressive overlap on an old land surface. A basal sandstone occurs everywhere, this grading upward and seaward into lutaceous deposits. At section I the series comprises beds *b* and *c* only, but at section II beds *a-c* are present.

section I. In general, it is safe to assume that in a case of this kind, where continuous transgression on a uniformly shelving shore has taken place, the basal bed of the section farther up the old shore is of later age than the corresponding lithic bed of the section farther seaward. There are many cases where relationships of this type must be considered in the correlation of strata.

We have so far considered only siliceous detrital material derived from an old land composed of crystalline or other siliceous rocks. We must now consider, in addition to these, the organic rocks and their clastic derivations, which play so important a rôle in the sedimentary series accumulating on the sea bottom. As noted in an earlier chapter, purely biogenic stratified deposits are formed by the accumulation of the various organic oozes on the sea-floor, such as foraminiferal, radiolarian, diatomaceous or pteropodan. Where clastic sediments are accumulating very slowly, as at a distance from shore, these organic oozes may constitute an important part, if not most, of the sediment. In such cases, the ooze being a calcareous one, the clay and other lutaceous beds forming in quieter water will shade off into calcareous sediments, and may even be entirely replaced by limestones of this type. Where coral reefs or shell heaps are forming off shore, the clastic derivations of these will become commingled with, and shade off into, the terrigenous sediments near shore. As explained in Chapter X, the coarsest fragments will remain near the reef, the calcarenytes coming next, and shading off into the finest calcilutytes. These calcilutytes may be gradually replaced shoreward by siliceous or argillaceous lutytes, or they or the calcarenytes may grade directly into the silicarenytes. Where this latter occurs, we have a seaward change from pure quartz sand (silicarenyte), through calciferous sandstone (calcareous silicarenyte) and siliceous calcarenytes to pure calcarenytes. This change is probably more often observed in the Palæozoic series than the change from siliceous to argillaceous sediments. (Fig. 145.)

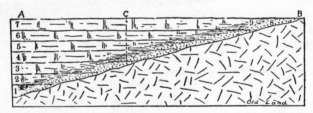

FIG. 145. Diagram showing regular marine progressive overlap; a basal sandstone is present, but this grades upward and seaward into calcareous deposits. The differences between sections A and C are readily seen.

Older examples. The type of overlap here described seems to have been by far the most general as recorded in both Palæozoic and Mesozoic deposits. An illustration is seen in the basal Ordovicic sandstone of Ontario, which on Lake Huron lies at the base of the Chazy series, but farther northeast is basal Trenton. The basal Cambric sandstone of Sweden also varies in age from Lower to Upper Cambric, though there is probably a series of unrecorded intervals during which retreat and erosion took place without the deposition of a basal sandstone by the readvancing sea. From the evidence of the dreikanter and other structural features it is known that this basal bed represents an old residual sandy covering of terrestrial origin, subsequently encroached upon by the sea. It is not improbable that wherever basal sandstones occur. extending upward through such a long series, as the entire Cambric in which there are, moreover, stratigraphic breaks, these sand stones are older continental deposits slightly reworked by an advancing sea. This appears also to be the case in the Cambric of North America. The basal Cambric sandstones and conglomerates of the southern Appalachian region underlie the Olenellus-bearing shales and limestones, while those of the Oklahoma and Ozark regions underlie beds generally referred to the Middle Cambric. Finally, in the upper Mississippi Valley the St. Croix sandstone series actually contains in its upper portion the Cambro-Ordovicic transition fauna. In many cases this northern "Potsdam" sandstone shows evidence of continental origin in pre-marine time by the occurrence of well-marked torrential cross-bedding in parts which apparently have not been reworked. In the North American Cambric there are numerous distinct breaks, the magnitude of which is not yet fully ascertained, except that it is now generally recognized that above the Middle Cambric there is a hiatus corresponding to nearly the whole of the Upper Cambric of the Atlantic coast. These breaks are, as a rule, not marked by retreatal intercalated sandstones. Further examples of overlap involving large portions of a system are shown in the North American Palæozoic by the entire absence of the Lower Cambric at St. John, New Brunswick, where the basal marine clastics belong to the Middle Cambric, while only 30 miles northeastward, at Hanford Brook, the Lower Cambric (Etcheminian) has a thickness of 1,200 feet. In Cape Breton this thickness measures several thousand feet. The well-known fact that the Cambric of Bohemia begins with the Paradoxides beds of Middle Cambric age, while Lower Cambric beds occur in western Europe, shows a pronounced eastward transgression of the Cambric sea in Europe with corresponding overlap of formations.

The basal Mesozoic sandstone of the Texas and Mexico regions furnishes another typical example of a rising basal bed in a transgressive series. In central Mexico this basal sandstone lies beneath Upper Jurassic limestones; on the Tropic of Cancer it has risen into the base of the Comanchic; on the Texas-Oklahoma line it has risen through the Lower Comanchic (Trinity) and lies at the base of the Fredericksburg or Middle Comanchic; and, finally, in central Kansas it has passed up to near the base of the Upper Comanchic or Washita series. There are, however, one pronounced (Paluxy) and several smaller sandstone members intercalated in the limestone series, and these mark either shoaling or an actual emergence of the sea-bottom.

In this case, as in the Cambric, the basal sands are most probably of continental origin reworked by the transgressing Comanchic sea. These basal sands indicate by their purity a distant source and long transportation, and the time interval during the Triassic and early Jurassic periods was ample to make possible an extended accumulation of widespread river and eolian sands derived in large part from the crystallines of the Canadian and western uplands, added to no doubt by contributions from uncovered Palæozoic and older sediments. A striking case of change in lithic character with progress of transgression is seen in the Cretacic series of southeast England and in that of northeast Ireland and the west of Scotland (Mull and Morvern). (Fig. 146.) In both cases the series begins with basal conglomerates, followed by sands, clays, and

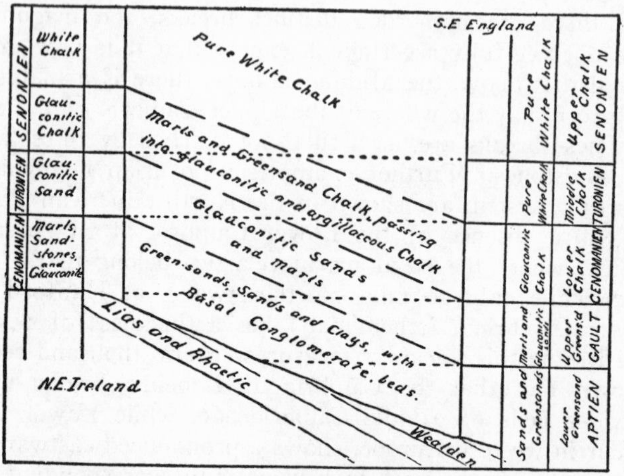

FIG. 146. Diagram showing overlap and change in lithic character of the Cretacic formations of England and Ireland, from southeast to northwest.

greensands. This is followed by (2) Glauconite sands and marls, then by (3) marls and Greensand chalk, passing into glauconitic and argillaceous chalk, and, finally, by (4) pure white chalk. In England the basal series (1) rests on the Weald clays, and is of Aptien age, while in Ireland it rests on Lias and is of Cenomanien age. In Scotland it also is of Cenomanien age. The next lithic series (No. 2) is of Albien (Gault) age in England, but of Turonien age in Ireland. The succeeding marls and Greensand chalk (No. 3) are of Cenomanien age in England, but of lower Senonien age in Ireland. Finally, the white chalk of England begins in the Turonien, but in Ireland and Scotland it occurs only in the upper Senonien. This illustrates not only the progressive overlap of the formations, but also the progressive overlap of facies in the same direction.

b. *Rate of Depression Exceeds Rate of Supply.* Under these conditions there will be a rapid transgression of the sea, and the meager supply of detritus will be spread thinly over the sea-floor, or, if the depression is a rapid one, in many places deeper water deposits may accumulate upon the original old land surface. Such cases are known and are probably less infrequent than one is led to suppose from the scattered observations available in the literature. Wilson (8:*148*) cites the case of a calcareous conglomerate of Black River age, carrying angular quartz fragments, molds of a Cameroceras and fragments of crinoid stems, which rests directly upon the Archæan red granite near Kingston Mills, Ontario. From the basin of the Moose River, Devonic corals have been reported, with their bases attached to an Archæan abyssolith. (Parks–6:*188*.) As under normal conditions of transgression, with an equivalent supply of detritus, the change in lithic character is a gradual one from coarse at the base to fine at the top, so, in any rapid or sudden transgression, we would expect to find an abrupt change from coarse material to fine, or from near-shore to off-shore deposits. Conversely, where we find a sudden change from coarse beds below to fine beds above, we may postulate a sudden relative change, either a sudden transgression or a sudden diminution in the supply of material. Sometimes a sudden transgression will transfer the shore zone, from which much of the detrital material is supplied, from one lithic formation to another, when the character of the deposit will change. Thus an abrupt change of sea-level may transfer the shore from a broad outcropping belt of quartz sandstones to a parallel belt of limestones, the sandstones being covered by the encroaching sea. As a result, the deposition of quartz sands may cease, and fine calcareous muds derived from the erosion of limestones may be deposited upon the coarse quartz sands without transition. Such a change appears to have taken place in eastern North America in late Siluric time, effecting a change from the Salina silicarenytes (Binnewater sandstones) to the fossiliferous limestones and water-limes (Rosendale cement) which overly them.

Where transgression takes place over an old peneplain surface, on which residual soil has accumulated during the long period of exposure, this ancient soil may be incorporated, without much change, as a basal bed. Where the soil is lutaceous, especially where it is a residual clay containing much carbonized vegetable material, as in the case of an old swamp-covered surface, a black carbonaceous mud will constitute the basal layer, which is succeeded upward by other beds of fine-grained terrigenous material or by limestones derived from organic sources. Such a black basal shale may also result from the washing of the residual black soil from the surface of the plain into the shallow encroaching sea. In any case, the basal black shale will rise diagonally across the planes of synchroneity, and, although it will constitute a lithic unit, it is not a stratigraphic unit, but made up of the shale ends of a successive series of deeper water formations. This relationship is shown in the following diagram. (Fig. 147.) An example of this type of basal bed is found in the Eureka (Noël) black shale of the Mississippi Valley. This formation rests generally upon eroded Ordovicic strata, the contact being a disconformable one. Upward it passes into limestones, which in southwestern Missouri

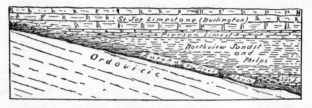

FIG. 147. Diagram of overlap of marine strata on basal black shale in southwestern Missouri and northern Arkansas.

are of Chouteau age, the shale itself carrying Kinderhook fossils, while in northern Arkansas it is succeeded by limestone carrying Burlington fossils. The same relationship exists in the southern Appalachian region, where the black shale has risen into the base of the Keokuk, if not higher. (Grabau–3.)

2. Regressive Movements.

c. *Rate of Depression Is Exceeded by Rate of Supply.* In this case accumulation will go on so fast as to fill in the shallow shore zone, when the coarse material begins to extend seaward, progressively overlapping the off-shore deposits in a seaward direction. We will thus have a gradual change in the character of the sediment from the lutaceous material at the bottom to arenaceous and sometimes coarser terrigenous material. This material will all be land-derived, and, as it is deposited rapidly, not a very thorough sorting can generally be expected. As the shore migrates seaward, subaërial deposits may accumulate above it. (Wilson–9: *119.*)

Local temporary increase in the rate of supply may be due to causes not readily determinable, but widespread and persistent changes must be regarded as indicative of climatic change. Before we accept such a climatic change, however, as the cause of a seaward migration of terrigenous deposits we must satisfy ourselves, if possible, that the migration in question is not due to a change in the rate of subsidence, the climatic conditions and, therefore, the rate of supply of detritus remaining the same. For it is evident that a gradual diminution of the rate of subsidence would produce practically the same results as a corresponding increase in supply.

II. STATIONARY SEA-LEVEL.

When the supply of detritus continues uniformly, while the sea-level remains stationary, a regression of the seashore will take place, but at a faster rate than would be the case if subsidence still continued, though at a diminished rate. The shore zone would creep out over the deeper water deposits, the transition from the one to the other being rather more abrupt than in the case of a slowly subsiding sea-floor. On the whole, however, stationary conditions produce a change of sediment differing in degree only from that incident upon a diminution in the rate of subsidence.

III. FALLING SEA-LEVEL.

The falling sea-level or rising land block is accompanied by a continuous regression of the seashore, and a consequent seaward migration of the shore zone with its attendant deposits. If the emergence is not too fast the waves will be able to remove much of the formerly deposited shore detritus and carry it seaward into the shoaling off-shore districts. Thus a bed of sand or conglomerate will advance seaward over the finer off-shore deposits, coming to rest upon these often without transition beds. Furthermore, the continuous movement of the clastic shore derivatives will tend, in the coarser material, to a perfect rounding off of the pebbles, and in general to a destruction of all but the most resistant materials. Thus a much washed-over sandstone or conglomerate may come to consist entirely of quartz, constituting a pure silica-renyte or silicirudyte. It is probably not saying too much that all pure quartz clastics, derived from a complex crystalline old land, and resting abruptly upon a clayey or calcareous off-shore deposit, represent the seaward spreading shore zone of a rising sea-floor, unless they are referable to continental deposits.

Characteristics of Regressive Deposits.

As the retreat of the sea from the land may under normal conditions be considered a process occupying a greater or less amount of time, it is evident that deposition at a distance from shore need not be interrupted. Thus, while within the zone of retreat for any given time period, no sedimentation will occur, such sedimentation may, nevertheless, go on at a regular rate beyond this zone. In other words, a certain thickness of off-shore deposits must be considered the depositional equivalent of a given time period, which in the shore zone is represented by a given amount of re-

Fig. 148. Diagram illustrating regressive overlap (off-lap) and the formation of a sandstone of emergence (x-y) into which the shore-ends of the successive members of the retreatal series (a-d) grade.

treat. Thus it is brought about that each successive formation of the retreatal series extends shoreward to a less extent than the preceding one. As each formation or bed passes shoreward into a coarser clastic it is evident that the shore ends of all the formations deposited during the retreat will together constitute a stratum of sandstone or conglomerate which in age rises seaward, since in that direction it is progressively composed of the ends of higher and higher formations. These relationships are shown in Fig. 148, where it will be noted that the diagonal rise of the shore-formed stratum is from the shore seaward, whereas in transgressive movements the shore-formed stratum or basal bed rises diagonally landward. In the series shown in the diagram, the beds a-d were successively laid down during the retreat of the sea from A to B. Each later formed bed comes to an end before it has reached the shoreward end of the preceding one, and each formation grades from a clayey or calcareous character landward into silicoarenaceous character. Thus b reaches landward to a less extent than a, the shore end of which, composed of quartz sands, remains exposed. The shore end of *b* is also composed of quartz sands, since during the formation of *b* the shore has migrated seaward. In like manner *c* does not entirely cover *b*, and *d* does not wholly cover *c*, each ending in a sand facies. Thus the sand ends of all the beds will be exposed at or just above sea-level, and constitute a continuous sand formation, which, however, is not of the same age at any two points along a line transverse to the direction of the shore. Such a sand formation will, however, be mapped as a unit, and receive a formational name. If the basal portion of such a sand formation is fossiliferous, it will contain in a seaward direction the fossils of successively higher formations. Thus the portion of the sandstone formation *x*, *y* in Fig. 148 will at *x* contain the fossils of formation *a*, and at *y* the fossils of formation *d*, while between these points it will contain the fossils of *b* and *c*, where it forms the end of these respective formations. When the land is sufficiently elevated during the retreat of the sea, stream erosion will set in and the material left by the retreating sea may be removed by the streams. Furthermore, if elevation of the land is responsible for the retreat of the sea, the streams coming from this higher land will bring more detritus, and hence, where erosion is not going on, deposition by rivers will further elevate the surface of the emerging coastal plain. The same thing is true also if the regressive movement is due to an increase in the supply of detrital material. In either case, pebbles and sands derived through the erosion of the old land or of old conglomerates and sandstones may be carried out for great distances over this emerging surface, while wind-assorted sands, with their grains rounded and pitted from attrition, may also accumulate over this surface. The peculiar structures of both torrential and eolian sands, *i. e.*, cross-bedding, ripples, etc., may thus be incorporated in this retreatal sandstone. Remains of land-plants and of land and fresh water animals may readily be entombed in the deposits thus accumulating upon the flat plain of retreat, and even coal beds may form and become embedded in sandstones the bases of which vary in age from place to place.

Burial of Retreatal Sandstones by Subsequent Transgressive Movements.

When the regressive movement of the shore has come to an end, and transgressive changes recommence, the upper portions of these migratory shore deposits may be worked over once more, and now partake of the character of a basal sandstone or conglomerate.

As the shore zone advances landward, finer deposits will be laid down over the coarser basal bed and thus the transgressive portion of such a sandstone or conglomerate will pass diagonally across the planes of synchroneity. The deposit resulting by the time the shore zone has returned to its former position will therefore be a composite formation including within it a hiatus, which may represent a considerable time interval, but is not recognizable by any structural character. The encroaching sea will work over the sand dune deposits and thus water-laid sandstone beds, composed of rounded translucent quartz grains and well stratified, will result. In the upper part of these worked-over sandstones marine shells and other remains may be included, the age of which changes shoreward, since the transgressive portion of this sandstone represents successively the ends of higher and higher formations, after the manner of a true basal sandstone of a transgressive series.

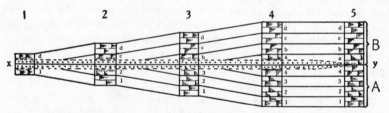

Fig. 149. Diagram showing the relationship of the strata in five successive sections, in a compound regressive-transgressive series. The intercalated sandstone x y encloses the hiatus. (See Fig. 150.)

The recognition of an intercalated shore formation of great areal extent between off-shore sediments as the product of combined regressive and transgressive movement must be based on a comparison of sections taken at intervals over the entire area covered by the formation in question. Such sections will show the intercalated shore formation (sandstone or conglomerate) to be in more or less intimate association with the lower beds of the underlying formation and the higher beds of the overlying formation at their shoreward ends, but, away from the shore, higher members of the lower formation and lower members of the higher formation will progressively appear until near the line of farthest retreat both lower and upper formation will be complete, while beyond that the intercalated bed will gradually lose its shore character and merge with the enclosing formations. This character of the sections is shown in the preceding diagram (Fig. 149). Formation A, consisting of divisions *1* to *4*, and formation B, consisting of divisions *a* to *d,* are both complete in section 5, which marks the farthest limit of retreat of the sea. Bed *x,* the intercalated shore formation, fades away in this section. In section 4 all the members of both formations are represented, but divisions *4* and *a* are not complete, while the intercalated bed *x* is prominent. In section 3, divisions *4* and *a* are wanting, and in section 2, divisions *3* and *b* are likewise wanting. In section 1, finally, all except the lowest division (*1*) of formation A, and the highest (*d*) of formation B, are missing. It would be obviously wrong to correlate division *l* of section 1 with the whole of formation A as exposed in section 5, or division *d* of section 1 with the whole of formation B of section 5. Yet such correlations have not infrequently been made in the past. In each of the above sections the intercalated sandstone or conglomerate may be intimately related to both overlying and underlying formations, and contain their fossils. Such a relation would

FIG. 150. Diagram of a compound regressive-transgressive series, showing the seaward decrease of the hiatus between the upper and lower part of the series. (See Fig. 149.)

show that the actual hiatus is represented by the middle part of the intercalated bed, which middle part may not infrequently be represented by continental deposits. Yet so intimate are the physical relationships between the bottom, middle and top of the intercalated formation that a separation into more than one formation is impossible. Thus in section 1 the intercalated formation *x* may have all the characters of a formational unit or a single stratum, and may grade upward into division *d* and downward into division *1,* so that to all appearance continuous deposition obtained in this locality. If the respective ages of divisions *d* and *1* are recognized, formation *x* will be likely to be considered the depositional equivalent of divisions *2* to *4* and *a* to *c* of section 5. Such is indeed the fact, except that the central portion of *x,* the terrestrial portion, whether represented by continental deposits or an unrecognizable erosion plane, represents all but the upper fraction of division *c,* and the lower of division *2.* The hiatus or stratigraphic break thus represented in the middle portion of the intercalated formation is a constantly decreasing one from section 1 to section 5. In each section it covers the interval of time between the emergence of the sea bottom at that point during the regressive movement and its resubmergence during the succeeding transgressive movement. This relationship may be expressed in the preceding diagram. (Fig. 150.) The following diagrammatic sections (Fig. 151) show the relation of a series of strata recording a transgressive movement followed by a regressive and again by a transgressive movement. *x-z* is the basal sandstone bed of the transgressive series, *x-y* the intercalated sandstone of the

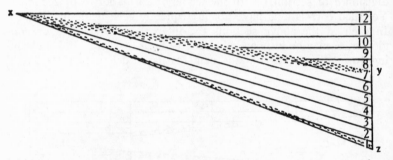

FIG. 151. Diagram showing the relationships of the strata in a transgressive-regressive-transgressive series. Basal sandstone *x z* and intercalated sandstone *x y* are both present.

regressive-transgressive series. Beds 1 to 3 are the first series of transgressive formations, beds 4 to 7 the regressive formations, and beds 8 to 12 the second series of transgressive formations.

EXAMPLES OF INTERCALATED SANDSTONES FROM THE PALÆOZOIC AND MESOZOIC FORMATIONS OF NORTH AMERICA.

The Saint Peter Sandstone. This is an exceedingly pure quartz sandstone of rounded, well-worn and pitted grains of nearly uniform size in any given region. It is widely distributed in central North America, lying generally between a member of the Chazyan and one of the Beekmantownian formations of the Ordovicic. In Minnesota it lies beneath the upper beds of the Stones River (Upper Chazyan), grading upward into and containing some of its characteristic fossils in the upper layers. Its base rests upon lower Beekmantown (Shakopee), into which it also grades in many sections, though in others it forms a sharp contact or even rests on an erosion plane of the dolomite. Where conformable it may contain lower Beekmantown fossils. Sometimes the lower beds are slightly disturbed, while the upper ones do not partake of such disturbance. This indicates an interval of time after the deposition of the lower beds, during which they were disturbed, and after which the higher strata were deposited upon them. Southward, higher members of the Beekmantown series come in beneath the Saint Peter sandstone and lower members of the Chazyan above it. In the Arbuckle Mountains the upper bed (here known as the Simpson formation) is about 2,000 feet thick, while the Beekmantown below the Saint Peter is of similar thickness. This sandstone thus has all the characteristics of a regressive-transgressive sandstone intercalated between limestones, and may be regarded as a typical example. (Grabau–3; 4.) (Fig. 152.)

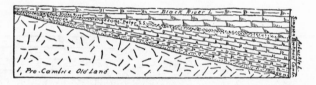

FIG. 152. Diagram representing the Cambric, Lower Ordovicic (Beekmantown), and Middle Ordovicic (Chazyan) formations, and the compound transgressive-regressive-transgressive overlaps between Oklahoma and Minnesota. The intercalated sandstone is the Saint Peter.

The Dakota Sandstone. This sandstone of Mid-Cretacic age has essentially the same relation to the enclosing calcareous strata as has the Saint Peter. It contains, besides, an abundant flora of terrestrial plants, so that its value as a record of complete emergence becomes even greater. In southern Kansas this sandstone lies at the top of the Fredericksburg division of the Comanchic, while in Texas it lies on top of the Washita or Upper Comanchic. In either case there is commonly a gradation from the limestones and shales to the sandstones. The top of this sandstone passes upward into the marine Eagle Ford formation in Texas, while further north, in Colorado and the Dakotas, it grades into the much later Benton beds.

B. NONMARINE PROGRESSIVE OVERLAP. This term is applied to the large structure normally produced during the formation of a great fan or subaërial delta, from the wash carried by the streams from the mountains and deposited upon the plains adjoining. Such a subaërial fan will of course grow in extent year by year, and in so growing the latest deposits, whether derived from the mountain or whether obtained through the reworking of the previously deposited portion, will as a rule extend further out into the plain than did those of previous periods of deposition. In other words, each later formation will overlap the previous ones by a margin commensurate with the increase in the size of the fan, and beyond the margin of the previously formed bed it will come to rest directly upon the floor of the plain. This overlapping of later formed over earlier ones will of course be a progressive one if the growth is continuous. The essential point of difference between this type of overlap and that formed in a transgressing sea is that in the subaërial fan the formations will primarily overlap one another *away from the source of supply of the material,* while in the marine progressive overlap the overlap is *toward the source of supply of the material.* The following diagrams will illustrate this differ-

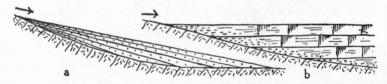

FIG. 153. Diagrams illustrating the relationship of the strata in nonmarine progressive overlap (*a*) and marine progressive overlap (*b*). The source of the material in each case is on the left.

ence, the source of supply in each case being on the left. (Figs. 153, *a, b.*) It should, however, be noted here (Barrell–1) that at the head of the delta an overlap toward the source of supply may occur, since with the aggradation of the delta plain and the consequent lowering of the river grade deposition may commence farther upstream. Such effects are seen in interior basins, where the upper beds extend farther toward the mountains from which the material has been derived. It appears to be shown also in the case of the Newark formation, where the upper beds extend farther north, overlapping the lower ones. (Kümmel–5 :*48.*) It may, however, be questioned whether headward overlapping of the formations is ever of marked character, since it is necessarily confined to the stream channels supplying the detritus and probably does not spread greatly in a lateral direction. In any case it cannot be compared in extent and importance with the overlap on the margin of the fan, which is always away from the source of supply.

The coarsest material of the subaërial fan will of course be deposited near the head of the delta. Finer material may be carried out for hundreds of miles across such a delta, as is abundantly shown by the delta plains of the Indus and Ganges and of the Huang-ho River. Occasionally pebbles well rounded may be carried out to great distances, and this is especially true of the well-rounded pebbles derived from older conglomerates. When the surface of the delta has become very flat, drainage obstructions may take place, in which case swamps and the deposit of carbonized plant remains will form. Thus a fossil delta of this type may include coal seams, the tops of which may again be eroded, or covered with a moderately coarse river deposit.

An essential feature of this type of overlap in purely nonmarine sediments is the relation which the beds have to the surface on which the overlapping edges rest. If this is an old land surface,

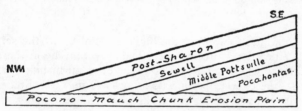

FIG. 154.   Diagram showing the westward overlap of the various members of the Pottsville series of eastern North America, upon the old erosion surface of pre-Pottsville age; the surface of supply is in the southeast.

e., without contemporaneous sediments of a marine origin, the evidence of the nonmarine origin of this overlapping series is complete. For it is manifestly inconceivable that clastic sediment will be carried across a body of water and be deposited upon the opposite shore in such a relationship as to suggest marine transgressive overlap.

THE POTTSVILLE SERIES, A TYPICAL EXAMPLE OF NONMARINE PROGRESSIVE OVERLAP. (Fig. 154.)

This is a deposit of quartzose clastics, consisting for the most part of rounded quartz pebbles embedded in a matrix of sand. In the eastern area the conglomerate is coarsest, the pebbles often reaching a diameter of several inches. They consist also of a greater variety of material, but westward, where the pebbles are smaller, scarcely any but those of quartz remain. Several distinct coal beds with associated shales occur, making identification of horizons possible. The formation is thickest in the eastern Appalachians and thins away westward by failure of the lower beds and overlap of the higher. The lowest beds are found in two localities in the eastern area, near Pottsville, Pennsylvania, and in the Pocahontas region of West Virginia and Virginia. From these two centers the deposits spread northward, westward and southwestward, each later division overlapping the preceding ones, until in western

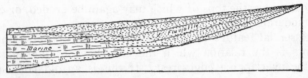

Fig. 155. Diagram showing replacing overlap of a nonmarine series over a marine one.

Pennsylvania and Ohio only the highest members of the series are present. Since the source of these beds can only be in the eastern Appalachians, where alone rocks capable of furnishing such material exist, the overlap becomes one away from the source of supply. Such an overlap might perhaps be produced under water if the overlapping marine sediments belonged to a spreading submarine delta. In this case the beds would become increasingly finer around the periphery of the submerged delta, and they would merge

Fig. 156. Diagram showing the relationship of the nonmarine Catskill and the marine Chemung in eastern North America. A Devonic example of replacing overlap.

into deposits of purely marine origin. Nor would the delta be of a size comparable to that of the Pottsville, which by its character, its coal beds and its overlap relations is shown to be of subaërial origin. There are to be sure one or more reported horizons of marine faunas, a brachiopod fauna having been found in the middle Pottsville (Horsepen) as far north as Sewell, on New River. If these organisms really indicate marine conditions and not secondary inclusions, this can only mean a momentary invasion of the delta area from a neighboring arm of the sea. Naiadites and "Spirorbis" have been found in the Lower Lykens division of the anthracite region of Pennsylvania, but these organisms do not necessarily indicate marine conditions.

C.   REPLACING OVERLAP.   This type of overlap occurs when a series of clastic sediments of terrestrial origin replaces a typical oceanic or thalassic series, or where continental clastics re-

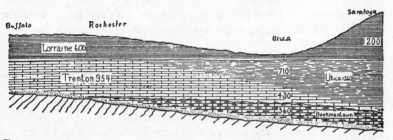

FIG. 157.   Diagram showing ·the westward replacing overlap of the Utica shale on the Trenton limestone, both being marine formations, but one (the Utica) terrigenous and the other thalassigenous.

place those formed in the sea (Fig. 155). The latter is associated only with a retreating seashore, and the overlapping of the nonmarine beds does not take place on the old land surface, but upon previously deposited and all but contemporaneous marine beds. Along the border line the two will blend, and it will appear as if the non-

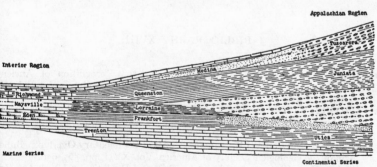

FIG. 158.   Diagram showing replacing overlap of terrigenous marine, followed by continental sediments on the east over marine limestones, etc., on the west.

marine series overlay the marine series, though in reality it is a case of replacement of the one by the other. A typical example of such a progressive replacement is seen in the Catskill sandstone, which is a nonmarine formation spread westward from its centers of origin, of which it appears there were at least two. The corresponding marine beds are the Chemung sandstones and shales, which may be regarded as the submerged continuations of the Catskill beds. Oscillatory conditions are indicated by occasional intercalations of the marine between the nonmarine layers. In the eastern area the series is represented wholly by the nonmarine Catskill; in the western it is represented wholly by the marine Chemung. Between these extremes marine Chemung is always overlain by nonmarine Catskill. These relationships are shown in the diagram on page 742. (Fig. 156.)

This type of overlap, though away from the source of supply, is not, however, limited to nonmarine deposits. It may likewise be shown by a spreading clastic shore deposit, which gradually replaces a limestone of neritic origin without actual emergence of the zone of shore deposits occurring. Or a current-borne type of terrigenous sediment may progressively replace a limestone of neritic origin. Examples of such replacement are found in the changing facies of the Trenton limestones, which (Grabau-4) are gradually replaced westward by the spreading Utica * type of deposit, which is of near-shore and probably shallow-water origin. This is illustrated in the diagram on page 743 (Fig. 157). A combination of this type and the replacing by sediments of continental origin is shown in Figure 158 on page 743, involving the Upper Ordovicic and Lower Siluric deposits of eastern North America.

BIBLIOGRAPHY XVIII.

1. BARRELL, JOSEPH. 1912. Criteria for the Recognition of Ancient Delta Deposits. Geological Society of America Bulletin, Vol. XXIII, pp. 377–446.
2. CROSBY, WILLIAM O. 1899. Archæan-Cambrian Contact near Manitou, Colorado. Bulletin of the Geological Society of America, Vol. X, pp. 141–164.
3. GRABAU, AMADEUS W. 1906. Types of Sedimentary Overlap. Bulletin of the Geological Society of America, Vol. XVII, pp. 567–636.
4. GRABAU, A. W. 1910. Physical and Faunal Evolution of North America During Ordovicic, Siluric and Early Devonic Time. In "Outlines of Geological History," etc., Chapter IV.
5. KUMMEL, HENRY B. 1898. Annual Report of the State Geologist of New Jersey for 1898. New Jersey Geological Survey.
6. PARKS, WILLIAM ARTHUR. 1899. The Nipissing-Algoma Boundary (Ontario). Ontario Bureau of Mines, Vol. VIII, pp. 175–196.

* Using this term in its broader sense, in which it is practically equivalent to the whole of the Trenton.

7. RUTOT, A. 1883. Les Phenoménès de la Sédimentation Marine. Études dans leur Rapports avec la Stratigraphie regionale. Bulletin du Musée Royal d'histoire naturelle de Belgique, Tome II, pp. 41-83.
8. WILSON, A. W. G. 1901. Physical Geology of Central Ontario, Canadian Institute Transactions, Vol. VII, pp. 139-186.
9. WILSON, A. W. G. 1903. The Theory of the Formation of Sedimentary Deposits. Canadian Record of Science, Vol. IX, pp. 112-132.

CHAPTER XIX.

METAMORPHISM OF ROCKS.

GENERAL DEFINITIONS. The term metamorphism, from the Greek μετά, interchange, and μορφή form (+ ism), has been applied to the process of alteration of rock masses in any manner whatsoever. The product of such metamorphism is metamorphic rock, often an entirely new substance so far as form and other physical characters are concerned. It is true that the term is seldom used in the comprehensive sense, metamorphism being generally considered as brought about by the agencies of heat and pressure, due to contact with heated bodies, or from being subject to dynamic disturbances. There can be no question, however, that these are only special phases of metamorphism, and that they cannot be separated genetically from the more quiet processes of alteration to which rocks are subject under ordinary physical conditions. As such, the weathering of rocks must be included. Metamorphism may bring about a change in one or more of the following characters: composition, texture, structure. The change in composition may be chemical alteration or mineralogical change, new minerals appearing in a rock as a result of metamorphism, and old minerals may disappear. Texture may be changed completely, as from compact limestone to crystalline marble, or special textures, characteristic of metamorphic rocks, may be produced, such as *cataclastic,* parallel orientation, etc. Original structures, such as flow structure, stratification, etc., may be obliterated and new ones produced, such as cleavage, fissility, joints, slatiness, schistosity and gneissosity (Van Hise–34).

THE FORCES PRODUCING METAMORPHISM. The forces at work in the production of metamorphism are given by Van Hise (34:45) as: 1, chemical energy; 2, gravity; 3, heat and light; while the agents through which these work upon the rocks are: (a) gases, (b) liquids, and (c) organic compounds. Organic compounds are mainly active in the surface belt where weathering of rocks takes place, but gaseous and liquid solutions * are agents everywhere present and active, within the known crust of the earth.

THE REGIONS OF METAMORPHISM. The regions where metamorphism of various kinds takes place are classified by Van Hise (34:43), according to depth, as follows:

I. The zone of *katamorphism,* or that zone in which simple compounds are produced from more complex ones, comprising (a) the belt of weathering, extending from the surface to the level of ground water, and (b) the belt of cementation, extending from the ground-water level to the next zone.

II. The zone of *anamorphism,* or that zone in which complex compounds are produced from simple ones.

Characteristics of the Zones of Metamorphism. The belt of weathering is the region of rock *destruction;* the belt of cementation is the region of rock *construction* and the zone of anamorphism the region of rock *reconstruction.* The zone of katamorphism is also the zone of fracture of rocks, where openings may exist. Van Hise has calculated that the maximum depth of this zone cannot be greater than 12,000 meters, and in most cases is probably much less. The zone of anamorphism also corresponds to the zone of rock flowage, where the pressure is greater than the strength of the rocks, and deformation will take place without fracture, but with rock flowage, which will not permit the existence of empty pore spaces.

Recent experiments on rock flowage made by Professors F. D. Adams (2) and L. V. King (21) at McGill University, Montreal, have shown that cavities can exist at much greater depths than 10,000 meters. They placed cylinders of granite, with holes bored through them, in a testing machine, and subjected them for seventy hours to a pressure of 96,000 pounds per square inch at a temperature of 550° C. After the experiment it was found that the hole was unchanged. The pressure obtained corresponded to that occurring at a depth of about 15 miles, but the temperature was that estimated to prevail in the earth's crust at a depth of only eleven miles.

---

* Solutions have been defined as "homogeneous mixtures which cannot be separated into their constituent parts by mechanical means" (Ostwald). They may consist of gases mingled with other gases, with liquids or with solids, of liquids mingled with liquids or with solids, and of solids mingled with solids. 'The solutions resulting from these various combinations may be gases, liquids, or solids or partly two or all." (Van Hise—34:59). The gases important in rock alteration are oxygen (O_2) sulphur (S_8 to S_2) water vapor (H_2O), ammonia (NH_3), carbon dioxide (CO_2), sulphurous oxide (SO_2), boric acid (H_3BO_3), hydrochloric acid (HCl) and hydrofluoric acid (HF). The liquid solutions are all water solutions.

KINDS OF METAMORPHISM.

Metamorphism is always a complex problem, but according to the dominant forces three distinct types have generally been recognized, viz., static, contactic (contagic), and dynamic. Static metamorphism is that process of alteration which goes on without the interference from *without* of forces producing deformation, or the invasion of heat from contact with a molten mass. It is essentially an endogenetic process, being concerned only with those forces universally active within the mass. These include chemical energy, gravitative rearrangement within the rock mass and the pressure due to its own mass, as well as the pressure resulting from the crystallization of the mass. Further, the influence of heat caused by these changes within the mass—but not invading heat (or cold) from without—and the influence of the omnipresent water and gases within the rock mass. This complex activity is essentially metasomatic and includes in reality two quite distinct processes: the destruction of rock masses by the atmosphere and water and the construction and reconstruction of rocks by the processes going on within the mass.

The process of weathering has been dealt with at length in earlier chapters; there remain for present consideration only the constructive and reconstructive processes of metamorphism. To the static phases of these processes of alteration the name *diagenesis* has been applied by Johannes Walther, the name itself having been used first by Gümbel in 1868 in his "Geognostische Beschreibung des ostbayerischen Grenzgebirges" for the more general processes of metamorphism. Andrée has proposed to restrict the term to those molecular and chemical transformations which the sediment undergoes under the influence of the medium in which it was deposited, and to which it is still subject after separation from this medium, through the ordinary circulating or vadose waters, in so far as these do not contain any foreign substances in solution, *i. e.*, such substances as are derived from outside of the sediment. He would include as chief of these changes: recrystallization, formation of concretions, lithification and desalinification. In so far as this restriction excludes changes due to percolating thermal waters or waters bearing mineral solutions, changes which may affect locally parts of various rock formations, this restriction seems warranted. Such changes are to be classed under the heading of contact metamorphism and are to be placed either with thermic metamorphism or are to be considered separately as hydrometamorphism. The name contact metamorphism is applied here to the reconstruction of rocks due to contact with (1) heated masses such as igneous bosses, dikes, sills, etc. (thermic metamorphism or *pyrometamorphism*); (2) mineralizing waters, or the alteration produced in the rock walls by the rising of heated or acidulated waters through fissures (*hydrometamorphism*). Since such fissures are generally closed shortly after by the formation of veins, no pronounced or extended alteration is produced in the wall rock. Finally, (3) vapors bearing or acting as mineralizers in passing through rock masses also produce profound local changes which would come under the same general heading of contact metamorphism (*atmometamorphism*). If the rock undergoes any change in character, when in contact with a glacier or ice cover, this too is to be classed as thermometamorphism, while contact with a heated meteoric body would also belong here. In all cases this is, therefore, to be regarded as a contact metamorphism. Grabau (16) has suggested for this process the name *æthoballism,* from αἶθός, fire, and βάλλω, to strike, which though emphasizing the heat element may, nevertheless, be expanded to cover all contact cases. Rocks altered in this manner would be designated æthoballic rocks. The essential of such changes is that they are local.

Dynamic metamorphism is a term restricted to the reconstruction processes initiated by tectonic movements, such as faulting, thrusting, gliding or folding of rocks. Since it generally affects extensive regions, it is also called *regional metamorphism,* as contrasted with the local contact metamorphism. The essential causes here are the pressure due to the tectonic movements, and the motion accompanying them, the result being a crushing, shearing and rearrangement of the component particles of rock, and often a recrystallization. A secondary factor is the heat developed during this movement. The alterations due to impact with meteoric bodies, whether hot or cold, must also be classed here, and it is not improbable that in the past they have played a considerable rôle. Finally, it must be considered whether the normal changes supposed to go on in the zone of flowage, under the immense pressure of the superincumbent rocks, do not in reality belong under the division of dynamic metamorphism. Grabau (16) has proposed the term *symphrattism* from συμφράττω, to press together, for this type of metamorphism, and for the rocks of this type he suggests the term symphrattic rocks.

As has been repeatedly emphasized, especially by Johannes Walther, metamorphic rocks of all kinds are naturally classed with the rocks from which they are derived, and not as a separate class.

STATIC METAMORPHISM OR DIAGENISM.

Of the diagenetic processes affecting rocks the following may be especially considered: (I) lithification, (II) recrystallization, (III) dolomitization, (IV) replacement of limestone by silica, etc., (V) desalinification, (VI) formation of concretions, (VII) hydration and dehydration.

I. LITHIFICATION OR INDURATION.

The lithification of a rock is not restricted to diagenetic processes, but may be greatly aided if not altogether caused by the other processes of metamorphism, especially the dynamic ones. Nor is lithification a natural result of aging, for time has little or no influence as a primary factor, though it may become important when lithification is primarily due to some other factors. As examples may be cited the still unconsolidated early Palæozoic sands and clays of the undisturbed plains of Russia, and the much metamorphosed Eocenic rocks of the Alps, or of the Coast Range of California. In the last two cases cited, the alteration of the rocks is of course due to the dynamic disturbances which have affected them, but consolidation by purely diagenetic processes of recent sediments is not unknown. Thus the consolidation of the coral sand of Bermuda furnishes a good example of a lithified rock of modern origin, while the Nagelfluh of Salzburg, Austria, and other districts illustrates the solidification of a clastic deposit of Pleistocenic origin. (See Chapter XIV, p. 601.)

Lithification takes place with varying rapidity in rocks of different origin. Thus pyrogenic rocks, lavas or intruded masses solidify comparatively rapidly through cooling. This results either in congelation into an amorphous mass or in crystallization—wholly or in part. Water solidifies with extreme rapidity by crystallization when subjected to the proper reduction of temperature. Snow crystals (atmogenic rocks) solidify somewhat more slowly from granular névé into glacier ice, a typical process of diagenetic metamorphism, though involving to a certain extent recrystallization. The same method of solidification probably affects most hydrogenic rocks. Organic rocks are solidified at the time of their formation, except organic oozes and granular organic rocks (pulverites, granulites, etc.), which may be combined into masses much as clastic rocks are. The lithification of clastic rocks is due to pressure-cohesion, to cementation, or to recrystallization.

The methods of lithification, not confined to diagenetic processes, however, may thus be tabulated:

1. Congelation—in amorphous bodies.
2. Crystallization—chiefly in pyrogenic rocks.
3. Recrystallization—chiefly in atmogenic and hydrogenic rocks.
4. Welding or pressure cohesion—chiefly in clastic rocks.
5. Cementation—chiefly in clastic and organic rocks.

Igneous rocks solidify by congelation into an amorphous glass (obsidian, etc.) or by crystallization. Atmogenic snow crystals consolidate into firn and glacier ice by a process of recrystallization, when the smaller crystals are destroyed to the gain of the larger ones. This is also true of granular hydrogenic rocks such as rock salt and gypsum. Hydrogenic rocks are also solidified through cementation by precipitated material of the same kind. Biogenic rocks are usually consolidated by the precipitation of calcium carbonate under the influence of decaying organic matter and the formation of ammonium carbonate.

Sphærites, granulites and pulverites, of whatever origin, are generally consolidated by the same agents which consolidate the clastic strata.

LITHIFICATION OR INDURATION OF CLASTIC ROCKS. Under this heading will also be included the granular or pulverulent endogenetic substances. The two chief methods are: (1) Pressure-cohesion, or welding, and (2) cementation. Recrystallization, especially through secondary enlargement, also consolidates loose material, but is more common in rocks already lithified. Though distinct processes, they seldom if ever occur wholly alone, both welding and cementation generally taking place at the same time, though in unequal amount. Recrystallization may accompany these processes.

1. *Welding.* (Van Hise–34: *595-597, 670-671.*) This is a process of mechanical consolidation caused either by the pressure of superincumbent rocks or by tectonic movements. This pressure results in bringing closely together the particles of which the rocks are composed. If water is present, this is squeezed out, while the mineral particles are mechanically readjusted with reference to one another. The particles will cohere, because they are brought so close together by the pressure that they are within the limit of molecular attraction of one another. This takes place especially in the zone of anamorphism, where the pressures in all directions are greater than the crushing strength of the rocks, and hence sufficient to bring the particles within the sphere of molecular attraction.

The depth at which this occurs varies with the rock substances, being comparatively moderate for plastic substances like coal and clay, and much greater for refractory rocks like quartzites, etc. (Van Hise–34: *671*.)

While universal within the zone of anamorphism, welding is not unknown in the belt of cementation of the zone of katamorphism. Here especially the lutaceous sediments are affected, the arenaceous and coarser clastics, especially when the particles are of uniform size, having too few points of contact for welding to occur. Thus quartz sandstone of nearly uniform grain may become slightly coherent by incomplete welding, with cementation weak or absent, and so constitute a "free-stone," so called on account of the ease with which it is quarried and cut. Many of the British cathedrals and abbeys, and some Continental ones as well, are built of rocks of this type, rocks which from their uniformity of grain and ready response to the gravers' tools made possible the elaborate carvings which adorn these structures. In not a few cases this rock seems to have been formed by the induration of former wind-blown sands. The slight cohesion of the round and uniform-grained Sylvania sandstone (Siluric) of Michigan, Ohio and Canada, and of the scarcely more coherent Saint Peter sandstone of the United States furnishes examples of cases where induration has scarcely been effected, though what there is may probably be referred to welding processes. This is seen in the fact that these sandstones are almost absolutely free from foreign matter, which might act as a cement, while, except in rare cases, secondary silica has not been deposited.

Cohesion may occur in lutaceous sediments without complete exclusion of water. Thus Becker (7: *131*) has shown that, "when the films of water between the particles become very thin, they may become an important factor in the coherence of the rocks. The molecular attraction of the water films and the adjacent particles, or their adhesion, and the cohesion of the molecules of the films may be sufficient to give the rocks a certain amount of strength." (Van Hise–34: *596*.) Thus muds and silts welded in this manner may have a marked coherence.

The squeezing out of the water, in whole or in part, the rearrangement of particles, and the partial compression of the particles themselves result in a reduction of volume. Thus a considerable reduction in the thickness of a formation may occur. Fossil shells or other organisms in such a formation may be pressed flat or crushed unless previously altered so as to be resistant. The generally flattened or crushed character of brachiopods and other shells in Palæozoic shales are good illustrations. If, however, a resistant structure, such as a calcareous or other concretion, exists in the rock, this will resist compression more than the enclosing mud, and so the layers of the latter may assume an upward or downward curving attitude arching over or under the concretion, or, if the latter is large, end abruptly against it, sometimes with the occurrence of slickensided surfaces on the exterior of the concretion. Stylolites also belong in this category of pressure structures. They will be more fully discussed beyond.

That rocks are ordinarily under great strain from lateral and vertical pressure has been shown by the fact that when the pressure is relieved, as in quarrying, expansion takes place, while upward bucklings of the quarry floor are also frequently observed. (Niles–24; 25; Johnston–20; Cramer–9; 10.)

The further phenomena resulting from pressure will be more fully discussed under *symphrattism* or dynamo-metamorphism.

2. *Cementation.* This is accomplished by the deposition, in the pores of the rock mass and between the particles, of a substance which will bind them together. The material is brought in solution by the percolating rain or ground water, and may be derived from a distance, from immediately adjoining formations, or from the formation in question itself. Thus the calcareous sands of the dunes on Bermuda are cemented by the rain water which percolates through them and which dissolves some of the lime only to redeposit it elsewhere in the same formation. The oölite grains of Gran Canaria in the Canary Islands are cemented by lime deposited by the sea water which is instrumental in forming these oölite grains. This, as in the similar cementation of organic lime accumulations, on coral reefs, etc., is brought about by the separation from the water of additional lime, through the decay of the organic matter and the formation of ammonium carbonates in the warm waters, this chemical reacting with the lime salts in solution in the sea water. Pleistocenic gravels are often cemented by the lime derived from a partial solution of the limestone pebbles which they contain or which are found in an overlying gravel or sand. Examples of this are not uncommon in limestone regions. The great Pleistocenic Nagefluh deposit of the Salzburg region is an example of the cementation of a deposit in this manner never buried under younger formations. The pebbles and grains of the rock are so firmly cemented that the galleries and crypts, cut into the formation and dating back to the third century, are still perfectly preserved. Pleistocenic delta deposits exposed near Lewiston, New York, and formed when the ice front rested near the Niagara escarpment, and before Lake Iroquois came into existence, have become consolidated

by lime cementation so as to form a fairly cohesive rock, showing well the oblique bedding of the fore-set beds.

The porosity of the rock is an important factor in aiding cementation. Other things being equal, the more porous rocks will have a better chance of cementation. Thus the Columbian gravels (Pleistocenic) of the Raritan Bay region in New Jersey are frequently cemented into a hard pebbly rock, the yellowish well-worn quartz pebbles being embedded in a deep brown sandstone cemented by iron oxide, the whole resembling a giant peanut brittle. The underlying Cretacic strata, on the other hand, are unconsolidated except where locally some of the sands are bound together by iron oxide. Certain layers in the Monument Creek Tertiary sandstone of Colorado Springs are strongly cemented by iron oxide, while the remainder of the sandstone mass is free from such cement. As a result, monuments are carved by the wind out of these rocks, the iron-cemented layers forming the capping stones of these monuments. In the Miocenic deposits of Baden, near Vienna, the shell-bearing pebble beds are often cemented by lime into a fairly resistant rock, while the clays are entirely unconsolidated.

The principal minerals deposited between the particles of a rock to form a cement are lime, iron and silica. Silica may be in the form of a colloidal cement, but in quartz sandstone it is far more often deposited in such a way as to have optical and crystallographic continuity with the silica of the grain it surrounds. This secondary enlargement of a quartz grain, forming more or less perfect crystals which interlock closely, is not an uncommon thing and may result in the formation of a hard and strongly indurated rock. Nevertheless, such close cohesion of new grown crystals does not always take place, and the mass will fall to pieces at the blow of a hammer, leaving a mass of angular quartz crystals which only under the microscope show that they represent the secondary development by addition of the originally more or less well-rounded quartz grains. This is not an uncommon source of angular quartz grains.

Van Hise mentions as the most important cementing substances: silica, iron oxide and aluminum oxide, among the oxides; calcite, dolomite and siderite among the carbonates, both hydrous and anhydrous silicates,* and marcasite and pyrite among the sulphides. (Van Hise–34 : *621-622*.)

The Keweenawan sandstone of Lake Superior may be cited as a case in which the cementation is largely due to the deposition of

---

* Among the hydrous silicates are: (1) zeolites and prehnite; (2) chlorites; (3) epidotes; (4) serpentine and talc. Among the anhydrous silicates are feldspars, hornblende and mica.

feldspar upon worn grains of that mineral, the old and new mineral being in optical continuity. (Van Hise–32.) The sandstone contains both orthoclases and plagioclases, and both are enlarged by deposition of new material in optical continuity with the old. Hornblende has also been found to be secondarily enlarged in old volcanic tuffs.

Quartzites and Novaculites.

When quartz sandstones are so completely cemented by secondary silica, whether deposited independently or in optical continuity with the original quartz grains, that the rock will break across the original grains rather than between them, the rock is called a *quartzite*. If the original grain of the quartz rock was a lutaceous one, the result of this excessive induration is a *novaculite*.

Lithification of Clastics Largely a Supramarine Process.

Since lithification of clastics by cementation and recrystallization requires the active circulation of ground water, it is apparent that it is chiefly effective after the deposits in question have been lifted above sea-level, if they originally were marine. This is not entirely true for processes of recrystallization, which may go on even beneath sea-level.

II. RECRYSTALLIZATION.

Recrystallization of the mineral constituents may affect all rocks, and occur under static, dynamic or contactic conditions. As a process of diagenism it often produces marked results, though these are never carried to the extremes which are attained when it acts as a process of symphrattism. When it takes place in unconsolidated material it may become a method of lithification, but it is more commonly found in rocks already consolidated by one or the other method. As a method of change from a less stable to a more stable form of mineral it is of the greatest importance. Thus the original less stable forms of $CaCO_3$, aragonite, ktypeit, found in marine oölites and organic deposits, are changed to the more stable form calcite. (See Chapter IX.) In the case of organic remains so altered, the finer structural features are commonly lost.

Recrystallization is especially effective in the more soluble rocks, such as limestones, gypsum and salt, though the secondary enlargement of quartz crystals in reality also belongs here. Gypsum, anhydrite, rock salt and granular snow are other substances easily subject to recrystallization. In this process the smaller particles are commonly dissolved and their material added to the larger ones. In the zone of katamorphism, solution and redeposition are going on throughout the limestone with the result that the entire mass is gradually recrystallized. This may affect both loose aggregates of calcite grains which thereby become consolidated, and it may affect indurated limestones which are then gradually altered toward the condition of marble. True marble is probably formed only under the influence of dynamic forces, but many recrystallizations come close to approaching this state.

It is often assumed that recrystallization has affected most of the older Palæozoic limestones, because of their lack of organic remains, which, it is argued, are destroyed by recrystallization. It may be questioned whether organic remains are ever destroyed by ordinary recrystallization, though there is no doubt of this when recrystallization under dynamic influences goes on. In the case of many of the older Palæozoic limestones, however, the absence of organic remains is a primary character. Many of these limestones were deposited as lime muds and silts derived from the erosion of still older limestones, and without the direct participation in their formation of lime-secreting organisms.

Rock salt deposits on recrystallization tend to become coarser, as in the case of the Polish deposits. The same is true for gypsum, which sometimes crystallizes out into masses of large dimensions. The largest found up to date in Utah measured in some cases 150 cm. in greatest dimension. When deeply buried, gypsum loses its water under the influence of pressure and recrystallizes into anhydrite. This brings with it a decrease of volume of 38%.

An important point for consideration lies in the fact that recrystallization is favored by pressure. The greater the pressure, the more likely is the deformation to be accomplished by recrystallization.

Pressure Phenomena Due to Recrystallization.

In rocks of homogeneous character and fine grain, recrystallization may have a deformative effect on the original structure lines and not infrequently upon the enclosing strata. This is especially well seen in the salt deposits of undisturbed regions, such as the Zechstein salt of north Germany and the Salina salt of New York.

In the former, where the enclosing rocks are undisturbed, the layers of brightly colored bittern salts and of gypsum often show a remarkable flexuous, sinuous or disrupted character not unlike a structure produced by strong compressive strains during tectonic deformation. That such deformation is not tectonic can often be shown by the undisturbed character of the enclosing sandstones and shales. Thus, in the Salina deposit of central New York, some of the alternating salt and gypsum layers occasionally show a pronounced flexing and overfolding, while others are wholly undisturbed. This is well shown in the following illustration reproduced from Everding (Fig. 159) and representing the endolithic deforma-

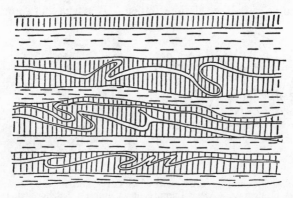

FIG. 159. Section of the potash layers of the Berlepsch shaft near Stassfurt. Scale 1:35. The vertically lined beds are carnallite; the beds with horizontal dashes are rock salt; the deformed layers (white) are kieserite. (After Everding.)

tion of the potash layers in the Berlepsch salt shaft near Stassfurt. Here the rock salt and the carnallite are apparently undisturbed, while the kieserite bands within the carnallite layers show most pronounced distortions in different directions. "The forces," says Arrhenius in this connection, "which have brought about this peculiar deformation, are evidently of very local character, and confined to the respective carnallite layers." Arrhenius concludes that tectonic forces cannot be the cause which produced these deformations. (Arrhenius–4.)

From the resemblance of the distorted layers to the convolutions of an intestine, this structure has come to be known in German scientific literature as "Gekröse" structure, a name first applied by Koken in 1900. (22.) The English equivalent of this term, proposed by me some time ago, and first used in print by Hahn (18), is *enterolithic* structure.

What is believed by many to represent extreme cases of deformation due to endogenetic causes is found in the remarkable salt domes of Louisiana and eastern Texas, and of North Germany, especially in middle and northern Hanover and Brunswick, extending as far as the Elbe. Similar occurrences are reported from Transylvania, on both sides of the Pyrenees, and from southern Algeria (Fig. 160).

These "salt domes" are elliptical in section, with folded, often much distorted layers of salt, gypsum, and in some sections potash salts, which rise through the enclosing strata, deforming them, and maintaining a plug-like relation to them. It is true that some writers

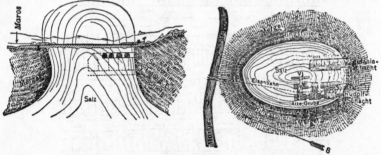

FIG. 160.   Section and ground plan of a salt dome in the Moros Valley, Hungary. (After Lamprecht in Fürer's Salzbergbau.)

(Stille, papers cited by Hahn–17) have explained these relationships as due to repeated foldings, but the consensus of opinion (Hahn–17) seems to be that, while some folding has undoubtedly occurred in certain places, the main force was the endogenetic one due to the crystallizing force of the salts and to metasomatic processes. (Arrhenius–4.)

Enterolithic structure is also a frequent occurrence in fine-grained limestones or dolomites. A remarkably fine example is seen in the basal "hydraulic" limestones of the Lockport series of Siluric age, in a section opened by the canyon of Niagara. The strata are finely shown along the railroad bed on the right bank of the canyon. This structure is equally well developed (Fig. 161) in the Upper Muschelkalk of the Neckar Valley, in Württemberg, Germany (Koken–22), and will probably be recognized in other formations. The essential feature is here, as pointed out by Hahn, that the deformation is in all directions,* not in certain ones, as would

---

* The multi- gyro- and a-polar deformations of Lachmann.

be the case in tectonic or in gliding deformations. Thus deformation is shown in whichever direction the section of the formation is cut, nor is there any evidence of slickensiding, such as is to be expected if the deformation is tectonic.

Koken, who described the disturbed layers of the Upper Muschelkalk of the Neckar Valley in detail, and originated the name *Gekrösekalk* for them, held that the folding and wrinkling were due to vertical pressure of overlying rocks upon the still plastic layers. He notes, however, that the folds are notably sharp and their limbs are thickened as is the case in deformations formed by swelling

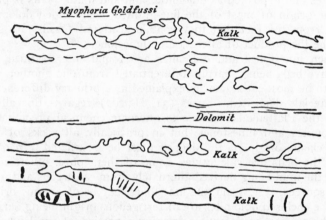

FIG. 161.   Enterolithic structure in the Upper Muschelkalk (Gekrösekalk) of the Neckar Valley in Württemberg, Germany.   (After Koken.)

masses, such as gypsum, but not through horizontal pressure. While it is not difficult to conceive that mere vertical pressure on still plastic layers can produce deformation of these layers, it is not quite clear what should cause the retention of plasticity in some layers and not in others. The deformed Muschelkalk layers are bluish, argillaceous calcilutytes, much like the similarly deformed layers of the Niagara section. In both cases internal pressure due to crystallization seems to have been an active agent in the deformation of the rock.

III.   DOLOMITIZATION OF LIMESTONES.

The change of limestones into dolomites, or dolomitization, has occurred in all geologic ages and is in progress to-day.   (Pfaff–26.)

True, not all dolomites are of secondary origin, some being no doubt deposited as dolomite rock in the beginning. Among dolomites of secondary origin we may distinguish those derived by the clastation and redeposition of older dolomites and those due to the replacement of limestones. Only the latter class belongs here, but the dolomites of clastic origin deserve brief attention. Here belong the many well-bedded, fine and uniformly grained rocks with few or no fossils which abound in many Palæozoic and later formations. As a typical example may be mentioned the Monroe (Upper Siluric) dolomites of Michigan, Ohio and Ontario, which have most probably been derived by the destruction of the older Niagaran dolomites and deposited as dolomitic sand and mud. This is probably the origin of most of the fine-grained, well-bedded dolomites which, from the fact that they contain scattered fossils, are seen not to be the product of alteration of limestone.

When limestones and dolomites are found interstratified, the successive beds being sharply differentiated from one another, this seems to be most satisfactorily explained as a primary difference in the materials deposited. Suess (31, II: *262*) regards this alteration in the Plattenkalke as due to alternate chemical precipitation of dolomites and limestones, but in practically all rocks of this type a clastic origin of the deposit must be postulated. In other words, the beds are calcilutytes, some of them pure, others magnesian, the mud being derived alternately from calcareous and magnesian sources. Or, again, the limestones may be of organic origin, while the enclosed dolomites are of terrigenous origin, being derived from the erosion of dolomites forming a portion of the land, and such alternation would have no more significance than alternations of limestones (of thalassigenous origin) and shales (of terrigenous origin). The possibility of secondary separation of a mixture of lime and dolomite grains by agitation of the water and the unequal settling according to specific gravity must not be overlooked.

Secondary dolomites due to diagenetic alteration processes may originate either before or after the original limestones are raised above the sea-level. (Steidtmann–30.) Such alteration may be primarily a process of leaching, either under the sea by sea water or by the ground water circulating through the upper zones of the earth's surface. By leaching out of the lime the proportion of the original magnesian content is greatly increased. Such differential leaching is due to the fact that calcium carbonate is several times as soluble as magnesium carbonate as first shown by Bischoff. When it occurs, one result is the rendering porous of the altered rock, which, if under pressure, may actually collapse. The process of alteration may on the other hand be one of secondary replacement of calcium by magnesium. Such replacement in the sea had apparently taken place in the case of coral rock reported by Dana (12: *393*) from the elevated reefs of Makatea Island in the Pacific; this rock contained 38.7% of magnesium carbonate, whereas such rock usually contains less than 1%. Similar alterations have been reported by others, thus Branner (8: *264*) found 6.95% of magnesia, equivalent to 14.5% $MgCO_3$, in reef rock of Porta do Mangue, Brazil; the corals of the reef containing only from 0.2 to 0.99% of MgO. Similarly Skeats (28) reports analyses of modern coral rock from the Pacific with 43.3% of $MgCO_3$. Such alterations have also been reported from Funafuti, the deep boring on which showed 16.4% $MgCO_3$ at a depth of 500 feet, 16% $MgCO_3$ at 640 feet, with much smaller but variable percentages above and below. A boring at Key West showed the highest percentage of MgO (6.7%) at a depth of 775 feet, the percentage of CaO at that depth being 46.53%. At a depth of 25 feet and 1,400 feet the two minima occurred (0.29% and 0.30% respectively).

Metasomatic replacement through the agency of ground water is also an active means by which dolomites are produced. In some cases it is less effective than submarine replacement, principally because sea water carries more magnesium than is found in such underground circulation. Where such magnesia is supplied, however, as in regions of decomposing magnesium-bearing rocks, this ground water replacement may be very effective. The magnesia is of course obtained from the belt of weathering where it occurs as carbonate in older dolomites, etc., or as silicate in crystalline rocks and minerals (garnet, staurolite, tourmaline, chondrodite, chlorite and the zeolites, etc.). The silicates are subject to carbonation (see *ante,* pp. 35, 178), and the carbonate then passes into solution and is carried downward to the belt of cementation, when, on coming in contact with limestones poor in magnesia, replacement takes place.

Local dolomitizations also occur, as for example at Aspen, Colorado, where hot magnesian spring waters rising through the limestone locally alter it to dolomite. These are, however, not diagenetic, but belong to the division of contact metamorphisms. In general limestones which have suffered orogenic disturbances are more commonly altered to dolomites than those not so disturbed. Thus (Van Hise–34: *801*) the Tertiary limestones of the Coast Range of California and of the Alps are more strongly magnesian than the undisturbed limestones of the same age. This is due to the fact that disturbed and shattered strata of mountain regions offer better access to waters bearing magnesium, through the agency of which the replacement is brought about.

The replacement of calcite by dolomite involves a contraction of 12.30%. Dolomites due to alteration will thus show a high degree of porosity unless they have been subjected to compression during orogenesis. Such porosity is shown in the early Palæozoic dolomites of the Mississippi Valley, and also in the Siluric and the Devonic dolomites of Michigan, Ohio and Canada. When the rock is under pressure, as in the zone of anamorphism, mashings and recrystallizations close the openings. It is also highly probable that pressure promotes dolomitization, since this means a decreasing volume, a result favored by pressure.

IV. Replacement of Limestones by Silica, Iron Oxide, Etc.

Metasomatic replacement of limestone by silica is a familiar phenomenon. In most cases the replacement affects chiefly certain parts of the limestones which by their structure seem best suited to such replacement. Such are the shells, corals and other organic remains embedded in Palæozoic or younger limestones where the enclosing matrix generally remains unaffected, though the fossil may be completely replaced. Oölitic limestones also suffer replacement by silica and in them often the steps of replacement are shown by the decrease in lime and the increase in silica. A mass of such siliceous oölite occurs in the lower Palæozoic rocks of central Pennsylvania, where it covers an area of about 40 square miles, with scattered extensions over a much wider area. Locally the oölite passes into chert. These siliceous oölites have been regarded as originating in rising hot springs containing silica in solution (Wieland–36:*262*), but others (Moore–23; Brown) hold that they represent replacements of originally calcareous oölites. This explanation is fully borne out by the analysis, and the incompleteness of the replacement in many cases. (See also Ziegler–37.)

Replacement of limestone by iron oxide is also a frequent occurrence. In the basal Siluric beds of Wisconsin, oölites, which from their character and appearance were most probably calcareous in the first place, have been changed to iron oxide (hematite). The so-called Clinton iron ore seems to be an example of metasomatic replacement of limestones, for here the organic fragments (brachiopod shells, Bryozoa, etc.) are replaced by iron oxide. In the Genesee gorge at Rochester the steps in replacement could formerly be observed, these being shown by the progressive increase in iron oxide and a corresponding decrease in calcium carbonate. It is true that these deposits have been regarded as formed directly in lagoons and cut-offs (Smyth–29) along the sea coast of the time, the iron being brought by the wash from the crystalline old land. This theory has, however, been discarded by some recent students of the subject in favor of the older replacement theory.

The replacement of calcareous bodies of organic origin by iron pyrites and other mineral substances will be more fully discussed in a later chapter.

V. DESALINIFICATION.

Among other diagenetic processes of importance may be mentioned the desalinification of old marine sediments. As already noted, the amount of salt absorbed by marine sediments varies greatly, chiefly in proportion to their pore space. (Gerbing–15: *85, 118.*) After these sediments are raised into the zone of circulating ground water, a slow removal of these salts takes place. Under arid climatic conditions, as already noted, this may go on more rapidly, and the leached salt may be redeposited in salinas and desert salt basins.

VI. FORMATION OF CONCRETIONS.

This has already been discussed at some length in a previous chapter (see pp. 718–720) and need be dwelt on only briefly here. Percolating waters carrying lime, silica or other substances in solution will deposit these in the strata at favorable localities, forming concretions of lime, of clay-iron-stones, or of silica. The first are common in calcareous shales, often growing to large size, with a corresponding deformation of the enclosing layers, through the pressure of the growing concretion. Not infrequently the concretions become confluent, forming a concretionary limestone bed. The nucleus of the concretion is very often some organic fragment or a shell. In the Champlain clays of Cumberland, Ontario, entire specimens of fish are common. Fish remains are found in similar concretions of the glacial and post-glacial clays of Norway, 16 species having been recognized so far.

The common types of concretion in the Mesozoic and Palæozoic shales are the septaria already described. These are often of great size, examples 10 feet in diameter occurring in the Devonic of New York. They not infrequently contain a fish bone as a nucleus, while the smaller ones commonly have a goniatite shell at the center. Frequently the stratification of the enclosing beds on either side appears to be continuous through the concretion, while the beds above and below are arched, owing to the pressure caused by the growing septarium. Some of this arching may be due to the compression of the shale around the resistant septarium.

Calcareous clay stones are also common in the loess, where they are known as Lösspuppen or Lössmännchen, by the Germans, as Fairy stones by the Scots, and as Imatra stones by the Finlanders. They form in parallel lines, giving the deposit the appearance of stratification, though the original bedding may have been quite diverse. The lines of concretions mark rather the successive levels of ground water than any structural features of the rock itself.

Claystone concretions of very regular form are found in the Champlain clays of the Connecticut Valley, while clay-iron-stones enclosing ferns, insects, crustacean and other remains, occur in the Carbonic shales of Grundy County, Illinois, the fossil-bearing concretions of Mazon Creek having become famous on account of their well-preserved organic remains.

A special form of calcareous concretion is known from the black Devonic shales of Michigan and Ontario, being especially abundant at Kettle Point, Lake Huron. These are spherical, or nearly so, and are composed of radiating crystals of calcium carbonate, which, growing outward, crowd the enclosing strata until they curve about the concretion. The structure resembles that of a fibrous wood, and fragments are not infrequently mistaken for "petrified" wood. Their manner of occurrence, growth and significance is fully discussed by Daly (11).

Concretions of iron pyrite and of marcasite are forming in many strata. Sometimes these are globular masses composed of crystals of pyrite, at other times they have a radial structure. Generally some object of organic origin forms the nucleus around which the concretion grows. In the Cretacic clays of New Jersey pyrite concretions are forming around fragments of lignite, all stages of incrustation and replacement being observable.

Siliceous concretions are common in calcareous formations. Thus flints characterize chalk, and chert layers abound in many limestones. Flints may occur in continuous layers in massive chalk beds in which their arrangement alone indicates stratification. As in the case of the concretions in the loess, these lines of flints need not have a necessary relation to the original stratification.

In many cases, however, the flints formed around a siliceous sponge or some other organism which acted as a nucleus to attract the silica in solution. Here the flints mark the original distribution of the organic remains in the strata. The source of the silica is to be found in the organic structures of silica scattered through the mass of the chalk. These are dissolved by the circulating waters and redeposited around the organic nucleus.

Chert concretions occupy the same relation to limestone that flints do to chalk. They too are derived from the organic silica enclosed in the deposit, and redeposited in favorable places. Confluent concretions of chert produce a more or less continuous chert bed such as is common in the Devonic limestones of eastern North America. Chert concretions may enclose organic remains, but they do not necessarily form around a visible nucleus. Van Hise holds that the heavier chert bands are formed first by the original segregation of siliceous organisms and the subsequent enrichment by silica-bearing ground waters of these siliceous strata.

VII. Hydration and Dehydration.

Hydration, or the union with water of originally anhydrous deposits, may produce profound results. Thus anhydrite is changed to gypsum with a corresponding swelling of the entire mass (see *ante,* p. 177) and the production of deformative structures. Dehydration of gypsum, on the other hand, produces a corresponding shrinking of the entire mass.

CONTACT METAMORPHISM OR ÆTHOBALLISM.

1. *Pyrometamorphism.* When rocks come in contact with heated igneous masses, as a result of subterranean intrusions, or of surface flows, they are more or less altered, especially along the contact, this alteration gradually decreasing in intensity away from the igneous mass, until its effect has been entirely lost. Such a phase of the contact metamorphism may be called igneo- or pyrometamorphism. It is especially manifested in the formation of new minerals along the contact zone and in the introduction of mineral substances from the igneous mass. A zonal arrangement is commonly formed, different alteration products arising at different distances from the igneous mass. Effects are felt by both the intruded and the intruding (or overflowing) rock; the former is *exomorphic,* the second *endomorphic.* The exomorphic effect from contact with dry heat is first of all a raising of the temper-

ature of the country rock adjacent to the igneous mass, such rise in temperature reaching even fusion point. Three stages of influencing the country rock are recognized: *baking, fritting,* and *vitrification.* As a result of baking, induration of unconsolidated material will occur without fusion. Hydrous minerals are dehydrated with a corresponding change, such as limonite to hematite, gypsum to anhydrite, etc. From carbonates the CO_2 is given off, changing limestone and dolomites to lime and magnesium oxides, respectively, which have a caustic reaction. Volatile gases are driven off, as in the case of coal which is changed to coke.

Fritting is partial fusion, carried to the point where the silica begins to act on the bases, forming an imperfectly melted or fritted mass. Vitrification results from complete fusion, the mass being transformed into a glass.

The effects of pyrometamorphism on clastic rocks are various. "Sandstones are decolorized and often fritted to a glistening enamel, like a porcelainic mass; where the cement is of a calcareo-argillaceous nature, this is melted into a glass; clay and mud are converted into porcelainite or brick, with marked change of color in many cases; tuffs and phonolites are so far vitrified as to acquire a character resembling that of obsidian; brown coal is altered into seam coal or anthracite, and these in other cases into a substance more resembling graphite, while in others (probably under less pressure) the coal is converted into coke; a prismatic structure is developed not only in clays and marls, but even in sandstones, in brown coal, in seam coal and in dolomite; limestones are altered into crystalline marble, often with complete effacement of their stratification and even of all traces of their fossils; the finer varieties of grauwacke and its associated shales are converted into hornstone, as in the classical region of the Brocken." (Irving–19: 76.) The effects of dry heat are very limited in extent, usually penetrating the rocks only for a short distance. Where hydro- and gaseo- (atmo-) metamorphism are also active, as is almost universally the case in pyrometamorphism, the alterations will be more extensive and widespread. The endomorphic effects, or those on the igneous mass itself, are largely confined to a more rapid solidification and hence the production of finer crystallization along the contact, owing to the chilling effect of the cool wall rock. The presence of water in the latter, of course, contributes to a much modified result, as already indicated in an earlier chapter (p. 312).

2. *Hydrometamorphism.* Contact with rising waters, whether hot or cold, carrying mineralizers, produces the second type of contact metamorphism to which the term *hydrometamorphism* may be

applied. As already noted, waters carrying magnesium locally alter limestone into dolomites. Sulphuretted springs on the Sinai Peninsula and at several points along the west coast of the Red Sea alter coral limestones to gypsum, and silica-bearing waters locally alter many reef limestones into siliceous rocks, as in the Upper Devonic coral reef limestones of Grund in Harz and elsewhere.

The greatest amount of alteration is, however, produced by the highly heated waters, given off by the igneous rock, or accompanying the intrusion. Here must be classed all the phenomena of secondary enrichment of the wall rocks of fissures, by the rising waters, though the actual deposits in the fissures themselves are to be classed as hydrogenic rocks. The subject is too special to be pursued here at greater length. The student is referred to the current works on ore deposits and to Van Hise's Treatise on Metamorphism. The work of geysers and hot springs not directly associated with volcanic intrusions, in so far as it affects the wall rock, must also be classed here. The deposits formed by these agencies, however, are hydrogenic deposits.

3. *Atmometamorphism.* Contact with rising vapors and gases, as in solfataras, fumaroles, etc., constitutes a third type of contact metamorphism, to which the term gaseo- or atmometamorphism may be applied. In its broadest sense the weathering of rocks in contact with the great gas envelope of the earth, the atmosphere, also belongs here, having the same relation to the intrusion of gases as the surface flow has to the intruded igneous masses. Practically, however, we may confine gaseous metamorphism to the work of hot vapors and gases emitted in connection with volcanic activity and always accompanying pyrometamorphism. Such effects are visible to-day in solfataras and fumaroles where the alteration of the wall rock is proceeding at a rapid rate.

The high temperature of the vapors and their high content of active chemical agents make their work of alteration much more effective than the work of water solution would be. The work of the gases at very high temperature is called fumarolic, while the work of the gases at lower temperature is solfataric.

The most important gases active in the fissures of the rock are: water vapor, sulphurous oxide (SO_2), chlorine (Cl_2), hydrochloric acid (HCl), hydrofluoric acid (HFl), hydrosulphuric acid (H_2S), sulphuric acid gas (SO_3), carbon dioxide (CO_2), oxygen (O_2) and hydrogen (H_2). Nitrogen is of course an abundant but essentially useless gas, and boric acid (H_3BO_3) is sometimes plentiful. Among the processes going on in atmometamorphism are the common ones of oxidation, hydration and carbonation. The last produces sodium carbonate, which is abundant at times. Chlorinization results in the formation of $NaCl$, KCl, NH_4Cl, $FeCl_3$, $CuCl_2$, $MnCl_2$ and other chlorides. By the action of sulphuric acid alums are formed, of which the potash and soda alums are the most abundant. Gypsum is formed by the action of the calcium-bearing compounds and sulphuric acid, this latter also forming Glauber's salts, sodium sulphate and potassium sulphate. The hydrosulphuric acid acting upon various compounds forms sulphides, and so in turn each acid acting upon the rocks forms compounds of various kinds.

These activities are of course not always sharply isolated. Indeed, solfataric and fumarolic actions are a common accompaniment of igneous activity and thus the alteration of the rocks is a complex of pyro-, hydro- and atmometamorphism.

4. *Biometamorphism.* A change in the rock due to contact with organisms, or *biometamorphism,* is of little effect, when we remember that the change must be produced by the physiological activities of the organism. Thus the changing of clay into bricks by baking is not primarily an organic process, though directed by man. It is a case of pyrometamorphism, even though the heat is artificially supplied. Disintegration of rocks by growing organisms is perhaps their only significant metamorphic activity.

DYNAMIC OR PRESSURE METAMORPHISM, OR SYMPHRATTISM.

When rocks are subjected to orogenic disturbances, their internal structure will be affected by the movement and pressure, and to some extent by the heat developed by these processes. The effect in slight deformations is often confined to the planes of gliding along which deformation has taken place. Here smooth gliding surfaces or *slickensides* are formed, often with the development of a thin layer of mineral matter, and marked by striations and flutings which indicate the direction of motion. Extreme polishing sometimes results from such movements. Here belong the glacial striations and groovings which are slickensides on a large scale.

The development of a mineral coating on the polished surface of the gliding plain may be the direct result of the energy liberated by the gliding process, or it may be the secondary deposit in the fissure, when the surface of the mineral will take on the cast of the striated surface. Hematite, chlorite, calcite, pyrite and other minerals have been active in such wise. In some cases, however, the mineral may have been deposited in the fissure before slipping took place. In such a case, the effect of movement is seen on the mineral.

In general, when extensive dynamic disturbances take place, resulting in crushing and mashing of the rocks, new minerals and new structures are developed. The former are numerous; among the latter are cleavage, fissility, and schistosity.

Different types of rocks suffer different alterations under the influence of the mass-mechanical motion characteristic of symphrattism. A few of these alteration products may be mentioned, but the student is referred to special treatises on the subject for more detailed information.

When coarse, clastic rocks, or rudytes, are subjected to dynamic metamorphism, there will generally result a recrystallization and granulation, and the development of schistose structure. This is especially the case in the matrix in which, owing to its great range in composition, a large variety of minerals may be developed. A schist conglomerate or conglomerate schist is produced, generally with the pebbles flattened and elongated and more or less granulated and recrystallized. With extreme movement, the pebbles may be flattened into laminæ or changed into a variety of minerals according to their original composition. A quartz pebble may thus be drawn out into a lamina of granulated quartz, often only as thin as cardboard or even as paper. Granite pebbles may be transformed into a micaceous lamina with quartz and feldspar grains. The material of the original pebble may become more or less commingled with the matrix so that the outline of the pebble disappears and finally all trace of the conglomeratic character is lost, the mass being a schist with laminæ of varying composition interspersed. The matrix may become progressively slate, schist and foliated schist, the particles at first winding in and out among the pebbles, but becoming more parallel as the pebbles disappear.

Impure arenytes and lutytes may suffer changes similar to those of the matrix of rudytes. Clastic gneisses and schists are thus produced, or exogneisses and exoschists, since they are derived from exogenetic rocks. They are distinguished from endogneisses and endoschists, or those produced from endogenetic (chiefly pyrogenic) rocks, by the parallel orientation of their mineral particles, which gives cleavage to the rock. This structure is almost if not quite universal with the schists and gneisses derived by the metamorphism of sedimentary rocks, but is commonly lacking in schists and gneisses produced from igneous rocks.

The alteration of other sedimentary rocks by dynamic metamorphism may be briefly reviewed. Thus quartz sandstone changes to quartzite and then to quartzite schist; arkoses into arkose schists, and arkose gneisses; grits into graywackes, graywacke slates, graywacke schists and graywacke gneisses, and shales or lutytes into lutyte schists and lutyte gneisses (pelite schists and pelite gneisses). Limestones are changed to marble and soft coals to anthracites and graphites. In general, pure sediments are the least altered, while mixed sediments are likely to produce the greatest variety of new minerals under metamorphism.

The Terms Slate, Schist and Gneiss.

The term slate, though generally used as a lithological term, is strictly applied only as a structural one. A slate is a metamorphic rock of a lutaceous texture and homogeneous character, splitting into parallel leaves, and whose mineral particles are for the most part so small as to be invisible to the naked eye. (See, further, Chapter XX.) A schist has been defined as "a rock possessing a crystalline arrangement into separate folia." (Geikie–14: *178*.) A typical schist has its cleavable minerals arranged in the same way and like one another and large enough to be for the most part visible to the naked eye. Mica is the most important cleavage-making mineral, and the most typical schist is one composed of quartz and mica scales, a quartz mica schist, more commonly spoken of as a mica schist.

Van Hise has urged the use of the term schist in a purely structural sense, much as the terms shales and slate should be used. This is in strict accord with the definition by Geikie given above. In mineral composition and in origin schists may vary greatly. Thus we may have the ordinary quartz mica schist, which contains quartz and mica in about equal proportions. Hornblende schists are schists containing hornblende and some other minerals, generally feldspar. Thus we may have a hornblende plagioclase schist. If the origin of the schist is known this may be indicated in the name, as arkose schist, silicirudyte schist, or if derived from an igneous rock such as gabbro it becomes a gabbro schist. Both composition and origin may be indicated, as in the name mica-quartz-feldspar-arkose-schist.

In certain petrographic circles, especially the German ones, the term schist was applied to rocks not only having a schistose structure, but also a definite composition. Thus quartz was considered essential in the formation of a schist and was assumed to be present. We thus had mica schists, hornblende schists, chlorite schists, etc., in which the other mineral was supposed to be quartz. If feldspar was present, the rock was called a gneiss. (Rosenbusch–27.) The structural use of the term seems, however, to be the preferable one.

Gneiss was originally defined as a banded or foliated rock having essentially the composition of granite, *i. e.,* quartz, feldspar and mica or hornblende. The quartz and feldspar were taken as distinctive minerals and the others added as qualifying prefixes. Thus, mica gneiss meant a schistose or foliated rock, consisting of quartz, feldspar and mica; and hornblende gneiss, the same combination with hornblende added or replacing the mica. Such gneisses were supposed to be metamorphic derivatives of granites. Since, however, many rocks, to which the name gneiss has been commonly applied, prove not to have the composition above given, the petrographic use of the name must be abandoned in favor of the structural use, or the use of the term gneiss as well as schist must be very much restricted. Van Hise's proposition to use the term as a purely structural one seems to be the most satisfactory solution, and accordingly we may define gneiss as a banded metamorphic rock in which crystalline structure has been developed and in which the bands are petrographically unlike one another and consist of interlocking mineral particles. The bands in different gneisses are of variable thickness, ranging from a fraction of a centimeter to many centimeters (Van Hise). There may also be a similar variation and range in thickness of the different bands of the same gneiss. Thus the fundamental distinction between gneiss and schist is the banded character of the former as compared with the homogeneous character of the latter. This homogeneous character is still more strongly expressed in the slates in which the cleavable mineral particles are not visible as they are in the schists.

Gneiss may be derived either from igneous or from sedimentary rocks. When derived from igneous rocks the parallel arrangement of the mineral particles which results in cleavage is more often lacking.

General Terms for Metamorphic Rocks.

Two terms have come into use for general designation of metamorphism in rocks. These are *meta* and *apo.* Meta is used as a prefix to any rock name and designates that the rock has been altered without stating how or to what degree. Thus we may say meta-arenyte, meta-shale, meta-granite, meta-diorite, etc. Rocks already metamorphosed to a certain degree may undergo a second set of changes producing meta-graywackes, meta-quartzite, etc. Here the rock was first metamorphosed to a graywacke or a quartzite, after which a second set of alterations occurred.

Apo is used as a prefix for rocks in which metasomatic changes have taken place without entire loss of original texture or structure. Thus a devitrified rhyolite is an apo-rhyolite. (Bascom–5.) This name applies especially to rocks which have undergone diagenetic alterations without loss of structure, though the chemical and mineral composition may differ greatly from those of the original rock. The term is useful to call attention to the original rock from which the new rock is derived. Thus quartzite is an apo-arenyte, graywacke an apo-grit, etc. When new structures are produced we obtain slates, schists or gneisses.

Variation in Metamorphism of Strata.

In a given series of metamorphosed strata a change may often be noted in the intensity of the metamorphism as one passes from point to point. This change may be along the strike of the strata or across it. In the first case, it is generally gradual, the profoundly metamorphosed strata of one region passing gradually into the slightly metamorphosed equivalent of another. Thus the three unconformable series of strata, the Archæan, the Lower Huronian and the Upper Huronian, are so closely mashed and altered in the western part of the Marquette district of Michigan as to appear completely conformable and suggest an inseparable series. In tracing the formations to the less metamorphosed central and eastern parts of the district, the three unconformable series are readily recognizable as well as the original character of the formations.

The change in the degree of metamorphism across the strike is generally more abrupt. "Thus the rocks at the crown of an arch or at the bottom of a trough may be only partly metamorphosed, while the same formations on the limbs of the folds may be profoundly metamorphosed, this being due to the difference in the amount of shearing in different parts of the folds, or to the dying out or change in character of orogenic movements across the strike." (Van Hise–33: 598-600.) This change is well illustrated in the Hudson River series, which in the Hudson Valley is practically unaltered, but eastward across the strike in the Taconic range becomes schists and gneisses, while in Vermont and parts of eastern New York the series changes to roofing slates.

Age of Metamorphic Rocks.

Rocks of all ages may become metamorphosed, but it may be stated for a restricted region that the metamorphosed rocks of that region are generally older than the non-metamorphosed rocks. Strictly considered, this should apply only to symphrattic rocks, since later rocks may be affected by an intrusive sheet or laccolith, the effect dying out upward and downward and thus not being noticeable in older and younger strata. Or a set of folded strata may be locally affected by intrusions which are visible in the newer and not in the older strata. Again different strata are differently affected by the heat of a dike which cuts all of them, and some in the middle of the series may be much altered, while lower strata may be less readily altered. Even symphrattic rocks are not equally altered throughout, some very resistant strata being scarcely affected by the agents which strongly metamorphose others.

While metamorphism is undoubtedly most marked in pre-Cambric and in early Palæozoic rocks, it is also known in rocks of later age, as shown by the metamorphic gold-bearing slates of Jurassic age in the Sierra Nevada and in Sonora, and the Eocenic marble of the Himalayas. See further, Correlation by Regional Metamorphism, Chapter XXXII.

BIBLIOGRAPHY XIX.

1. ADAMS, FRANK D. 1912. An Experimental Contribution to the Question of the Depth of the Zone of Flow in the Earth's Crust. Journal of Geology, Vol. XX, pp. 97–118. (See also King–21.)
2. ADAMS, F. D., and COKER, ERNEST G. 1906. An Investigation into the Elastic Constants of Rocks, more Especially with Reference to Cubic Compressibility. Carnegie Institute of Washington, Publication No. 46. Ibid. American Journal of Sciences, 4th series, Vol. XXII, pp. 95–123.
3. ANDRÉE, KARL. 1911. Die Diagenese der Sedimente, ihre Beziehungen zur Sedimentbildung und Sediment Petrographie. Geologische Rundschau, Bd. II, pp. 61–74; 117–130.
3a. ANDRÉE, K. 1912. Die geologische Bedeutung des Wachstunsdruchs Kristallisierender Substanzen. Geologische Rundschau, Bd. III, pp. 7–15.
4. ARRHENIUS, SVANTE. 1912. Zur Physik der Salzlagerstätten. Meddelanden från K. Vetenskapsakademiens Nobelinstitut, Bd. II, No. 20, pp. 7–25.
5. BASCOM, FLORENCE. 1897. Aporhyolite of South Mountain, Pennsylvania. Bulletin of the Geological Society of America, Vol. VIII, pp. 393–396.
6. BASCOM, F. 1900. Volcanics of Neponset Valley, Massachusetts. Bulletin of the Geological Society of America, Vol. XI, pp. 115–126.

7. BECKER, GEORGE F. 1895. The Torsional Theory of Joints. Transactions of the American Institute of Mining Engineers, Vol. XXIV, pp. 130–138; 865–867.

8. BRANNER, J. C. 1904. The Stone Reefs of Brazil, Their Geological and Geographical Relations, with a Chapter on the Coral Reefs. Bulletin of the Museum of Comparative Zoölogy, Vol. XLIV, 285 pp., 95 plates. Ibid. 1905. Geological Society of America. Bulletin, Vol. XVI, pp. 1–12, pls. I–II.

9. CRAMER, FRANK. 1890. On a Recent Rock Flexure. American Journal of Sciences, 3rd series, Vol. XXXIX, pp. 220–225.

10. CRAMER, F. 1891. On the Rock Fracture at the Combined Locks Mill, Appleton, Wisconsin. Ibid., 3rd series, Vol. XLI, pp. 432–434.

11. DALY, REGINALD A. 1900. The Calcareous Concretions of Kettle Point, Lambton County, Ontario. Journal of Geology, Vol VIII, pp. 135–150.

12. DANA, JAMES D. 1890. Corals and Coral Islands, 3rd edition.

13. EVERDING, H. 1907. Deutschlands Kalibergbau. Festschrift zum 10ten Allgemeinen deutschen Bergmannstage zu Eisenach, Vol. I, pp. 25–133 (especially pp. 50, 83, 88).

14. GEIKIE, A. 1893. A Textbook of Geology, 3rd edition.

15. GERBING, J. 1909. Chemische Untersuchungen von Meeresboden-Meereswasser- und Luft-Proben der deutschen südpolar Expedition. 1901–1903, Bd. VII. Berlin.

16. GRABAU, A. W. 1904. On the Classification of Sedimentary Rocks. American Geologist, Vol. XXXIII, pp. 228–247.

17. HAHN, F. FELIX. 1912. The Form of Salt Deposits. Economic Geology, Vol. VII, pp. 120–135 (and papers cited there).

18. HAHN, F. F. 1912. Untermeerische Gleitungen bei Trenton Falls (Nord Amerika) und ihr Verhältniss zu ähnlichen Störungsbildern. Neues Jahrbuch für Mineralogie, u. s. w., Beilage Bd. XXXVI, pp. 1–41, taf. I–III.

19. IRVING, A. 1889. Chemical and Physical Studies in the Metamorphism of Rocks. Longmans, Green & Co., London.

20. JOHNSTON, JOHN. 1854. Notice of some spontaneous movements occasionally observed in the sandstone strata in one of the quarries at Portland, Connecticut. Proceedings of the American Association for the Advancement of Science, 8th meeting, 1854, pp. 283–286.

21. KING, L. V. 1912. On the limiting strength of rocks under conditions of stress existing in the Earth's interior. Journal of Geology, Vol. XX, pp. 119–138.

22. KOKEN, ERNEST. 1902. Ueber Gekrösekalke des obersten Muschelkalkes am unteren Neckar. Zentralblatt für Mineralogie, etc., 1902, No. 3.

23. MOORE, ELWOOD S. 1912. Siliceous oölites and other concretionary structures in the vicinity of State College, Pennsylvania. Journal of Geology, Vol. XX, No. 3, pp. 259–269.

24. NILES, WILLIAM H. 1876. The Geological Agency of Lateral Pressure in Quarrying. Proceedings of the Boston Society of Natural History, Vol. XIV, pp. 1–8.

25. NILES, W. H. 1876. The Geological Agency of Lateral Pressure Exhibited by Certain Movements of Rocks. Ibid., Vol. XVIII, pp. 272–284.

26. PFAFF, F. W. 1895. Beiträge zur Erklärung über die Entstehung des Magnesits und Dolomits. Neues Jahrbuch für Mineralogie, u. s. w., Beilage Bd. IX, pp. 485–507.

27. ROSENBUSCH, H. 1898. Elemente der Gesteinslehre. Stuttgart.
28. SKEATS, E. W. 1903. The chemical composition of limestones from upraised coral islands, with notes on their microscopical structure. Bulletin of the Museum of Comparative Zoölogy, Vol. XLII, pp. 53–126.
29. SMYTH, C. H., JR. 1892. On the Clinton Iron Ore. American Journal of Sciences, 3rd series, Vol XLIII, pp. 487–496.
30. STEIDTMANN, EDWARD. 1911. The Evolution of Limestones and Dolomite. Journal of Geology, Vol. XIX, pp. 323–345; 392–428.
31. SUESS, EDUARD. 1910. The Face of the Earth, Vol. II (English translation by Sollas and Sollas).
32. VAN HISE, CHARLES R. 1884. Enlargement of Feldspar Fragments in Certain Keweenawan Sandstones. Bulletin of the United States Geological Survey, No. 8, pt. I, pp. 44–47.
33. VAN HISE, C. R. 1896. Principles of North American Pre-Cambrian Geology. 16th Annual Report of the United States Geological Survey, pt. I.
34. VAN HISE, C. R. 1904. A Treatise on Metamorphism. United States Geological Survey, Monograph XLVII.
35. WALTHER, JOHANNES. 1894. Einleitung in die Geologie, Lithogenesis der Gegenwart.
36. WIELAND, G. R. 1897. Eopalæozoic Hot Springs and the Origin of the Pennsylvania Siliceous Oölites. American Journal of Science, 4th series, Vol. IV, pp. 262 et seq.
37. ZIEGLER, VICTOR. 1912. The Silicious Oölites of Central Pennsylvania. American Journal of Science, 4th series, Vol. XXXIV, pp. 113–127.

CHAPTER XX.

DEFORMATION OF ROCK MASSES.

Having in the preceding chapters dealt at length with the subject of rock formation or *Lithogenesis,* we must next turn our attention to the subject of rock deformation or *Orogenesis, i. e.,* the making of mountain structures.

As the result of rock deformation a number of distinct structural features come into existence, some of which have already been noted in the preceding chapters. Deformation may be classed as endogenetic or exogenetic, *i. e.,* produced by internal or external causes, respectively. Internal causes are diagenetic, such as chemical change, recrystallization, etc., while external causes include pressure and motion due to gravity, to tectonic disturbances, etc. The following types of deformation may be considered:

I. *Endogenetic.*

    1. Endolithic brecciation.
    2. Enterolithic structure.
    3. Contractive joints (prismatic) (basaltic).

II. *Exogenetic.*

    A. *Gravitational Deformations.*

        a. *Structures Due to Movement.*

    4. Intraformational brecciation.
    5. Gliding deformations.
    6. Surface deformation through creep.

        b. *Structures Due to Compression.*

    7. Squeezed-out strata.
    8. Shaliness.
    9. Slatiness.

        c. *Of Complex Origin.*

    10. Pressure sutures and stylolites.
    11. Cone-in-cone structure.

B. *Tectonic or Orogenic Deformation.*

12. Tectonic joints.
13. Earthquake fissures.
14. Slaty cleavage.
15. Fissility.
16. Schistosity.
17. Gneissoid structure.
18. Folding—Anticlines, synclines, isoclines, fan folds, monoclines, etc.
19. Domes and basins.
20. Faulting.

C. *Contact Deformations.*

21. Prismatic structure.
22. Insolation joints.

D. *Complex Structures Partly Due to Deformation.*

23. Metamorphism.
24. Disconformity and unconformity.

ENDOGENETIC DEFORMATIONS.

1. *Endolithic Brecciation.* This term is applied to brecciation of strata caused by forces acting from within the mass, such as crystallization and especially swelling or hydration, as in the case of gypsum, etc. In this last case it is only the extreme of enterolithic structure. Similar structures are produced by contraction of the rock mass on drying and the disruption into blocks or cakes which are subsequently enclosed by later deposits and form an endostatic rudyte. Examples of such have recently been described by Hyde (11 : *400-408*) from the Coal Measures of Ohio. Beds of fresh-water limestone intercalated in the series and deposited in a playa lake were subject to periodic drying, as a result of which the surface for several acres was broken up into polygonal blocks of various sizes, the surfaces of which were frequently covered by the shells of the animals killed in the drying of the lake. The fragments seem to have been exposed for a while to weathering and were then covered by a second flooding. Where the covering deposits were muds, the limestone fragments form a striking series of pebbles in a lutaceous matrix and often weather out in relief. Many intraformational conglomerates may have such an origin. Such breccias are of course closely similar to intraformational breccias due to gliding movements as described under Section 4.

2. *Enterolithic Structure.* This has already been discussed in the preceding chapter. In so far as it can be shown that this structure is a purely diagenetic one, brought about by the swelling of the mass either through crystallization or hydration, it properly belongs to endogenetic deformations. If, on the other hand, it should be proven that enterolithic structure in some rocks is produced by the pressure of the overlying mass and the consequent creep and rearrangement of the particles under pressure, such deformation must be classed under the gravitational section of the exogenetic class.

The important distinction between enterolithic and other deformations, such as folding under lateral pressure, or gliding in a given direction, lies in the fact that the enterolithic structure folds in all directions—is apolar or multipolar instead of unipolar.

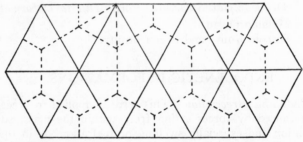

Fig. 162. Diagram illustrating the formation of contraction joints and of desiccation fissures. The normal form is hexagonal, but, as shown in the left-hand member, an irregular pentagonal form is developed when one side is suppressed.

3. *Contraction Joints—Basaltic Jointing.* This is seen in the formation of mud cracks in lutaceous sediments such as clay or argillo-calcareous mud and in the development of prismatic jointing in cooling basalt and other igneous rocks. In the latter case the prisms always form at right angles to the enclosing surface, such as the upper and lower surface of a sill or laccolith, when the prisms will be vertical or curved, or the lateral walls of a dike, when the prisms will be horizontal. The prevalence of six-sided forms in these prisms suggests that the crystallizing force centers about equidistant points in the magma, each of which will draw an equal amount of the surrounding matrix toward it from all sides. This results in other equally spaced points between these around which the tension in all directions is greatest. Since the points around which attraction takes place are all equally distant from one an-

other, they form the apices of a series of equilateral triangles and the points around which the greatest tension is focused will be the centers of these triangles. The smallest number of cracks about these central points which will relieve the tension in all directions is three. If these cracks are symmetrically arranged about the point, the angle between any two of them is 120°, which is the angle between the two sides of a hexagonal prism. As shown in the diagram (Fig. 162), this uniform contraction about equidistant points will result in the formation of a set of uniform hexagonal prisms. Unequal development or failure of the cracks to develop about one of the points may lead to five-sided or other irregular prisms.

Drying mud will in like manner cause a development of a series of prisms which typically are hexagonal, but from lack of homogeneity of the material through unequal drying, or from some other cause, are frequently irregular polygons. The prisms are seldom very high, though in exceptional cases the cracks may penetrate to a depth of ten feet. In general a fraction of an inch is the usual height of the dried mud prisms, the sides of which are slightly raised, giving a concave surface. (See *ante,* Chapter XVII.)

Prismatic jointing is also sometimes found in undisturbed hydrogenic rocks. Examples of these occur in some gypsum beds of the Paris Basin. It is quite probable that this structure is due to pressure exerted by hydration of anhydrite and so belongs to the diagenetic processes.

DEFORMATIONS DUE TO EXTRANEOUS CAUSES— EXOGENETIC DEFORMATIONS.

This type may be divided into (A) Gravitational, (B) Orogenic, and (C) Contactic.

A. GRAVITATIONAL DEFORMATIONS.

a. *Structures Due to Movements.*

4. *Intraformational Brecciation.* This has already been discussed in the chapter on Autoclastic rocks, but is again mentioned here as a structural feature. It is probably in all cases an extreme of the next type, and so may be considered in connection with that subject. Here belong the edgewise conglomerates of many limestone formations.

5. *Subaquatic, Gliding-deformation.* Offshore deposits of sediments on a gently sloping sea or lake bottom may suffer from time to time deformation of the surface layers through gliding or slipping down the gently inclined sea floor. Such deformation has been repeatedly observed in modern deposits. The best known modern examples are those which affected the village of Horgen on the lake of Zurich in 1875, and the village of Zug in 1887. Both of these have already been described in Chapter XV, p. 658. The most remarkable fact about the gliding in Zug was that it took place on an average grade of 6% (3° 26'), while the larger and more

Fig. 163. Folding accompanying subaquatic gliding in Miocenic marl of Oeningen—natural size. (After Heim.)

pronounced movement occurred on a grade as low as 4.4% (a trifle over 2° 31'). The material which thus slid into the lake was brecciated and folded with overfolds, overthrusts, reversals of layers, excessive strata, etc., and furnishes an excellent guide to the interpretation of similar movement in the past. Among the chief points in which these folds differ from those produced diagenetically by swelling of gypsum, or by pressure of overlying masses, is that they are of the nature of normal folds due to lateral compression and so show movement in one direction only, whereas in the case of the other deformations movements in several directions are shown. Furthermore, the axes of the folds are thickened in the gliding as in normal tectonic folds, instead of the limbs, as is the case in folds due to swelling.

Examples of fossil subaqueous solifluction.

A. *Miocenic sublacustrine glidings of Oeningen.* The Miocenic marls of Oeningen, noted for their wonderful remains of insects, etc., show in the midst of these beds a strongly folded layer, lying between horizontal beds of the same character. These foldings are so pronounced that they inevitably suggest lateral compression as the cause of their production, yet the entirely undisturbed charac-

FIG. 164. Folding accompanying subaquatic gliding in Miocenic marl of Oeningen. One-half natural size. (After Heim.)

ter of the enclosing strata forbids such an assumption. Another feature which indicates gliding is the independence of the folded beds from the basal beds, against which the limbs commonly abut directly. The axes of the folds are notably thickened, while the limbs are thinned by compression exactly as in tectonic folding. (Figs. 163, 164.)

B. *Jurassic deformations* of this type are known from the Solnhofen Plattenkalke, where the so-called distorted layer (*krumme Lage*) furnishes a good example. The zone has a thickness of 1 to 1.5 meters, and in it are found all the phenomena of folding, including folds 5 meters in length. Here the glidings took place in the periodically submerged lagoons within the reefs and the calcareous nature of the material probably insured a partial cementation before the gliding took place. (See Fig. 95, p. 440.)

C. *Triassic examples* are known from the Muschelkalk of Germany, especially the Main region, but not all of the disturbances found in this formation and so fully described by Reis (20) belong

FIG. 165. Deformation due to subaqueous gliding, Muschelkalk, Franken (Germany) 1:50. (After Reis.)

here. The enterolithic structure described by Koken (13) from the Neckar Valley must certainly be removed from this category of deformation due to submarine glidings.

D. *Devonic examples* of this class have been figured by Sir Wm. Logan from the Cape Bon Ami limestones of Lower Devonic age from Gaspé (Logan–15:*392*) where in division 4 and less

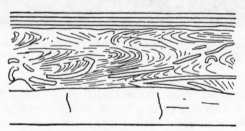

FIG. 166. Deformation due to subaqueous gliding, Muschelkalk, Franken (Germany) 1:50. (After Reis.) ˋ

than 400 feet above the base of the entire series is a bed seven feet thick made up of several thin layers of limestone and limestone shale and presenting a series of wrinkles or contortions from which the overlying and underlying beds are free. The series now dips at an angle of 24° southwest. The folding in some cases has been so intense as to cause a brecciation of the limestone beds. (Fig. 167.)

E. *Ordovicic examples* of this type are beautifully exposed in the walls of the gorge of East Canada Creek at Trenton Falls, N. Y. Here there are at least three such disturbed zones, one well

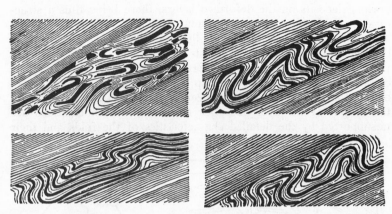

FIG. 167. Corrugated limestone beds, showing the effects of subaqueous gliding. Gaspé limestone, Canada. Scale about 1:200. (After Logan.)

shown below the Lower or Sherman Falls, one just below the High Falls (now replaced by a high dam), and a third higher up. All of these show a wonderful series of folds and overthrusts, the zones varying in thickness up to 4 meters, and, as is to be expected, dying

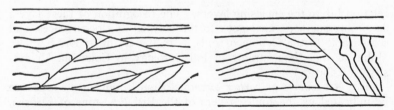

FIG. 168. Deformation due to subaqueous gliding. Trenton limestone, Trenton Falls, N. Y. 1:75.
(After Hahn.)

FIG. 169. Deformation due to subaqueous gliding, Trenton limestone, Trenton Falls, N. Y. 1:100.
(After Miller.)

out after a while, though traceable for some considerable distance. The upper and lower layers are not disturbed, but absolutely normal, not even showing evidence of excessive compression. The layers involved in the folding are not always the same, sometimes they are granular limestones with abundant organic remains, but more often they are calcilutytes. The fossils are often broken, but no recrystallization occurs; the appearance is such as would be expected from the result of gliding of a mass of imperfectly lithified lime mud. The overlying layers have all the characters of normal deposits on the deformed layers, there being thus a structural unconformity, though without a hiatus. (Figs. 168, 169.) These disturbances at Trenton Falls have been variously explained, the general conclusions of geologists being either: (1) that they were truly tectonic—lateral pressure having resulted in the folding of certain strata while others took up the thrust without deformation, or (2) that they were due to squeezing out of certain layers under the weight of the overlying rock masses. Both explanations are unsupported by the detailed characteristics of the folds and their

FIG. 170. Edgewise conglomerate, Beekmantown limestones, Center county, Pennsylvania. (After Hahn.)

FIG. 171. Section across the two interlocking stylolites, shown in Fig. 172, much reduced. (After Wagner.)

relationship to the enclosing layers. The recognition of these layers as gliding surfaces, analogous to the Horgen-Zug occurrences, and comparable to the Oeningen folds, is to the credit of Dr. F. Felix Hahn, at that time curator in Palæontology in Columbia University. (Hahn–7.)

F. *A Cambric or earlier example* of such movements seems to be indicated by the folded layers of the Biri limestone of Mjösen, Norway, described by Rothpletz (21). This limestone contains certain layers "which are deformed in a singular manner without the enclosing layers partaking of such deformation. It appears as if, during the tilting, these layers had not enough stability, and collapsed within themselves, so that between the more stable layers there occurred a movement in which the enclosing strata had no part." (Rothpletz–21 : *28.*) The characters of these foldings seem in every way analogous to those of the younger formations described.

Finally, it should be mentioned that in the unconsolidated deposit of the Pleistocenic such deformations occur, though some of them, no doubt, are due to glacial thrust. The deformation of the Tertiary beds of Martha's Vineyard may possibly belong to this category.

Deformation through gliding may result in complete brecciation of the deformed layers. The fragments may lie in all positions, as in the case of ordinary "intraformational conglomerates," or they may consist of thin cakes, many of which in the gliding process have assumed a vertical position in the mass. This forms the so-called "edgewise conglomerate" common in the Ordovicic limestones of the Appalachian region. The characteristics of all these formations seem to point to rather shallow water as the place of deposition of these strata, and the possible periodic exposure and partial hardening of the surface layers. A different explanation has, however, been given for these by Seely and amplified by Brown (1).

6. *Surface Deformation Due to Creep.* As already noted (p. 543), vertical strata, especially of a shaly or slaty character, are subject to deformation in portions of their exposed ends by the creep of the surface soil down a sloping hillside composed of thin strata. A bending in the direction of movement is generally found to occur after a while. Such deformation is of slight importance, and is probably never preserved in the older rocks.

b. *Deformations Due to Vertical Pressure of Overlying Rock Masses.*

7. *Squeezing Out of Layers.* This may occur in cases where certain beds are especially susceptible to such deformation. Fine-grained, homogeneous strata seem to be most readily affected in this way. An enterolithic structure similar to that produced by swelling masses (gypsum, salt) is thus produced, the effect being similar whether the pressure originated from the swelling of the mass itself or from the weight of the overlying rock. Koken believes that the enterolithic structure in the Muschelkalk of the Neckar Valley (*Gekrösekalke*) is due to vertical pressure and squeezing out of these layers. (*Ante,* Fig. 161.)

8. *Shaliness* is the property of lutaceous rocks, rich in clay, to split with concave or "shelly" surfaces in a general way parallel to the bedding planes. The structure is a secondarily derived one, due to vertical pressure and the character of the rock. It seems to be best developed in calcareous shales. That it is a secondary structure is shown by the fact that the splitting will sometimes pass

across a fossil, a part of which remains with either portion of the split mass.

9. *Slatiness.* This term is applied to the structure developed by many siliceous and carbonaceous argillutytes of splitting into thin layers or plates parallel to the bedding and with essential regularity of surfaces similar to true slaty cleavage. The Genesee and Black Portage shales of New York, the Black Shale of Ohio and Michigan and others of their kind show this feature well. It is shown in the undisturbed Jurassic lutytes of Württemberg, which are split into slate blocks to all appearance comparable to slates from disturbed

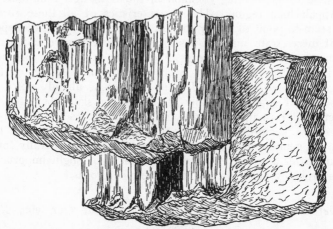

FIG. 172.   Stylolite from Trigonodus limestone (Muschelkalk) of Frauenthal. Three-quarters natural size.   (After Wagner.)   (See Fig. 171.)

regions. Finally a certain slatiness is observed in the Plattenkalke of the Upper Jura in the Solnhofen region, where layers are split thin enough for roofing slate purposes.

In all these cases the region is undisturbed, and the slaty structure is parallel to the bedding. It is apparently developed as the result of pressure of the overlying rock masses, and, when exposed to erosion, it is developed by the weather in the same way that slaty cleavage is developed by the weather.

c. *Of Complex Origin.*

10.   *Pressure Sutures and Stylolites.** In massive limestones are not infrequently found irregular sutures or seams, which pene-

---

* For a recent comprehensive survey of the subject together with discussion of all the theories of origin advanced, and reference to literature, see Wagner–24.

trate the rock usually in a direction parallel to the bedding planes. These sutures (*Drucksuturen* of the Germans) range from a scarcely visible size to projections an inch or more in length. They interlock on opposite sides in a most complicated manner, which has led to their comparison with the sutures of a skull (Vanuxem). Such sutures have been found in limestones of widely varying geological ages and in different parts of the world. They seem to pass by gradation into the true stylolite structures which generally occur in the same or in similar limestone beds. Stylolites generally occur along a horizontal plane of separation, and consist of flutes and slickensided columns of limestone, varying in length up to 4 inches or more, and in diameter up to two or more inches and projecting alternately from the upper and from the lower layer at right angles. At the end of each column is usually a cap of clay, which weathers out in the cliff, leaving hollow cavities. That these structures are due to pressure is suggested by the fact that the fracture line often passes across recognizable organic remains, the two parts of which are displaced in opposite sides of the fracture plane. The structure thus resembles minute faulting, the flutings on the sides of the column being analogous to the slickensides formed at the fault planes. Stylolites are often mistaken for corals or other organic remains. Not infrequently a shell or other fossil remains caps the stylolite, and determines the outline of the fluted column.

Ordinary pressure work has, however, not taken place here, for nowhere is there any evidence of deformation of the beds by crowding or compression above the columns, which project from one face of the suture into the hollows of the other. In other words, if the interlocking of the notch-like projections were due to simple compression before or after solidification, then wherever a hollow occurs there should be evidence above and around that hollow of compression and movement to crowd away the material so as to produce that hollow.

That the structure was produced after the solidification of the rock is shown by the fact that the surfaces of separation are sharp, that the sides are striated and that all evidence of massive deformation or squeezing is wanting. The most satisfactory theory yet advanced to explain these remarkable structures is that they are the result of unequal solution along sutures or fracture planes. If solution takes place on the concave surfaces of both the upper and lower face of the fracture, the result must be the production of a series of tooth-like projections from both sides of the fissures, which, owing to the pressure of the overlying rock, interpenetrate more and more as room is made by solution. In other words, the rock opposite the end of each tooth-like projection is dissolved away—the hollows are deepened, and thus the teeth, by gliding under pressure, penetrate deeper and deeper into the opposite bed, while at the same time they become longer by the deepening of the hollows which surround and isolate them. The residual clay, left on solution, comes to rest as a cap on the top of the stylolite, protecting this top from solution.

It is not necessary that the suture or dividing plane should be irregular to begin with. Unequal solution on opposite sides of the plane is sure to occur, since rocks are seldom so homogeneous that all parts are equally soluble. Such irregularity once produced, it will continue to be augmented, for the greatest amount of pressure

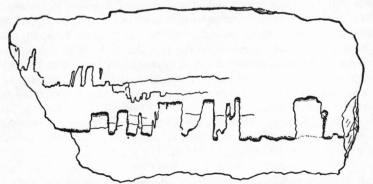

FIG. 173.　Sketch of a portion of a limestone face of white Jura β in Talheim, showing stylolites. (After Wagner.) The spaces resulting (black) are filled with calcite. (After Wagner.) (Much reduced.)

will occur where the rocks on opposite sides come in contact. The projecting mass, especially if it is crowned by a fossil which is less readily soluble than the enclosing rock, generally suffers the least solution, while the hollow opposite into which it presses suffers the largest amount of solution. The protecting cap of clay also helps this process. The sides of the growing teeth are free from pressure, so solution is absent here, and deposition even may occur. (Figs. 171-173.)

The length of the individual stylolite tooth serves as a fair measure of the amount of material removed by solution from both sides of the fracture plane.

11. *Cone in Cone.* This is a structure sometimes found in lutaceous rocks, particularly in calcareous or ferruginous argillutytes. It consists of a number of crenulated or corrugated conical

layers one within the other. In the beds they are seen to consist of two sets interlocking from opposite sides, the top and bottom of the beds affected being formed by the bases of the two sets of cones.

Professor Marsh (16) has suggested that this structure is the result of concretions forming under pressure. It has also been held that crystallization of the calcium carbonate in the bed is responsible for the formation of this structure.

B. Tectonic or Orogenic Deformations.

Of late the term tectonic has come to be more specially applied in geology to larger rock structures, due to disturbances such as accompany and bring about the formation of mountains. In other words, orogenic disturbances have come to be considered the chief causes in the production of tectonic features. Lateral pressure seems to be the chief active agent responsible for such deformation, but it is by no means certain that the products of such lateral compression are always distinguishable from those of vertical compression by the superincumbent strata.

The various types of tectonic deformation will be considered, beginning with tectonic jointing.

d. *Deformation Resulting in Fractures and Related Structures.*

12. *Joints.* Rocks separated into more or less regular blocks by natural fissures are said to be jointed. Joints may be due to shrinkage on cooling, or on desiccation, forming shrinkage joints, already discussed, or they may be caused by folding or other tensile stresses, giving *tension joints,* or finally they may be due to compression on folding, forming *compression joints.* Both tension and compression joints frequently occur together. In tension joints the surfaces will be rough if the rock is arenaceous or rudaceous and the grains weakly held. If the rock is lutaceous or otherwise a strong, tolerably homogeneous rock, the fracture will be smooth and sharply cut. Faulting and slickensiding may develop along such joints when subjected to pressure, and deposit of mineral matter will take place along the joint surfaces.

Daubrée (3) has shown by experiments with glass plates that, if a brittle stratum is subjected to torsion, when the limit of elasticity is reached it will break, with two sets of parallel fractures forming nearly a right angle with each other (Figs. 174, 175).

Crosby (2) has shown that, if a shock were sent through the strata before this limit was reached, the fracture would be produced in a similar manner. The shock may be produced by the giving way of the first portion of the bed, in which torsion has been carried beyond the resisting strength of the bed, or it may have extraneous causes.

The slight amount of torsion required in a brittle bed is easily accounted for by differential uplift of the bed. It may be illus-

FIG. 174. Illustration of Daubrée's method of breaking a sheet of glass by torsion to produce intersecting joints.

FIG. 175. Arrangement of fractures in glass plate broken by torsion. (Daubrée.)

trated by the torsion produced in a large sheet of stiff cardboard lifted slightly by one corner.

Compression joints are produced in the folding of rocks. Simply folded rocks will have joints in two planes at right angles to each other. Joints of this kind are closely related to fissility, which is distinguishable only by the greater number and closer approximation of the shearing planes. "The same compression might produce fissility along one set of shearing planes and joints along another." (Van Hise—23: *671*.)

Minor characteristics of joint faces.

Feather fracture. This, as shown by Woodworth (26), is characteristic of the joint surfaces of certain fine-grained phyllites or siliceous lutytes. It consists of a "delicate tracery of feathery lines diverging from a roughly outlined axis, which traverses the face of the joint block in a plane parallel with the stratification. When the axis of the feather fracture departs from this plane it becomes sinuous." (Woodworth–26.)

Dendritic markings. These are formed on the joint planes of fine-grained rocks, and are due to the arborescent deposit of earthy oxide of manganese or of iron. They may be compared to the plumose frost traceries on window panes. In the so-called landscape marble, this deposit has penetrated the entire rock, and is seen on all polished sections. Dendrites of iron pyrites and other minerals are also known. Not infrequently they are mistaken for vegetable impressions.

Widening of joints.

Joints of tectonic origin may be widened by separation of the blocks, by solution or erosion of their sides, and in other ways. The Olean conglomerate on the hills of southwestern New York furnishes a good illustration of widening of joints by separation of the blocks. Here huge masses 40 feet in height and of similar basal dimensions have been formed in the coarse conglomerate, and the blocks have in many cases slid far enough apart to open passageways between them. These street-like passageways between the blocks have given the region the name of Rock City. The gliding of the masses is favored by the soft, clayey strata underlying and by the constant erosion which is going on on the hillsides.

Joints in limestones are commonly widened by solution of the wall rock, which when continued long enough will produce cavern-like passages and eventually caves. The peculiar character of the Karst regions of the world is accounted for by such solution. (See *ante,* p. 133.) Not infrequently partly widened fissures are filled with clay, sand, gravel or other substances from above, constituting a clastic "dike." Sandstone dikes are especially common, though not always originating in solution fissures (see beyond). Fissures thus filled are common in most modern limestone masses, covered by drift deposits. A remarkable example of a Devonic fissure in Niagaran limestone, filled with fossiliferous Upper Devonic shales, has been described by Weller from Illinois (25).

Widening of joint fissures by erosion is of common occurrence. The most active agent is often the wind, which cuts away at the sides of the prism produced by the joints, and narrows it until only a pillar, isolated from its neighbor, remains behind. All stages of such erosion along joint cracks may be seen in the Tertiary sandstone of Monument Park, Colorado, where in the ledges the beginnings of this erosion work are seen, while scattered through the park are numerous isolated stone pillars, generally capped by a ferruginous block of greater resistance, the last remnants of an extensive formation which formerly covered the entire region.

13. *Earthquake Fissures.* A well-known phenomenon accompanying more or less violent seismic disturbances is the opening of fissures in the rock by the tearing asunder of the mass. Such fissures may remain open or be filled subsequently by the washing into them of surface material, or they may be filled at the time of formation by material violently injected into them from above. Recent fissures have been described by Whimper and others. (See Chapter XXIII.) Examples of such fissures are sometimes found in the fossil state. Thus the Upper Siluric limestones and dolomites of western New York and Ontario are traversed by vertical fissures, which show evidence of violent disruption, and into these fissures sands representing the Oriskany period were injected. These sands apparently rested on the old erosion surface of the Siluric limestone before the shock came. The shock was a pre-Middle Devonic one, for Middle Devonic (Onondaga) strata rest upon this mass without showing any evidence of being affected by the shock. One of the best examples of this group has been described from the cement quarries of North Buffalo.

"The total depth of the fissure as now exposed with its filling of sandstone is in the neighborhood of 10 feet. The dike is squarely cut off at the top, where the Onondaga limestone rests on its truncated end and on the limestones flanking it. The Onondaga limestone is entirely unaffected by the dike, being evidently deposited after the formation and truncation of this remarkable mass of sandstone. The width of the fissure is scarcely anywhere over 2 feet, but lateral offshoots extend for many feet into the walls of Bullhead [and Bertie] limestone. These offshoots or rootlets of the dike are irregular, commonly narrow, and often appear as isolated quartz masses in the Bullhead or Waterlimes, the connection with the main dike not being always observable. Such masses of sandstone have been noted at a distance of 20 or 30 feet from the main dike. They are always small. The dike itself has been traced for more than 30 feet in an east and west direction in the sloping walls of the quarry. The walls of this ancient fissure are very irregular, angular masses of the limestone projecting into the quartz rock, while narrow tongues of sandstone everywhere enter the limestone. Extensive brecciation of the limestone has occurred along the margin, and the sandstone there is filled with angular fragments of the limestone, which show no traces of solution, or wear by running water. These limestone fragments are themselves frequently injected with tongues of the quartz sand. The nature of the contact between the quartz and the limestone, the trituration of the latter, and the inclusion of individual grains of quartz sand in a triturated mass of limestone, the presence of cavities along the contact filled with recrystallized calcite, the presence of elongated limestone "streamers" in the quartz mass near the contact, all "point to a cataclysmic origin of the fissure . . . and a more or less violent injection of the sand. . . . It seems also certain that the fissure was formed after the deposition of a considerable mass of sand over the . . . limestone, and that the formation of the fissure and the injection of sand from above occurred simultaneously. In no other way can we account for the inclusion of horses of the wall rock, often of considerable size, and the injection of the sand into all the fissures and crevices; nor can we readily explain on any other hypothesis the trituration of the limestone along the borders, which clearly indicates a violent contact between the sand and the already consolidated limestone. The supposition that the fissure is due to a violent disruption of the wall . . . is further borne out by the numerous minute faults which occur in the Waterlimes in the vicinity of the fissure and elsewhere." (Grabau–5 : *360-361*.)

14. *Slaty Cleavage.* Slaty cleavage (Leith–14) is the property of strata to split or "cleave" along certain planes which as a rule have no relation to the planes of stratification. This property is especially well developed in argillutytes, resulting in the formation of "slates," from which the term slaty cleavage has been derived. Slate is therefore a structural term, and has no lithic significance, except in so far as the structure is best developed in the clastic rocks of lutaceous texture, and generally in part at least of argillaceous composition. This rock structure has been explained as "due to the arrangement of the mineral particles with their longer diameters or radial cleavage, or both, in a common direction, and that this arrangement is caused, first and most important, by parallel development of new minerals; second, by the flattening and parallel rotation of old and new mineral particles, and, third, and of least importance, by the rotation into approximately parallel positions of random original particles." (Van Hise–23: *635.*) (See also page 770.)

The original cause of these changes is the lateral compression of the rocks due to orogenic disturbances. Cleavage may be considered as separation of the laminæ, potentially developed in the rock. The actual cleavage or splitting is subsequently developed by the frost, or other atmospheric agent, or by the hand of man.

Coarse-grained rocks are seldom affected by cleavage. Limestones likewise offer great resistance to compression, and are not generally cleaved. Thus cleavage may often be developed in a stratum of argillaceous lutytes, while adjoining arenytes or calcareous beds will be unaffected. This sometimes gives rise to the appearance of an unconformity.

Cleaved strata commonly have their original bedding structure obliterated. Only in exceptional cases are the bedding planes preserved, when the strata are differently colored or when a change in texture occurs. In such cases ribbon slates or banded slates are produced. In cleaved fossiliferous strata the fossils may sometimes be detected on the weathered surfaces of the bedding plane, the position of which they indicate. A very general distortion of the fossils accompanies the formation of cleavage, so that in many cases the remains are no longer recognizable.

Unless the relation of cleavage to the bedding is detected, an erroneous conception of the structure of a country is obtained. Strata which are strongly cleaved generally appear to be vastly thicker than they really are, and unconformities are sometimes considered to exist between strata where in reality the bedding planes are perfectly concordant. If, however, a formation with slaty cleavage is overlain by one without such structure, although of a composition which would permit its development as readily as would the underlying rock, a discordance of relation is indicated, though in the absence of other evidence this is not fully demonstrated. (Van Hise–23 : 726.)

15. *Fissility* is the structure found in some rocks, "by virtue of which they are already separated into parallel laminæ in a state of nature." It thus differs from cleavage, where this separation is only potential. Fissility belongs in the zone of fracture, while cleavage belongs in that of flowage. Both occur and grade into each other in the zone of combined fracture and flowage.

16. *Schistosity.* This structure is the result of intense metamorphism under pressure, and is characterized by the development of planes of cleavage due to the presence of large, cleavable particles. It is essentially comparable to slaty cleavage, except that metamorphism has gone farther and the rock has become crystalline. Schistosity may be developed in rocks of many kinds, both clastic and igneous. Foliation is another term applied to these rocks.

The structure is essentially due to recrystallization of the rock on mashing. It is often not apparent in fresh rocks, but, as in the case of slaty cleavage, is developed on exposure to the atmosphere.

17. *Gneissoid Structure.* This structure, like schistosity, results from intense mashing and recrystallization of rocks subjected to symphrattic metamorphism. Gneissoid structure is essentially characterized by banding, the bands being of unlike composition. The mineral particles also interlock so that the cleavage is much less perfect than in schists. Usually it is parallel to the banding, but this is not always the case. Gneissoid structure may be developed in igneous and in clastic rocks. In the former case we have granite-gneisses, diortite-gneisses, etc., in the latter arenyte or sandstone gneisses, rudyte gneisses or conglomerate gneisses, etc.

e. *Deformations Due to Folding, and to Folding and Erosion.*

18. *Folding.* Rock folds are among the most conspicuous and easily recognized tectonic features. They vary greatly in magnitude, from the minute wrinkles formed in the axes of larger folds, to those whose limbs are many miles apart. In regions of erosion generally only a part of the fold is found, the folded strata having been truncated and cut down until only portions of the limbs remain. In this way the appearance of tilted strata is produced, these tilted strata being, however, only the remnants of great folds.

The form of folds is very variable, but it has been possible to select a number of distinct types, of which the others are variants. These distinct types are (a) *anticline,* (b) *synclines,* (c) *isoclines,* (d) *fan folds,* and (e) *monoclines.* Compound anticlines are *anticlinoria* and compound synclines are *synclinoria.*

(a) *Anticlines.* In this type the sides or *limbs* of the fold typically slope away from the plane of the axis on either side. The sloping portions are known as the *limbs* of the anticline, and the amount of slope as compared with the horizontal is the angle of *dip.* All folds are wrinkles in the earth's crust, and if followed far enough along the axis they will die out. The amount of inclination of the axis of the fold, also measured from the horizontal, is called the pitch. Every anticlinal axis pitches in two directions, *i. e.,* toward the two ends of the folds. A short anticline in which the two axes are of approximately equal length is a *dome.*

(b) *Synclines.* When the limbs of the fold dip toward the axis a trough fold or syncline is produced, the axis of which pitches toward the center of the fold. A short syncline, in which the two axes are of nearly equal length, is a *basin.*

Anticlines and synclines may be either symmetrical or asymmetrical, according as the limbs are equal in length and inclination, or unequal. Anticlines may be erect or recumbent. In the latter case one limb of the anticline is *overfolded,* and the strata composing it are overturned.

FIG. 176. Anticlinal fold near St. Abbs Head, Scotland. (Geikie.)

FIG. 177. Two anticlines enclosing a syncline truncated above. (Geikie.)

(c) *Isoclines.* When the limbs of a fold are parallel an isocline is produced. The limbs of such a fold may stand vertically or they may be inclined. In the latter case some portion of the strata involved will always be overturned, *i. e.,* their original surface now

FIG. 178.   Synclinal fold near Banff, Scotland.   (After Geikie.)

lies below. Nearly horizontal isoclines are produced by overfolds and underfolds.

In a region of isoclinal folds, the most important problem confronting the stratigrapher is the recognition of the repetition of strata and the proper relationship between them. It is evident that a succession of strata, such as is shown in Fig. 179, *a,* may be interpreted as all belonging to one limb of a fold, and therefore representing a continuous series, or as representing one or more isoclinal folds. According to the first interpretation, the sediments have great thickness, and there is a recurrence of similar beds, while, according to the second interpretation, the series is much thinner and the recurrence of beds is only apparent, there being an actual repetition of the same beds. The problem is often a difficult one to solve, and depends upon the identification of the similar beds as parts of the same bed. A knowledge of the degree of folding characteristic of the region in question and a knowledge of the characters and thicknesses of the formations involved in other and undis-

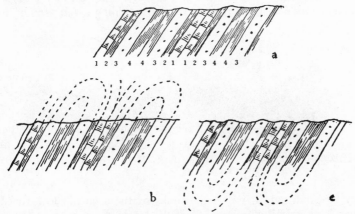

FIG. 179. Isoclinal strata, showing repetition of strata (*a*) and two methods of reconstructing them (*b, c*).

turbed regions will often serve to settle the question. If more than two kinds of beds are involved, the order of repetition will often give a clue to the original condition. Thus in a closely folded district, the strata within the same fold will be repeated in inverse order, as shown in Fig. 179, *a*.

This generally is conclusive evidence of repetition by folding. If this point is settled, the next question is: Which bed is the upper and which is the lower of the series? If the character of the folds can be determined by inspection, the proper relation will at once appear, for if, when beds 4 and 4 come in juxtaposition, they present the upper ends of the fold, *i. e.*, they are parts of an anticline, bed 4 is the oldest and originally the lowest of the series (Fig. 179, *b*).

If, however, the two limbs of the folded bed 4 join below the surface in a concave or synclinal fold, bed 4 is the youngest of the series, and formerly overlay all the others. When the actual type of folding cannot be observed, an examination of the beds themselves will often reveal their relationships. Thus, if bed 3 shows normal ripple marks, footprints or other markings (see Chapter XVII) on the surface of any layer facing bed 2, it is evident that the surface of 3 next to bed 2 was the upper surface of that bed, and that the strata are related, as in Fig. 179, b, bed 3 being older than bed 2. If, however, bed 3 shows on the side of its layers facing bed 2 the natural molds or reverse impressions of the markings named, it is evident that that is the lower side of the bed, and that 3 therefore overlies 2 and is younger, as shown in Fig. 179, c.

(d) *Fan folds.* In regions of sharp folding a fan type of fold

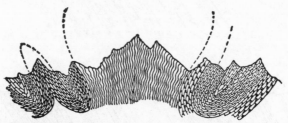

FIG. 180. Generalized section of the fan fold of the central massif of the Alps. (After Heim.)

may be produced, in which the limbs of the arch dip toward each other for a certain distance. Here the lower or concave portions of the fold are pressed inward with the result that the beds at the center of the fold are squeezed out or pinched. This type of fold is characteristic of the Alps and other strongly folded districts (Fig. 180).

(e) *Monoclines.* Typically a monocline is a part of an anticline, cut off by faulting or erosion. Simple monoclines are those in which the strata have no further continuation. Thus the Front Range of the Rocky Mountains is flanked by a series of simple monoclines, all of which face, with their erosion slopes, the crystalline axis of these mountains. In many cases the continuation of these folds is, however, on the opposite side of the crystalline axis. The Blue Ridge extending from New Jersey for the entire length of the Appalachians is a variable series of eastward facing monoclines. The Appalachians themselves are for the most part composed of complementary monoclines, these representing the opposite limbs of anticlines with the axis opened by erosion. Simple flexures of strata are sometimes spoken of as monoclines, but these are in reality strongly asymmetrical anticlines. They may be spoken of as monoclinal flexures, but should not be spoken of as monoclines. (Figs. 181-183.)

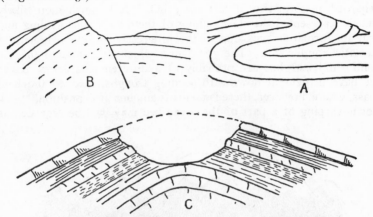

FIG. 181. A, recumbent isoclinal fold, with over- and underfolds. B, monocline due to faulting. C, corresponding monoclines, due to erosion of an anticline.

Anticlinoria and synclinoria. When a succession of anticlines has such a relationship as to make a large anticline, it is called an anticlinorium. The central massif of the Alps may be taken as an illustration. In like manner a large synclinal fold composed of a succession of minor folds is a synclinorium. Such a condition exists

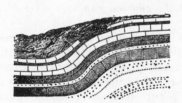

FIG. 182. A simple monoclinal flexure.

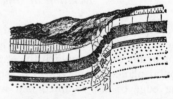

FIG. 183. The same passing into a fault.

in the Mount Greylock massif of western Massachusetts. (Figs. 184, 185.)

Geosyncline and foredeep. The term "geosyncline" was proposed by Dana for the long trough which formed to the east of the Appalachian old land during Palæozoic time. In this trough some

40,000 feet of strata, partly of marine and partly of continental origin, were deposited. It is evident that there must have been a gradual downbending of the old land to permit this extensive series of deposits to accumulate. This depression should not, however, be regarded as primarily of tectonic origin. It is much more likely that it represented the slow sinking of the crust under loading and that its formation was due to the progressive reëstablishment of isostatic equilibrium. The *foredeeps*, which are situated off the continental margins, are probably of a different character. Here we have in general downward-bending troughs, next to the land mass, where, however, there is no great amount of deposition. Such down-warping of a part of the ocean bed may well be regarded as

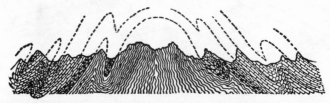

FIG. 184. Anticlinorium. Generalized section in the Alps. (After Heim.)

of tectonic origin, serving to relieve the accumulating stresses in the earth's crust. An examination of the ocean bottom charts will locate the existing foredeeps. (See further, Chapter XXIII.)

Relation of dip, strike and outcrop.

Dip has already been defined as the inclination of the strata from the horizontal. Strike may be defined as the compass-bearing of the line of intersection which the stratum in question makes with a horizontal plane. It may also be spoken of as the compass-bearing of the edge of the inclined bed when cut off by a horizontal plane. The direction of strike is determined by compass, with reference to the true north and south line, *i. e.,* the meridian. A wrong direction is often furnished by the outcrop of the stratum on a sloping surface. If the slope of the surface and the dip of the strata are in the same direction, varying only in amount, or if the slope and dip are in exactly opposite directions, no difference will be observed between outcrop and strike. (Fig. 186a.) Again, if the strata stand vertically, no difference will be observed between outcrop and strike (Fig. 186b), no matter what the surface slope. In all other cases, however, the outcrop on a sloping surface will differ in direction from the true strike of the strata, and is apt to mislead unless this fact is borne in mind. In general, it may be said that the lines made by the intersection of inclined strata with a sloping surface have their *down-slope end* deflected in the direction of the dip of the strata. (Fig. 186c.) If the dip is vertical, this deflection will not alter the direction. If the lines of inter-

FIG. 185. Synclinorium. Mt. Greylock, Mass. (After Dale.)

section run at right angles to the slope of the surface, there is no down-slope end, and hence no deflection. (Fig. 186a.) Again, it should be stated that the true strike and the true dip are always at right angles to each other, and any slope whose intersection with the inclined stratum makes a line at right angles to the line of dip must show the true strike in the outcrops in its surface. (Fig. 186a.)

In the diagram, Fig. 186c, the inclined plane, A B C C′ A′ has its outcrop and strike coinciding where cut by the horizontal surface

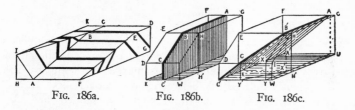

FIG. 186a.   FIG. 186b.   FIG. 186c.

E F G H, but where cut by the inclined surface D E H I the outcrop is deflected toward the down-dip side. It is evident from comparison with Fig. 186b that any vertical plane, as A B X Y Z, whose intersection with the horizontal surface coincides with that of the inclined plane A B C C′ A′, will intersect the inclined surface along a line B X continuous with the line A B and having the same compass direction. This is evidently the true strike, and the angle X B C marks the angle of deflection from this direction of the intersection of the inclined plane on the sloping surface, *i. e.*, the angle of deflection of the strike. Its projection on a horizontal plane is the angle Y′ X′ Y.

The amount of deflection of the strike, by a sloping surface, may be seen by the following consideration: Given a stratum dipping due west, at an agle of 45 degrees, a horizontal surface intersecting this will show the true strike due north and south. Given a second surface, whose intersection with the horizontal surface is at right angles to the strike, i. e., due east and west in the given case, and which also intersects the inclined plane. If this surface is tilted to the vertical, i. e., if the beds are seen in vertical section at right angles to the strike of the inclined bed, the outcrop or intersection of this stratum with the surface will coincide with the dip, i. e., the

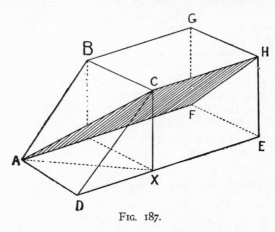

Fig. 187.

line of outcrop as marked by compass direction has been deflected 90° by a tilting of the surface to the extent of 90°. If the surface is tilted 45°, the line of intersection as marked by compass direction will evidently lie halfway between the two or N. 45° E. by S. 45°. (Fig. 187.) Thus in the model the shaded bed A C H F is inclined at 45° from the horizontal, while the surface A B C D is also inclined 45° from the horizontal, but in a direction at right angles to that of the bed A C H F, i. e., its intersection with the horizontal surface is at right angles to the strike of the bed. Thus, by construction, X Y = X C = X D, hence A X, being the diagonal of the square A D X Y, makes an angle of 45° with D X E and with the direction of C H. It is evident that the line of intersection C H between the inclined bed and the horizontal surface B C H G is the true strike. It is also the strike of the vertical bed C H E D. The line C D, the intersection of this vertical plane with

the sloping surface A B C D, has the same compass direction as
C H, and hence represents the true strike. The line A C, however,
the intersection between the surface A B C D and the plane A C
H F, is deflected 45° from that direction, since its direction corresponds to that of the line A X, the diagonal of the square A D X Y.

With a constant surface, as given, and sloping at 45°, the outcrop of a vertical stratum will have no deflection from the line of
strike. As the stratum becomes inclined from the vertical the down-
slope end will be deflected in the direction of dip, a degree for every
degree of departure of the dip from 90°. When 45° of dip are
reached the deflection will be 45°. With decreasing dip, *i. e.,* its
approach to 0°, the deflection will approach 90°, which is reached
when the strata are horizontal. When the slope of the postulated
surface is other than 45° the deflection of the strata must be calculated. Designating the dip of the stratum by θ, the angle of inclination of the sloping surface from the horizontal by ϕ and the deflec-
tion of the outcrop by ψ, we have $\tan \psi = \cot \theta \tan \phi$ or $\psi = \tan^{-1} (\cot \theta \tan \phi)$.

It sometimes happens that only the outcrop of inclined strata is
visible on the surface of a region, the angle of dip not being ascertainable. In such a case the angle of deflection (ψ) can often
be measured directly by taking a reading of the true strike on a
horizontal portion of the surface and another of the apparent strike
on a sloping surface, where the intersection with the horizontal is
at right angles with the strike. The angle of slope of this surface
(ϕ) must also be read by the clinometer. Thus with the values of
two terms of the equation ascertained the third or angle of dip
(θ) may be readily found by the formula $\tan \theta = \tan \phi \cot \psi$ or
$\theta = \tan^{-1} (\tan \phi \cot \psi)$.

An example may further illustrate this: Given an inclined
stratum of which the true strike as shown by the intersection with a
horizontal surface is N. 10° E., while the apparent strike on an inclined surface of the postulated direction of slope is N. 30° W., the
angle of deflection of outcrops between horizontal and inclined surface, *i. e., ψ*, is therefore 40°. The angle of slope of the inclined
surface may be assumed as 30°. Thus the dip is: $\tan \theta = \tan$
30° cot 40° or 0.6882608; $\therefore \theta =$ about 34° 32'. The direction of
dip is to the east, since the deflection was to the west.*

The above formulas apply only to the case where the inclined
surface intersects the horizontal along a line at right angles to the
true strike, *i. e.,* when the directions of slope of the inclined strata
and surface are at right angles to each other. When the direction
of slope of surface varies from this, the amount of deflection will

increase or decrease according as the direction varies toward or away from that of the inclined strata. Thus the more nearly the direction of slope of the inclined surface approaches that of the inclined strata, the more nearly will the amount of deflection approach 90 degrees, while the more the direction of slope approaches the opposite of that of the strata the more nearly will the true strike be approached. The following formulas will serve in such a case. In Fig 188.

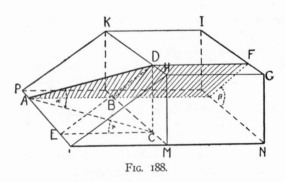

Fɪɢ. 188.

Let A D represent the outcrop of a stratum along a sloping hill-side.

D B represent the dip of the stratum.

a = outcrop dip, or the angle C A D made by the line of outcrop A D with a horizontal plane obtained by placing the clinometer on the line of outcrop A D.

β = the angle of dip of the stratum, B D K or C B D in diagram.

γ = the angle by which the outcrop is shifted by the slope of the hill (A C E).

$$\text{Then } \sin \gamma = \frac{\tan a}{\tan \beta} \text{ or } \gamma = \sin^{-1} \left(\frac{\tan a}{\tan \beta} \right)$$

$$\text{and } \tan \beta = \frac{\tan a}{\sin \gamma} \text{ or } \beta = \tan^{-1} \left(\frac{\tan a}{\sin \gamma} \right)$$

* It should be noted that, as viewed from above, the deflection is in the direction of the dip, but, as viewed from below, looking up the plane, the deflection is in the opposite direction. This must be borne in mind when the compass direction is read; that on a northward sloping plane will be read from above, that on a southward sloping plane from below.

The following method is given by Keilhack (12:65, 66) for the determination of the true dip and strike when observations are possible only on vertical cliffs or quarry walls (Fig. 189):

Given two dip observations on vertical quarry walls, one of 65°, on a wall, the compass alignment of which is N. 45° W., and one of 45° on a wall, the alignment of which is N. 65° E. Draw two lines at a b and a c, the former at an angle of N. 45° W., and the latter N. 65° E., so that they intersect in the point a. At the point a erect perpendiculars to a b and a c. Lay off equal distances on these from a, locating the points e and d, respectively. At d lay off the

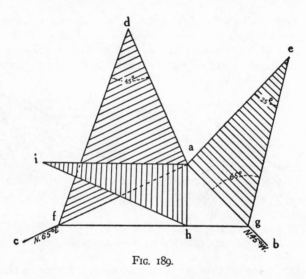

FIG. 189.

complement of the angle observed on the wall represented by a c, that is, the complement of 45°, which is 45°. At e lay off the complement of the angle observed on the wall represented by the line a b, that is, the complement of 65°, which is 25°. Complete the right angle triangles by continuing the hypothenuses until they meet the lines a c and a b, at f and g, respectively. Join f g by a line which represents the true strike of the strata, which if a c and a b are properly oriented can be readily measured. Drop a perpendicular a h from a to f g. This is the direction of dip toward either a or h, as the case may be. Erect a perpendicular to a h at a, and lay off the length a d (=a e), on it, locating point i. Connect i and h, then the angle i h a is the angle of true dip. This will be readily understood if the three shaded triangles are bent at right angles to the plane of the paper, either up or down, until the three sides $a\,d$, $a\,e$ and $a\,i$ coincide with the apices of all three ($d\,e\,i$), meeting in a common point. The triangles $a\,d\,f$ and $a\,e\,g$ would then represent the walls of which the original dip measurements were made, the angles in each case being represented by the angles $a\,f\,d$ and $a\,g\,e$, respectively. A plane resting on the three hypothenuses would represent the inclined stratum.

Strike as affected by pitching axis of folds.

As long as the axis of an anticline or syncline continues horizontal, the outcrops of the beds exposed by planing off the summit of the fold in a horizontal surface will be in the form of parallel bands, the lowest appearing at the center and the repetition of the

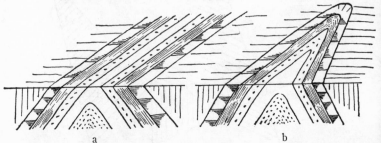

a   b

FIG. 190. *a*, Eroded anticline with horizontal axis. *b*, Eroded anticline with pitching axis, showing resulting outcrops of strata.

beds being in the same order from the center outward in both directions. (Fig. 190, *a*.)

When the axis of the fold is inclined the strike of the strata on opposite sides of the axial plane will converge and finally meet. (Fig. 190, *b*.) In an anticlinal fold the inner strata are the older; in a synclinal fold the inner strata are the younger.

Folding as indication of unconformity.

In a complexly folded region an unconformity may sometimes be detected between two formations not actually seen in contact by the fact that the lower formation is folded much more strongly than the upper one. In this case it is apparent that the lower formation was folded and truncated before the upper one was deposited, after which both were again folded. (See Fig. 191.)

The trend of the Appalachian folds.

The Appalachians furnish a good example of an extended line of folding formed at approximately the same time, *i. e.,* the end of the Palæozoic. They show a remarkable series of curves of varying size, which, with reference to the land, may be called convex or land lobes, when they bulge seaward, and concave or sea lobes, when they extend back into the land. (See the map, Fig. 192.) Beginning in the southwest, we have the following:

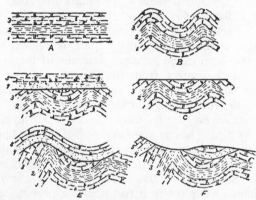

FIG. 191. Diagrams showing the steps by which complexly folded strata are produced. A—C, deposition, folding and truncation of first series; D—F, deposition, folding and erosion of second series, the folding and erosion also affecting the first series.

1. *Louisiana sea lobe,* extending from Texas to central Mississippi with the apex near Little Rock, Arkansas, and with probably a subordinate land lobe at McAlester in Oklahoma.

1a. *Mississippi land lobe,* extending through northern Mississippi and northwestern Alabama.

2. *Birmingham sea lobe,* a small lobe in central Alabama.

2a. *Rome land lobe* with a moderate curve.

3. *Knoxville sea lobe,* with its apex looping around the Knoxville area.

3a. *Alleghany land lobe*—along the main line of the Alleghany Mountains of Virginia.

4. *Pennsylvania sea lobe,* a marked lobe with the apex in central Pennsylvania, the trend changing to nearly east.

4a. *New York land lobe,* the apex being near New York City.

5. *Champlain sea lobe,* east of the Adirondacks.

5a. *Maine land lobe,* along the northwesern boundary of Maine.

6. *Gaspé sea lobe,* a pronounced lobe, the trend actually changing to southeast (40°).

6a. *Cape Breton land lobe,* the change of trend being near Sydney, Cape Breton, the trend again turning northeastward and continuing thus through Newfoundland.

19. *Domes and Basins.* Domes are shortened anticlinal structures with the dip of the strata away from the center in all directions or *quaquaversal.* These dips may vary greatly in different domes. In some cases they are so low as to be scarcely or not at all perceptible (Cincinnati dome); in others they may be 45° or over (Black Hills dome). Many of the low-dipping domes are perceptible as such only by the erosion which has removed their central portion, often leaving a topographic depression. Such low domes have also been called *parmas,* after one of the low east and west ranges which project from the western side of the Urals (which have a north-south trend), and which are formed by gently folded strata, the folds dying out in the plains.

Basins are the reverse of domes, the strata all dipping toward the center. As a rule, basins are composed of gently dipping strata only so that their basin character is recognized only by the rimming outcrops of the lower strata after erosion (Michigan basin, Paris basin, etc.). Between two basins lies generally a more sharply marked anticline, while between two domes a pronounced syncline often occurs. Sometimes the basin structure is ascertained by the location by borings all over the area of the summit (or bottom) of a certain formation, such as a coal bed or a marked sandstone. Thus the basin structure of Iowa is beautifully brought out by the series of contours connecting areas of equal depression beneath the surface of the summit of the St. Peter sandstone. (Iowa Geol. Survey, Vol. VI, p. 316, map.)

Eastern North America is marked by a number of distinct basins and domes, many of which are indicated by the outcrops, while others are recognized only from their general relationship and the occurrence of separating anticlines or synclines. All of these basins and domes owe their final character to the Appalachian folding, but some of them apparently existed during much of Palæozoic time. The accompanying map (Fig. 192) shows the location of these domes and basins. It will be observed that the outermost basins are generally embraced by convex lobes of the Appalachian system, while the concavities of that system are opposite domes or opposite anticlines separating basis. (See also Ruedemann–22; Willis–30.)

The principal basins so far determined are in the northeast, the

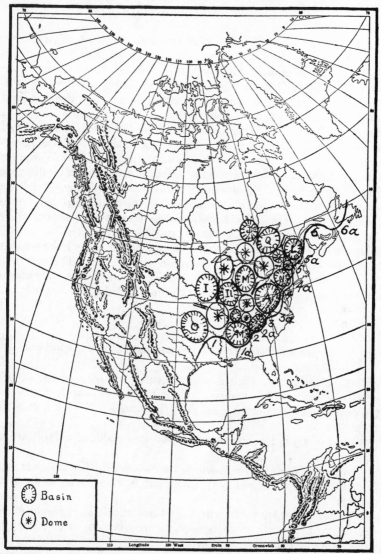

Fig. 192. Map of North America, showing the sinuous trend of the Appalachian folds (see text) and the domes and basis. A=*Alleghany* basin; AM=*Alabama-Mississippi* basin; I=*Iowa* basin; Il=*Illinois* basin; J=*James Bay* basin; L=*St. Lawrence* basin (Montreal, etc.); M=*Michigan* basin; N=*New York* basin; O=*Oklahoma* basin; o=*Ottawa* basin; Q=*Quebec* basin. The line or lines between basins represent anticlines. The domes are: The *Adirondack;* west of this the *Ontario;* north of this the *North Ontario;* southwest of this the *Wisconsin* dome. In the southern area are: the *Cincinnati,* the *Nashville,* and the *Ozark* domes.

St. Lawrence, the Quebec, the Ottawa, and the New York. The Frontenac axis separates the last two basins, and joins the Adirondack dome to the Ontario dome. Northwest of the latter is the North Ontario dome, the Temiscaming syncline separating the two. To the north of this is the James Bay Basin. Next southward of this series is the Alleghany basin, embraced by the Alleghany land lobe of the Appalachians on the east. Northwest of this is the Michigan basin, these two being separated by the Toledo anticlinals. Northwest of the Michigan basin is the Wisconsin dome, which is separated from the North Ontario dome by the deep Superior synclinals. Southwest of the Wisconsin dome is the Iowa basin, and southeast of this the Illinois basin, with the Keokuk anticline between. The Illinois and Michigan basins are separated by the Kokomo anticline. The Cincinnati dome is enclosed by the Illinois, Michigan and Alleghany basins, and south of it is the smaller Nashville dome, with small basins on either side. The southern tier is formed by the Alabama-Mississippi basin in the embrace of the Mississippi land lobe, the Ozark dome, and the Oklahoma basin.

f. *Deformations Due to Dislocation of Strata. Faulting.*

20. *Faults.* "A fault is a fracture in the rock of the earth's crust accompanied by a displacement of one side with respect to the other in a direction parallel with the fracture." (Reid, etc.–18; 19.)

"*A closed fault* is one in which the two walls of a fault are in contact."

"*An open fault* is one in which the two walls of a fault are separated. The same fault may be closed in one part and open in another."

"*A fault surface* is the surface of fracture. It is rarely plane, but where it is without notable curvature over any area it may be called a *fault plane* for that area.

"*A fault line* is the intersection of a fault surface with the earth's surface."

"*The shear zone:* When a fault is made up of a number of slips on closely spaced surfaces, the section of the earth's crust containing these minor faults is called 'shear zone.' This name would also apply to the brecciated zone, which characterizes some faults."

"*A horse* is a mass of rock broken from one wall and caught between the walls of the fault. (Fig. 193a.)

"The fault strike is the direction of the intersection of the fault surface, or the shear zone, with a horizontal plane." The same precautions apply here as in the case of the strike of the strata on a sloping hillside. (See p. 800.) The term "trend" would be better and would avoid confusion.

"The fault dip is the inclination of the fault surface, or shear zone, measured from a horizontal plane. It is never greater than 90°."

"The hade is the inclination of the fault surface or shear zone, measured from the vertical; it is the complement of the dip." Hade is to be preferred to dip to avoid confusion with dip of strata. (See beyond.)

"The hanging wall is the upper wall of the fault." It generally overhangs the vertical.

"The foot wall is the lower wall of the fault." It generally projects footwise at the base.

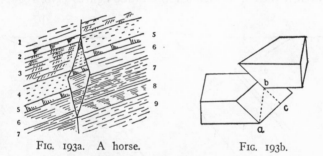

Fig. 193a. A horse.   Fig. 193b.

In stratified rocks faults may be parallel in strike to the strike of the strata, when they are called *strike faults,* or the strike may be approximately at right angles to the strike of the strata, when they are called *dip-faults.* The *bedding fault* is a special type of strike fault, in which the fault plane and bedding plane coincide. Between the strike faults and the dip faults are many directions giving oblique faults. When the general structure of a region is considered, the faults may be called *longitudinal,* when their *strike* (or trend) is parallel to this structure, or *transverse,* when it is across the structure.

The *slip* of a fault is the displacement on the fault surface. The *net* slip is the actual amount of movement between points on the opposite walls originally in contact. The *strike* * *slip* (trend-slip)

---

* Strike and dip here refer to the strike and dip of the fault, not of the strata. Trend and hade would be better.

is the component of the slip parallel with the strike, and the *dip-slip* (hade slip) the component parallel with the dip. Thus (in Fig. 193b) *a b* is the net slip, *a c* the strike-slip and *b c* the dip-slip.

The shift is the relative displacement of the rock masses outside of the zone of displacement, and is used when there are many minor slips making up the shear zone or when the strata in the neighborhood of the fault are bent. It is the relative displacement which would exist had there been only one slip of the same magnitude as the combined minor slips.

Features shown in section of faults.

Throw is the vertical displacement of the strata, as seen in sections, even if the slip is inclined, *d e* in the figures (No. 194, A B).

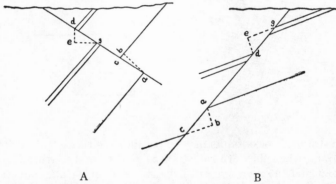

A   B

FIG. 194.   Sections of faults: A, with dip of fault plane across strata; B, with dip of fault plane in same direction as dip of strata.

Heave or horizontal throw is the horizontal displacement of strata seen in section, as *e g* in the figures (No. 194, A B).

Stratigraphic throw. This is the distance between the two parts of a disrupted stratum measured at right angles to the plane of the stratum. (*a b*, Fig. 194, A B.)

The stratigraphic heave, or *dip throw,* is the displacement of the strata in section in the direction parallel to the strata, as *c b* in Fig. 194, A B. In Fig. A it signifies shortening and overlapping of the strata, in Fig. B, lengthening by separation of the strata.

*Features shown in surface appearance of faults, i. e., map features
of faults.*

These features are seen in strike and oblique faults. In the
former the apparent horizontal displacement or *offset* is measured
along the fault line, and is the same as the actual horizontal distance between the ends of the corresponding strata (*a b*). (Fig.
195 A.) This is the same as the trend-slip, but is probably never or
but seldom the actual or net slip. In oblique faults the offset is

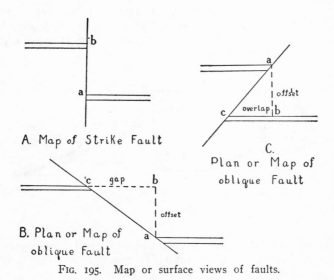

A. Map of Strike Fault

C.
Plan or Map of
oblique Fault

B. Plan or Map of
oblique Fault

FIG. 195. Map or surface views of faults.

measured at right angles between the two ends of the disrupted
strata, as (*a b*) in Figs. 195 B and C, where the trend-slip is
marked by *a c*. In Fig. B, the strata are disrupted and pulled apart;
the distance thus separated is the *gap*. In Fig. C the ends are
pushed past each other, making an *overlap, c b*.

Classification of faults.

Faults have been classified with reference to direction, as *strike*
(and bedding), *dip* and *oblique* faults. With reference to their
movements, they may be classified into *normal* and *reverse* faults,

and with reference to the force producing them they may be classified as *gravity* and *thrust* faults.

With reference to direction. The classification with reference to direction has already been in part explained. It includes strike faults, dip faults and oblique faults, with reference to the strata. With reference to each other, they may be parallel, intersecting or radial, the last when radiating roughly from a point. With reference to a geological region whether raised or depressed (geologically, but not necessarily topographically), they may be peripheral, when running along the periphery of the geological formation, or cross-faults when they cut across it.

With reference to movement. Movement is relative. If the stratum of the hanging wall in any given section is lower, it is designated a *normal fault*. If the stratum of the hanging wall is higher, it is a *reverse fault*.

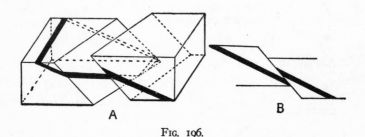

FIG. 196.

With reference to cause. In most cases normal faults probably mean a tension and a down-sinking of the hanging wall, accompanied by an elongation of that part of the crust. In this case the normal fault would also be a *gravity fault*. In like manner the reverse fault generally implies an upward movement of the hanging wall with consequent foreshortening of the crust by overlapping under pressure. In such a case the reverse fault is also a *thrust fault*. Under certain conditions, however, a gravity fault may in section show the conditions of a reverse fault (Figs. 196, A B), for, though the hanging wall has slipped down, owing to the oblique character of the displacement and the dip of the strata, the beds seem actually to have slipped up over each other.

In like manner a thrust fault may in section show the characters of a normal fault, the ends of the strata on the hanging wall being actually lower than on the foot wall. This is shown in Figs. 197, A B.

Terms applied to rock masses formed by or bounded by faults—but not topographically distinguishable from surrounding masses.

1. *A horst* is a mass geologically elevated relatively to the surrounding region and separated from it by faults.

2. *A fault basin* is a region geologically depressed relatively to the surrounding region from which it is separated by faults.

3. *A fault block* is a mass bounded on at least two opposite sides by faults. It may be geologically elevated or depressed relatively to the adjoining region, or it may be geologically elevated

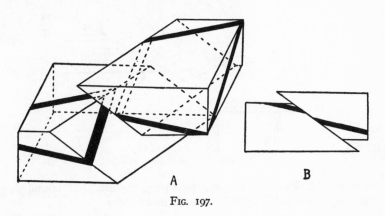

Fig. 197.

relatively to the region on one side and depressed relatively to that on the other.

4. *A fault ridge* is a relatively elongated fault block lying between two faults with roughly parallel trends.

5. *A fault trough* is a relatively depressed (geologically) fault block lying between two faults with roughly parallel trends.

Terms applied to the topographic expression of faults.

1. *Fault scarp*—a scarp or cliff presenting the original surface form of the displacement.

2. *Graben,* or fault scarp valley—a long, narrow topographic depression, the surface expression of a new fault trough. Ex. Rhine Graben; Purgatory Chasm, near Sutton, Mass. It is bounded on both sides by fault scarps facing inward.

3. *Fault scarp ridge*—a topographic ridge bounded by two roughly parallel fault scarps which face outward or toward the surrounding low country.

4. *Fault scarp block*—a topographic block bounded on all sides by outward facing fault scarps.

5. *A tilted block*—a topographic block bounded on all but one side by fault scarps facing outward. The excepted side may be faced by the fault scarp of another tilted block.

6. *A fault scarp basin*—a topographic basin bounded on all sides by fault scarps facing inward.

7. *A complex scarp basin*—a topographic basin bounded on

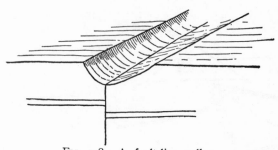

Fig. 198. A fault-line valley.

most of its sides by fault scarps facing inward, but bounded by warpings or in other ways on one or more sides.

Secondary features due to erosion.

1. *Fault-line scarp.* (Davis–4.) This is the fault scarp resurrected in the second cycle of erosion, after the obliteration of the original fault scarps. This may face either way and may be greater or less than the original fault scarp. If it faces in the same direction as the original fault scarp it is *resequent;* if in the opposite direction it is *obsequent.*

2. *Fault-line valley*—a valley cut out along an old fault-line after the obliteration of the original fault scarp. (Fig. 198.)

3. *The graben and fault scarp basin,* the fault scarp ridges, fault scarp block and tilted block may all be destroyed by erosion and then resurrected in the second cycle of erosion. Such cases may be designated by prefixing the word erosion—an erosion graben, erosion fault scarp basin, erosion fault scarp ridge, etc. See, further, Davis (4) and Hobbs (9a); also Chapter XXI.

Stratigraphic significance of faults.

From the stratigraphic viewpoint, strike faults are of the greatest importance, for they often lead to a duplication of strata or to the elimination of certain beds. Many mistakes in stratigraphy have been made because of the nonrecognition of such faults. The Ogden quartzite, for example, regarded as a distinct formation in the western Ordovicic, has been shown to be a repetition of a lower formation due to overthrust. In the Helderberg region of New York, near Kingston, duplication by overthrust has led to the confusion of the stratigraphy. The overthrust New Scotland beds were originally described as the Upper Shaly (Port Ewen), and the higher formation was held to have the same fossils as the lower one.

In discussing the effects of strike faulting on the apparent succession of strata, eight principal cases may be considered:

A. *Gravity faults.* (Figs. 199, A-G.)
1. Dip of fault plane with dip of strata, but at greater angle. (Fig. A.) In this case elimination of beds will take place.
2. At smaller angle. In this case repetition of beds will take place. (Fig. B.)
3. Dip of fault planes against dip of strata. In this case repetition of beds will result. (Figs. C-E.)
4. Dip of fault plane vertical (hade o). The "down dip" portion descends. In this case elimination of beds results. (Fig. F.)
5. The "up dip" portion descends. In this case repetition results. (Fig. G.)

B. *Thrust faults.* (Figs. 199, H-J.)
6. Dip of fault plane with dip of strata, but at greater angle, repetition results. (Fig. H.)
7. Dip at smaller angle—elimination results. (Fig. I.)
8. Dip of fault plane against dip of strata. In this case elimination of strata results. (Fig. J.)

A consideration of the diagram, Figs. A to J, will show that the plane of faulting cuts the inclined strata so as to leave a portion which is limited below by the fault-plane, but may extend indefinitely upward except as limited by the earth's surface. This portion may be called the "up-dip" end of the strata (see the figures). The other part is limited above by the fault plane, and may extend indefinitely downward. This is the "down-dip" end (*d*) of the strata. When the fault plane cuts the obtuse angle between the strata and the surface, *i. e.,* when its dip is greater than that of the strata, the "up-dip" end lies on that side (to the right of the plane in the figures). When it cuts the acute angle, *i. e.,* dips at a less angle than the strata, the up-dip end lies on the acute side (left side of the fault plane in the figures). With the part thus oriented, the

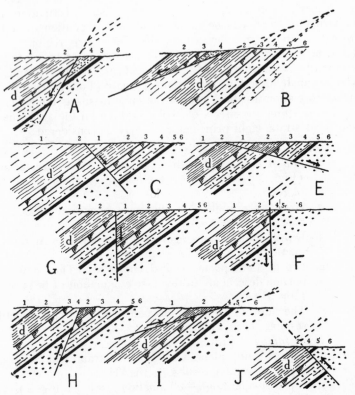

FIG. 199. Sections showing the effects of strike faults in eliminating beds (A, F, I and J) and in repeating beds (B, C, E, G, and H).

general law may be stated that, if the "up-dip" end moves down, we have repetition of strata, while, if the up-dip end moves up, elimination of strata results. Conversely, when strata are repeated or eliminated, the up-dip end must be assumed as having moved either down or up. If the angle of the fault plane is ascertained, the fault will appear to be either thrust or gravity, according to the greater or less angle of inclination of the fault plane, as compared with the strata, and the repetition or elimination of the strata. The general rule can be easily ascertained at any time by a consideration of the simple case shown in Figs. F-G. There it will be readily seen that, when the up-dip end is moved up, elimination results, and when it is moved down repetition occurs, or, to put it the other way, when the down-dip end moves up repetition occurs, but when the down-dip end moves down elimination occurs.*

Faults as indications of unconformity.

If in two superposed formations of similar character and susceptibility to faulting the lower is more complexly faulted than the upper, the indications are that the lower was faulted before the upper was deposited upon it, and that then the two formations are unconformably related.

Relation of folds, faults, cleavage, fissility and joints.

Van Hise has emphasized the close relationships existing between these structures, which may in general be considered as different manifestations of the same forces—thrust and gravity—acting upon heterogeneous rocks under varying conditions. When rocks are under less weight than their ultimate strength, while being rapidly deformed, they will break, with the formation of crevices, of joints, faults, brecciations or fissility, as a result of extensive fracturing. Such rocks are then regarded as being in the *zone of fracture*. When rocks are buried to such a depth that the weight of the superincumbent strata exceeds their ultimate strength, they will flow as plastic material under deforming strains and folding without fracture results. The depth at which this takes place marks the position of the *zone of plasticity and flowage*. The depth at which flowage occurs varies with the character of the rock. For soft shales, Van Hise estimates that probably 500·meters or less of overlying strata will prevent the formation of crevices and fractures to any considerable extent, while for the strongest rocks a depth of perhaps 10,000 meters is required to reach this condition. Cleavage normally belongs in this zone. Between these two is the zone of combined fracture and plasticity. In this zone all the structures occur together in complex relationship. Folds may pass into faults and faults into folds. Fissility and cleavage occur side by side.

* This may be condensed into the slogan—down, down, out.

Downward probably most faults pass into flexures, these flexures dying out at still greater depth. Van Hise thinks that 5,000 meters is a possible depth, at which important faults disappear, though some may extend to the depth of a number of miles. Others, however, regard the necessary depth as very much less.

C. Contact Deformations.

Under this heading may be placed changes in the rock mass as a whole, produced by contact with a deforming agent. The deforming force is heat or cold, and the agents conveying the former are igneous masses (intruded or extruded), hot waters or gases, and the direct rays of the sun. Heating rock masses by any of these agents results in expansion of the rock. The agents conveying cold are glaciers and the cold atmosphere. Their action on the rocks results in contraction. The chief structures produced by these agents singly or in conjunction are prismatic jointing and insolation joints.

21. *Prismatic Jointing Due to Contact with Igneous Masses.* When igneous masses come in contact with sedimentary rocks a prismatic structure is not infrequently developed. This has been noted in clays, marls, sandstones, brown coal, seam coal and even in dolomites. Beautiful examples of this structure are found in the coal seams of Ayrshire.

In all cases of prismatic jointing thus produced, the columns diverge perpendicularly from the surface of the igneous mass which caused the alteration. When the latter is vertical, the columns are horizontal; when it undulates, the columns follow its curvature. It is most probable that this structure is developed as the result of *expansion* of the heated rocks. That such structure can develop under pressure due to expansion is shown by an experiment in which prismatic structure is formed in a box of powdered starch stored for some time in a moist region. The swelling of the starch exerts a pressure in all directions against the sides of the enclosing box, and after a time a series of prismatic columns is developed which radiate from the center outward, being at right angles in most cases to the enclosing walls. Prismatic structure produced by swelling seems also to have occurred in nature, as is shown in the gypsum beds of the Paris Basin (probably originally deposited in part at least as anhydrite), where, as observed by Jukes, some beds are divided from top to bottom by vertical hexagonal prisms. I this structure is due to swelling on hydration, as in the case of the starch cited, it belongs properly under the subject of diagenetic alterations. Thus there are at least three ways in which prismatic structure is produced:

1. Contraction and shrinking, on cooling or drying.
2. Expansion and pressure by heating from without.
3. Expansion and pressure by swellings from hydration.

22. *Insolation Joints.* These are joints produced in massive rocks, such as granite, etc., by the alternate expansion and contraction to which they were subjected under the diurnal heating and cooling. Such joints are parallel to the surface subjected to change in temperature, and are close together in the outer portion of the mass, but farther apart at a depth. They serve an excellent purpose in quarrying operations, which in such rocks would be more difficult otherwise.

D. STRUCTURES IN PART DUE TO DEFORMATION AND IN PART TO EROSION.

23. *Disconformity and Unconformity.* Strata separated by an unrepresented time interval are generally spoken of as unconformably related. Two types of such unconformable relation may be recognized, the *stratic* where the stratification of the formation on both sides of the plane of nonconformity is parallel or nearly so, and the *structural,* where the two sets of strata are inclined at a greater or less angle with reference to each other.

For the first type, in which no folding of the older set of strata is involved, the term *disconformity* has been proposed (Grabau–6: *534*), with the corresponding limitation of the term *unconformity* to the second type, or that in which folding plus erosion of the first set of strata precedes the formation of the second set.

Crosby (2a) has called attention to the unsatisfactory character of the prefix *dis,* since it means divergence rather than parallelism. He prefers to divide unconformity into para-unconformity (parunconformity)—the disconformity of Grabau, and clino-unconformity (clinunconformity) for the angular type with discordant strata. Heim (9) had previously proposed the term *paenaccordanz* for approximate conformity with the strata nearly parallel. This, as Crosby says, is not quite the equivalent of the parunconformity, which implies crustal oscillation, rather than deformation, whereas Heim's term suggests rather gradation between true conformity or *accordanz,* and unconformity or *discordanz.*

Disconformity (Parunconformity, Paenaccordanz). When strata are elevated without folding or other disturbances, and subjected to a prolonged period of erosion, after which their truncated edges are covered by other strata, either marine or nonmarine, a stratic unconformity or disconformity (parunconformity, paenaccordanz) is produced. Here a hiatus, measured by the length of time during which the lower strata were exposed to erosion, plus the amount worn away during this exposure, separates the two series. While this hiatus measures the unrepresented strata it must be borne in mind, however, that it does not represent the length of time during which deposition was interrupted in the region in question. The amount of nondeposition can be determined only when the

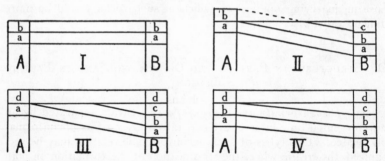

FIG. 200.   Diagrams illustrating the development of disconformities.

amount of erosion during the elevation of the region is known. We may assume two locations A-B, where elevation may occur or some other changes by which deposition continued uninterruptedly at B, while erosion replaced it at A. (Fig. 200, I-IV.) Under assumed conditions a formation *c*, equal in thickness to formation *a*, may be deposited at B, while *b* is eroded at A. If later deposition becomes uniform again in both localities, *d* will rest conformably on *c* at locality B, but disconformably on *a* at A. The hiatus at locality A comprises formations *b* and *c*, but the actual time interval is measured only by the deposition of formation *c* at locality B. In this case the erosion at A was assumed to equal the amount of deposition at B, and hence the hiatus at A represents twice the amount of the time interval involved, as developed at B.

If erosion at A exceeds deposition at B, then the hiatus at A representing a definite time interval will be greater than twice the depositional equivalent of that time interval at B, by an amount proportional to the excess of erosion over deposition. If erosion at A is exceeded by deposition at B, then the hiatus at A will be smaller than twice the depositional equivalent by a corresponding amount. When the amount of erosion is zero at A, the hiatus will be represented by the deposit at B above, when formation *d* will rest disconformably on *b* at A, instead of resting on *a*. (Fig. 200, IV.)

The disconformity at A may be scarcely indicated in the strata, and, if it were not for the fact that formations elsewhere found intercalated between the two strata (as at B) are missing here, the disconformity would not be recognized at all. Very many such disconformities exist in our formations, but few of them are readily recognized on account of the parallelism of the strata. Sometimes an erosion interval and the subsequent encroachment of the sea are indicated by the existence of a basal conglomerate in the later formation, which includes fragments of the earlier one. In some cases, where a rapid transgression of the sea took place, or where fine, residual soil on the old surface is but slightly reworked, such basal rudytes may be wanting; and the two formations follow apparently with perfect conformity upon each other. This is the case with the black Chattanooga shale, where it rests upon the Rockwood clays in the Appalachians. The hiatus here comprises the whole of the Devonic and part of the Siluric as well, yet the contact, though abrupt, appears like a conformable one. Careful examination should, however, reveal in such cases a more or less imperfect upper surface of the lower bed, where some traces of erosion are still visible. When this upper surface is an undoubted deposition surface, *i. e.*, when it shows no traces of erosion whatever, and when furthermore the succeeding beds show no evidence of derivation from the underlying bed, the existence of a disconformity may be doubted.

Examples of contacts where disconformities have been assumed, but are not supported by evidence of erosion, are the contact between the pyritiferous Brayman shale and basal Siluric sandstone (Binnewater) in the Schoharie region, and the Oriskany-Esopus contact in the Helderbergs of eastern New York. In the former case the Brayman shales are known to be of Salina age, while the sandstones on which they rested were regarded as of Lorraine age. There is, however, no evidence of a hiatus comprising most of the Siluric between these two formations, the basal arenyte being too intimately related to the shale and of the same age. The hiatus, known to exist in this region, occurs at a lower level, unless, indeed, as has recently been suggested by Ruedemann and others, the Brayman shale is Upper Ordovicic. The Oriskany-Esopus contact of the Helderbergs also has the aspect of a conformable one. This

conformity if fully established has even a more far-reaching significance. Where a marine formation is abruptly succeeded by a continental formation, the existence of a possible hiatus between the
two must be taken into consideration. Recently the tendency has
manifested itself in certain quarters to greatly multiply the number

Fɪɢ. 201. Basal Palæozoic sandstone resting unconformably upon gneissoid
granite, Williams Canyon, Colorado. (After Hayden.)

of disconformities. (Ulrich–22a.) In many cases the apparent
absence of a formation between two others is merely due to a
change in facies so that the formation is actually present, but in a
different lithic or faunal facies or both.

Unconformity (Clinunconformity, Discordanz). (Figs. 201-202.)

Fɪɢ. 202. Unconformity at Siccar Point, Scotland. *a a*, Ordovicic strata,
d, á, d, Old Red Sandstone. (After Lyell.)

The structural unconformity is readily recognized and the one
generally detected wherever it occurs. This type of unconformity involves the folding of the older strata, and the subsequent
erosion of the folds followed by the deposition of the later strata
upon the eroded edges of the older beds. This type of unconformity

may often become complicated by further folding and erosion, when the complex relationship shown in Fig. 191 is produced.

In all cases of structural unconformity a considerable time in-

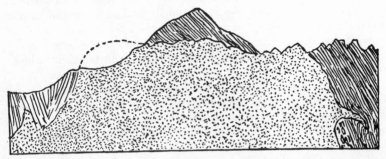

Fig. 203. Cross-section of the Aletschhorn, showing inverted unconformity of schists upon the laccolithic crystallines. (After Baltzer.)

terval remains unrecorded. This is measured by the amount of folding and erosion which the strata have undergone. In this circumstance it is often the case that the last deposited strata prior to the time that folding and erosion commenced were folded down to

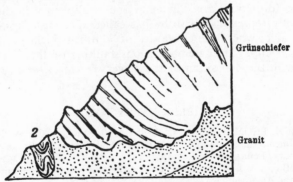

Fig. 204. Detail of the peak of the Aletschhorn. 1, dragging of greenslate at granite contact; 2, infolding of greenslate into the granite.

such an extent that they were preserved from complete removal by erosion. Especially is this the case when the folding has been so intensive as to place the strata in parallel positions, i. e., isoclinal folding. In this case the actual time interval, during which no deposition went on in the region in question, may be determined by a comparison of the ages of the youngest stratum in the folded series with that of the first stratum unconformably overlying the series.

Unconformities and disconformities are often suggested by the occurrence of dikes of igneous material in the lower rocks, which do not penetrate the upper beds. Stronger folding or faulting in the lower than in the upper series also suggests an unconformity, as shown below. As a unique example of an indicated disconformity may be cited the sandstone dikes filling fissures in the Siluric limestones of western New York and Canada, the overlying beds being wholly unaffected by these fissures and dikes because a later deposit. Faulting affecting a lower set of strata, but not a higher one, also indicates a disconformable relationship, and a hiatus representing a sufficient time interval to allow for the removal of the fault scarps of the lower series.

The appearance of an *inverted unconformity*, where the later strata end abruptly against the older ones, may be produced by intense folding of the rocks of a complex region, as shown in the figures of the structure of the Aletschhorn on page 825. (Figs. 203-204.)

Conformable or accordant strata may also show a variety of aspects. Crosby has shown that on the Atlantic coastal plain of North America, the strata wedge out landward.* This wedging conformity, where the formations are thinner in one locality than in the other, though fully represented, Crosby has called *sphenoconformity,* and its correlative, where the strata are of uniform thickness, he calls *planoconformity*. If contemporaneous faulting of the older series goes on with the deposition of the newer, *fractoconformity* is produced.

BIBLIOGRAPHY XX.

1. BROWN, THOMAS C. 1913. Notes on the Origin of Certain Palæozoic Sediments, Illustrated by the Cambrian and Ordovician Rocks of Center County, Pennsylvania. Journal of Geology, Vol. XXI, pp. 232–250.
2. CROSBY, WILLIAM O. 1893. The Origin of Parallel and Intersecting Joints, American Geologist, Vol. XII, pp. 368–375.
2a. CROSBY, W. O. 1912. Dynamic relation and terminology of stratigraphic conformity and unconformity. Journal of Geology, Vol. XX, No. 4, 1912, pp. 289–299.
3. DAUBRÉE, AUGUSTE. 1879. Études synthétiques de Géologie Experimentale, pp. 300–374.
4. DAVIS, WILLIAM M. 1913. Nomenclature of Surface Forms on Faulted Structures. Bulletin of the Geological Society of America, Vol. XXIV, pp. 187–216.

* A part of this is no doubt due to actual breaks in the series, which disappear seaward.

5. GRABAU, AMADEUS W. 1900. Siluro-Devonic Contact in Erie County, New York. Bulletin of the Geological Society of America, Vol. XI, pp. 347–376.

6. GRABAU, A. W. 1905. Physical Characters and History of Some New York Formations. Science, N. S., Vol. XXII, pp. 528–535.

7. HAHN, F. FELIX. 1912. Untermeerische Gleitung bei Trenton Falls (Nord Amerika) und ihr Verhältniss zu Ähnlichen Störungsbildern. Neues Jahrbuch für Mineralogie, etc. Beilage Band XXXVI, pp. 1–41, Taf. I–III, 1912.

8. HEIM, ARNOLD. 1908. Ueber rezente und Fossile Subaquatische Rutschungen und deren Lithologische Bedeutung. Neues Jahrbuch für Mineralogie, etc., 1908, pt. II, pp. 136–157.

9. HEIM, ARNOLD. 1908. Die Nummuliten- und Flysch-bildungen der schweizer Alpen (discusses Accordanz, Discordanz, Paen-accordanz). Abhandlungen der schweizerischen Palæontologischen Gesellschaft, XXXV, 1908, p. 173.

9a. HOBBS, WILLIAM H. 1911. Repeating Patterns in the Relief and in the Structure of the Land. Bulletin of the Geological Society of America, Vol. XXII, pp. 123–176, pls. 7–13.

10. HOW, JOHN ALLEN. 1913. Joints. Encyclopedia Britannica, 11th edition, Vol. XV, pp. 490–491.

11. HYDE, J. E. 1908. Desiccation conglomerates in the Coal Measures-limestone of Ohio. American Journal of Science, Vol. XXV, pp. 400–408.

12. KEILHACK, KONRAD. 1908. Lehrbuch der Praktischen Geologie, 2te auflage, Stuttgart.

13. KOKEN, E. 1902. Ueber die Gekrösekalke des Obersten Muschelkalkes am Unteren Neckar. Centralblatt für Mineralogie, etc., 1902, pp. 74 et seq.

14. LEITH, C. R. 1905. Rock Cleavage. Bulletin of the U. S. Geological Survey, no. 239.

15. LOGAN, SIR W. 1863. Geology of Canada, 1863, pp. 391 et seq.

16. MARSH, OTHNIEL C. 1868. On the origin of the so-called lignites or epsomites. Proceedings of the American Association for the Advancement of Science, Vol. XVI, pp. 135–143.

17. MILLER, W. J. 1909. Geology of the Remsen Quadrangle. New York State Museum Bulletin 126, 1909.

18. REID, H. F.; DAVIS, W. M.; LAWSON, A. C.; and RANSOME, F. L. 1912. Proposed Nomenclature of Faults. Advance Publication, Geological Society of America, Bulletin 24.

19. REID, H. F.; DAVIS, W. M.; LAWSON, A. C., and RANSOME, F. L. 1913. Report of the Committee on the Nomenclature of Faults. Geological Society of America Bulletin, Vol. XXIV, pp. 163–186.

20. REIS, OTTO M. 1909. Beobachtungen ueber Schichten-folge und Gesteins-ausbildungen in der fränkischen Unteren und Mittleren Trias. I. Muschelkalk und Untere Lettenkohle. Geognostische Jahreshefte, Bd. XXII, 1909 (1910), pp. 1–285, plates I–XI.

21. ROTHPLETZ, A. 1910. Meine Beobachtungen ueber den Sparagmit und Birikalk am Mjösen in Norwegen-Sitzungsbericht. K. bayrischen Akademie der Wissenschaften, Mathematisch-Naturwissenschaftliche Klasse, Bd. XV, 1910, 65 pages and maps.

22. RUEDEMANN, RUDOLF. 1910. On the Systematic Arrangement in the elements of the Palæozoic platform of North America. New York State Museum of Natural History, Bulletin 140, pp. 141–149.

22a. ULRICH, E. O. Revision of the Palæozoic Systems. Bulletin of the Geological Society of America, Vol. XXII, pp. 281–680.

23. VAN HISE, CHARLES R. 1904. A Treatise on Metamorphism. United States Geological Survey, Monograph XLVII.

24. WAGNER, GEORG. 1913. Stylolithen und Druck-suturen. Geologische und Palæontologische Abhandlungen (Koken), N. F., Band XI (XV), Heft 2, pp. 101–127, taf. X–XII. (With literature.)

25. WELLER, STUART. 1899. A Peculiar Devonian Deposit in Northeastern Illinois. Journal of Geology, Vol. VII, pp. 483–488.

26. WOODWORTH, J. B. 1896. On the fracture system of joints, with remarks on certain great fractures. Boston Society of Natural History Proceedings, Vol. XXVII, pp. 163–183, pls. 1–5.

Supplementary.

27. BÖHM, A. (Edler von Böhmersheim) 1910. Abplattung und Gebirgsbildung. Leipzig und Wien; p. 83.

28. POKELS, F. 1911. Aenderungen der Rotationsgeschwindigkeit der Erde als geologischer Faktor. Geologische Rundschau, Band II, pp. 141–144.

29. TAYLOR, F. B. 1885. On the Crumpling of the Earth's Crust. American Journal of Science. 3rd ser., Vol. XXX, pp. 259–277.

30. WILLIS, BAILEY. 1907. A Theory of Continental Structure Applied to North America. Geological Society of America. Bulletin Vol. XVIII, pp. 388–412.

CHAPTER XXI.

THE PRINCIPLES OF GLYPTOGENESIS, OR THE SCULPTURING OF THE EARTH'S SURFACE.

During every geological period the complementary processes of erosion and deposition were in evidence, sometimes the one predominating and sometimes the other. Deposition added material to the crust locally, erosion removed it elsewhere. The results of erosion in terms of form are the relief features, and the process viewed from this angle is a process of sculpturing. The genesis of land forms is thus in large part a genesis by sculpturing or *glyptogenesis.**

At all times, wherever land existed, erosion produced its characteristic forms, controlled to a large degree by the character of the material on which the forces of erosion were at work. Many of the old erosion forms were buried beneath accumulations of new rock material, and were thus preserved in a fossil form. Where much deformation and alteration of the rocks has since occurred, those older land forms may have become unrecognizable. Nevertheless, in many cases they are still in part preserved, and from a study of modern types we may gain a sufficient insight into the order of the development to enable us to reconstruct ancient examples from partly preserved remains.

THE CYCLE OF EROSION. It is needful at the outset for us to have a clear conception of the entire cycle of erosion as expressed in land forms. Beginning with the young or newly formed land, which may be a recently emerged coastal plain, a dome, anticline, fault block, etc., the development of a drainage system as outlined in Chapter III brings with it a progressive sculpturing and the production of a series of topographic features, which carries the landscape through all stages of youthfulness to maturity and on toward old age. With the completion of the cycle in a moist climate the condition of a peneplain is reached, when the region is worn down to essential uniformity, with but little elevation above sea-level.

* From γλυπτός, carved, and γένεσις, origin

The encroaching sea may finish this surface into an almost absolutely level plane of marine planation. In an arid climate a more or less sloping plane (conoplain) or a series of planes will be formed in the old age of the landscape, these depending for their character, slope, and elevation on the forces controlling the local base level of erosion.

After the cycle has thus been completed, a new one may be inaugurated by an uplift of the land or lowering of the sea-level or other base-level of erosion or by a climatic change, etc. Thus a second cycle of erosion will be inaugurated which, if left undisturbed, will continue to its end, and a second peneplain or chonoplain is produced. The cycle may at any time, however, be interrupted by a premature rejuvenation, the earlier cycle remaining thus incomplete.

Considering the principal land forms resulting from land sculpture, we may first note the characteristics of immature stages, and later on those of the completed cycle. Strata unaffected by orogenic disturbances will be considered first, and later on those which have suffered deformation. The types to be discussed include the forms resulting from the normal sculpturing of 1. the coastal plain, 2. the monoclinal strata, 3. the dome, 4. the anticline, 5. the basin, and 6. the syncline. Faulted structure (7) will be briefly noted, and after this the peneplain (8) will be considered more at length.

A. EROSION FEATURES IN UNDISTURBED STRATA.

1. THE COASTAL PLAIN.

The submerged deposits on the continental or island margin, of which the sub-coastal plain is composed, represent most typically a series of clastic sediments, in part land-derived and in part thalassigenous or derived from organic or biogenic, rarely chemical, deposits formed in the sea. Stratification is well developed, and the phenomenon of progressive overlap is generally well marked. Regressive phenomena, accompanied by landward erosion and seaward retreat of shore features, and transgressive phenomena accompanied by overlap of the upper beds of later formations on the eroded surfaces of earlier ones, are all commonly represented in the structure of the sub-coastal plain. When this is elevated into a coastal plain by epeirogenic movements, or into a mountain by orogenic disturbances, these structures will to a greater or less extent influence the erosion topography induced upon these surfaces.

The coastal plain has normally a gentle dip seaward, while, close

o the margin of the old land, the upper thin edges of the last de-
osited layer, provided continuous subsidence precedes the elevation
f the coastal plain, lap over the earlier layers and rest directly
pon the old land.   These overlapping edges of the strata are gen-
rally the first to be removed again, and in their place will appear a
hallow valley running parallel to the upper edge of the coastal plain,
he *inner lowland* of the normal coastal plain erosion topography.

 Dissection of the Coastal Plain.   Streams originating upon the
oastal plain as the "run-off" of the rain and snow-fall, continue
own the slope of the surface to the sea in more or less parallel
ines, and with more or less directness, according to the angle of
lope.   These *consequent* streams, together with the *extended conse-
uents, i. e.,* the old streams of the old land, now extended across
he coastal plain to the new sea margin, will incise more or less

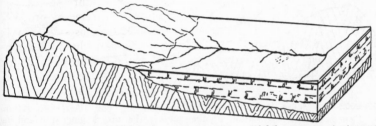

FIG. 205.   The emerged coastal plain with the youthful consequent streams
          bearing a few simple insequents.

parallel channels across the coastal plain.   When these channels are
cut down to the level of the "ground water," they will be supplied
by springs with a permanent stream, whereupon down-cutting may
proceed at an accelerated pace.   Along the margin of the main
streams, lateral tributaries will begin, and, cutting headward, will
soon diversify the original channel of the streams.   These lateral
branches are the "insequent" streams of the physiographer, since
they are not consequent upon a constructional slope.   Insequent
streams, furthermore, cut their channels backward from the edge of
a stream, and only deepen their channels as the channels of the consequents to which they are tributary are deepened.   Consequent
streams, on the other hand, cut their channels downward, headward
extension being generally a secondary mode of growth.   Near the
old land the insequents will remove the feather edges of the coastal
plain strata, as indicated above, and here will come into existence a
stripped belt, expressed topographically in a broad, shallow valley,
the inner lowland, containing the enlarged insequents, now more

generally spoken of as the *subsequents*. This inner lowland is bounded on one side by the stripped slope of the old land and on the other by the cut edges of the coastal plain strata. If these latter contain resistant members of limestone or sandstone, they will present an escarpment or cliff of some steepness. As the inner lowland is widened and deepened the cliff increases in height because lower and lower members of the coastal plain series are discovered by the removal of the overlapping higher members. This will continue until the consequent has reached a condition of grade, and so will arrest further deepening of the channels of its tributaries. Beyond this point the cliff will be gradually lowered, through continued backward pushing, until the plane of erosion and the sloping

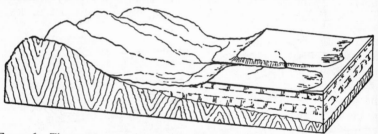

FIG. 206. The same coastal plain as shown in Fig. 205. After dissection and the formation of the cuesta; the broad inner lowland is occupied by the subsequents.

surface of the coastal plain intersect near the seashore, when the condition of peneplanation is reached.

The topographic element produced by the dissection of the coastal plain is known as the *cuesta*. Its main elements are the "inface" or cliff facing the old land, and the gentle outward slope conforming to the slight inclination of the coastal plain strata, and formed by its top member. Between the cuesta and the old land is the stripped belt or inner lowland, occupied by the subsequent stream. This is tributary to the consequent stream, which dissects the cuesta transversely. (Figs. 205, 206.)

Deposition in dissected coastal plain. A moderately dissected coastal plain in which transverse consequent and longitudinal subsequent valleys are formed may be affected by partial subsidence, in which case erosive activity not only comes to a standstill, but deposition will actually take place in the valleys, if subsidence has been sufficient to result in the entrance of the sea into the valleys, and the consequent drowning of the same. Examples of drowned consequent valleys are seen to-day in Chesapeake and Delaware bays which dissect the Atlantic coastal plain of North America. A drowned subsequent valley or inner lowland is seen in Long Island Sound, the northern edge of Long Island forming the more or less ice-disturbed and moraine-covered escarpment, the inface of a normal cuesta, now largely submerged. Deposits of the present geologic epoch are being formed within these valleys, which were cut in the partly consolidated Tertiary and Cretacic clays and sands, the stratification of which is almost horizontal. The result of such deposition will be that horizontally stratified modern deposits come to rest upon the Cretacic or later strata of similar position which form the bottoms of these eroded valleys, and that laterally they will become continuous with or merge into the horizontal beds of Cretacic or Tertiary age, of the valley sides and of the rewashed material of which these modern strata will in part at least be composed. Since these old drowned valleys have in places a width of a score of miles or more, and since it is not at all unlikely that conditions like the present one may have existed at different stages in the formation of the Atlantic coastal plain, of North America— not to mention earlier coastal plains of this and other countries— the significance of these facts becomes apparent. The commingling of the older and newer organic remains is another feature characterizing such deposits. Thus, in Chesapeake Bay, modern oyster shells are found attached to oyster shells of Miocenic age.

Effect of dissection and peneplanation of coastal plain strata on outcrop. Where normal deposition with continuous subsidence and progressive overlapping of strata occurs the undissected coastal plain will show on elevation the highest stratum only, which then rests directly by overlap against the old land. The formation of the inner lowland results in the exposure of a belt of lower strata next to the old land, while the edge of the higher stratum is farther and farther removed from the old land. As the inner lowland is widened and deepened, lower strata appear by erosion of the overlapping ones, and the map of a strongly dissected coastal plain region will show several belts of strata next to the old land, the lowest exposed one being nearest it. These belts of strata will also appear on the banks of the consequent streams, but will progressively disappear below the valley bottoms in a seaward direction and from the lowest to the highest. When the coastal plain has been reduced to a peneplain, the various strata composing it will outcrop in a series of more or less parallel bands from the lowest next to the old land to the highest of the series. This last will appear as a belt near the point where the coastal plain passed beneath the sea-level at the time the peneplanation was completed. Thus a glance at the geologic map of New York State shows a series of color bands representing the various strata of an ancient (Palæozoic) coastal plain, the lowest appearing around the Adirondack old land and along the border of the crystallines north of Lake Ontario, while each later one is further and further removed southward, until the latest, the Carbonic strata, scarcely extend into New York State at all. Now, most if not all of these strata once extended far toward, if not entirely to, the Adirondacks, and to the Laurentian old land in Canada. Their present distant outcrop is in large measure due to peneplanation across gently inclined strata. Subsequent erosion has, of course, pushed the edges of many of these strata further south than where they were left at the end of the period of peneplanation, but the amount of this later removal was small as compared with the greater separation of outcrops effected by peneplanation. It was formerly thought that the outcrop of the edges of strata along the margin of the old crystalline land marked their former extent. Since the strata of eastern North America crop out in a series of belts margining the old-land, each later formation falling short of the preceding one, it was believed that North America rose by a series of steps, the sea, at the end of each period, retreating to the region near which the next later formation now comes to an end. From the characters of the formations, however, it appears that they accumulated in a subsiding sea, and that each formation in turn overlapped the preceding ones, with few exceptions.

The present appearance of the outcrops is due wholly to erosion, the higher formations having suffered most. Many of the later Palæozoic strata of the eastern United States derived their clastic material from the Appalachian region on the southeast, and their northwestward limit in some cases was far beyond the border lines of the present Canadian old land, a great portion of which may in fact have been entirely submerged during a part of the Palæozoic. That the erosion of the strata continued until peneplain conditions were reached is shown, not only by the fact that the remnants of this old surface in the eastern United States form parts of a somewhat warped plain rising southward, but also and more especially by the fact that this surface is not formed by a single hard stratum, but by various hard beds which have been beveled across. Thus the Alleghany plateau of western New York, which is a characteristic part of this old peneplain, is composed of the beveled edges of successively higher southwestward dipping strata as shown in the following diagram. (Fig. 207.)

This beveling of the strata can be interpreted only as the result of peneplanation, in other words, when the level of erosion was reached, erosion could go no further because this surface stood so close to sea-level that the streams could not cut lower. Subsequent elevation would permit of the cutting of lowlands on the softer strata (5, 9 and 12), leaving the harder ones in relief.

That this beveling of the strata is due to erosion and not to a

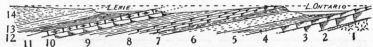

FIG. 207.   Section across New York State, from Ontario to the Pennsylvania line, showing the peneplanation of the strata along the dotted line, and the subsequent carving of valleys on the softer strata. 1, Archæan; 2, Potsdam or Beekmantown; 3 and 4, Black River-Trenton; 5, Utica-Lorraine; 6, Queenston; 7, Medina-Clinton-Rochester; 8, Lockport-Guelph; 9, Salina; 10, Bertie-Cobleskill; 11, Onondaga; 12, Marcellus; 13, Hamilton; 14, Genesee-Portage-Chemung. 2-6, Ordovicic; 7-10, Siluric; 11-14, Devonic.

shoreward thinning is shown by the fact that the material of the strata does not change toward the beveled portion as it would if that part had marked a progressively retreating shore accumulation, while the fact that the lowest portion of the beds extends farther than the higher portions shows that the thinning cannot represent an overlapping transgressive series. The following diagrams illustrate the thinning of the strata by overlap and by beveling. (Figs. 208, A B.)

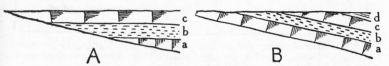

FIG. 208.   Diagram illustrating the thinning of strata: A, by overlap; B, by beveling through erosion.

Ancient Coastal Plains Showing Cuesta Topography.

Looking over the geological maps of the world, many examples of ancient coastal plain strata, in which a cuesta topography has been revived after peneplanation, are found. The Palæozoic strata of New York and Canada furnish excellent examples, though part of the topography is drowned, or obliterated by subsequent deposits. (Figs. 209, 210.)

A nearly continuous cuesta inface may be traced along the south shore of Lake Ontario from Rochester to Niagara, and thence northwestward through Canada, the Indian Peninsula between Georgian Bay and Lake Huron, and across the Manitoulin Islands. Turning westward on these islands, it passes through the Northern Peninsula of Michigan, and then turns southward, forming the peninsula between Lake Michigan and Green Bay, beyond which it continues southward through eastern Wisconsin.

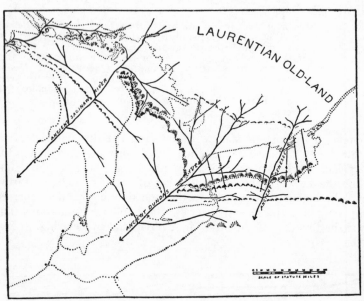

FIG. 209. Map showing the probable drainage and topography in eastern North America during Tertiary time, when a revived cuesta-topography was produced.

The cuesta is cut out of the Lower Siluric formations which here consist of the capping hard Niagaran (Lockport) limestones and dolomites, underlain by softer shales and sandstones, into which the inner lowland has been cut. In New York the softer strata are thickest while the overlying hard beds thin eastward. Here the inner lowland is very deep, approaching in places a thousand feet below the top of the cuesta. Most of it is submerged by the waters of Lake Ontario. Eastward from Rochester the cuesta becomes less defined, owing to the failure of the hard capping stratum, and it finally unites with the next higher cuesta to the south, to form the Helderberg escarpment. Westward the limestone thickens, and hence the escarpment becomes bold, but the inner lowland suffers. In Western Ontario this inner lowland is largely obliterated by drift deposits, but it appears again in the basin of Georgian Bay. The basin of Green Bay likewise occupies a part of the inner lowland in its western extension, south of which the deposits of drift somewhat obscure it. There is, however, a chain of small lakes (Winnebago, etc.) which shows its continuation. Lake Winnipeg

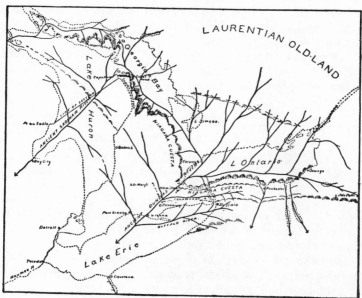

Fig. 210. A later stage, showing probable river adjustment by capture, etc., as deduced from the present topography. The partial blocking of the valleys by glacial drift, the glacial over-deepening of others, and the subsidence of the land on the northeast, produced the present topography and drainage.

in Canada lies in a similar inner lowland faced on the west by a cuesta inface of the Niagaran formation. In a few places the cuesta is broken by ancient or by modern stream channels. The most pronounced of the former is at the western end of Lake Ontario (Dundas Valley) and in the channel connecting Georgian Bay with Lake Huron, and continued in Saginaw Bay (Saginaw River Valley). (Grabau–16: 37-54.) The most pronounced of the modern stream channels are those of the Genesee and the Niagara.

North and west of this cuesta series, i. e., nearer to the old land, are several smaller cuestas, less continuous, but still in places quite pronounced. These are carved out of the Ordovicic limestones, where they rest on softer shales or sandstones. (Wilson–31.) South of the Niagara cuesta are several others cut into the Devonic strata. The most pronounced is that of the Onondaga limestone crossing the Niagara River at North Buffalo and extending east across the State until it culminates in the Helderberg edge northwest of Albany. This extends northwestward from Buffalo, and crosses Lake Huron as a submerged ridge, finally reappearing in Mackinac Island, beyond which it merges with the cuesta formed by the Hamilton strata, which continues southward along the eastern border of Lake Michigan.

Throughout western New York and Canada this cuesta is buried under drift, but in Lake Huron, though submerged, it forms a cliff 400 feet high. (Fig. 211.) A still higher but generally less

FIG. 211. Cross-section of Lake Huron, from Point au Sable (a) across nine-fathom ledge (b) to Cape Hurd (c), showing the submerged cuesta and inner lowland.

pronounced cuesta extends eastward across central and southern New York, formed by the sandy Upper Devonic strata. Eastward this, too, merges into the Helderberg escarpment.

The Palæozoic outcrops of northern Europe also fall into line as parts of a series of discontinuous cuestas. Thus the drowned region of the Baltic shows an Ordovicic cuesta series, partly submerged in the islands of Öland, Dagö and the coast of Esthonia, the infaces of which faced the old land of Sweden and Finland. The drowned inner lowland includes the Kalmar Sund in Sweden and the Gulf of Finland in Russia. A second discontinuous cuesta formed of Siluric rocks runs in a general way parallel to the first and farther to the south and east. This comprises the islands of Gotland and Ösel, and continues in the Baltic provinces of Russia. Central Europe has its main Mesozoic cuestas in the Swabian Alp which extends across southern Germany as a bold escarpment of horizontal Jurassic limestones from Württemberg to the borders of the Bohemian forest.

England, too, has its Palæozoic cuesta in the westward facing Wenlock Edge of Siluric strata. It has two distinct Mesozoic cuestas: one in the range of oolite cliffs which extends from Dorset to the Yorkshire coast and forms the Cotswold hills of middle England with the Worcester lowland in front of it, and the other in the chalk cliffs which extend in like manner from the Channel to Flamborough Head, and forms the Chiltern hills of middle England, the Oxford lowland lying to the west of them. (Fig. 212.)

All of these topographic features are revived, being probably in the second if not later cycle of erosion. The coastal plain of Alabama, on the other hand, furnishes an example of a cuesta apparently in the first cycle. The cuesta itself is formed by the Tertiary strata of the coastal plain, the inface rising rather abruptly 200 feet above the lowland and being locally known as Chunnenugga ridge. On the broad upland dissected by short streams running down the

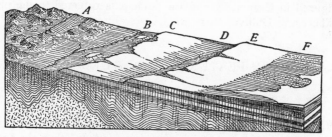

Fig. 212. Stereogram of the Mesozoic coastal plain of central England: A, old land of Palæozoics (Wales); B, Worcester lowland on Triassic sandstone; C, Cotswold hills or Oolite cuesta; D, Oxford lowland on Upper Jurassic and Lower Cretacic clays, etc.; E, Chiltern hills or chalk cuesta; F, Tertiary coastal plain. (After Davis.)

inface (obsequent streams) lie the "hill prairies," the surface being formed by a resistant limestone bed. This slopes south to the coast and supports the "coastal prairies." Extensive pine forests also grow on this surface. The inner lowland, which lies between the inface and the old land formed by the rocks of the Appalachians, is so level that rainfall drains slowly and roads are impassable in wet weather. "It is called the 'Black Prairie' from the dark color of its rich soil, weathered from the weak underlying limestone. This belt includes the best cotton district of the state." (Davis–5:135.)

Minor Erosion Forms of Horizontal Strata. Among these is the *mesa* or flat-topped table mountain, the surface of which is formed by a resistant capping stratum. It is limited on all sides by erosion cliffs, and it may constitute one of the last remnants of a once widespread series of formations. The name "mesa" is also sometimes applied to a tableland cut out of a peneplaned region, where the strata are disturbed or where the material is crystalline rock. Its restriction to an erosion remnant of horizontal strata is desirable. When the mesa has been reduced to small dimensions so that it has no longer an extended flat top—the name *butte* applies, though here again the designation is not always uniform, for the name is applied to hills of varying origin, even to volcanic cones. Restriction here would serve the cause of accuracy and precision.

A *tepee-butte* is a conical erosion hill, so named from its resemblance to the Indian wigwam or tepee. Tepee-buttes abound in the region east of the Front Range in Colorado, where they are formed by the resistance to erosion of a core of organic limestone which is surrounded by soft, easily eroded shale. These have been described and figured in Chapter X and the student is referred to the paper by Gilbert and Gulliver there cited.

B. EROSION FEATURES IN DISTURBED STRATA.

2. THE MONOCLINE.

When the old land, together with the edge of the coastal plain lapping onto it, suffers an uplifting which does not affect the coastal plain strata at a distance from the old land, a monoclinal structure

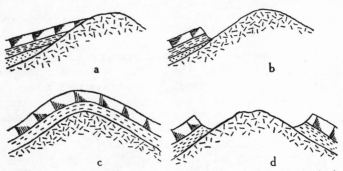

FIG. 213. Diagrams illustrating the formation of a simple hog-back (a, b), and of complementary hog-backs (c, d).

is given to the edge of these coastal plain strata. On these up-bending ends of the strata erosion will proceed in much the same manner as in the normal coastal plain, and a topography comparable to the cuesta and differing from it only in the greater inclination of the component strata will be produced. The resistant stratum will produce a ridge, one side of which is composed of the steeply dipping surface of the resistant stratum and comparable to the gentle outward slope of the cuesta surface, while the other is formed of the eroded edges of the strata composing the ridge, and is comparable to the inface of the cuesta. (Fig. 213, a b.). Topographic elements of this type are common on the flanks of the Rocky Mountain Front Range where they are familiarly known as "hog-backs." In some cases these hog-backs may, however, be parts of normal anticlines of which the crystalline mountain mass was the original core. The outcropping edges of the component strata will not appear different on the map from those of the normal cuesta, and the phenomenon of overlap is perhaps as frequently preserved in this case as in that of the dissected normal coastal plain.

3. Erosion Features of the Structural Dome.

Wherever strata are locally uplifted into the form of a broad, flat dome, as in the case of the Black Hills, a radial arrangement of consequent streams will come into existence, and a series of radial consequent valleys will be incised in the surface of the dome. The birth of numerous insequent streams at the summit of the dome will cause a gradual opening up of a series of summit valleys. If the surface stratum is a resistant one, while the stratum next below is readily eroded, a compound summit valley, drained by tributaries of the various consequent streams, will come into existence on the soft stratum, while the eroded edge of the hard stratum will surround this valley as a series of ramparts broken at intervals by the breaches through which the drainage is carried out. The character of the enclosing rampart will be that of a breached circular hog-back with an erosion inface and a steeply inclined outward slope. Continued erosion by the tributary (subsequent) streams will widen the circumference of the rampart by pushing it down slope, and thus increasing the size of the summit valley. If a second resistant layer is discovered beneath the soft layer on which the valley was opened, it may be breached in a manner similar to the first, and a second inner set of encircling hog-back ridges may come into existence surrounding an inner valley opened up on a second soft layer. Several sets of such encircling hog-backs may thus be produced, two sets always being separated by a circular valley which drains through one or more branches in the outer hog-back ring. If the level to which erosion is carried, i. e., base-level, is reached while the center is still composed of a soft stratum, a central lowland will remain as in the case of the Weald of southeastern England. If, however, erosion goes on until the underlying crystallines are exposed a central mountainous area will remain as in the case of the Black Hills. (Fig. 214.)

In outcrop, an eroded dome will show the strata in a series of concentric rings, the oldest at the center and the youngest outer-

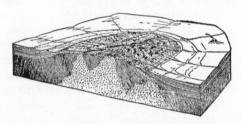

FIG. 214. Stereogram of the Black Hills dome, showing the mountainous center formed by the resistant crystallines, and the rimming hog-backs and valleys. (After Davis.)

most. As in the case of the cuesta and the monocline, the ultimate result of erosion of such a dome is the obliteration of the ridges, and the reduction of the dome as a whole to peneplain condition. When that has occurred all the strata involved will be beveled off toward the center of the dome, their lower edges projecting farthest up onto the dome. (Fig. 215, A.) A structure of this kind is not infrequently mistaken for a marginal thinning of strata on the shore

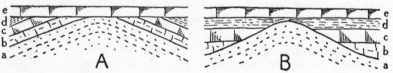

FIG. 215. Diagrams illustrating the thinning of strata under cover toward the center of a dome: A, by erosion; B, by overlap.

of an island. In this case, however, the strata should overlap each other, and the higher portions reach farthest onto the dome. (Fig. 215, B.) The thin overlapping edges, moreover, should be of a clastic character, and composed in part of material derived from the shore of the island, while, in the case of the eroded dome, the strata on both sides, being part of a formerly continuous whole, should be of the same character, and show no shore features on the thin edge. Furthermore, strata deposited in this area, subsequently to the erosion of the dome (Fig. 215, A, b d e) would progressively come to rest upon the beveled edges of older and older strata, in the direction of the center of the dome, the relation being an unconformable one. This same type of structure might, of course, be produced by a gradually retreating sea from a rising island, so that each succeeding stratum reaches to a less distance than the preceding. In that case, however, the ends of the successive strata would show shore characteristics, and fragments of the lower might be enclosed in the higher formations.

The Cincinnati and Nashville domes are typical examples of low domes with very gently inclined strata formed and eroded during Palæozoic time. As pointed out repeatedly by Dr. Foerste (15) and others, the lower Siluric (Niagaran) strata found on the flanks of the dome conform in character to the first of the two cases cited, all the evidence pointing to the fact that the Niagaran strata formerly extended across the domes, which therefore formed in late Siluric or early Devonic time. As the eroded edges of the strata are disconformably overlain by Mid-Devonic limestones, or by Upper Devonic or younger black shales, it is evident that the erosion of the dome preceded Mid-Devonic time. This probably occurred during the Helderberg period, while the greater part of North America was above sea-level.

Subsequently to the deposition of the higher Palæozoic over this pre-Devonic truncated dome, one or more additional domings took place, followed by erosion which again exposed the lowest central strata.

4.   Erosion Features on the Anticline.

The anticline differs from the dome chiefly in the fact that the longitudinal axis is many times longer than the transverse. Since the anticline must come to an end in either direction by a downward pitching of the axis, the characteristics of the simple anticline may be considered those of an excessively elongated dome. While domes, however, generally occur singly, anticlines occur most commonly in series, a number of parallel anticlines being separated by synclines. The erosion structure of such anticlines is in general similar in each anticline to that of the dome, except that the subsequent valleys and the hog-back ridges are parallel, instead of circumferential, and the transverse consequent gorges in the ridges are parallel instead of radial. The most important difference lies in the duplication of the structure in each anticline and its complication by the intervening synclines. The resultant outcrops have been discussed in the preceding chapter.

When anticlines are partly eroded a series of monoclines or hog-backs results, similar in character to that formed by the uplifted upper end of the coastal plain as above described. Monoclines formed by breached anticlines usually occur in pairs opposing each other as in the Appalachians of to-day, but monoclines without a corresponding opposite occur which in reality represent one limb of an anticline of which the other limb has been entirely removed. (Fig. 216.) Thus the monocline which forms the Front Range of the Appalachians in New Jersey, Pennsylvania and southward

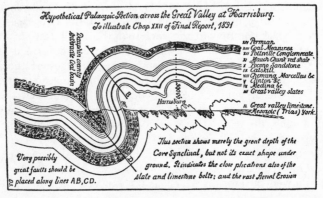

FIG. 216. Section of the Appalachian folds near Harrisburg, to show the removal of the eastern part of the folds by erosion.

represents merely the western limb of an anticline, the eastward continuation of which has been entirely removed by erosion. This was accomplished by peneplanation which cut below the axes of the synclines into the underlying more intensely folded rocks in which the Appalachian folds are not recognizable. The same is in part true of the monoclines facing the Front Range of the Rocky Mountains. The Triassic and Cretacic strata most probably once extended across what is now the front range axis, and this was perhaps true of much of the Palæozoic series as well. From the fact that the axis of the long Front Range anticline was a granite one, erosion, which removed the formerly continuous sediments, left it in relief, so that it holds the same relation to the flanking monoclines on either side that the central crystalline mass of the Black Hills holds to its encircling hog-backs. (Fig. 213, c, d, p. 840.) The completion of the cycle of erosion in a region of monoclinal flexures results in the formation of a peneplain across which rivers wander with little or no regard to the underlying structure. As already outlined, the mapping of the outcrops of the strata on such a surface would form a series of color bands parallel for a long distance, but uniting when the pitch of the anticline carried the strata below the erosion surface. The central color band of the eroded anticline would, of course, represent the oldest formation, while on either side of this would be bands corresponding on opposite sides and representing the successively younger formations from the center outward (Fig. 190, a, b, p. 806; see also Figs. 217, 218.)

Elevation of the peneplain and renewal of the erosive processes will result in the revival of the topography, since the harder layers

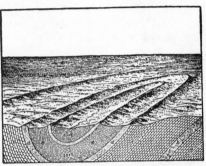

Fig. 217. Anticlinal fold with pitching axis, truncated across the top. The harder beds form monoclinal ridges; the valleys were cut on soft strata. (After Willis.)

Fig. 218. Synclinal fold with pitching axis eroded. The harder beds form monoclinal ridges. (After Willis.)

will again be carved into relief by the concentration of the erosive processes on the softer layers. The Appalachians furnish an instructive example of such a revived topography—they are at present in the second if not in a later cycle of erosion.* This fact is well brought out by the numerous entrenched transverse streams which cross the monoclines more or less at right angles. These streams, of which the Susquehanna is a good example, came into existence on the tilted peneplain, and their constant downward cutting made possible the openings of the longitudinal valleys on the softer strata, by the tributary streams.

* This is graphically expressed by the formula $n^{th} + 1$ cycle suggested by Davis for such cases, where it is known that the region is not in the first cycle of erosion, but where it is impossible to say how many cycles have been completed. Thus n may stand for one or for more than one.

5. The Basin.

The basin is the complement of the dome, representing the downward arching of the strata. As in the dome, the basin may be gentle, with strata so slightly inclined as to seem horizontal or it may be a pronounced one with highly inclined sides. The former is represented by the Paris Basin and the Michigan Basin and is in many respects the most significant type to the stratigrapher, being often difficult to detect. The Paris Basin represents a case in which the successive strata have been breached by radial consequent streams running from the surrounding higher old-land to the lower center, while their tributaries carved out circumferential valleys bounded by *outward* facing cliffs of the "inface type." The dissected basin at this stage differs from the dissected dome in having its oldest formations on the outside, the circumferential valleys

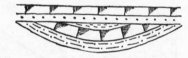 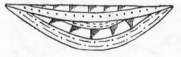

FIG. 219.   Strata of a basin, trun-   FIG. 220.   The same series after a
cated and covered by horizontal   second folding and truncation.
strata.

being cut out of higher and higher strata toward the center, while in the dome the youngest formations are on the outside, and the successive circumferential valleys are cut on lower and lower strata toward the center. In the basin the infaces or escarpments face outward; in the dome they face inward. The Paris Basin is most probably to be regarded as a region in the second cycle of erosion, having been peneplained once, after which the topography has been revived by a resumption of stream activity.

The Michigan basin forms an interesting example of a compound type. At the beginning of Devonic time, the basin was formed, after which erosion beveled off the margins, leaving the successive formations superimposed after the manner of a nest of plates, the highest being the smallest, while the edges of the successively lower ones project beyond the higher. Across this series were deposited the Devonic and later strata, after which a second downward arching took place, followed by beveling of the edges of this later formed basin. Thus the highest formations occupy the center of the area and are surrounded by the rims of successively lower formations. (See Figs. 219 and 220.) The dome and basin have generally a definite relation to each other. Thus in Europe the Weald dome lies north of and immediately adjacent to the Paris Basin, while in North America the Michigan Basin is surrounded by domes. As already outlined in the preceding chapter (see map, Fig. 192), these domes and basins suffered simultaneous deformations at at least two distinct periods, but some of the domes and perhaps some of the basins may have suffered repeated deformations throughout Palæozoic time.

6. The Syncline.

This corresponds to a much elongated basin, and the characteristics it exhibits will be essentially those of the basin except that, instead of radiality or concentric arrangement, many of the features will be characterized by parallelism of arrangement. The characteristics of synclines as of anticlines are best exhibited in the Appalachian region of North America and the Jura Mountains of Europe.

7. Erosion Features in Faulted Strata.

These have already been discussed. to some extent in Chapter XX. Some special features are shown in Figs. 221 and 222.

8. The Completion of the Cycle.

The Peneplain. When the surface of a country is worn to so low a relief that the streams have practically ceased eroding and are throughout in a graded condition, the surface of the region may be considered as in the peneplain state. This is by no means a perfectly level surface, but rather one of a rolling or undulating topography, and not infrequently erosion remnants or *monadnocks* rise considerably above the general level of the peneplain. Since streams erode their beds until every portion is graded, the stream bed represents a continuous gentle slope to sea-level. As long as the relative position of land and sea remains stable, reduction of the relief will progress, and the surface of the land will approach closer and closer to the level of the sea. If that could be reached, the region would be reduced to base-level. It is obvious, however, that as the relief is reduced more and more, the rate of reduction rapidly decreases, so that the process of base-leveling goes on at a progressively diminishing rate.

While the harder or more resistant strata of any region are the last to be reduced to the level of the peneplain, they eventually also succumb, and the surface of the peneplain thus shows a lack of conformity to the structure of the country. This lack of conformity to structure is one of the most characteristic features of a peneplain, and the one by which it is most readily recognized. When the peneplain is gradually submerged beneath a transgressing sea, the final inequalities may be smoothed off by marine planation. In this manner erosion surfaces of remarkably level character may be produced, such as are seen on the Archæan granites of the Manitou

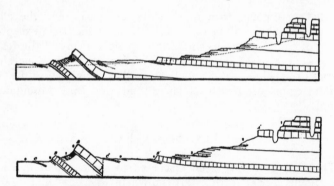

Fig. 221. Section on San Juan River, Colorado, showing erosion escarpments in horizontal and tilted strata.
Fig. 222. The same section interpreted by the assumption of a fault.

region in Colorado, where the early Palæozoic sandstones rest upon a surface almost as level as a table top. (Crosby–1.) (Fig. 52, p. 310.) Where transgression of the sea is gradual and uniform on a peneplain surface, a basal conglomerate or sandstone is formed which everywhere rests directly upon the old peneplaned surface. The age of this sandstone or conglomerate will, however, vary as pointed out in Chapter XVIII, being younger shoreward and older seaward. Where monadnocks rise above the level of the submerged peneplain, these will be gradually buried under the accumulating coastal plain strata, which along their contact with the monadnock will be of a more or less coarsely fragmental character. A typical example of a monadnock buried in coastal plain strata, and now partly resurrected by erosion, is found in the Baraboo ridges of southern Wisconsin. An example of a monadnock being partly buried by marine sediment is found in the island of Monhegan, off the coast of Maine, which is still partly above the level of the sea, though the peneplain from which it rises is here completely submerged.

In an old region, where peneplanation has long been in progress, the surface is formed by a layer of atmoclastic material of greater or less depth. With this are mingled peat and other phytogenic material, while here and there may occur a deposit of wind-blown matter. On this surface the rivers will assume a meandering course which has no regard to the underlying structure. When such

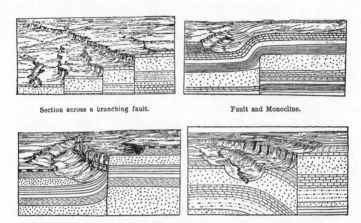

Section across a branching fault.   Fault and Monocline.

Fault with thrown beds flexed upward—a dragged fault.   Fault with thrown beds flexed downward.

FIG. 223. Erosion scarps formed in horizontal and in flexed strata, compared with erosion and fault scarps in faulted strata.

material is exposed to the activities of a slowly encroaching sea, it will be pretty thoroughly sorted and the finer material carried seaward to settle in quieter water. But if transgression is rapid, other sediments may be deposited over the ancient soil, which will remain relatively undisturbed. Such ancient buried soils are sometimes met with in the geological series marking former periods of extended peneplanation.

The Relation of the Peneplain to Sedimentation. A region of low relief will furnish only the finest material for its rivers to carry, and hence the sea bordering a peneplained country will receive only the finest lutaceous sediment which is washed from the lands by the rains and swollen streams. Thus lutaceous sediments, often heavily charged with decaying organic matter, may accumulate in the form of extensive mud flats or deltas. The present Mississippi and Nile deltas are examples, being composed only of the finest mud. The Black Devonic shale of Michigan and Ohio also appears to represent a deposit of this type, as already outlined in a previous chapter.

When the continent has been worn so low that little or no sediment is carried into the sea, organic deposits may accumulate close to the shore. Since rivers, even in low countries, are probably never without their modicum of silt, it follows that pure organic accumulations can be formed near shore only where large rivers do not discharge. A consideration of the chalk beds of England and Ireland shows them to be part of a series of coastal deposits in a slowly westward transgressing sea. This is partly shown by the westward overlapping of the successive members on an eroded pre-Cretacic peneplain. Thus while the basal conglomerates, sands and greensands of southeastern England are of Aptien age and rest disconformably upon the Wealden, the basal Cretacic conglomerates, sandstones and greensands of northeast Ireland and of Mull and Morvern in Scotland are of Cenomanien age. Here the Aptien and the Gault have been overlapped, while the Cenomanien of the northwest has the characteristics held by the Aptien in the southeast. The Cenomanien in the southeast is a glauconitic chalk, and is succeeded by the pure chalk which begins with the Turonien. In the northwest the Turonien is still a glauconite sand to be succeeded by lower Senonien glauconitic chalk and only toward the last by pure chalk. (See Fig. 146 in Chapter XVIII, page 730.)

It is thus seen that the great mass of organic material which forms the chalk was deposited in comparatively shallow water not very remote from the coast, and this suggests that the land of that time must have been in a state of peneplanation. The micro-organisms of the chalk bear out this interpretation, for shallow water benthonic forms predominate. The possibility of eolian deposition of some chalk beds, mentioned in an earlier chapter, must not be overlooked.

Dissection of the Peneplain. If a peneplain is elevated, with or without tilting, a new cycle of erosion commences; all the streams will be revived, and they will incise their valleys, thus dissecting the peneplain. At first the stream valleys are relatively insignificant as compared with the broad, gently rolling upland of the elevated peneplain. But as the valleys are widened, the interstream portions are reduced and the upland dwindles into a series of ridges and peaks which eventually become lowered, so that a new peneplain is produced. Thus the second cycle of erosion is completed. While the upland portion of the elevated peneplain is still broad, the character of the old peneplain surface is easily seen. As the valleys become widened and the interstream portions reduced, the old peneplain level is less and less readily recognized, the uniform agreement in height of the interstream ridges being the most conspicuous feature. It can, however, be shown that uniform height of interstream ridges may also be brought about in a country where the original surface was very diverse, if the streams are uniformly spaced. (Shaler–27.) This is especially true if the streams are of approximately equal power, and the rate of erosion is thus more or less uniform.

Age of the Peneplain. It is evident that the peneplain is of later age than that of any of the strata affected by the erosion in the formation of the peneplain. In the case of folded strata which have become peneplaned the commencement of peneplanation may be regarded as simultaneous with the folding, and since in a strongly folded region even the latest strata deposited may be involved in the folds and so protected from complete erosion, we may not be far wrong in considering that folding and peneplanation begin shortly after the deposition of the youngest stratum involved. It must, however, be borne in mind that folding of strata without fracture takes place at some distance below the surface (see Chapters XIX and XX), and that therefore a series of perfect folds in any given series of strata suggests that these strata were at considerable depth below the surface at the time of the formation of the folds. Under such conditions, when perfectly folded strata are found near the surface of a peneplain, it is not likely that the later strata, deposited before the commencement of folding, are included within the folds. Thus within some of the strongly folded strata of the Hudson River group in Albany County, N. Y., only middle and earlier Ordovicic strata are involved so far as known, though there is every reason for believing that the folding did not take place until late Ordovicic, if not early Siluric time.

In the case of horizontal strata which have been peneplained, the latest preserved stratum is not to be regarded as the last one deposited before elevation and erosion, for this would allow no removal of strata by erosion during the peneplanation. In general we may consider that the amount of rock removed from a given region during a stated period of elevation and erosion is proportional to the distance of that region from the point where erosion was replaced by deposition, *i. e.,* from the seashore or piedmont plain of the period. Exceptions to this must, however, be recognized where local conditions limited or accentuated erosion, as in the case of a warped surface where some portions of a given formation were raised excessively and so became subject to pronounced erosion, or where other portions were proportionally more depressed and so escaped great erosion, or where other causes were active.

The end of the period of peneplanation is commonly marked by the age of the strata overlying the peneplain surface. Here, however, it must be borne in mind that slow subsidence of a peneplain surface produces a gradual deposition of formations which successively overlap each other, each later one in turn coming to rest upon the old peneplain surface beyond the edge of the preceding one. Thus, the pre-Cambric peneplain of North America is overlain by Lower or Middle Cambric strata in the southern United States, by Upper Cambric strata in the Upper Mississippi Valley and northeastern New York, by Lower or Middle Ordovicic in northwestern New York, by Middle, and later Ordovicic, in portions of Canada, and by later formations in other parts. In each case the age of the peneplain terminates with the age of the overlying bed, while the part still above water continues to be subject to erosion. Thus these higher portions continued to be peneplained, though at an exceedingly slow rate, long after the southern end of the peneplain was buried under thousands of feet of strata.

High-Level Plains of Arid Regions. In arid regions, where the rainfall is insufficient, and where a large part of the erosive work is done by wind, high-level plains of erosion comparable to peneplains, but having no definite relation to sea-level, may come into existence. Under the influence of arid erosive forces, the initial relief of even a rugged region will gradually become extinct, partly by erosion and partly by filling of the desert basins with waste. The process has been fully described by Davis (12) and enlarged upon by others. A few quotations from Davis will serve to point the essentials of the process and its results: Under the conditions cited "the most perfect maturity would be reached when the drainage of all the arid region becomes integrated with respect to a single aggraded basin-base-level, so that the slopes should lead from all parts of the surface to a single area for the deposition of the waste. The lowest basin area which thus comes to have a monopoly of deposition may receive so heavy a body of waste that some of its ridges may be nearly or quite buried. Strong relief might still remain in certain peripheral districts, but large plain areas would by this time necessarily have been developed. In so far as the plains are rock-floored, they would truncate the rocks without regard to their structure." (12: 389.)

"As the dissected highlands of maturity are worn down, the rainfall decreases, and the running streams are weakened and extinguished; thus . . . the winds in time would appear to gain the upper hand as agents of erosion and transportation. If such were the case, it would seem that great inequalities of level might be produced by the excavation of wide and deep hollows in areas of weak rocks. As long as the exportation of wind-swept sand and of wind-borne dust continued, no easily defined limit would be found for the depth of the hollows that might thus be developed in the surface, for the sweeping and lifting action of the wind is not controlled by any general baselevel. In an absolutely rainless region there appears to be no reason for doubting that these abnormal inequalities of surface might eventually produce a strong relief in a still-standing land of unchanging climate; but in the actual deserts of the world there appears to be no absolutely rainless region; and even small and occasional rainfalls will suffice, especially when they occur suddenly and cause floods, as is habitual in deserts, to introduce an altogether different régime in the development of surface forms from the rock hills and hollows which would prevail under the control of the winds alone. The prevailing absence of such hill-and-hollow forms, and the general presence of graded wadies and of drainage slopes in desert regions, confirm this statement."

"As soon as a shallow wind-blown hollow is formed, that part of the integrated drainage system which leads to the hollow will supply waste to it whenever rain falls there; the finer waste will be blown away, the coarser waste will accumulate, and thus the tendency of the winds to overdeepen local hollows will be spontaneously and effectively counteracted. As incipient hollows are formed in advancing old age, and the maturely integrated drainage system disintegrates into many small and variable systems, each system will check the deepening of a hollow by wind action; hence no deep hollow can be formed anywhere, so long as occasional rain falls." (12-391-392.)

With the continuance of the processes and the further disintegration of the drainage, the surface is slowly lowered, leaving only those rock masses projecting as monadnocks or "Inselberge" which most effectually resist dry weathering. The production of the Inselberg landscape chiefly by eolian agencies has already been considered in an early chapter.

"At last, as the waste is more completely exported, the desert plain may be reduced to a lower level than that of the deepest initial basin" which originally was a temporary recipient of the waste, "and then a rock-floor, thinly veneered with waste, unrelated to normal baselevel, will prevail throughout—except where

monadnocks still survive." (12: *393.*)   This condition of widespread desert-leveling has actually been reached in the Kalahari
region of South Africa, as described by Passarge—and these examples of the final stage, Davis holds, justify the assumption that
the various stages, through which they must have passed to reach
this last stage, and the characters of which can easily be deduced
theoretically, may actually find representation in the arid regions
of the world.   Furthermore, fossil examples of such desert-leveled
plains, as well as examples of stages which precede the final stage,
ought to be looked for in the sections of the earth's crust, and we
can no longer assume that any level plain, recent or fossil, is a
normal peneplain; the possibility that it may be a high-level desert
plain must not be overlooked.

Some criteria for distinguishing modern peneplains from desert
plains are given by Davis.

"A plain of erosion lying close to sea-level in a region of normal
climate, and therefore traversed by rivers that reach the sea, but

FIG. 224.   Erosion-buttes (Zeugenberge) near Guelb-el-Zerzour.   The erosion
is mainly eolian.   (After Walther.)

that do not trench the plain, might conceivably be a depressed desert
plain standing long enough in a changed climate to have become
cloaked with local soils; but it is extremely unlikely that the depression of a desert plain could place it so that it should slope
gently to the seashore, and that its new-made rivers should not
dissect it, and that there should be no drifted sands and loess
sheets on adjoining areas, and no signs of submergence on neighboring coasts.   An untrenched plain of erosion in such an attitude
would be properly interpreted as the result of normal processes, long
and successfully acting with respect to normal baselevel." (12:
397-398.)

"In the same way a high-standing plain of erosion in a desert
region might be possibly explained as an evenly uplifted peneplain
whose climate had in some way been changed from humid to arid,
whose deep weathered soils had been removed and replaced by
thin sheets of stony, sandy, or saline waste, and whose residual
reliefs had been modified to the point of producing shallow basins.
But in this case there should be some indications of recent uplift
around the margin of the area, either in the form of uplifted marine

formations whose deposition was contemporaneous with the erosion of the peneplain, or in the form of fault-escarpments separating the uplifted from the non-uplifted areas. Moreover, it is extremely unlikely that the uplift of an extensive peneplain could place it in so level a position that it should not suffer dissection even by desert agencies; hence a high-standing desert plain is best accounted for by supposing that it has been leveled in the position that it now occupies." (12 : 398.)

"It should not, however, be overlooked that there is some danger of misreading the history of a depressed desert plain which has been by a moderate amount of normal weathering and erosion transformed into a normal peneplain; and of an uplifted peneplain which has been by a moderate amount of arid weathering and erosion transformed into a typical desert plain; the danger of error here is similar to that by which a peneplain, wave-swept and scoured during submergence, might be mistaken for a normal plain of marine abrasion." (12 : 399.)

"If an old rock-floored desert plain be gently warped or tilted, marine submergence is not likely to follow immediately, but the regular continuation of general degradation will be interrupted. The patches and veneers of waste will be washed from the higher to the lower parts of the warped surface; the higher parts, having an increased slope, might be somewhat dissected, and would certainly be exposed to more active degradation than before, until they were worn down to a nearly level plain again. The lower parts would receive the waste from the higher parts, and the continuance of this process of concentration would in time cause the accumulation of extensive and heavy deposits in the lower areas. Such deposits will be, as a rule, barren of fossils; the composition, texture and arrangement of their materials will indicate the arid conditions under which they have been weathered, transported, and laid down; their structures will seldom exhibit the regularity of marine strata, and they may reach the extreme irregularity of sand-dune deposits. If warping continues, the desert deposits may gain great thickness; their original floor may be depressed below sea-level, while their surface is still hundreds or thousands of feet above sea-level." (12 : 400-401.)

Examples which serve to illustrate such deposits have been described from South Africa (Passarge) and West Australia, where barren sandstones of continental origin surround the monadnocks ("Inselberge"). Ancient examples seem to occur in the great deposits of barren Uinta sandstones 12,000 to 14,000 feet thick in some localities which lie at the base of the Palæozoic series in the region of the present Wasatch Mountains. The basal Palæozoic sandstones of eastern North America, from a few feet to over a thousand feet thick ("Potsdam" sandstone), also have many characters pointing to such an origin. In this case, of course, the transgressing Palæozoic sea modified the deposits to a certain degree and redeposited a part of them as fossiliferous marine sands and clays.

"If a change from an arid toward a moister climate causes a drainage discharge to the sea, a dissection of the plain will ensue. The valleys thus eroded cannot expectably exhibit any great degree of adjustment to the structures, because the stream courses will result from the irregular patching together of the preëxisting irregularly disintegrated drainage. This peculiar characteristic, taken together with the absence of neighboring uplifted marine deposits, will probably suffice in most cases to distinguish desert plains, dissected by a change to a moister climate, from peneplains dissected in consequence of uplift; but there still might be confusion with peneplains dissected by superposed streams." (12:401.)

Locally, around individual mountains in an arid climate, a surface sloping outward in all directions partly due to erosion and partly to deposition is produced by the forces operative under such conditions. Such a plane, though never very perfect, will have the appearance of a broad-based cone—the center of which is the undissected mountain remnant. Dr. Ogilvie (21) has described these as forming around the laccoliths of the Ortiz Mountains in New Mexico—and has named them "conoplains." They are essentially elements in the stages of desert planation.

C. MINOR EROSION FEATURES.

Many of these have already been noted in previous chapters. We may recall the grooves formed by eolian corrasion in the Libyan limestone plateau and the erosion needles capped by Operculina in the Libyan desert (p. 52); the Yardangs of central Asia and

FIG. 225. Erosion features (Schichtenköpfe) in inclined Cretacic limestones. Chiefly eolian. Abu Roasch. (After Walther.)

the erosion monuments of Monument Park, Colorado (p. 53) ; the facetted pebbles (p. 54) ; erosion forms produced by solution (pp. 174-176), by waves (pp. 221-226), by rivers (pp. 246-257), and by ice (pp. 263-265). A striking example of eolian erosion is further shown in Fig. 225, where alternating hard and soft limestone strata

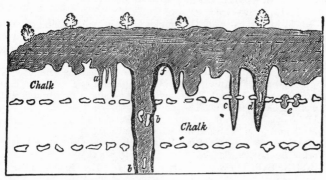

FIG. 226. Solution fissures in chalk, forming organ-pipe structure. The hollows are filled with sand and clay from above. (After Lyell.)

inclined at a considerable angle were carved into fantastic forms by wind. Another example, illustrating the effect of solution on limestone, is given in Fig. 226, which shows the solution fissures in chalk and other limestone regions where cylindrical depressions often occur in great numbers, and close together, forming geological "organ pipes" (*Geologische Orgeln*) (Fig. 136, p. 698). Broad kettle-like hollows or *dolinas* are also produced by solutions on joint-cracks. These may be up to 1 km. in diameter and 30 meters in depth.

BIBLIOGRAPHY XXI.

1. CROSBY, WILLIAM O, 1899. Archæan Cambrian Contact near Manitou, Colorado. Geological Society of America Bulletin, Vol. X, pp. 141-164.
2. DAVIS, WILLIAM MORRIS. 1896. Plains of Marine and Subaerial Denudation. Geological Society of America Bulletin, Vol. VII, pp. 378-398.
3. DAVIS, W. M. 1899. The Peneplain. American Geologist, Vol. XXIII, pp. 207-239.
4. DAVIS, W. M. 1899. The Geographic Cycle. Geographical Journal (London), Vol. XIV, pp. 481-584.
5. DAVIS, W. M. 1899. Physical Geography. Ginn & Co.
6. DAVIS, W. M. 1899. The Drainage of Cuestas. London Geologists' Association Proceedings, Vol. XVI, pp. 75-93, 16 figures.
7. DAVIS, W. M. 1900. The Physical Geography of the Lands. Popular Science Monthly, Vol. LVII, pp. 157-170.

8. DAVIS. W. M. 1901. Peneplains of Central France and Brittany. Geological Society of America Bulletin, Vol. XII, pp. 480–487.

9. DAVIS, W. M. 1901. The Geographical Cycle. Verhandlung des 7ten Internationalen Geographischen Kongresses, pt. II, pp. 221–231.

10. DAVIS, W. M. 1902. Base-level Grade and Peneplain. Journal of Geology, Vol. X, pp. 77–109.

11. DAVIS, W. M. 1905. Leveling without Base Leveling. Science, N. S., Vol. XXI, pp. 825–828.

12. DAVIS, W. M. 1905. The Geographic Cycle in an Arid Climate. Journal of Geology, Vol. XIII, No. 5, pp. 381–407.

13. DAVIS, W. M. 1905. The Bearing of Physiography on Suess' Theories. American Journal of Sciences, Vol. XIX, pp. 265–273.

14. DAVIS, W. M. 1905. The Complication o the Geographical Cycle. Compte Rendu, 8th International Geographical Congress, pp. 150–163.

15. FOERSTE, A. E. 1902. The Cincinnati Anticline in Southern Kentucky. American Geologist, Vol. XXX, pp. 359–369.

16. GRABAU, A. W. 1901. Geology and Palæontology of Niagara Falls and Vicinity. N. Y. State Museum Bulletin No. 45.

17. GRABAU, A. W. 1908. Pre-Glacial drainage in Central Western New York. Science, N. S., Vol. XXVIII, pp. 527–534.

18. JOHNSON, DOUGLAS W. 1903. Geology of the Cerillos Hills. (Laccolith and Dome Mountain Dissection.) School of Mines Quarterly, Vol. XXIV, pp. 173–246; 456–600.

19. JOHNSON, D. W. 1905. Youth, Maturity and Old Age of Topographic Forms. American Geographical Society Bulletin, XXXVII, pp. 648–653.

20. KEYES, C. R. 1903. Geological Structure of New Mexican Bolson Plains. American Journal of Science, Vol. XV, pp. 207–210.

21. OGILVIE, IDA H. 1905. The High Altitude Conoplain: A topographic form illustrated in the Ortiz Mountains. American Geologist, XXXVI, pp. 27–34.

22. PASSARGE, SIEGFRIED. 1904. Die Kalahari. Berlin.

23. PASSARGE, S. 1904. Rumpffläche und Inselberge. Zeitschrift der deutschen geologischen Gesellschaft, Bd. LVI, pp. 193–209.

24. PASSARGE, S. 1904. Die Inselbergelandschaft im tropischen Africa. Naturwissenschaftliche Wochenschrift. N. F., Bd. III, pp. 657–665.

25. PENCK, A. 1883. Einfluss des Klimas auf die Gestalt der Erdoberfläche. Verhandlungen des 3ten deutschen Geographentages, pp. 78–92.

26. PENCK, A. 1905. Climatic Features in the Land Surface. · American Journal of Science, Vol. XIX, pp. 165–174.

27. SHALER, N. S. 1899. Spacing of Rivers with Reference to the Hypothesis of Base-Leveling. Geological Society of America Bulletin, Vol. X, pp. 263–276.

28. WALTHER, JOHANNES. 1891. Denudation in der Wüste. (See Bibliography II.)

29. WALTHER, JOHANNES. 1900. Das Gesetz der Wüstenbildung (2nd ed., 1912).

30. WILSON, ALFRED W. G. 1903. The Laurentian Peneplain. Journal of Geology, Vol. XI, pp. 615–669.

31. WILSON, A. W. G. 1904. Trent River System and St. Lawrence Outlet. Geological Society of America Bulletin, Vol. XV, pp. 211–242.

32. WILSON, A. W. G. 1905. Physiography of the Archæan Areas of Canada. International Geographical Congress, 8th report, pp. 116–135.

D. THE PYROSPHERE.

CHAPTER XXII.

GENERAL SUMMARY OF PYROSPHERIC ACTIVITIES.

The activities of the pyrosphere are judged by their surface manifestations, and by the observations on results of igneous activities in the past. So far as the pyrosphere itself is concerned direct observation is, of course, out of the question, nevertheless much may be learned regarding its probable character by experimentation and the study of igneous activities in the laboratory, as well as in the field, while much more may be inferred from a logical interpretation of past igneous work in portions of the earth's crust exposed as a result of dislocations, or of prolonged erosion, or of both. No attempt is made to discuss volcanic activities in anything more than a summary manner, though the subject is of vast geological importance. The science of pyrology or vulcanology has already developed a literature which only a specialist may hope to master. The list given at the end of this chapter is an extremely fragmentary one, but it contains a sufficient number of general works in which the subject is treated from a comprehensive viewpoint, and which will open for the student the gateways to the special fields of research in which ground has been broken.

VOLCANIC ACTIVITIES.

TYPES OF VOLCANIC ACTIVITIES. These may be purely explosive or purely extravasative or, what is more frequent, a combination of both in varying proportions. According as the one or the other prevails, the form of the resulting deposit will vary from simply conical in the first to flat and plain-like in the second case.

SUBDIVISION WITH REFERENCE TO LOCATION. Volcanic manifestations may take place either on the surface of the lithosphere (effusive) or within the earth's crust (plutonic, intrusive). In the latter case direct observation of such manifestations is impossible, but their characters may be inferred from the results of past intrusive and plutonic manifestations as indicated by the characteristics of intrusive and deep-seated (plutonic) igneous masses. (See *ante,* Chapter VII.)

Extrusive manifestations may further be divided into the terrestrial and the submarine, the latter again being withdrawn from direct observation, except when their results appear above the surface of the sea, after prolonged existence. Indirect observation on the results of submarine eruptions is likewise scanty, mainly because, in the case of older volcanics, it is at present difficult to distinguish with certainty between submarine and subaerial eruptions, and many so-called submarine lava flows must probably be relegated to the subaerial type.

In discussing the types of eruptions, the primary division into *explosive* and *extravasative* will be kept in mind, and under each of these will be noted the subaerial or terrestrial and the submarine types.

Explosive Eruptions.

Terrestrial Type. Volcanoes of purely explosive type are probably very rare, though the "maare" craters may be classed here. In the typical examples of the Eifeler Maare, no volcanic cone exists; instead, there is merely a more or less circular opening, the result of the explosion, and this has subsequently been filled with water. Lapilli, bomblets, and even large bombs often abound in the neighborhood of the maare craters, but lava flows are typically absent. The coarse and fine lapilli of the maare region in the Eifel and Rhein districts form stratified deposits which have all the appearance of stratified sands of clastic origin. As outlined in Chapter VI, the lapilli are not to be regarded as pyroclastic in the true sense of the word, but rather as granular pyrogenics, being primarily of endogenetic origin, and classifiable as pyrogranulites rather than as pyrarenytes. True pyroclastics are, of course, also associated with the deposits of lapilli and bombs, these resulting from the clastation, by eruptive explosion, of already consolidated rock masses, either of igneous or of "sedimentary" origin. The vicinity of the Laacher See, the largest and most picturesque of the explosive craters of Germany, is characterized by deposits of volcanic bombs and tuffs, of trachyte, mingled with clastic fragments of granite and various metamorphic rocks, brought up by the explosion from great depths below the cover of Devonic strata.

Some of the bombs consist of a remarkable mixture of crystals, characteristically developed at great depth within the earth's crust, such as sanidine, olivine, hornblende, garnet, etc. (Walther–41: *170-171*.)

A modern case of such an explosion without lava extrusion occurred in Japan in 1888, the explosion being a sudden and violent one, and tearing away the side of a volcano which had not been active for at least a thousand years. The air was filled with ashes and débris as in a typical volcanic eruption, and a large tract of the adjacent region was devastated and many lives lost.

Coon Butte, in Arizona, has also been regarded by Gilbert (11:*187*) as a possible example of such an explosive eruption— though he also suggests the possibility that it was formed by the impact of a meteorite. Both theories have had their advocates, the former origin being favored by Chamberlin and Salisbury (4:*596*), while the latter is especially defended by Fairchild (8).

The cinder cone. While the explosion-craters seen in the Maare represent probably a single eruption, or one which, with slight intervening pauses, lasted only for a comparatively short time, the more general examples of explosive volcanoes last sufficiently long to build up a *cinder cone.* Such eruptions may be of comparatively limited duration, and may occur at short intervals, as in the volcano Stromboli in the Æolian Islands north of Sicily (*Strombolian type*), where the interval of explosion is from 1 to 20 minutes, as shown by the "flash" of this "Lighthouse of the Mediterranean"; or it may be of a more violent character and occur at great intervals with dormant or "strombolian" periods intervening. Such is the case in Vulcano of the same group of islands, and in other violent volcanoes (*Vulcanian type*) which have an interval of decades (moderate phase), or of centuries (grander phase).

Material of the cinder cone. This includes the bombs, the lapilli, and the volcanic sand, ash, and dust which fall in the immediate vicinity of the crater. Not all the ejected material falls here—much being carried to a distance, this distance increasing with increasing fineness of material. Even large bombs may be hurled beyond the actual radius of the cinder cone, one such, fully three feet in diameter, being hurled to a distance of a mile and a half during the eruption of Vulcano in 1888 (Hobbs–15:*119*). A remarkable example of the propulsion of volcanic ejecta has been described by Hovey (17:*560*) in the eruption of Mont Pelée in 1902. Frequent explosions of dust and lava-laden clouds have brought material enough from the crater to fill the gorge of the Rivière Blanche. "The lower portion of the gorge has been entirely obliterated and the adjoining plateau elevated, while the upper and deeper portion near the center has been almost filled by ejecta. The dust-flows are the material left behind by the dust-laden clouds of steam. The exploding clouds of steam were so overloaded with dust and larger fragments of comminuted lava, that they flowed down the slope of the mountain and the gorge, like a fluid propelled at a high velocity by the horizontal or partly downward component of the force of the explosion. Many large fragments of solidified lava were carried down the gorge by these clouds. Such blocks 10 to 15 feet in diameter were not uncommon" (17:560).

Lapilli vary in size from that of a walnut to dust. The term is somewhat loosely used, and should be restricted to pyrogenic material in a state of division, i. e., pyrogranulytes and the smaller pyrosphærytes (more rarely pyro-pulverytes) which by their appearance show that they were unconsolidated or at least in a plastic state on eruption. (See *ante,* Chapters VI and XII.) The sand and dust are, for the most part, true pyroclastic material characterized by angularity of outline and density of material.

The forms of cinder cones. Cinder cones are essentially local accumulations of unconsolidated materials, and so their form is determined by the general laws which govern the accumulation of such material, modified, of course, by the special influences characteristic of the mode of accumulation. The form will also vary in accordance with the prevailing size and character of the material, being steeper for coarse and gentler for fine material, and gentler also for rounded material (lapilli) than for angular. There will be further variation induced by the abundance or scarcity of water vapor, condensed into rain in the vicinity of the eruption, the variation being analogous to that found in the slopes of alluvial cones and dry "cones of dejection," or between that of alluvial cones of dry and pluvial regions. "Speaking broadly, the diameter of the crater is a measure of the violence of the explosion within the chimney. A single series of short explosive eruptions builds a low and broad cinder cone. A long-continued succession of moderately violent explosions, on the other hand, builds a high cone with crater diameter small if compared with the mountain's altitude, and the profile afforded is a remarkably beautiful sweeping curve." (Hobbs–15:123.) Owing to the fact that material near the summit lies at the maximum angle of repose, while that lower down generally has a lower angle—the product of change wrought by time and by the addition of material fallen from the sky upon the surface of the original slope—the form of the lateral curve of the cinder-cone will be a faintly concave one, whereas that of a lava cone is more typically convex. This is shown in the following sketch of a cinder cone (Fig. 227) and appears further in Fig. 232.

Monte Nuovo, in the Bay of Baie, near Naples, is an example of a cone composed almost entirely of loose cinders. This volcano had its birth within historic time, arising on the borders of the ancient Lake Lucrinus on September 20, 1538, and attaining a height of 440 feet. Other volcanoes largely composed of cinders have arisen within the knowledge of man. Among them are Jorullo (Mexico), 1759; Pochutla (Mexico), 1870; Camiguin (Philippine Islands), 1871; a new mountain of the Ajusco Mountain group (Mexico), 1881; and the new mountain of Japan formed on September 9, 1910, and rising to a height of 690 feet.

Both Jorullo and the new Camiguin volcano started from fissures in level plains. The former arose in the night of September 28, 1759, 35 miles distant from any then existing volcano, and its sum-

Fig. 227. Campo Bianco, in the Island of Lipari. A pumice-cone, breached by the outflow of an obsidian lava stream.

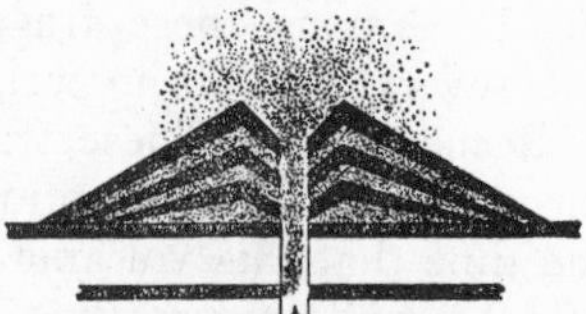

Fig. 228. Experimental illustration of the mode of formation of volcanic cones composed of fragmental materials. (After Judd.)

mit has since reached an elevation of 4,265 feet above sea-level. The Camiguin volcano had a growth period of four years during which it reached a height of about 1,800 feet.

Consolidation of cinder cones. Unless extravasations of lava should punctuate the eruptions of cinders, the cinder-cone is not likely to be thoroughly consolidated, but remains rather in the condition of an ash or sand heap. Diagenetic processes will, of course, go on throughout the mass and thus consolidation may be brought about, aided by the metamorphosing effect of the steam and hot vapors accompanying each eruption, and penetrating more or less through the mass of accumulated material (atmo-metamorphism).

Submarine Explosive Eruptions. Explosive eruptions are probably as common in the littoral belts of the sea as they are on land, and, indeed, near the margins of the lands they, in common with the extravasative eruptions, may be more frequent than elsewhere, as discussed beyond. There is no reason for doubting that explosive eruptions also occur on the floor of the deeper sea—though examples of such cinder-cones rising from the abyssal sea-bottom are unknown.

The Mediterranean has been the region best known for submarine volcanic eruptions. Of these a number have been of the explosive type, though more generally the compound (explosive and extravasative) type prevailed. The most noted of the recorded submarine eruptions "occurred in the year 1831, when a new volcanic island (Graham's Island, Ile Julia) was thrown up, with abundant discharge of steam and showers of scoriæ, between Sicily and the coast of Africa. It reached an extreme height of 200 feet or more above sea-level (800 feet above sea-bottom) with a circumference of 3 miles, but, on the cessation of the eruption, was attacked by the waves and soon demolished, leaving only a shoal to mark its site." (Geikie–9:*250.*) "The upper part of this volcanic cone, above the sea at least, seemed to have been solely composed of ashes, cinders, and fragments of stone, commonly small. Among these fragments of limestone and dolomite, with one several pounds in weight, of sandstone, were observed. (De la Beche–6:*95.*) These fragments were broken off from the rocks through which the eruption passed on its upward way. "During the time that this volcanic mass was accumulating, a large amount of ashes and cinders must have been mingled with the adjacent sea before it reached its surface, and no slight amount would be distributed around, when ashes and cinders could be vomited into the air. Add to this the quantity caught up in mechanical suspension by the breakers and there would be no small amount to be accumulated over any deposits forming, or formed, on the bottom around this locality . . ." (De la Beche–6:*95, 96*). These deposits included, of course, abundant remains of organisms, killed by the explosive eruption. Another example of a volcano formed in the historic period is Sabrina Island in the Azores, off the coast of St. Michaels. Here a submarine eruption built a cone of loose cinders to a height of about 300 feet, and a circumference of about a mile. This, too, soon disappeared under the subsequent attack of the waves.

"The formation of this island was observed and recorded. It was first discovered rising above the sea on the thirteenth of June, 1811, and on the seventeenth was observed by Captain Tillard, . . . from the nearest cliff of St. Michael's. The volcanic bursts were described as resembling a mixed discharge of cannon and musketry; and were accompanied by a great abundance of lightning." (De la Beche–6:*123.*) A sketch made at that time is here reproduced (Fig. 229). A similar occurrence is recorded from the west coast of Iceland, where, in the early summer of 1783, arose an island of volcanic nature about thirty miles from Cape Reykjanaes. In less than a year, however, it had again been washed away by the waves, leaving only a submerged reef or shoal from five to thirty fathoms below sea-level.

Numerous submarine eruptions which never reach the surface no doubt occur over many portions of the ocean floor. In these both cinders and lava enter, sometimes one and sometimes the other

FIG. 229. Sketch of the submarine volcanic eruption which, in June, 1811, formed Sabrina Island, off St. Michaels in the Azores. (After De la Beche.)

predominating. On the floor of some parts of the deep sea volcanic ejectamenta are abundant, and these are in part at least due to submarine explosive eruptions.

Extravasative Eruptions.

Terrestrial Type—Fissure Eruption. The fundamental characteristics of this type are best developed in the great fissure eruptions which have resulted in the formation of extensive lava fields, and in the broad flat lava domes of the Hawaiian group. The fissures from which the great lava extravasations take place are generally ranged parallel with and near to the coast and seem to be especially prevalent where the edge of the land drops off rapidly to deep sea. The most stupendous modern examples of fissure eruptions are those of eastern Iceland. In this island occur a number of distinct and parallel clefts arranged in two dominant series, one extending northeast and southwest, the other north and south. "Many such fissures are traceable at the surface as deep and nearly straight clefts or *gjâs,* usually a few yards in width but extending for many miles. The Eldgjá has a length of more than 18 English miles and a depth varying from 400 to 600 feet." (Hobbs–15:*99.*)

According to Thoroddsen, the lava wells out quietly from the whole length of some of these fissures, overflowing on both sides without the formation of cones. These fissures, therefore, constitute connecting dikes, such as are known to occur under the older lava flows of this type. At three of the wider portions of the great Eld cleft of Iceland the lava has welled out quietly without the formation of cones, flooding an area of 270 square miles. Upon the southern narrower prolongation of the fissure, however, a row of low slag cones appeared, and this is a feature characteristic of other fissures in Iceland, as well as the great Skaptar fissure reopened in 1783, emitting great volumes of lava. Subsequently the eruptive processes became concentrated at the wider portions of the fissure and a row of small cones was left over the line of the fissure. Upon this fissure, too, stands the large volcano of Laki. The great eruptions and the larger volcanoes are generally found at the intersection of two fissures, as in the case of the great eruption of Askja in 1875, and of the volcanoes of Java. On a small scale, the formation of volcanoes along fissures is shown in the frozen surface of the lava lake in the caldron of Kilauea, where miniature volcanoes form whenever the crust which hardens in the lava-lake becomes fissured.

The connection of volcanic activities with fissuring of the earth's surface is further shown in the great rift-valley of eastern Africa, where extensive outpourings of lava have covered portions of the valley floor, while volcanoes of great height and comparatively recent origin have arisen within the valley, as in the case of the Mfumbiro Mountains, already referred to, which block the rift-valley north of Lake Kivu and which rise to great altitudes, the crater rim of the still active volcano Kirungo-cha-Gongo rising to 11,350 feet above the sea-level, while Karisimbi reaches an altitude approaching 14,000 feet. (Fig. 21, p. 125.) The valley floor on which these volcanoes arose was considerably less than 4,000 feet above sea-level; indeed, this same valley floor in the region of Lake Tanganyika to the south actually descends below sea-level.

The most gigantic outpouring of lavas from fissures occurred in late Tertiary or early Quaternary time in western North America. There lava floods formed the great plains of the Snake River region in southern Idaho, and the vast basaltic plateau of Washington, Oregon, and northern California. This lava field has more or less interrupted extensions through Nevada, Arizona, New Mexico, and the western half of Mexico south into Central America and northward through British Columbia to the Alaskan Peninsula and the Aleutian Islands. (See the Geological Map of North America.) The main lines of fissures were probably parallel to the Pacific coast, but of this nothing is visible, except the general trend of the lava sheets from north to south. The area covered by the lava outpourings aggregates 200,000 square miles, while the thickness of the sheet averages 2,000 feet and reaches in some places 3,700 feet. The comparatively recent origin and the location of the lava plateau have precluded much destructive work by the surface agents, although the Snake River has cut a series of picturesque gorges through it. The cones now rising from this surface indicate localization of eruption subsequent to the outpouring of the lava floods. Prismatic structure is well developed in parts of these lava sheets. Intercalated river sediments often separate successive flows.

Remnants of early Tertiary basaltic lavas are now found in numerous places in northeast Ireland, western Scotland, the lower Hebrides, the Faroe islands, and faraway Iceland. These, famous for their columnar partings (Giants' Causeway, Fingal's Cave, etc.), were probably part of a once continuous lava field, now dismembered by the agents of erosion, not the least of which is the sea. Numerous dikes of similar material occur in regions from which this lava has apparently been eroded, and these dikes probably mark the fissures through which this welling-up of the lava took place.

These dikes are extremely abundant in the northwest of Scotland (Peach and Horne–28) and range eastward across Scotland and the north of England and Ireland. They have been traced from the Orkney Islands southward to Yorkshire and across Britain from sea to sea over a total area of probably not less than 100,000 square miles. This may indicate the former wide extent of this basaltic lava field which then rivaled the younger one of western America. When erosion has been carried far enough in the great lava plateau of western North America, to remove a considerable portion of the lava sheet, there will no doubt appear an equally

vast number of dikes, which represent the filling of the fissures
through which the lava reached the surface.

A Cretacic example of such outpouring of basic lava, rivaling
in extent that of the northwestern United States, is seen in the great
bed of Deccan trap which forms the surface of the Deccan Plateau
in India. Here the depth of the lava is from 4,000 to 6,000 feet.
Where the basement rocks on which this trap sheet rest are exposed
by erosion along the margin of the plateau dikes of basalt are seen
penetrating them, representing in part the fissures through which

Fig. 230. End of the lava flow of 1881 near Hilo, Hawaiian Islands. The
lava surface is a typical pahoehoe surface. (After Dutton.)

the lava reached the surface. No cones or definite vents have been
found.

What appears to be a pre-Palæozoic example of such eruptions
is seen in the great Keweenawan lava sheets which represent a prolonged succession of outpourings in the Lake Superior region,
aggregating an enormous amount variously estimated as reaching
the great thickness of 15,000 or 25,000 feet. Here, too, there is
little evidence of explosive or other concentrated volcanic activity.

The lava dome. Where eruptions are concentrated about a
single opening a mountain of lava will be built up which rises in
proportion to the frequency of the eruption and the volume of lava
poured out. Where fragmental material is absent, as in the Hawaiian volcanoes, the slope is a very gentle one, though the actual

height is great. Though now rising to nearly 14,000 feet above sea-level these volcanoes began as submarine eruptions, starting on the floor of the deep sea and having a total height of 20,000 or 30,000 feet. The visible portion is less than a hundred miles in diameter, but the actual base is probably much more than twice that. The two active volcanoes are Mauna Loa, the rim of which is 13,675 feet above sea-level; and Kilauea, which is less than 4,000 feet high and appears to rest on the flanks of the larger volcano. The craters, or caldera, have each a circumference exceeding seven miles, being irregularly elliptical in outline with the sides descending in a series of steps to the central pit, which is formed by the "frozen" surface of the lava. The floor of the pit of Kilauea is a "movable platform" of frozen lava which rises and falls with the variation in

FIG. 231. View of Kilauea caldera from the Volcano House. (After Dutton.)

the pressure of the lava beneath. The difference in height between 1823 and 1884 was estimated by Dutton (7:127) to be nearly 400 feet.

"Beneath the floor of the caldera," says Dutton, "we may conjecture the existence of a lake of far greater proportions than those which now expose a fiery surface to the sky. The visible lakes might be compared to the air-holes in the surface of a frozen pond." The proof for this is found in the fact that new eruptions are not overflows of the open pools of lava, but break out anywhere in the floor of the caldera. (Fig. 231.)

Acid lava domes. Lavas of the acid type are, as a rule, too viscous to form mountains of gentle slope, occurring more often as steep-sided domes, especially if the lava is only semi-fluid. This is well shown in Figure 232, where, in the Auvergne district of France, a trachyte cone of highly viscid lava was extruded between cinder cones. The domed character of the extravasated pustular cone contrasts strongly with the concave surfaces of the cinder cones. The results of experiments recorded in Figures 228 and 233 show the fundamental differences between fragmental cones and domes of pustular lava.

The spine of Pelée. What is regarded by many as a most stupendous example of the extravasation of a viscous mass of andesitic lava—which cooled as it was extravasated—is found in the remarkable spine of Mont Pelée which formed after the great eruption of 1902. According to Hovey (16; 17; 18), this spine was a lava mass pushed up vertically without spreading, the mass cooling either in the upper part of the conduit or upon its appearance at the surface, so that no extended flow was possible. The spine grew at an average of forty-one feet per day during a period

Fig. 232. The Grand Puy of Sarconi, in the Auvergne, composed of trachyte, rising between two breached scoria-cones. A typical example of a pustular cone formed of highly viscid lava.

Fig. 233. Experimental illustration of the mode of formation of volcanic cones composed of viscid lavas.

of eighteen days out of the new cone, which itself had attained a height of 1,600 feet during the last ten days of May, and was of the same character as the spine. As the spine rose 1,100 feet above this new cone in October it appears that the total elevation of this mass above the top of the cone as it existed prior to the eruption of May, 1902, was 2,700 feet. (See, further, Heilprin–12; Hill–12a; Jaggar–20 and Russell–34a.)

Composite Lava and Cinder Cones.

Volcanic cones built by a combination or an alternation of the explosive and extravasative activities are by far the most common. They generally have pronounced slopes and are more resistant than cones built wholly of cinders, because the lava binds together the loose material into a complex mass. This is sometimes accomplished by the formation of radial dikes, as in the case of Ætna. These represent lateral fissuring of the cone and the filling of these fissures by lava (Figs. 234, 235). The lava sometimes extended through these fissures, building up secondary cones or monticules on the flank of the main cone, as in the case just cited. Fissuring of the cone is of common occurrence in volcanoes, the lava of many of them rarely or never overflowing the crater, but finding an outlet at a lower level through the side of the volcano. If parasitic cones (monticules) are built up over such a fissure these may remain the site of eruption for a long period, but sooner or later they are likely to become extinct, and then they may be buried by later flows and ejectamenta. Cinder cones, which are relatively weak structures, will be breached if a subsequent lava stream is poured out, and this

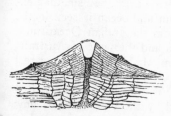

FIG. 234. Diagram illustrating the formation of parasitic cones (monticules) along lines of fissures formed in the flanks of a great volcano. (After Judd.)

FIG. 235. Basaltic dikes projecting from stratified scoria or tuff in the walls of the Val del Bove, Ætna.

will issue from their sides. (Fig. 227.) Large composite cones may be breached by explosive eruptions and the shifting of the center of the eruption. A new cone may be built up within the breached outer rim of an original large caldera, as in the case of Vesuvius, which was built within the breached rim of the extinct Monte Somma. The displacement of the eruptive point may be a gradual one, when a series of adjoining cones will result, all but the youngest being breached on the side toward the direction of migration of the cones. Examples of such consecutively breached cones are found in the volcanic region of central France (Mont Doré Province), and elsewhere. Many variations and combinations occur, and the student is referred for the details of these phenomena to the numerous general treatises, some of which are listed at the end of the chapter.

Compound volcanoes, such as Vesuvius, have alternating periods of light (or *Strombolian*) and violent (or *Vulcanian*) activity. During the former cinder cones are built up which are destroyed again, in part or entirely during the violent periods, when crater formation is the marked characteristic. It is during this period of activity that the extravasative eruptions are in the ascendency, and at this time also fissuring of the volcano takes place, with all the varied activities which accompany such a state.

Submarine Cones. Submarine cones of pure extravasation are apparently illustrated by the Hawaiian Islands, though the early history of many of these volcanoes is shrouded in obscurity. Submarine cones of the composite type are well known, however. Probably many of the volcanoes of the Mediterranean began as submarine volcanoes and subsequently reached the surface. Volcanoes of this type are also known from the Aleutian island group (Jaggar–21), while volcanoes apparently rising from the abyssal portions of the sea abound in the western Pacific. A singular example of a volcanic peak projecting from mid-ocean is seen in the little island of St. Paul, which rises from the Indian Ocean midway between the southern end of Africa and the west of Australia and more than 2,000 miles distant from Madagascar, the nearest mass of dry land. This little island, scarcely 2½ geographical miles long and about 1½ miles broad, is the mere summit of a volcano. The crater has been breached by the waves and is now occupied by the sea, the break in the rim being nearly dry at low tide. (Figs. 236, 237.)

Mud Volcanoes. Of an origin fundamentally the same as that for lava volcanoes are the mud volcanoes found in various regions of the world, but not associated with igneous eruptions. They occur in Sicily, the Apennines, Caucasus, and on the peninsulas of Kertch and Taman bordering the Black Sea, as well as in India. They find their chief activity in the escape of various gases, which play much the same part as does the escaping steam in igneous volcanoes. Hydrocarbons, carbon dioxide, nitrogen, and naphtha are some of the gases emitted. The mud volcanoes of Sicily have been explained as due to the slow combustion of sulphur beneath the surface. Whatever the causes, these volcanoes are manifested on the surface in mounds or hillocks of mud. They generally occur in groups and range in elevation up to several hundred feet, while during periods of explosion they throw mud and stones up into the air to much greater heights. They are built up by successive outpourings of mud, which harden and form a foundation for later mud flows. "In the region of the Lower Indus, where they are abundantly distributed over an area of 1,000 square miles, some of them attain a height of 400 feet, with craters 30 yards across."

(Geikie–9 :245.) These are not to be confused with the mud flows which form on the sides of volcanoes from the saturation of dust

FIG. 236.   View of the Island of St. Paul in the southern Indian Ocean, showing the breach in the rim of the extinct volcano and the crater
flooded by the sea.   (From a sketch by Charles Vélain in Haug.)

and cinders by rain.   Such flows always occur in regions of igneous extrusion on the sides of igneous volcanoes, while mud volcanoes may occur in any region where gases accumulate beneath the sur-

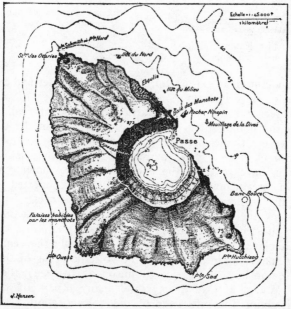

FIG. 237.   Map of the Island of St. Paul in the southern Indian Ocean.   A
breached volcano.   (After Charles Vélain in Haug.)

face in large enough quantities to be forced out.   Neither should these mud volcanoes be confused with mud mounds, cones, or craterlets which form along earthquake fissures where the release of pressure sends forth a stream of water carrying sand and mud with it. (See farther in Chapter XXIII, on Seismology.)

Dissection of Volcanoes. When volcanoes have become extinct the ordinary forces of erosion set in and progressive destruction goes on. The rapidity with which this takes place varies, of course, with the nature of the material, the prevailing strength of the erosive forces, and with other factors. Many of the Tertiary volcanoes of the Eifel in Germany and of the Auvergne district in France are still almost perfect, while others of earlier date show all stages of dissection. Of interest in this connection is the Kammerbühl near Franzensbad in northern Bohemia, which

FIG. 238. The Kammerbühl, an old volcanic hill in Bohemia.

FIG. 239. Section of the Kammerbühl, showing the probable former outline of the volcano: *a*, metamorphic rock; *b*, basaltic scoriæ; *c*, plug or neck of basalt; *d*, stream of basalt; *e*, alluvial beds.

Goethe pronounced an extinct volcano, though Werner had explained its character as originating, in common with those of others of similar aspect, through the combustion of a bed of coal. Goethe predicted the finding of a core of volcanic rock in the center of this hill were a tunnel driven into it horizontally. The excavating of this tunnel in 1837 verified this prediction, while more recent excavations have revealed the entire structure, showing that the small lava stream on the side of the hill was connected with the central plug or neck and rested on basaltic scoria. The above figures show the appearance of this hill and the structure ascertained by these excavations. (Figs. 238, 239.)

In extensively dissected volcanoes often only the central neck or plug remains, as in the case of the volcanic necks of the Mount Taylor Region in New Mexico (Johnson—22:303-324), the Leucite Hills of Wyoming (Kemp—25), and many others of this type. Dikes dissecting the tufa beds of old volcanoes often stand out in bold relief owing to the steady removal of the easily eroded tufa enclosing them. Examples of such are known from many localities. The geological map of the Spanish Peaks region in Colorado shows excellently the numerous radiating dikes which center in the old volcanic necks of that region.

Where extinct volcanoes have been subject to the attack of the waves of the sea sections are often cut which reveal their structure. This is the case in the island of St. Paul, already noted, and in Vulcanello on the shores of the Island of Vulcano in the Mediterranean. Some of the outlying islands of the Sandwich or Hawaiian group likewise represent partly dissected extinct volcanic cones whose sides, moreover, are deeply gullied into a series of parallel valleys so sharply divided one from the other as to effectively isolate certain of the organisms inhabiting them. (See Chapter XXIX.)

Finally, the destruction of volcanoes by their own explosive activity may be noted. Examples are furnished by the Vesuvian eruption of A. D. 79, which shattered the cone of Monte Somma; by the Japanese volcano Bandai-san, of which a considerable portion was blown out in 1888; and by the Javanese volcano Krakatoa, which was practically blown to pieces on August 26 and 27, 1883, furnishing the most stupendous example of volcanic activity in modern times. "After a series of convulsions, the greater portion of the island was blown out with a succession of terrific detonations which were heard more than 150 miles away. A mass of matter estimated at about $1\frac{1}{8}$ cubic miles in bulk was hurled into the air in the form of lapilli, ashes, and the finest volcanic dust. . . . The sea in the neighborhood was thrown into waves, one of which was computed to have risen more than 100 feet above tide-level, destroying towns, villages, and 36,380 people." (Geikie–9:*212*.) The oscillations of the wave were noted at Port Elizabeth, South Africa, 5,450 miles away, having traveled with a maximum velocity of 467 statute miles per hour. The air waves generated traveled from east to west and are supposed to have passed three and a quarter times around the earth (82,200 miles) before they died away. The barometric disturbances, passing round the globe in opposite directions from the volcano, proceeded at the rate of almost 700 miles per hour.

Special Erosion Features. An interesting type of erosion has been observed on some steep-sided volcanoes, such as those of the islands of St. Vincent and Martinique. Vast amounts of dust were deposited during the eruption of May, 1902, and these formed a bed varying from a few inches to many feet in thickness, and extending over an area of 50 square miles on each island. The heavy rains that followed the eruption turned this dust into a cement-like mud which was firm enough to remain in place and which, during the eruptions of September and October of the same year, was covered by a new layer of coarser ejectamenta. In the valleys the permanent and periodical rivers were loaded with the new ash to such an extent as to form viscous streams, which, however, had great powers of erosion, on account of the steep slope of the declivities down which they flowed. The bottoms and sides of the gorges were deeply grooved by the sand carried down in this manner by the flowing water.

"During the great eruptions the ejected material was drifted into large beds in the gorges extending radially down the Soufrière [on St. Vincent Island]. The massing of material was most important in the gorge of the Wallibou River on the west, and in that of the Rabaka River on the east, side of the island. In these gorges the bed of new material reached a thickness of from 60 to 100 feet. This enormous amount of material was almost entirely washed out of the gorges during the first rainy season following the eruptions of 1902. Not less than 150,000,000 cubic feet of ashes have been washed out of the Wallibou gorge itself, without taking into account the thousands of cubic yards of fresh ash removed from the watershed of the river during the same period. All this material was, of course, transported directly to the ocean." (Hovey–18:560.)

FORMATION OF THE LAVA.

Since it is very unlikely that at any point within the earth's crust the temperature is sufficiently high to melt rocks (see Chapter I) at the increased fusing point caused by the increase in pressure downward, it follows that some other factors must be taken into consideration in explaining the liquefaction of rock. We must, therefore, seek either for causes producing an increase of temperature, or for such producing a decrease of pressure. The former may be found in the energy liberated by radio-active substances, such as are found in practically all the rocks of the earth's crust, as well as in the water and the air. Since, says Chamberlin (3:679), "radio-activity increases as we go from air to water, from water to sediment, and from sediment to igneous rock, it might be inferred . . . that radio-activity would be found to reach its maximum concentration in the heart of the earth, and certainly that the deeper parts would be as rich as the superficial ones." This, however, would imply a more rapid increase in temperature than observation indicates. Strutt (quoted by Chamberlin) has computed that, if the quantity of radio-active substances known to exist in surface rocks is also found throughout the rocks of the upper 45 miles of the earth's crust, the rise in temperature equal to that observed in deep wells and mines would be produced by this cause alone, irrespective of any other source of heat. Whether this distribution is equal, or whether it increases or decreases downward, can not, at present, be determined; but it is seen that if we start with an original increase in temperature downward the amount added to it by radio-activity might serve, locally, to overcome the opposing effects of pressure in raising the fusing point, whereupon reservoirs of molten rock would be formed which would become the source of volcanic activity.

If excessive temperature increase is not to be accepted as the cause of rock fusion at a depth, we must turn to a local decrease of pressure to permit the lowering of the fusing point of the rocks. This would be effected by the formation, locally, of rock arches within the crust capable of maintaining the weight of the superincumbent portion of the crust. Such arches, or domes, by relieving the pressure, would permit the liquefaction of the rock mass for some distance beneath them, provided the temperature is sufficiently high, and so furnish the requisite conditions for volcanic activities.

Arches of this type might be expected to form along the margins of the continent where the down-warping of the continental edges takes place. Now, it is precisely along these lines, where the continental margin drops off steeply to the deep sea, that the great volcanic phenomena of the past have been located, while the distribution of most of the modern volcanoes of the earth is essentially in harmony with this idea. Thus by far the largest number of still active or but recently extinct volcanoes are ranged in belts or lines parallel to the margins of the continents or within the oceanic areas. The most important belt of volcanic activity surrounds the Pacific Ocean, the deepest and perhaps the oldest of the oceans of the earth, and the one which has experienced the least change. This belt includes the volcanic mountains of the west coasts of South and Central America, of Mexico, and of the western United States and Canada to Alaska and the Aleutian Island chain. It is continued along the eastern coast of Eurasia, and through the Malaysian islands to New Zealand, the belt being finally closed by the volcanoes of Victoria Land, King Edward Island, and West Antarctica. It is significant that the belt for the most part is paralleled by an inner one of exceptional depressions the great fore-deeps of the marginal Pacific. That these are produced by downwarping or faulting seems certain, and this would imply an arching or unwarping of the adjoining continental margins.

BIBLIOGRAPHY XXII.

1. ANDERSON, TEMPEST. 1903. Volcanic Studies in Many Lands. John Murray, London.
2. BONNEY, T. G. 1899. Volcanoes, Their Structure and Significance. John Murray, London.
3. CHAMBERLIN, THOMAS C. 1911. The Bearing of Radioactivity on Geology. Journal of Geology, Vol. XIX, pp. 673–695.
4. CHAMBERLIN, T. C., and SALISBURY, ROLLIN D. 1906. Geology, Vol. I. Henry Holt & Co., New York.
5. DANA, JAMES D. 1890. Characteristics of Volcanoes, with contributions of Facts and Principles from the Hawaiian Islands. Dodd, Mead and Company, New York.
6. DE LA BECHE, HENRY T. 1851. The Geological Observer, Philadelphia.
7. DUTTON, CLARENCE E. 1884. Hawaiian Volcanoes. Fourth Annual Report of the United States Geological Survey, 1882–83, pp. 81–219.
8. FAIRCHILD, HERMAN L. 1907. Origin of Meteor Crater (Coon Butte), Arizona. Bulletin of the Geological Society of America, Vol. XVIII, pp. 493–504, pls., 54–56.
9. GEIKIE, ARCHIBALD. 1893. Text-book of Geology, 3rd edition. Macmillan & Co.
10. GEIKIE, A. 1897. The Ancient Volcanoes of Great Britain, 2 vols. Macmillan & Co.
11. GILBERT, G. K. 1893. Report on Coon Butte, Arizona. Fourteenth Annual Report of the United States Geological Survey, pt. I, p. 187.
12. HEILPRIN, A. 1904. The Tower of Pelée. Philadelphia.
12a. HILL, R. T. 1905. Pelée and the Evolution of the Windward Archipelago. Bulletin of the Geological Society of America. Vol. XVI, pp. 243–288, 5 pls.
13. HITCHCOCK, C. H. 1909. Hawaii and Its Volcanoes. Honolulu.
14. HOBBS, WILLIAM H. 1906. The Grand Eruption of Vesuvius in 1906. Journal of Geology, Vol. XIV, pp. 636–655.
15. HOBBS, W. H. 1912. Earth Features and Their Meaning, an Introduction to Geology. Macmillan Company, New York.
16. HOVEY, E. O. 1903. The New Cone of Mont Pelée and the Gorge of the Rivière Blanche, Martinique. American Journal of Science, Vol. XVI, pp. 269–281.
17. HOVEY, E. O. 1904. New Cone and Obelisk of Mont Pelée. Bulletin of the Geological Society of America, Vol. XV, pp. 558–560.
18. HOVEY, E. O. 1904. Some Erosion Phenomena Observed on the Islands of Saint Vincent and Martinique in 1902 and 1903. Ibid., pp. 560–561, pls. 57–58.
19. HOVEY, E. O. 1905. Present Conditions of Mont Pelée. Bulletin of the Geological Society of America, Vol. XVI, pp. 566–569, pl. 92.
20. JAGGAR, THOMAS A. 1904. The Initial Stages of the Spine on Pelée. American Journal of Science, 4th series, Vol. XVII, pp. 39 et seq.
21. JAGGAR, T. A. 1908. The Evolution of the Bogoslof Volcano. Bulletin of the American Geographical Society, Vol. XLV, pp. 385–400, 8 figs.
22. JOHNSON, DOUGLAS W. 1907. Volcanic Necks of the Mount Taylor Region, New Mexico. Bulletin of the Geological Society of America, Vol. XVIII, pp. 303–324, pls. 25–30.

23. JOHNSTON–LAVIS, H. J. 1891. The South Italian Volcanoes. Naples. 342 pp.

24. JOHNSTON–LAVIS, H. J. 1909. The Eruption of Vesuvius in April, 1906. Transactions of the Royal Dublin Society, Vol. IX, pt. VIII, pp. 139–200.

25. KEMP, JAMES F., and KNIGHT, W. C. 1903. Leucite Hills of Wyoming. Bulletin of the Geological Society of America, Vol. XIV, pp. 305–336, pls. 37–46.

26. MOORE, J. E. S. 1903. The Tanganyika Problem. Hurst and Blackett, London.

27. OMORI, F. 1911. The Usu-san Eruption and Earthquake and Elevation Phenomena. Bulletin of the Earthquake Investigation Committee, Japan. Vol. V, pp. 1–37.

28. PEACH, BENJAMIN, and HORNE, JOHN. 1907. The Geological Structure of the North-west Highlands of Scotland.

29. RATH, G. VON. 1872. Der Aetna. Bonn.

30. RECLUS, JEAN JACQUES ÉLISÉE. 1906–1910. Les Volcans de la Terre. Belgian Society of Astronomy, Meteorology and Physics of the Globe.

31. ROYAL SOCIETY OF LONDON. 1888. The Eruption of Krakatoa and Subsequent Phenomena. Report of Special Committee. London. 494 pp.

32. RUDOLPH, E. 1887. Ueber Submarine Erdbeben und Eruptionen. Gerlands Beiträge zur Geophysik, pp. 133–365; ibid., 1895, pp. 537–666; ibid., 1898, pp. 273–336.

33. RUSSELL, I. C. 1897. Volcanoes of North America. Macmillan, New York.

34. RUSSELL, I. C. 1902. Geology of Snake River Plains, Idaho. Bulletin United States Geological Survey, No. 199. (Abstract: Bulletin of the Geological Society of America, Vol. XIII, 1902, p. 527; and Science, Vol. XV, 1902, pp. 85–86.)

34a. RUSSELL, I C. 1905. The Pelée Obelisk. Science N. S. Vol. XVIII, pp. 792–795.

35. SCROPE, PAULET. 1858. The Geology of the Extinct Volcanoes of Central France. John Murray, London.

36. THORODDSEN, TH. 1905. Die Bruchlinien und ihre Beziehungen zu den Vulkanen. Petermann's Mittheilungen, Bd. LI, pp. 1–573.

37. THORODDSEN, TH. 1906. Island, IV. Vulkane. Petermann's Mittheilungen, Ergänzungsheft 153, pp. 108–111.

38. THOULET, J. 1903. Les Volcans sousmarins. Revue des Deux Mondes. 73ième année, 5ième période, T. XIII, pp. 611–624.

39. VERBECK, R. D. M. 1885. Krakatau. Batavia. 557 pp., 25 pls.

40. WALTERSHAUSEN, SARTORIUS VON. 1880. Der Aetna. Leipzig. 2 vols.

41. WALTHER, JOHANNES. 1910. Lehrbuch der Geologie von Deutschland. Quelle und Meyer. Leipzig.

E. THE CENTROSPHERE OR BARYSPHERE.

CHAPTER XXIII.

DIASTROPHISM, OR THE MOVEMENTS TAKING PLACE WITHIN THE EARTH'S CRUST AND THEIR CAUSES.

In discussing the subject of diastrophism under the heading of the Centrosphere, it is intended to emphasize the fact that the great mass of such movements is directly or indirectly induced by gravity, *i. e.*, the terrestrial phenomenon of weight or downward acceleration,* which has for its two components the gravitation or attracting force between bodies and the centrifugal force due to the rotation of the earth on its axis.

Other forces which induce earth movements have their origin in the interior heat of the earth; in chemical combination; in molecular attraction and repulsion; in radio-activity; in electrical and vital energy; in the centrifugal energy due to the rotating of the earth on its axis and its revolution around the sun; in the attraction of the moon and sun; and in the radiant energy of the sun. Impact with heavenly bodies may be further mentioned as a source of possible energy. But all of these, except perhaps the last, are of minor significance as compared with gravity as the great source of energy influencing earth movements. The displacement of the earth's center of gravity through any cause, and the consequent displacement of the earth's axis, would also be a direct cause of the setting free of a vast amount of available energy.

CLASSIFICATION OF EARTH MOVEMENTS.

Earth movements may be classified either as local disturbances or as widespread or regional ones. The movements are manifested

* The amount of downward acceleration is about 385.1 inches (978 centimeters) per second at sea-level at the equator, and 387.1 inches at sea-level at the poles, diminishing slightly on mountain tops. The centrifugal force at the equator is $\frac{1}{289.4}$ of gravity.

as seismic disturbances, of which *earthquakes* and *sea-quakes* are the recognized effects, while the products of the disturbances are *tectonic structures*.*

Not all tectonic structures are accompanied in their formation by seismic disturbances, for some deformations may go on so gradually, and at such a uniform rate, that no surface manifestations are felt. In this class fall especially the large or epeirogenic earth movements, and the bradyseisms noted below.

CLASSIFICATION OF SEISMIC DISTURBANCES.

Not all seismic disturbances are due to earth movements, as the term is here used, for volcanic activities, especially of the explosive type, may generate such disturbances, these being sometimes of considerable magnitude, as in the case of the explosive eruption of Krakatoa in 1883. As there illustrated, the three inorganic spheres—the litho, hydro, and atmosphere, not to mention the biosphere—were disturbed by this explosion, and earthquakes, sea-quakes, and air-quakes † resulted. The air-waves which characterized the last passed around the earth several times, while the sea disturbances or *tsunamis* ‡ generated were noticeable more than five hundred miles away.

Recognizing the different modes of production of earthquakes, seismologists have divided them according to origin into: (Suess–38.)

1. Dislocation or fault earthquakes.
2. Volcanic, or explosive earthquakes.

* The term *tectonic*, originally applied to all structures, has come of late to be more especially applied to structures due to earth movements, or deformation structures. These include faults, folds, torsion joints, etc., but not stratification, unconformity, overlap, flow-structure, or any other *original* structures, nor such secondary structures as concretions, enterolithic deformation, or any other structures due to diagenetic or contactic metamorphism.

† If we consider that the term *seisma* refers to the trembling or shaking of the *geos*, or earth as a whole (geoseism), and not merely to the tremblings of the land, we may extend the meaning of the term seismology so as to cover the shaking or trembling of any portion of the earth as the result of such disturbances. We could thus distinguish: *lithoseisma*, or earthquakes proper (land-quakes); *hydro-* or *thalassoseisma* or sea-quakes and *atmoseisma*, or air-quakes. The *bioseisma* are, of course, a universal accompaniment of all these disturbances.

‡ The Japanese term for the "tidal wave," or "sea-wave" of sea-quakes. Suggested for general adoption by Hobbs (17).

The first type of seismic disturbance may be spoken of as *bary-seismic*,* and the second as *pyroseismic*,† these terms indicating the ·relationship of the disturbances to the respective spheres. Hoernes (19) has designated as a third type the results of incaving of the roofs of fissures (*Einsturzbeben*) which characterize the Karst region of the Dalmatian coast. This, however, is to be classed as a special phase of the dislocation (baryseismic) type, since such cavings-in of cavern roofs are merely special phases of faulting. In the same way, we must class under the volcanic or explosive (pyroseismic) type the tremors resulting from explosions of gunpowder or dynamite, and of gases, in mines and elsewhere, which may not be sufficient to affect the seismograph, but are certainly noticeable as sea-quakes (submarine explosions) and as air-quakes. These, as well as the disturbances due to incaving, may be dismissed without further notice.

The Volcanic or Pyroseismic Type of Earthquake. This is, of course, an accompaniment of volcanic activities; but such disturbances are not necessarily always felt, for, even if they occur, they may be so slight as to escape notice.

The Tectonic or Dislocation (Baryseismic) Earthquake. This is a jar occasioned by the breaking of rock under strain. "The strain may be caused by the rising of lava in a volcano or by the forces that make mountain ranges and continents." The rupture of the rock mass "may be a mere pulling apart of the rocks, so as to make a crack, but examples of that simple type are comparatively rare. The great majority of ruptures include not only the making of a crack but the relative movement or sliding of the rock masses on the two sides of the crack; that is to say, instead of a mere fracture, there is a geologic fault." (Gilbert–13:2.)

The walls of the fault plane may eventually become cemented together, but they will remain as a plane of weakness for a long time, so that repeated slipping may take place, making the region one of frequent earthquakes. This has been the case in the repeated California earthquakes, of which the San Francisco quake of 1906 is the most recent. The fault-line there extends for several hundred miles northwest and southeast and nearly parallel to the coast. The "Fossa Magna" crosses Japan from north to south, while the southern border lands of Afghanistan have such an habitual earthquake-producing fault-line extending for 120 miles.

The faulting or slipping which produces the earthquake may

---

* From the Greek βαρύς = heavy, + σεισμα = earthquake; signifying that weight or gravity is the dominant factor in their production.

† From the Greek πῦρ = fire, + σεισμα = earthquake.

be deepseated or may reach the surface. The depth to which the dislocation penetrates may be very great—it may pass from the zone of fracture into that of flowage; but the origin of the shock is probably never deeper than 30 geographical miles, and usually does not exceed 5 to 15 miles. (Hovey–21 :*244.*) The point or locus of origination of the earthquake is variously called the *seismic center, centrum, hypocenter, origin,* or *focus.* This, though conveniently regarded as a point, is really a space of three dimensions which in different cases varies much in size and shape and may be of great magnitude. The part of the earth's surface which is vertically above the center is the *epicenter* or epicentral or epifocal tract.

SURFACE MANIFESTATIONS OF BARYSEISMIC DISTURBANCES.

The surface manifestations of an earthquake-producing fault or other tectonic movement may, so far as the lithosphere is concerned, be classed as *rifting,* as *slipping,* and as *disruption.* The first is mere separation, the second involves displacement. It is to the latter movement that the term faulting is commonly applied.

Rifting.

As a result of rifting, fissures will open in the earth (Fig. 240) and these may remain open or be filled by injected material. So far as arrangement is concerned these fissures may be in *parallel* series, as in the case of the fissures formed by the earthquake of Sinj, Austria, in 1898, in which slipping also occurred along each rift. Or, again, these fissures may *radiate* from a center, branching repeatedly. Such fissures were formed during the Calabrian earthquake of 1783. Finally, fissures formed during earthquakes may be irregularly intersecting, forming a network. This type has been observed at Aigon in the Balkans after the earthquake of December 26, 1861; in Owens Valley, California, after the earthquake of 1872 (Whitney); and in Ecuador, where it is a very characteristic feature of the Andes region. Whimper (43) says of these: "In no other part of Ecuador is there anything equaling this extraordinary assemblage of fissures, intersecting one another irregularly and forming a perfect maze of impassable clefts . . . the cracks are all V-shaped and, though seldom of great breadth, are often very profound, . . . Several, at least, have been formed within the memory of man, while others are centuries old."

These intersecting fissures are locally known as earthquake "quebradas."

Fissures often open and close repeatedly, even during the same

FIG. 240. Small earthquake fissure and fault in the Arizona desert. (After Branner.)

disturbance; sometimes in closing, the walls are pressed violently together, while shattering of the adjoining rock masses occurs, with the formation of autoclastic material or fault-breccias. This gen-

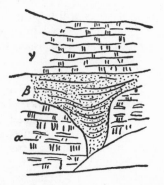

FIG. 241. Section of one of the sandstone pipes in limestone on the eastern coast of Anglesey in Wales. (After Greenly, from Hobbs.) *a*, cherty limestone; *β*, sandstone pipe; *γ*, cherty limestone.

erally falls into the fissure, more or less filling it, or it marks the sides of the fissure for some distance outward.

Filling of the Fissures. Sandstone Dikes. Fissures formed by earthquakes may remain open for a longer or shorter period of time, becoming gradually filled up by débris which falls in from above, or is washed into them. Such is the case in several vertical fault fissures at Meriden, Connecticut, which have been filled by infiltration of trap fragments and sandstone from above. (Davis, in Diller–8:*442*.)

Davis says: "These fractures traverse a sheet of lava and are chiefly filled with angular trap-fragments, but the interstices are occupied with sandstone, not in fragments as if it had fallen in with the pieces of trap, but in a close-fitting mass, as if it had settled down in the form of separate particles derived from the sandstone originally overlying the trap sheet, thus, in a general way, taking a structure conformable to the blocks of trap that it surrounds, but showing also a tendency to a transverse or horizontal stratification. It seems probable that these fissures were filled gradually by infiltration from above . . ."

In some cases, however, such fissures are filled at the time of their formation by sand violently injected into them either from below or above. Cases of mud and sand welling up from volcanic fissures have been frequently observed, and seem to be a general accompaniment of such fissures near the surface. In some cases, as in the earthquake of Chemakha, Turkestan (Feb. 12, 1902), "salty plastic mud exuded from the open faults and built up high hillocks of the pasty material, which were surmounted by craters" (Hobbs–18:*134*). Subsequent movement along the plane caused a displacement in these "mud volcanoes" to the extent of 1.5 meters in some cases. Sand and mud injections of this type are known from older geological formations, where they form sandstone dikes. Thus Newsom (33:*233*) describes a sandstone dike 2½ to 5 feet wide from California, in which the upward bending of the shales on either side is regarded as proving its injection from below. Others from the same general region are also described. Violent injection into an earthquake fissure of loose sand, which covered the surface of the rock, seems to have taken place in the case of the Lower Devonic sandstone dike (injected into Upper Siluric strata) at Buffalo, as described in a preceding chapter. For a general summary of sandstone dikes with references to the literature, the student is referred to Newsom's article (33).

Craterlets. Analogous to the injected sandstone dikes are the craterlets formed by sand and mud ejected with water from earthquake fissures. One such has already been noted in connection with the Chemakha earthquake. Others were noted in the Charleston earthquake of 1886. Some of these which were aligned along fissures measured 20 feet in diameter, while the water and sand ejected from them shot in some cases 20 feet into the air. Many of the craterlets, especially those formed during the Calabrian earthquake, are merely funnel-shaped holes in the ground, and so resemble the volcanic explosion craters. (Fig. 242.) Such craterlets formed in the Mississippi Valley during the earthquake of 1811. They were commonly surrounded by a ring of sand and carbonized wood, sometimes as much as 7 feet in height. They have a diameter ranging from 20 to 100 feet, and some were sounded to a depth of 20 feet or over.

Much sand and water is ejected from these and is spread over the surrounding country, which may thus be blanketed by a

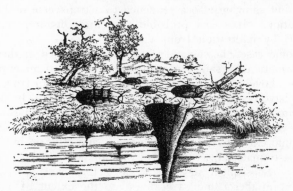

Fig. 242. Funnel-shaped holes formed during the Calabrian earthquake of 1783. (C. Vogt.)

layer of sand brought from below, the analogue of a lava flow. Sulphuretted hydrogen frequently accompanies these eruptions.

Fossil examples. Ancient craterlets of the type above described have been noted in some cases. Thus, on the coast of East Anglesey, in Wales, sandstone pipes have been observed, penetrating the Ordovicic limestones, and having a general funnel form comparable to the funnels formed by the Calabrian earthquake. They are continuous above with a spreading blanket of sandstone, which may be the ejected layer of sand. The entire series is again covered by the Ordovicic limestones of the region. A section of this, copied from Hobbs, is shown in Fig. 241. Care must, however, be exercised to distinguish these fissures from the solution fissures subsequently filled by sand and forming the organ-pipe structure described in a preceding chapter.

Slipping.

When differential movements of the two sides of a fracture occur a fault results. This movement may be horizontal, diagonal, or vertical. The displacement may be profound or very slight. It may be sudden or by a series of progressive slips, or it may be the resultant of a series of slips in various (even opposite) directions, and of varying amounts. The California earthquake of 1906 and the Japanese earthquake of 1811 were caused by slips of large amplitude along well-defined seismotectonic lines. The frequent New England quakes are due to a relatively large number of slight adjustments along joint planes. These minor slippings may be so slow as to produce no perceptible seismic disturbances, though they may find a surface expression in minute faults. Here, probably, belong the numerous minute post-glacial faults of New England and eastern New York. (Woodworth–45.)

The local rise and fall of the land in response to adjustment to stresses, but without violent shocks, or abrupt ruptures, may be considered as forming cne end of the series of earthquake-producing disturbances. To these the name *bradyseisms* has been given, and they are well illustrated by the changes of level recorded in the ruins of the Temple of Jupiter Serapis in the Bay of Naples, already referred to in an earlier chapter.

On the surface the fault is expressed by the dislocation of structures, such as fences, roadways, and parts of buildings, bridges, railroad tracks, or of natural objects, such as trees, etc., while if the slipping has a vertical component, a fault scarp will result. These phenomena, and the types of faults and their effects, have been discussed in Chapter XXI. When successive shocks from various directions are experienced, a vortical movement of objects may result, as in the case of statues turned on their pedestals. The various effects of such shocks on buildings and other structures are fully illustrated in the reports on the recent Californian and other earthquakes.

Block Movement. The faulting may be manifested as a block movement, strips of land dropping or rising and forming rift valleys (Gräben) or fault blocks. On a large scale, these form fault-block mountains. Such faulting occurred in connection with the Owens Valley earthquake of 1872, the resulting scarps reaching in some cases a height of ten feet or more. At Big Pine, California, a tract of land 200 to 300 feet wide sank, some portions being depressed 20 feet or more, leaving vertical walls on either side.

(Johnson–23.) During the earthquake of Yakutat Bay, Alaska, in 1899, great sections of the country moved as individual masses, some blocks being elevated, some depressed, the extent of the differential movement reaching 30 to 47 feet. Portions of the seashore were elevated; beaches only recently abandoned being now at a considerable height above the sea, while many of the depressed areas became submerged. Similar block movements occurred during the great Icelandic earthquake of 1896.

Disruptive Effects of Earthquakes.

The more pronounced earthquake shocks often have a very destructive effect on the rocks of the earth's surface. Land slips of great extent may be set in motion by them. A piece of land one mile long fell from the cliff at Scilla during the Messina earthquake.

Darwin describes the overwhelming forces of the earthquake of February 20, 1835, in Chile. He particularly notes the effects on the islands in Concepcion Harbor, where upward of a hundred villages were destroyed and where rocks from beneath the sea were broken off and cast high up on the shore. "One of these was six feet long, three broad, and two thick." Darwin describes the destruction on Quiriquina Island as follows: "The ground in many parts was fissured in north and south lines, perhaps caused by the yielding of the parallel and steep sides of this narrow island. Some of the fissures near the cliffs were a yard wide. Many enormous masses had already fallen on the beach, and the inhabitants thought that when the rains commenced far greater slips would happen. The effect of the vibration on the hard primary slate, which composes the foundation of the island, was still more curious: the superficial parts of some narrow ridges were as completely shivered as if they had been blasted by gunpowder. This effect, which was rendered conspicuous by the fresh fractures and displaced soil, must be confined to near the surface, for otherwise there would not exist a block of solid rock throughout Chile . . . I believe this convulsion has been more effectual in lessening the size of the island of Quiriquina than the ordinary wear-and-tear of the sea and weather during the course of a whole century." (Darwin–6, *Chap. XIV.*)

Effects of Earthquakes on Topography.

Many minor changes in topography in regions of frequent seismic disturbances may have their origin in the earth tremors.

Changes due to displacement are not to be classed in this category, as they are due to the same cause which is responsible for the earthquake, namely, the faulting. But topographic changes caused by the shaking of the earth are properly classed here. Such are the formation and sudden drainage of lakes; the blocking of rivers by land slips; the shifting of river channels in level delta regions, and other changes. After the Indian earthquake of 1897 no less than 30 earthquake lakes were produced. The earthquakes of 1811-12 caused the appearance of many new lakes along the lower Mississippi, owing, probably, to the local settling of the river sediment. One of these is Reelfoot Lake, in Obion county, Tennessee, which has a length of more than 20 miles and a width of seven miles; the water in places covering the tops of submerged cypress trees. Near Little Prairie a lake, many miles in length but only from 3 to 4 feet in depth, came into existence. Upon its disappearance it left behind a stratum of sand. On the other hand, Lake Eulalie, 300 yards long and 100 yards wide, was suddenly drained through parallel fissures which opened in its bottom. Many other examples of this kind might be cited.

This same earthquake was responsible for a local and temporary reversal of the current of the Mississippi. Similar phenomena have been observed in other rivers.

SUBMARINE EARTHQUAKES AND SEA-QUAKES.

As might be expected, seismic disturbances are common along the borders of the Pacific, where, as before noted, we have the regions of down-warping, and, therefore, the region of stresses and of readjustments to these stresses. From their proximity to the sea the latter is, of course, strongly affected by the shocks, and sea-quake waves, or *tsunamis*, are the result. These, on account of their height and velocity, are exceedingly destructive. Perhaps the most memorable one is that which destroyed Lisbon in 1775. The sea-quake originated on the ocean floor fifty or more miles off the coast of Lisbon, and the vibrations were transmitted along the surface of the water in a series of monstrous waves. The greatest of these was sixty feet high, and was followed by others of decreasing height. Spending their strength on the coast of Spain the waves passed on with diminished amplitude, but were felt even on the shores of the West Indies, across the whole expanse of the Atlantic.

Even greater distances have been traveled by tsunamis, as, for instance, those originating in an earthquake at Concepcion, Chile, which "set in motion a wave that traversed the ocean to the Society and Navigator Islands, 3,000 and 4,000 miles distant, and to the Hawaiian Islands, 6,000 miles." (Dana–5:*213*.)

The velocity of these mighty waves has been ascertained, and is seen to be far greater than that of ordinary sea-waves, though it does not equal that of earthquakes proper. "The waves of the Japan earthquake crossed the Pacific to San Francisco, a distance of 4,525 miles, in a little more than twelve hours, and, therefore, at a rate of 370 miles per hour, or over six miles per minute. The waves of the South American earthquake of 1868 ran to the Hawaiian Islands at a rate of 454 miles per hour." (Le Conte–26:*131*.)

Seismic disturbances are not confined to the shore, however, but also occur under the sea. Both pyroseismic and baryseismic disturbances are likely to affect the water and produce pronounced disturbances. That faulting occurs on the bottom of the deep sea is shown by soundings and studies of cable routes. The frequent breaking of the cables, accompanied by thrusting and fraying, furnishes visible evidence of such disturbances. Precipices from 3,000 to 5,000 feet in height have been detected by soundings in the Mediterranean, a difference in depth of 2,000 feet having been noticed between the bow and the stern of the cable repair ship. The earthquake of October 26, 1873, caused the cable to break 7 miles from the cable office at Zante, Greece, by the formation of a submarine fault scarp 600 feet in height, the change in depth being from 1,400 to 2,000 feet. Similar breaks, with the formation of submarine fault scarps more than a thousand feet in height, have been reported from the same region. Submarine earthquakes ought to be distinguished from sea-quakes proper. The latter always accompany the former and may even accompany earthquakes originating in the land near the sea. On the other hand, true sea-quakes, or thalassoseisma, may be formed by causes which will not produce earthquakes, as, for example, submarine explosions. The latter represent a submarine pyroseismic disturbance (whether of a submarine volcano or a submarine mine), and this is the only kind of directly induced sea-quake or thalassoseisma possible. Secondarily induced or communicated thalassoseisma are, however, the most frequent type, and here belong, besides the effects of many volcanic explosions on the sea coast (*e. g.*, Krakatoa), the great series of baryseismic disturbances or tectonic faultings.

Air-quakes.

What is true of the sea is in an even greater measure true of the atmosphere. This, like the water, is too mobile to permit the setting up of strains within its mass, and so baryseismic disturbances cannot originate in the atmosphere any more than they can in the hydrosphere. Such disturbances may, however, be communicated from the baryseismic disturbances of the land. Originally induced pyroseismic disturbances are, however, as readily produced in the air as in the water, and they are more readily transmitted, owing to the greater mobility of the atmosphere over that of the water.

Periodicity of Earthquakes.

Periods of strong seismic disturbances (macroseisms) are known to alternate with periods of relative quiescence, or only minor disturbances (microseisms). In Japan the seismic periods recur about once in thirteen years, though observations at Kioto indicate a period as short as six and one-fourth years. Too little is yet known to warrant predictions of recurrences of earthquakes.

Movements Due to Displacement or Migration of the Poles.

The theory of pole migration, or the shifting of the earth's axis of rotation with reference to the earth itself, together with the accompanying changes in the form of the earth, in distribution of land and sea and in climatic belts, has ever proved attractive to speculative geologists who sought for means of accounting for the ascertained variations in the surface characters of the earth in the past. Thus, evidence is accumulating which points to a widely different position of the earth's axis during Palæozoic time from that which it held during the Mesozoic and subsequent periods. This evidence is furnished in part by the occurrence of mild climate, and even of tropical vegetation, in regions having an arctic climate at present, and in part by the presence of glacial deposits where tropical conditions prevail to-day. It is further found in the occurrence of sediments which indicate the existence during Palæozoic time of easterly winds where now the westerlies prevail. (See *ante,* Chapters II and XIV, also Fig. 128, page 636.)

A wealth of biological evidence has been accumulated which

also seems to point to the phenomenon of polar migration. (Simroth-37.) The signs further point to the existence, in the border regions of the present Atlantic, of large continental masses which became submerged with the close of the Palæozoic. Thus Appalachia, the source of clastic sediments in eastern North America during the whole of Palæozoic time, disappeared at the end of that period; the disappearance being coincident with, or closely related to, the formation of the Appalachian folds. Similar conditions have been ascertained for western Europe. As demonstrated in an earlier chapter, the clastic sediments of North America indicate that in Palæozoic time this continent came under the influence of the trade winds, at least so far as the eastern portion is concerned, while in Mesozoic and later time it had passed into the region of the westerlies. This suggests that the end of Palæozoic sedimentation was brought about by a profound change in physical geography which affected not only North America, but also the earth as a whole. A comparatively rapid shifting of the position of the earth's axis would be sufficient explanation of the profound changes which brought about the all but universal extinction of life, so that only the pelagic and deep-sea types of the oceans (especially of the Pacific), and the terrestrial types in the interior of the continents, remained unaffected. These probably formed a source from which the earth was repopulated after the widespread extermination of life on the margins of the continents and in shallow water. That migrations of the poles occurred before and after this great cataclismic shifting is indicated by the nature of the sediments, the changes in climate and life during the successive periods, and, especially, by the occurrence of glacial conditions in Pleistocenic times in regions not now subject to such conditions. (See *ante,* Chapters II and VIII.) The map (Fig. 245), copied from Walther, shows the location of the Pleistocenic ice sheets, and the suggested position of the pole, to account for its occurrence. All such wanderings of the poles, however, if they occurred, are insignificant in comparison with the catastrophic change which brought to an end the period of Palæozoic sedimentation and biologic development.

THE PENDULATION THEORY. Though frequently suggested as a possible cause of changes in the geologic development of the earth, the theory of polar migration seems to have been first definitely formulated by Paul Reibisch in 1901. Reibisch developed the theory of polar pendulation, or swinging, *i. e.,* a back and forth migration of the poles along certain well-defined paths. Dr. Heinrich Simroth, of the University of Leipzig, developed this theory more fully in his book, "Die Pendulations Theorie," fortifying it by a wealth of illustrations furnished by the distribution of animals and plants in both the present and past geologic periods. Simultaneously with Reibisch, the theory of polar migrations was formulated by Dr. D. Kreichgauer (25), who approached the subject from a purely geological point of view. He endeavored to explain the changes of climate in past geological periods by a change in the position of the earth's equator and therefore a shifting of the north pole, which he thought had migrated 180° since Cambric

FIG. 243. Map showing the hypothetical wanderings of the earth's North Pole during the successive periods of its history. (After Kreichgauer.)

time, having been at the beginning of that period where the south pole is now. Kreichgauer's map, showing the migration of the poles, is here reproduced. (Fig. 243.) As Simroth points out, however, Kreichgauer did not consider the phenomenon of polar pendulation.

The theory of polar pendulation, as formulated by Reibisch (34) and developed by Simroth (37), postulates the existence of two "oscillation poles" (*Schwingpole*) in addition to the two rotation poles. These oscillation poles lie in the region of modern Ecuador, on the one hand, and of Sumatra, on the other. The meridian which passes through the rotation and oscillation poles forms the *culmination* circle (*Kulminationskreis*), and it divides the earth into a Pacific and an Atlantic-Indian hemisphere. (Fig. 244.) Each hemisphere is again divided by the equator into a northern and a southern quadrant. The meridian of 10° E. longitude from Greenwich, which bisects each hemisphere, is called the *oscillation circle,* because it is upon it that the poles swing back and forth. The culmination circle is so called because each point reaches its closest approximation to the poles when it crosses this circle.

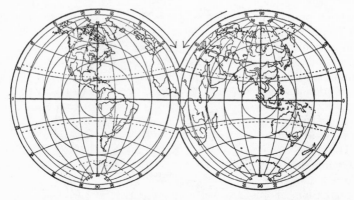

FIG. 244. Map of the earth, divided by the *oscillation circle* (near the meridians of 10° E. and 170° W. of Greenwich) into two hemispheres, according to the theory of P. Reibisch. The *oscillation poles* form the centers of the hemispheres. The vertical meridian is the *culmination circle* (80° on the left, 100° on the right). The concentric rings around the oscillation axis mark the paths along which the points cut by them move during the pendulation. (After Simroth.)

The form of the geoid, *i. e.,* the difference in length of the axis of rotation and the equatorial diameter, amounting to more than 40 kilometers (43 km., or nearly 27 miles; see *ante,* Chapter I), is responsible for the transgressions and regressions of the sea, and the elevation and subsidence of the land. The sea, the mobile element, assumes the flattened geoid form with every position of the axis of rotation, but the land, owing to its greater rigidity, does not so readily assume this form. Hence, as every point approaches the pole during the pendulation, the waters recede from it, while at the same time they rise over the points approaching the equator. The differences between rise and fall of the water are greatest on the oscillation circle and decrease progressively to the oscillation poles, where they are zero. A point on the oscillation circle, which lies 10,000 meters below sea-level when under the equator, would, by the time that it has come to lie at the pole (after a rotation of 90°), lie 10,000 meters above sea-level. It must be remembered that every point on the globe is nearest to the pole as it crosses the culmination circle, which, together with the ends of the axis of rotation, may be regarded as having a fixed position in space. At the moment of crossing, therefore, the point has its greatest elevation above sea-level, while, as it passes away from the culmination circle, the sea-level will rise, where previously, during the approach, the sea-level fell. This seems to be illustrated by Florida, which at present lies under the culmination circle. The eastern half has a rising sea-level and would, therefore, be passing away from it, while the western half has a falling sea-level, *i. e.*, the land emerges, and this section would, therefore, be approaching the culmination circle. All this would indicate that the earth is swinging in such a way that the north pole is migrating toward Behring Sea, which thus becomes a region of emergence, and away from the Greenland-Iceland region, where, it has been supposed, the pole had its location in Pleistocenic time. (Fig. 245.) (See *ante,* Chapter II.)

Owing to the proximity of Florida to the oscillation poles (where emergence and submergence are zero), the total amount of oscillation of the sea was never great, and hence old coral reefs which grew near the surface go only to the depth of 50 feet. In Funafuti, on the other hand, which lies not far from the oscillation circle (under which the greatest variation of sea-level occurs), the reef corals grew to a depth of more than 600 feet. (See *ante,* Chapter X.) The coral islands of the North Pacific lie in the quadrant approaching the pole and the culmination circle, and hence they show at the present time a retreating sea-level; as in the case of the Hawaiian Islands. The islands of the South Pacific, on the other hand, are moving toward the equator, and hence, in this case, submergence is taking place. In the Indian Ocean, again, the region north of the present equator is one of rising sea-level (submergence of reefs and islands), while that south of the equator is one of falling sea-level (emerging reefs). This would explain why the Maldives, north of the equator, are apparently being submerged, while the Cocos Islands to the south are rising out of the water.

The regions around the oscillation poles were always tropical regions, as compared with the regions near the oscillation circle. In the former, therefore, life conditions changed little and slowly, and so they are the regions where ancient types persisted, while the region near the oscillation circle (northern North America, northern Eurasia, western Europe, Africa, and Antarctica), on the contrary, showed the greatest oscillation in climate and in life during the successive periods of the earth's history.

When we next consider what effects the shifting of the poles would have on the form of the lithosphere we realize that, while it would be more gradual than the effect on the hydrosphere, it

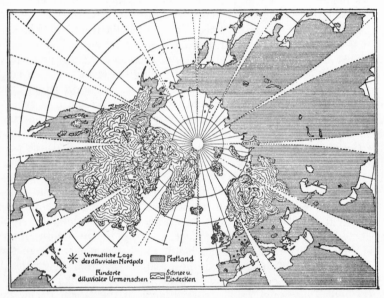

Fig. 245. Map of the Pleistocenic Ice Period, showing the distribution of the ice and the hypothetical North Pole. (After Walther.) The black dots in western Europe indicate the localities where remains of early man have been found.

must still result in a series of important changes, if the hypothesis of pendulation is correct. The influence of the centrifugal force on the equatorial region is manifested by an expansion or stretching of the equatorial zone, and this will result in the formation of depressions, through the sinking of fault blocks. Depressions in the present surface of the lithosphere are most marked in the quadrant now approaching the equator, near which lie all the large terrestrial or submarine trenches and deeps. Thus the great submarine depressions of the present day, the Tonga and Kermadec deeps, lie in the South Pacific quadrant, whereas similar depressions in the land, such as the Caspian and the Dead Sea, etc., lie in the North Atlantic quadrant, which also approaches the equator. It should be noted, however, that the Marian depression with the deepest submarine pit, the Nero deep, lies mostly north of the equator and therefore in the opponent quadrant. However, its proximity to the equator (less than 20° N.) is evident, and it may be regarded as still retaining the characters acquired as it passed under the equator. In like manner, the greater part of the African rift valley lies in the south Atlantic-Indian quadrant, though again within 20 degrees of the equator.

Conversely, regions approaching the poles are regions of shrinking land, and hence regions where mountain-making through folding is marked.

Ingenious and suggestive as this theory is, and much as it seems to throw light on many geological as well as biological phenomena, it is still too new and too little tested to receive more than respectful attention. As a working hypothesis in the attempt to interpret the history of the earth, it is likely to be of much value. (See the application of this theory by Yokoyama to the interpretation of the Pleistocenic problem, given in Chapter II.)

In this connection may also be mentioned the recent studies by Eugenio Jacobitti (22), who, attacking the problem as a study in geology, finds the wanderings of the poles to be of a more irregular character, through the various geological periods, as illustrated in the subjoined figures reproduced from his paper. (Figs. 246, 247.) He also reconstructs a series of charts showing the position of the equator in the successive periods. All such reconstructions are, of course, premature, and must be taken as suggestions rather than as demonstrations. What is probably the most complete attempt at restoration of the earth's surface during a period of different polar location is that made by Koken (23a) for the Permic. His map not only locates the poles but also the lands and seas of the period, as well as the ocean currents, etc. See *ante,* page 536.

It may again be remarked here, as was stated in Chapter II, that astronomers have generally looked with disfavor on such speculations, though George Darwin concedes the possibility of the pole having wandered some 10 or 15 degrees from its original position, provided the degree of rigidity of the earth is not so great as to be inconsistent with a periodic readjustment to a new form of equilibrium. Sir William Thompson (Lord Kelvin), for one, readily entertained the idea of such changes. He says: "We may not merely admit, but assert as highly probable, that the axis of maximum inertia and axis of rotation, always very near one another, may have been in ancient times very far from their present geographical position, and may have gradually shifted through 10,

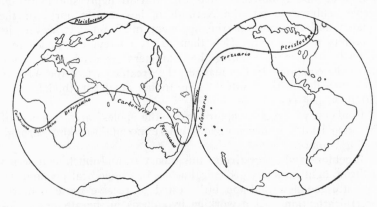

FIG. 246. Map of the hemispheres, showing the hypothetical migration of the North Pole during the successive geologic periods. (Jacobitti.)

20, 30, 40, or more degrees, without there being at any time any perceptible sudden disturbance of either land or water." (42:*11*.)

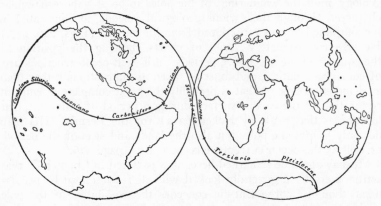

FIG. 247. Map of the hemispheres, showing the hypothetical migrations of the South Pole during the successive geologic periods. (Jacobitti.)

Various theories have been advanced to account for and explain such wanderings of the poles, but at present the whole subject is too little investigated to make their discussion profitable. Geologists must first gather a larger body of facts, which will tend either to prove or disprove these theories, before the discussion of causes need be undertaken.

Determined Migrations of the Poles.

That the poles, *i. e.*, the points of intersection between the earth's axis of rotation and the surface of the earth, are not actually fixed, but wander about within small limits, was first recognized toward the end of the nineteenth century. From thousands of careful observations on latitude made in recent years in

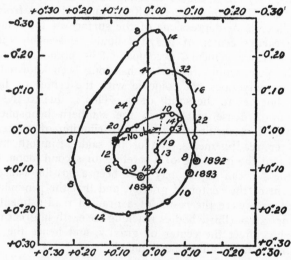

FIG. 248. Map showing the ascertained migration of the North Pole from 1892 to 1894 (after Milne); the figures indicate the number of large earthquakes in each period.

Europe and America this wandering has been determined to lie within a circle 40 or 50 feet in diameter. It has a curiously irregular, but somewhat spiral path, and completes its erratic circuit in about 428 days. The path described by the North Pole between the years 1892 and 1894 is shown in the above map by Milne, in which each year is divided into ten parts. (Fig. 248.) The figures show the number of earthquakes which occurred in each period, the largest of them, as John Milne has pointed out, coinciding with the sharpest curvature in the path of the pole. As Milne suggests, both the abrupt curvature and the sharp earthquake may be the result of sudden readjustments, due to the redistribution of material on the earth's surface by currents and by meteorological agents.

Accompanying the changes of position of the poles, is, of course, a change in the position of the equator, the plane of which is always at right angles to the axis of rotation of the earth. A further result of such changes is a variability of terrestrial latitudes generally.

It is now commonly admitted that the movement of large bodies of water, or of air, over the surface of the globe, and, more especially, an accumulation of vast masses of snow and ice in different regions, may all be causes effecting slight displacements of the earth's axis. More pronounced effects might follow from widespread upheavals or depressions of the surface of the lithosphere.

If the earth's center of gravity should be sensibly displaced, momentous rearrangements, accompanied by pronounced wanderings of the pole, would result. It has long been known that the center of gravity does not coincide with the center of figure of the earth, but lies to the south of it. This is due to the greater aggregation of dense material in the southern hemisphere, but whether this is a result of original distribution of matter, or is due to later readjustments, cannot be said. Simroth has even suggested that the in-falling of a satellite, or second moon, into the earth in the African region may have been a possible cause of the displacement of the center of gravity, and that the pendulations of the earth's axis were the result of a gradual readjustment. That meteoric or extra-telluric bodies reaching the earth in great numbers may sensibly affect the center of gravity, and hence the position of the earth's axis, cannot be doubted.

EARTH MOVEMENTS AND GEOSYNCLINES.

As already noted in Chapter XX, the term geosyncline was applied by Dana (in 1873) to the great earth troughs, whether simple or compound, which are formed in regions of excessive deposition, the Appalachian region being taken as the type of such troughs. The idea of great downward bowings under heavy load was developed much earlier by James Hall, who held that this downward-bending was in direct response to the load added by the sediment, and thus, in effect, constituted an isostatic readjustment. Dana, on the other hand, regarded the downward bending as primary, and of the nature of a fold due to compressive strains, and the filling by sediment as a secondary consequence. Among subsequent authors, Haug (14, 15) has greatly extended this idea, and has included under this title all great submarine depressions parallel to land areas, such as the great depressions of the Pacific coast. (See Chapter III and Figures 16 and 17, pages 101 and 105.) These "fore deeps" (*Vortiefen*) are undoubtedly the direct result of deformation under strain, but they are not areas of excessive deposition. Indeed, sedimentation here goes on with extreme slowness, and is confined to materials normal to the deep sea. Haug has identified among many of the deposits bathyal sediments (see Chapter XV), which he regards as accumulations in geosynclines, and he holds that the great thickness of these deposits indicates a progressive deformation of the region of deposition. He finds that many bathyal sediments pass laterally into neritic or shallow-water deposits, though other deposits in the geosynclines are throughout of

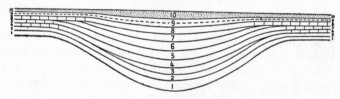

FIG. 249.   Diagrammatic section of a geosyncline according to Haug. The numbers 1-10 indicate the successive strata, which are complete in the center of the geosyncline but incomplete on its margins, where thinning away of beds and overlap of others is characteristic. (After Haug.)

neritic origin. Haug does not, apparently, recognize the presence of continental sediments in the geosynclines, though he finds these on the margins. This type of sediment is, however, eminently characteristic of the Appalachian region throughout, and is included in the main mass of the sediment itself.

The bathyal origin of many of the sediments in the geosynclines of the Alpine region and elsewhere is by no means wholly established, and it may be questioned whether, on the whole, sediments of that class are abundant or widespread. The frequent marginal disconformities in the sediments of most geosynclines lead one to the supposition that, after all, many of the so-called bathyal deposits may be of littoral (neritic) origin, and that, furthermore, repeated laying bare of the margins of the geosyncline permitted erosion of the already deposited sediments.

Haug recognizes the shading away of the sediments by overlap and by thinning toward both sides of the geosyncline (Fig. 249) and he explains this by the supposition that the geosyncline was located between two continental masses and not, as held by American students, on the borders of the continent. He holds that the geosynclines are zones of weakness and mobility between two relatively stable masses.

The Himalayas are chosen by Haug as an illustration of a great geosyncline (in pre-mountain time) formed, not on the border of a sea, but between two continental masses, the stable Indian land mass on the south and a similar land mass on the north. In spite of this location, he holds that Palæozoic and Mesozoic sediments in this geosyncline are none of them of a littoral (neritic) character. The chains of central Europe are in like manner regarded by Haug as occupying the sites of former geosynclines. If the expanded Mediterranean basin of Mesozoic time is to be considered in the light of a geosyncline, the bathyal nature of some of the sediments therein, or at any rate their thalassogenic character, may be readily conceded. It may be questioned, however, if the use of the term geosyncline for an intracontinental sea with abyssal regions (i. e., a mediterranean) is permissible. Certainly such a condition did not prevail in the Palæozoic of the Appalachian region. Here an accumulation of 40,000 feet of sediment was accompanied by a downward bowing of the sea-floor bordering the old Appalachian continent. But this was probably never of great depth, nor was there, as a rule, a land mass to the west of the region of sedimentation. Indeed, as has already been pointed out, and, as has elsewhere been discussed by the author in great detail, the prevailing sediments were of shallow water and terrestrial type. As stated in Chapter XX, it seems best to restrict the name geosyncline to such regions of deposition, and use the name fore-deep for regions known to have descended to bathyal or abyssal depths. That these fore-deeps are due to tectonic movements is freely conceded, but the geosyncline of the Appalachian type is most probably due to isostatic readjustments incident upon the loading of the earth's surface along the line of subsidence. This does not imply, however, that the subsequent folding of these strata is due to any other cause than that of yielding under compressive strain. Such an origin alone seems to be possible, in view of the many features which can be explained only as originating under compressive stresses.

GEOSYNCLINES THE SITES OF OROGENIC DISTURBANCES. As long ago pointed out by Hall and Dana, and as emphasized by Haug the geosynclines are the sites of subsequent foldings of the strata or, conversely, the regions of folded mountains are the sites of former geosynclines. Bailey Willis (44) has pointed out that the gradual downward sinking of the strata in the geosyncline gives them an individual steepness along the margin of the depression, and that this initial dip forms the beginning of the deformation, and determines the subsequent folding under the influence of lateral pressure. The folds of the Appalachians are asymmetrical anticlines, with the steeply inclined, vertical, or even overturned limb on the northwest or away from the present ocean. It must, however, be remembered that the present Atlantic coast is near the western border of the old Appalachian land, and that hence if the folds occurred before this land mass disappeared by subsidence, the thrusting, which was from the east or southeast, was performed or transmitted by this ancient land mass. In this westward thrusting many folds were not only overturned, but thrust-faults of considerable magnitude were developed. Thus the crystalline range of the Hudson Highland was thrust northwestward over the Palæozoic strata (Berkey) and numerous other overthrusts were developed in the Palæozoic and older strata along the entire Appalachian range.

FORESHORTENING OF THE CRUST. During the folding of the Appalachians there was, of course, a considerable amount of foreshortening of the earth's crust. Lesley long ago estimated the movement to have extended over a distance of forty miles, while Claypole, considering the major folds, arrived at the approximate conclusion that a section of the earth's surface measuring originally one hundred and fifty-three miles had been compressed into sixty-five miles. (4.)

Recently R. T. Chamberlin (2) has published the results of some careful measurements of the Appalachian folds in the district between Harrisburg and Tyrone, Pennsylvania, and these have furnished more exact data for the estimation of the amount of crustal foreshortening, and have likewise thrown some light on the form and thickness of the crust involved in the folding. He concludes that, so far as his measurements warranted, and postulating the correctness of the assumed basis of investigation, the region west of Harrisburg showed 81 miles of strata compressed into 66 miles. The uncertainties of this result lie in the difficulty of eliminating the amount of loss due to thickening and thinning of strata in various parts of the fold; the variation in closeness of folding; or the subsequent relaxation of the strata under the influence of gravity, with resultant gliding on the limb of the fold. These uncertainties can make such estimates only approximate.

HEIGHT OF THE FOLDS. Assuming that, when the folding of

the Appalachians commenced, the strata were practically horizontal and the upper surface of the youngest beds essentially at sea-level, and assuming, furthermore, that the higher Carbonic and Permic beds of the region (above the Pottsville) was 1,100 feet thick, Chamberlin concludes that 3 miles represents the average height of the top of the restored Pottsville conglomerate over the area from Tyrone to Harrisburg, i. e., the vertical deformation was of that amount.

There are here several assumptions which need careful consideration before we can regard this as anything more than a very general estimate. In the first place, if we regard the late Palæozoic sediments as terrestrial in type rather than marine, as their nature seems to indicate, we can not assume an initial horizontality with the upper strata at sea-level throughout. Even on the basis of the gentle gradient of the present delta-fan of the Huang-ho the elevation at the heads of the delta plains would be some 500 feet or more above sea-level, and from the coarseness of the material in the deposits it is likely that this elevation was a thousand feet, if not more.

In the second place, it appears that the estimate of the original thickness of the post-Pottsville Palæozoic is much too low. A comparison of the thickness of the Pottsville and Kanawha formations between the eastern and western portions of their outcrops shows the thickness of these two formations in the western region to be only one-fifth or one-sixth that of the part preserved in the eastern Appalachians. Since the sediment of the later formations was also derived from the Appalachian old land, and since the nature of the deposit suggests a similar origin of the later strata, it does not seem amiss to consider that a similar eastward increase in thickness originally obtained in the case of these higher strata as well. This would make the Allegheny alone some 1,500 or more feet in thickness in the Appalachian region, while the remaining formations, if increased at the same rate, would aggregate 11,000 or 12,000 feet, making a total above the Pottsville in round numbers of about 13,000 feet of strata. This is not an improbable thickness when we consider the 15,000 feet of late Tertiary delta deposits of the Siwalik formation of India (see *ante,* Chapter XIV).

CHARACTER AND THICKNESS OF THE DEFORMED MASS. On the assumed elevation of about 3 miles for the entire area, Chamberlin figures out the thickness of the part of the crust involved in the folding. Since different sections have been differently affected he considers each independently with the following results:

Section Number	1	2	3	4	5a	5b
Original length of tract, in miles (a)................	17.8	16.3	13.56	14.44	9.6	9.5
Length after folding, in miles (b)................	14.9	15.2	12.1	12.10	7.37	4.75
Mean elevation through folding, in miles (c)..........	3.45	2.37	2.88	2.71	2.36	5.75
Deduced thickness of crustal block, in miles (x)	17.7	32.7	23.8	14.00	7.8	5.71

The formula for ascertaining (x) is $x = \dfrac{bc}{a-b}$

The following diagram, copied from Chamberlin, shows the location of the sections, the extent of the folding and the cal-

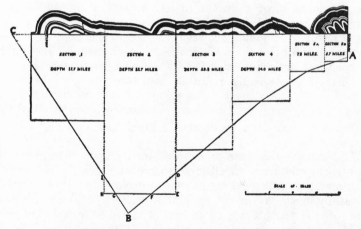

FIG. 250. Plot of the Tyrone-Harrisburg folded section, representing the thickness of the deformed shell beneath each of the six blocks as developed by Chamberlin's method of measurement. The lines A-B and B-C are drawn through the middle points of the bottom lines of each of these blocks, except section 2, the apex block. The triangle G, B, F is drawn equal in area to the sum of the triangles G, H, I and D, E, F. The whole deformed mass appears, subject to the necessary limitations, to be the triangular block A, B, C. (After R. T. Chamberlin.)

culated thickness of the block affected. (Fig. 250.) It shows strikingly the fact that, where the crust is folded intensely, the thickness of the crust involved is least; where folding is slight, it is greatest. In any case, folding is shown to be a superficial phenomenon, a conclusion which must have an important bearing on the mechanics of folding. As shown by the section, the eastern portion suffered most, the western portion was the next most affected, while the intermediate ones suffered the least. The form of the entire block affected is that of a triangular prism, the lower bounding planes being shear-zones. This is the form which such a block should assume theoretically, two sets of planes of greatest tangential stress developing at right angles to each other, and approximately at an angle of 45 degrees to the direction of greatest pressure, though varying with the nature of the material and other factors. (Becker–1:50; Hoskins–20:865; Leith–27:121.) Experiments by Daubrée have shown this to be the type of fracture developed in compressed blocks where a triangular prism is developed with faces approximately at 45 degrees to the direction of pressure. In the experiment the prism was lifted without folding, the other parts being thrust under it on both sides (Fig. 251). The extensive development of over (or under) thrusts along the western margin of the folded Appalachian region is quite in harmony with this principle. It should, however, be mentioned here that there is some evidence that the folds of the Appalachians were not purely asymmetrical anticlines, modified by overthrust, but that the Appalachians had originally a fanfold structure.

Changes Due to Extra-Telluric Influences.

The impact of a mass of meteoric matter upon the surface of the earth would form an effective source of energy, which would set into motion geological agents of vast magnitude. If the mass is sufficiently large, as in the case of a satellite, a great displacement of the earth's center of gravity would result, with the attendant phenomena already outlined. If the earth were bombarded by a vast number of meteoric bodies, if, in other words, a swarm of meteors should descend upon the earth, changes affecting the entire earth might take place. Among these might be the all but universal extermination of life, as well as the modification of the lithosphere and hydrosphere, and perhaps the atmosphere as well. The heat of impact might result in nearly universal metamorphism of the rock masses of the earth, with the accompanying destruction of the record of life in these rocks. It might be asked if some such catastrophe may not have altered the surface of the earth in pre-Cambric time, inaugurating the forces which produced the widespread metamorphism and exterminating most of the organisms which had reached a high state of development prior to the opening of Palæozoic time. Such catastrophic occurrences are within the range of possibility, and, indeed, the rising school of astro-geologists regards the origin of the earth itself as due to accretion of planetary matter, rather than to the development by condensation from an original nebular condition. If the accre-

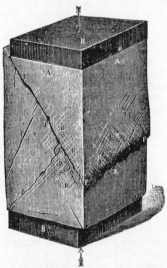

Fig. 251.   Prism of wax, deformed under pressure, between two iron plates (B, B) and exerted in the direction shown by the arrows. Two main sets of fissures are formed nearly at right angles to each other (FF, f) leaving a triangular prism between them. RR, plexus of fine fissures at right angles to one another. Scale 1 :75. (After Daubrée from Haug.)

tion theory of earth-building, whether from planetesimals or from meteorites, should become established, the recurrence of such an event—the repetition of the celestial bombardment to which the earth owed its origin—is brought within the range of probability, and thus the stupendous problem of the origin of the great difference everywhere observed between the Cambric and the undoubted pre-Cambric * rocks may be brought a step nearer solution.

* Some of the undisturbed clastic rocks now referred to the pre-Cambric have not yet been proven to be such. The occurrence of disconformities between Middle Cambric or late Lower Cambric and underlying unaltered sediments is not conclusive evidence of the pre-Cambric age of these sediments, especially if they are of continental origin.

BIBLIOGRAPHY XXIII.

(See also Bibliography xx, pp. 826–828.)

1. BECKER, G. F. 1893. Finite Homogeneous Strain, Flow and Rupture of Rocks. Bulletin of the Geological Society of America,Vol. IV, pp. 13–90.
2. CHAMBERLIN, ROLLIN T. 1910. Appalachian Folds of Central Pennsylvania. Journal of Geology, Vol. XVIII, No. 3, pp. 228–251.
3. CHAMBERLIN, THOMAS C., and SALISBURY, ROLLIN D. 1906. Geology, Vol. I.
4. CLAYPOLE, E. W. 1885. Pennsylvania Before and After the Elevation of the Appalachian Mountains. American Naturalist, Vol. XIX, pp. 257–268.
5. DANA, JAMES D. 1895. Manual of Geology, 4th edition. American Book Co.
6. DARWIN, CHARLES. 1841. The Voyage of the *Beagle*.
7. DAVISON, CHARLES. 1905. A Study of Recent Earthquakes. Contemporary Science Series, London.
8. DILLER, J. S. 1889. Sandstone Dikes. Bulletin of the Geological Society of America, Vol. I, pp. 411–442, pls. 6–8; with discussion by Davis.
9. DUTTON, CLARENCE E. 1904. Earthquakes in the Light of the New Seismology. New York and London.
10. FALB, R. 1871. Grundzüge einer Theorie der Erdbeben und Vulcanenausbrücke. Graz.
11. FALB, R. 1874. Gedanken und Studien über den Vulkanismus, etc.
12. GILBERT, GROVE KARL. 1893. Continental Problems. Bulletin of the Geological Society of America, Vol. IV, pp. 179–190.
13. GILBERT, G. K.; HUMPHREY, RICHARD; SEWELL, JOHN S., and SOULÉ, FRANK. The San Francisco Earthquake and Fire of April 18, 1906, and their Effects on Structures and Structural Material. United States Geological Survey Bulletin 324.
14. HAUG, ÉMILE. 1900. Les geosynclinaux et les aires continentales. Contribution à l'étude des transgressions et des régressions marines. Bulletin de la société géologique de France, 3rd series, Vol. XXVIII, pp. 617–711, 3 figs.
15. HAUG, É. 1907. Traité de Géologie. T. I.
16. HAY, ROBERT. 1892. Sandstone Dikes in Northwestern Nebraska. Bulletin of the Geological Society of America, Vol. III, pp. 50–55.
17. HOBBS, WILLIAM H. 1907. Origin of the Ocean Basins in the Light of the New Seismology. Bulletin of the Geological Society of America, Vol. XVIII, pp. 233–250, pl. 5.
18. HOBBS, W. H. 1907. Earthquakes. D. Appleton and Company, New York.
19. HOERNES, RUDOLPH. 1893. Erdbebenkunde. Die Erscheinungen und Ursachen der Erdbeben, die Methoden ihrer Beobachtung. Leipzig.
20. HOSKINS, L. M. 1896. Flow and Fracture of Rocks as Related to Structure. Sixteenth Annual Report of the United States Geological Survey, 1894–95, Pt. I, pp. 845–872, figs. 163–169.
21. HOVEY, E. O. 1909. Earthquakes: Their Causes and Effects. Proceedings of the American Philosophical Society, Vol. XLVIII, No. 192, pp. 235–258.
22. JACOBITTI, EUGENIO. Mobilitá dell 'Asse Terrestre. Studio Geologico. Torino.

23. JOHNSON, WILLARD D., and HOBBS, W. H. 1908. The Earthquake of 1872 in Owens Valley, California. Abstract: Science, N. S., Vol. XXVII, p. 723.

23a. KOKEN, E. 1907. Indisches Perm und die permische Eiszeit. Neues Jahrbuch für Mineralogie, etc., Festband, pp. 446–545, Map.

24. KOTO, B. 1893. On the Cause of the Great Earthquake in Central Japan, 1891. Journal of the College of Science, Imperial University, Tokyo, Vol. V, pp. 295–353, pls. XXVIII–XXXV.

25. KREICHGAUER, D. 1902. Die Aequatorfrage in der Geologie. Steyl.

26. LE CONTE, JOSEPH. 1902. Elements of Geology, 4th edition. D. Appleton.

27. LEITH, C. K. 1905. Rock Cleavage. United States Geological Survey Bulletin 239.

28. MARTIN, LAWRENCE. 1910. Alaskan Earthquakes of 1899. Bulletin of the Geological Society of America, Vol. XXI, pp. 339–406, pls. 29–30.

29. MALLET. 1862. The Great Neapolitan Earthquake of 1857. 2 vols.

30. McGEE, W. J. 1893. A Fossil Earthquake. Bulletin of the Geological Society of America, Vol. IV, pp. 411–414.

31. MILNE, J. 1898. Earthquakes and Other Earth Movements. 4th edition.

32. MONTESSUS DE BALLORE, F. DE. 1906. Les Tremblements de Terre. Paris.

33. NEWSOM, JOHN F. 1903. Clastic Dikes. Bulletin of the Geological Society of America, Vol. XIV, pp. 227–268, pls. 21–31.

34. REIBISCH, PAUL. 1901. Ein Gestaltungsprincip der Erde. 27ter Jahresbericht des Vereins für Erdkunde zu Dresden, 1901, pp. 105–124; II, ibid., 1905, pp. 39–53.

35. ROSSI, M. S. DE. 1879 and 1882. La Meteorologia Endogena. 2 vols.

36. RUDOLPH, E. 1887–1898. Ueber submarine Erdbeben und Eruptionen. Beiträge zur Geophysik. Vol. I, 1887, pp. 133–365, pls. IV–VII; Vol. II, 1895, pp. 537–666; Vol. III, 1898, pp. 273–336.

36a. SIEBERG, AUGUST. 1904. Handbuch der Erdbebenkunde. Braunschweig.

37. SIMROTH, HEINRICH. 1907. Die Pendulations-theorie. Leipzig.

38. SUESS, EUARD. 1875. Die Entstehung der Alpen. Vienna.

39. SUESS, E. 1886. Ueber unterbrochene Gebirgsfaltung. Sitzungsberichte der königlichen Akademie der Wissenschaften zu Wien. Bd. XCIV, Abth. 1, pp. 111–117.

40. SUESS, E. 1898. Ueber die Asymetrie der nördlichen Halbkugel. Ibid., Bd. CVII, Abth. 1, pp. 89–102.

41. TAYLOR, FRANK BURSLEY. 1903. The Planetary System. Published by the author, Fort Wayne, Indiana.

42. THOMPSON, SIR WILLIAM. 1876. Report of the British Association. Report of Section 81.

42a. VAN HISE, C. R. 1898. Earth Movements. Wisconsin Academy of Arts, Sciences and Letters, Transactions, Vol. xi, pp. 465–516.

43. WHIMPER, EDWARD. 1892. Travels Among the Great Andes of the Equator. 2nd edition.

44. WILLIS, BAILEY. 1893. Mechanics of Appalachian Structure. Thirteenth Annual Report of the United States Geological Survey, Pt. II, pp. 211–281. (See also reference 30, on page 828.)

45. WOODWORTH, J. B. 1907. Postglacial Faults of Eastern New York. New York State Museum Bulletin 107, pp. 5–28, 5 pls.

F. THE BIOSPHERE.

CHAPTER XXIV.

SUBDIVISION OF THE BIOSPHERE. CLASSIFICATION AND GENERAL MORPHOLOGICAL CHARACTERS OF ORGANISMS.

The organic world or biosphere falls naturally into two great subdivisions or kingdoms, the phytosphere, or plant kingdom, and the zoösphere, or animal kingdom, though organisms occur or have occurred which are not readily placed in either division. The detailed study of organisms has developed the sciences of phytology (botany) and zoölogy, with its many subordinate sciences. As ordinarily understood, these sciences deal with the plants and animals of the present, or Holocenic, geological epoch, while those of the many epochs of the earth's history anterior to the present are reserved for the palæontologist. Such a division, however, is illogical, for the life of the earth has been continuous and its development has been progressive from the earliest time to the present day. The scientific palæontologist can not neglect the study of the existing organisms, nor can the scientific zoölogist and botanist, or student of the present living world, neglect the organisms of the past. Palæozoölogy cannot be divorced from zoölogy, nor palæobotany from botany. From the nature of the organic remains of former periods it follows, however, that the palæontologist lays most stress upon the hard parts of organisms, or those capable of preservation, in former as well as the present geological periods, while the botanist and zoölogist in the study of the modern floras and faunas tend to lay more stress upon the soft tissues which perish readily and so are not, or only rarely, preserved in the case of ancient forms of life.

There are, however, good reasons for believing that the hard parts of organisms form in some respects a more reliable index to their relationship than do the soft parts. This is especially the case in animals which build external hard parts which increase by serial addition, without change of the older parts deposited. In such cases we are certain to get a complete record of the individual development of the animal from the youngest stages in which such structures are formed to the adult or even old age stage. Thus, in the case of the molluscan shell, for example, we have a complete record of the individual development or ontogeny, all the changes being indicated in the successive whorls or areas of the shell, from the initial shell-plate to the adult. Moreover, such shells will preserve the detailed features assumed necessarily by the mantle of the animal in conformity with development and increase of internal organs, features which are evanescent in the soft parts and can in many cases not even be observed.

What has just been stated is true mainly of animals whose hard parts are external structures, retained throughout life and increased by addition in one region only. Such additions are recognizable by the formation of growth lines, and they are typically shown in the shells of the Mollusca, as already noted. Brachiopoda also show such changes in external form but there are, in addition, changes in interior structures, for the study of the development of which a complete series of individuals, representing all the stages, is needed. Corals likewise show their growth lines, and sections made across the older part in most cases show the progress of development of the individual. Other invertebrates are less satisfactory. While the serial development of parts can be made out in the plates of an adult echinoderm, yet the fact that each plate changes with the progress of development interposes certain difficulties in the study of the life history, and for its complete determination individuals of various age stages are needed. This is also true of the vertebrated animals where the internal skeleton or external armor changes with the growth and development of the individual, and where, therefore, skeletons of the young as well as the adult are needed to determine the entire life history.

PLANTS AND ANIMALS AS INDICATORS OF THE AGE OF THE PERIOD IN WHICH THEY OCCUR.

Since we have realized, by a prolonged study of modern as well as ancient organisms, that animals and plants have gradually increased in complexity of structure and diversity of form, from the earliest times to the present, it has become possible to use the remains of organisms embedded in the strata as indices of the chronology of the earth's history, and by extensive collection of facts from all geological levels, and over wide areas, to build up an organic succession which parallels the stratigraphic succession in the development of the earth's crust. It has been found that certain groups of organisms did not extend beyond a certain time period in the earth's history, and so their occurrence in the strata indicates the upper age limit of these strata. Thus, trilobites are known only from Palæozoic formations—hence the finding of one of these extinct organisms stamps the strata in which it occurs as of Palæozoic age. More restricted occurrences of special forms have made it possible to recognize the geological levels with greater precision, thus the trilobite Paradoxides characterizes only the Middle Cambric rocks of the earth's crust in certain regions, while the trilobite Holmia characterizes the lower Cambric strata in the same regions. Again, the Hydrozoan *Dictyonema flabelliforme* is of world-wide distribution in the basal Ordovicic strata. Organisms used in this manner become indices of geological horizons and, since all but those of the present geological period occur only in fossil form, the term "index fossil" is properly applied to them. This subject will be considered further in a subsequent chapter.

CLASSIFICATION OF PLANTS AND ANIMALS.

The classification of plants and animals is a process of assortment into natural groups, or groups of related types, and the arrangement of these groups in a natural order, according to their genetic relationship. Groups of various denominations are recognized, the smallest of those in general use being the *species*. Smaller groups, known as *varieties* or as *mutations*, are, however, included within the species. Species are grouped into *genera*, each genus comprising one or more species. The generic and specific name of an organism are always used together in speaking of any particular species, since the same specific name may be used for a species of another genus. Thus, the fossil brachiopod genus Productus includes among its many species *Productus muricatus*. Likewise the fossil pelecypod genus Actinopteria has among its species *Actinopteria muricata*, while another brachiopod genus, Strophalosia, also has a species *Strophalosia muricata*. These three species, though they have the same specific name, are not at all related to each other, belonging to distinct genera, one of which belongs to a different division or *phylum* of the animal kingdom from that to which the other two belong.

Naming of genera and species. (18.) The generic name is always a noun, and is commonly derived from the Greek, though generic names derived from the Latin are not uncommon. Names compounded from the two languages are undesirable. The name should always express some prominent character of the genus, as Orthoceras, from the Greek ὀρθός (orthos), meaning straight, and κέρας (ceras), meaning horn, the essential form of the genus being that of a straight horn. Names are, however, not always chosen with such direct meaning, while not infrequently the derivation of the name is obscure or fanciful. Proper names are frequently chosen for generic names, as Hyattella for a genus of brachiopods, the name being given in honor of the great American palæontologist, the late Alpheus Hyatt. In the formation of such names the original name is reduced to the genitive case, and the termination is in a (a, ia, iia, oia, æa, ella, etc.). When the original name ends in y this letter is treated as a consonant and the termination is added. Example: from Gray we may derive Grayia, Grayella, Graysia, etc. In all cases the form of the word must be the Latin form, the Latin equivalent of the original Greek being used. The gender of the generic name is the same as in the language from which it is derived. If the generic name is a compound of two or more words, the terminal word determines the gender. Thus, in Orthoceras, the terminal ceras is neuter in the Greek, and hence all names ending in this manner are neuter. The same is true of the words nema (thread), stoma (mouth), and desma (band), often employed as endings. Special uniform endings are often employed in the naming of genera within certain classes, such endings having reference to the class. Thus pora and phyllum are the common terminations for corals, the former being used in the poriferous corals, as Aulopora, Syringopora, Tubipora, etc., and the latter in the septate corals, especially the Tetraseptata; example: Cyathophyllum, Heterophyllum, etc. In graptolites the termination graptus is common. In Cystoidea, Blastoidea, Crinoidea and Echinoidea the common terminations of the generic names are cystites, blastus, crinus, and echinus, respectively, though these are by no means exclusively employed. Examples are: Pleurocystites, Cryptoblastus, Encrinus, Eucalyptocrinus, etc., and Rhoëchinus. In Bryozoa trypa and pora are frequent endings; example: Callotrypa, Bythopora. In Cephalopoda ceras is the prevailing termination, as in Orthoceras, Gephyroceras, Phylloceras, Lytoceras, etc., though in some orders of ammonites (e. g., Discocampyli) the termination ites is the prevailing one; example: Ceratites, Stephanites, etc. Among Reptilia saurus is a common termination; example: Mosasaurus, Stegosaurus, etc., and names of fossil birds not infrequently have the termination *pteryx* (wing); example: *Archæopteryx, Megalopteryx,* etc.

The generic name is always written with an initial capital. Specific names, on the other hand, have the value of adjectives and should always be written with a small initial letter, even though they are derived from proper names. It should be noted, however, that this rule is not universally accepted.

The gender of the specific name, as expressed in its termination, should agree with that of the generic name. Thus, the specific name in the above examples is *muricatus* in Productus, which is masculine, and *muricata* in the other two genera, which are feminine. In general, the specific name is derived from the Latin, while all other words are rendered in the Latin form. Names of persons are frequently used for the formation of specific names, an appropriate termination being added. Geographical names likewise are commonly used for the formation of specific names. The more common terminations of specific names thus derived are: *anus, a, um* (pertaining to), as *americanus, linnæanus;* further, *ensis, is, e* (belonging to a locality), as *cincinnatiensis, canadensis, chicagoensis, kentuckiensis* (final a or e when occurring in the original word is dropped and terminal y changed to *i*); and finally, *i* as *halli, knighti,* etc., a common termination for names derived from persons. Common terminations for names derived from other words are: *atus, a, um,* as *costatus, lobatus, galeatus; formis, is, e,* as *tubiformis, filiciformis,* etc.; *inus, a, um,* ex: *rugatinus; oides* (added only to words derived from the Greek), as *discoides,* etc., and others.

Priority and Synonymy (13; 14; 15). Since there is such a vast number of specific names in natural history, and since it often happens that the same species receives distinct names by different authors, owing to ignorance or ignor'ance of each other's works, it is necessary to have a fixed standard by which the name which is to survive is invariably chosen. The standard is priority—the name used in the first description of the species being adopted, even if a later proposed name is more suitable. All later names become synonyms. In certain cases, however, exceptions to this rule are allowed. Thus, if the original description is too poor, so that the true characters of the genus and species cannot be ascertained, a later name, proposed with a better description or illustration, is often accepted. Where a name has long been in general use the discovery of a prior name ought not to overthrow the established usage, especially if the older name has itself come into use for another species. Thus *Spirifer mucronatus* has become the widely accepted name for the species described by Conrad as *Delthyris mucronata* in 1841. One of the numerous varieties of this species had, however, been described by Atwater in 1820 as *Terebratula pennata*, and it has hence been argued that *Spirifer pennatus* and not *Spirifer mucronatus* should be the name of the species. *Spirifer pennatus* has, however, come into use for another species, described under that name by Owen in 1852. The adoption of Atwater's name requires not only the discarding of a well-known and appropriate name, but also requires the substitution of another name for Owen's *Spirifer pennatus*. This strict adherence to the rule of priority in this case would lead to so much confusion that it is much better to make an exception and retain the names which have been so extensively used in the literature.

In the example cited, the name *pennatus* has been given to two species of Spirifer by different authors. That we may know which species is meant, it is necessary to write the name of the author after the specific name. Thus, in the case cited, the names should be written: *Spirifer pennatus* (Atwater) and *Spirifer pennatus* Owen. This custom of adding the author's name is a general one, and should always be observed in all but the most general discussions. When the author of the species has placed it in the wrong genus, or if the species is subsequently referred to a new genus, the author's name after the species is placed in parentheses, and frequently the name of the person who first placed the species in the correct genus is added. Thus, in the examples cited above, Conrad described his species under the generic name Delthyris, but it belongs to the genus Spirifer; hence the name is written *Spirifer mucronatus* (Conrad). Since Billings was the first to place the species in the genus Spirifer, his name may be added, viz., *Spirifer mucronatus* (Conrad) Billings; but this method is not always adopted. Sometimes the form *Spirifer mucronatus* Conrad sp. is used.

Synonymy.

No genus can have two species of the same name. If two authors describe, under the same name, two different species of the same genus, the one to which the name was first applied retains it, the name becoming a synonym so far as the other species is concerned; for this later-described species a new name must be proposed. When reference to the first-described species is made, it is often desirable to note the fact that the name has been applied to another species to avoid possible confusion. Thus Dunker in 1869 described and named *Fusus meyeri*, a modern species, and Aldrich in 1886 described a Tertiary species as *Fusus meyeri*. Reference to the former would thus be made as follows: *Fusus meyeri* Dunker 1869 (non Aldrich 1886). Since Aldrich considered his species a true Fusus he was forced to change its name on discovering that the name had been preoccupied for that genus. So in 1897 he proposed the name *Fusus ottonis* for this species. It appeared, however, that Aldrich's species is not a true Fusus, but belongs to a series of distinct origin. The name Falsifusus (Grabau) was, therefore, proposed for it, with the present species as the type, and, since this genus has no other species by the name of meyeri, it became proper to retore that specific name to its original rank. Thus we now have the synonymy of this species as follows (omitting references to authors which did not change the name):

FALSIFUSUS MEYERI—(Aldrich) Grabau.

    1886 *Fusus meyeri* Aldrich....................................*
    not *Fusus meyeri* Dunker, 1869.............................
    1897 *Fusus ottonis* Aldrich................................
    1904 *Falsifusus meyeri* Grabau............................

In this case the specific name *ottonis* not only becomes a synonym, but, so far as Fusus is concerned, it is dead and cannot be used again, even for a new species of Fusus. Unless this rule is observed much confusion is likely to arise. Should the generic name Falsifusus be found invalid, however, the type species *Falsifusus meyeri* being proved a true Fusus after all, the specific name *ottonis* will have to be restored to its original rank, the species in question being then *Fusus ottonis*. The general rule is that no specific name which has become a synonym in a genus can ever be used again for another species of that genus, though it may be used for species of other genera. If an old comprehensive species is divided into a number of species the original name is retained for that subdivision to which it was originally applied, or to which the diagnosis corresponds most closely. For the other subdivisions new names must be proposed. If two authors describe the same species under different names, the name given in the earlier description is retained, the other one becoming a synonym. If a species is transferred from one genus to another, in which there is already a species of that name, that one of the two species to which the specific name in question was first applied retains it, while the

---

* The dotted lines take the place of the reference to the literature where this name was used.

other species takes the oldest tenable synonym applied to it, if such exists, otherwise it receives a new name.*

Manuscript Names, List Names (Nomina Nuda). Sometimes authors propose names in manuscript, or in lists with the intention of giving descriptions later, but the manuscripts are not published or the descriptions not written. Such a *nomen nudum* has no standing, unless a subsequent describer chooses to adopt it and give the original proposer credit for the name. Thus U. P. James in 1871 listed *Ambonychia costata* in his catalogue of Lower Silurian (Ordovicic) Fossils of the Cincinnati group, proposing the name without description. Meek in 1873 described the fossils for which James had proposed the above name, which Meek adopted, and credited to James. In this case the description was based on the material originally named by James, so that there could be no question regarding the applicability of the name. Even so, many subsequent writers have credited the name *costata* to Meek, refusing to recognize James' claim to priority. In general, manuscript names and list names are best discarded.

Generic Names as Synonyms. As a general rule, a generic name can be used but once in natural history, even if the genus to be named belongs to a wholly distinct phylum of the animal or plant kingdom. Thus in 1835 Swainson proposed the generic name Clavella for an Eocenic gastropod shell, but this name had been preoccupied in 1815 by Oken for a crustacean. The name Clavilithes was therefore proposed by Swainson in 1840 for his shell. Many authors, however, consider that preoccupation of a name disqualifies it for subsequent use only if both cases are within the same phylum, and in the case cited Clavella is retained by some for the gastropod as well as for the crustacean. The stricter rule, however, which allows one name to be used once only is the better, since it avoids all ambiguity.† When species described under different generic names are found to belong to one genus, the oldest of the generic names applied to them is retained, the others becoming synonyms. Such synonyms ought not to be used again, but relegated to the limbo of invalid terms. If, however, the supposed generic identity of the species is shown to be untenable, the original name or names must be restored to rank. Thus naturalists have commonly regarded the generic name Cyrtulus, proposed by Hinds

*For further extensive discussion of this question see recent numbers of Science.

† For the generic names used in zoölogy up to 1879, see Scudder (25). For those used subsequently see the annual lists published by the Zoölogical Society of London in the Zoölogical Record (complete index every ten years, 1865–1906), continued in the International Catalogue of Scientific Literature since 1907.

in 1843 for a modern gastropod, as a synonym of Clavilithes, proposed by Swainson in 1840 for a Tertiary one, and relegated the name Cyrtulus to the limbo of dead terms. As the types of these genera are, however, widely distinct, the name Cyrtulus must be restored to its original significance.

When a genus includes several distinct groups of species, each of which is subsequently raised to the rank of an independent genus, the original name should be retained for the group considered most typical by the original author, or corresponding best to his diagnosis. New names must be given to the other groups. Thus the name Clavilithes has been restricted to that group to which the generic characters, as described by Swainson, best correspond (*C. parisiensis*, etc.), while another group included by Swainson under the same generic name has been separated under the term Rhopalithes (*R. nœ*, etc.).

TYPES.

A *type* in natural history is the material used in describing, defining, and illustrating a species or genus, etc. Two kinds of types are recognized—Primary or Proterotypes and Secondary or Supplementary types or Hypotypes (Apotypes). Typical specimens (Icotypes) not used in the literature, but serving a purpose in identification, are further recognized.

Terms Used for Specific Types. The following terms have been proposed and have come into more or less general use (24) for types of species:

    I. Primary types (Proterotypes).
        a. Holotypes.
        b. Cotypes (Syntypes).
        c. Paratypes.
        d. Lectotypes.
    II. Supplementary types (Hypotypes or Apotypes).
        e. Autotypes (Heautotypes).
        f. Plesiotypes.
        g. Neotypes.
   III. Typical specimens (Icotypes).
        h. Topotypes.
        i. Metatypes.
        j. Idiotypes.
        k. Homœotypes.
        l. Chirotypes.
    IV. Casts of Types (Plastotypes).

I. Among the primary types a *holotype* is the original specimen selected as the type, and from which the original description (*protolog*), or the original illustration (*protograph*), is made. A *cotype* (*syntype*) is a specimen of the original series when there is no holotype, the describer having used a number of specimens as of equal value.

A *paratype* is a specimen of the original series when there is a holotype. When the original describer selected one specimen out of the number used to be the type *par excellence, i. e.,* the holotype, the remainder of the specimens used in the original description constitute the paratypes.

A *lectotype* is a specimen chosen from the cotypes subsequently to the original description to represent the holotype.

II. Among the supplementary types:

An *autotype* (*heautotype*) is a specimen not belonging to the primary or proterotype material and identified with an already described and named species and selected by the nomenclator himself for the purpose of further illustrating his species.

A *plesiotype* is a similar specimen but selected by some one else than the original describer of the species.

A *neotype* is a specimen identified with an already described and named species, and selected to represent the holotype in case the original material (all the proterotypes) is lost or too imperfect for determination. A neotype must be from the same locality and horizon as the holotype or lectotype which it represents.

III. Among typical specimens or Icotypes:

A *topotype* is a specimen (not used in the literature) from the same locality and horizon as the holotype or lectotype.

A *metatype* is a topotype identified by the nomenclator himself.

An *idiotype* is a specimen (not used in the literature) identified by the nomenclator himself, but not from the original locality or horizon of the holotype or lectotype with which it is identified, *i. e.,* not a topotype.

A *homotype* (*homœotype*) is a specimen (not used in the literature) identified by a specialist, after comparing with the holotype or lectotype.

A *chirotype* is a specimen upon which a chironym or manuscript name (a name never published) is based.

IV. Casts of type material (*plastotypes*) may be used or not in descriptions or illustrations. They are accordingly *holoplastotype* or any other *protoplastotype*. *Hypoplastotypes* and *icoplastotypes* also may be made, but are generally of comparatively little value.

GENERIC TYPES. Species upon which genera are based are *genotypes.** Three kinds of genotypes may be recognized:

Genoholotype—the original species on which the genus is founded, or the species selected by the author from those originally described as the type of the genus.

Genosyntype—one of a series of species upon which a genus is founded when there is no genoholotype.

Genolectotype—a species subsequently selected from the genosyntypes to represent the genoholotype.

Selection of the Genotype or Type Species of a Genus.

Many genera are monotypic, *i. e.*, had only one species when founded, though others may subsequently have been referred to them. The original species upon which the genus is founded in such a case is the true genotype or genoholotype. When a genus is founded on a group of species (heterotypic) the originator of the genus should select one species as the genoholotype. This has not always been done, especially in the case of the older genera, the genus being founded on a group of species or genosyntypes described at the same time. It then becomes the duty of the first reviser of the genus to select the type species (genolectotype) from the original species (or genosyntypes). Two principal methods are used by naturalists in such cases—the *first species method* and the *elimination method*. The first of these methods appears to be the simplest one, since the species first described by the author of the genus is taken as the type. It sometimes happens, however, that the first species is not the most typical of the genus as defined by the author, or it may have been subsequently separated from the other species and perhaps placed in a genus by itself, the diagnosis of which differs from the original one, or is more circumscribed than it. In such a case it is the practice to choose the genolectotype from the remaining species of the original group. Often several sections have been separated from the original group and placed in distinct genera. By this process of elimination the genotype thus becomes restricted to the remaining species (genosyntypes), one of which must be selected. This selection is to be done by the first reviser of the old genus and his designation of the genolectotype will stand. Occasionally it may happen that all the original species have been removed to new genera, in which case the last one so

---

* This name has recently been employed by zoölogists and botanists in a very different sense (see Osborn–19).

removed is to be taken as the type of the restricted genus, the new name applied to it becoming a synonym.

The application of the first species rule to the determination of the type of the genus may lead to a great many unnecessary and undesirable changes, but where possible it is best applied, as being the most readily carried out. Where, however, this would lead to confusion in the nomenclature, the elimination rule is best followed. (For illustration and discussion see Stone–26; Allen–12 and subsequent articles in Science.)

Union of Genera into Groups of Higher Taxonomic Value.

Sub-families, Families, Super-families. Genera are united into families, the name of the family being generally derived from its principal genus or the one longest known. The termination of families in zoölogy is generally *idæ* (short i), as *Terebratulidæ* from *Terebratula*. Families are often divided into sub-families, the names of which terminate in *inæ* (long i), as *Terebratulinæ*. In Botany the family generally ends in *aceæ*, as *Rosaceæ*, but there are a number of exceptions to this rule. Sub-families in botany end in *eæ* or *ineæ*, the name in each case being derived from the principal genus. Super-families—in which a small group of related families are united, are sometimes made use of. The names of these end in *acea*, the name being derived from the principal family. Ex.: *Terebratulacea.*

Sub-orders, Orders. The important division of next higher rank is the *order*, which often comprises a number of *sub-orders*. The names of these divisions have no uniform ending in zoölogy, though the terminal letter is commonly *a*, the termination *ata* being most common. Other terminations are: *ia*, *oida* or *oidea*, *acea*, *era*, etc. In botanical nomenclature the orders end in *ales*.

Groups of Higher Rank. Above the orders we have in ascending rank: (*super-orders*), (*sub-classes*) *classes*, (*sub-types*) *phyla* (or *types*), *sub-kingdom*, *kingdom*. When a taxonomic division of higher rank takes its name from a genus the name of which is afterward found to have been preoccupied, and so has to be changed, the name of the higher division must also be changed.

The law of priority is not strictly applied to names of divisions of higher rank than genera, since newly discovered facts often make a change in the classification necessary when the substitution of a new for an old term becomes desirable. A uniform termination for the names of divisions higher than families is much to be desired.

Faunas and Floras. An association of all the animals in a given locality constitutes the fauna of that locality, while a similar association of the plants produces the flora. In the study of past geologic epochs it is often necessary to speak of the totality of animal or plant life in any given formation. This constitutes the fauna and flora, respectively, of that formation. It matters not whether the formation is great or small—whichever is considered—all the animal remains found in that formation together make up the fauna of that formation, and all the plant remains constitute its flora. To designate the fauna and flora of a time period we may conveniently employ the terms *chronofauna* and *chronoflora,* or *chronobios* for both. Each chronofauna or flora comprises numerous geographic faunas or floras, and these may be designated the *locofauna* and *locoflora,* or, in its entirety, the *locobios.* We must, of course, realize that the terms fauna and flora refer to the assemblage of animal and plant life as a whole, in the time-period of the formation, and at the locality where the formation now occurs, and that therefore the fossil remains of a given bed do not adequately represent the fauna or flora of that time, since many types have not been preserved. Hence the term fossil faunas is useful as indicating that only a certain portion of the original fauna, *i. e.,* that preserved as fossils, is spoken of. Thus we may speak of the fossil fauna of the Hamilton period of western New York, by which we would mean that portion of the western New York locofauna of the Hamilton chronofauna which has been preserved.

TABLE I. SUBDIVISIONS OF THE PLANT KINGDOM.

Phanerogamous plants.

PHYLUM V. SPERMATOPHYTA or seed plants.
    Class 2. *Angiospermæ* (covered seed-plants).
        Sub-class 2. Dicotyledoneæ (seed-leaves 2).
        Sub-class 1. Monocotyledoneæ (seed-leaves 1).
    Class 1. *Gymnospermæ* (naked-seeded plants).
        Order V.   Ginkgoales
        Order IV.   Gnetales (joint firs).
        Order III. Coniferales.
           Family 2. Pinaceæ.
           Family 1. Taxaceæ.
        Order II.   Cycadales (cycads, sago palms).
        Order I.   Cordaitales (Cordaites).

Cryptogamous plants.

PHYLUM IV. PTERIDOPHYTA or Fern Plants (Vascular Cryptogams).
    Class 6. *Felicinæ.*
        Order IV.   Marattiales (Ringless Ferns).
        Order III. Feliciales (True Ferns).

Order II. Cycadofiliciales.
Order I. Hydropteridiales.
    Family 2. Salviniaceæ.
    Family 1. Marsiliaceæ.

Class 5. *Ophioglossinæ.*
Order I. Ophioglossales.

Class 4. *Lycopodinæ.*
Order IV. Isoëtales.
Order III. Lepidodendrales.
    Family 2. Sigillariaceæ.
    Family 1. Lepidodendraceæ.
Order II. Selaginellales.
Order I. Lycopodiales (Club-mosses).

Class 3. *Psilotinæ.*
Order I. Psilotales.

Class 2. *Sphenophyllinæ.*
Order II. Cheirostrobales.
Order I. Sphenophyllales.

Class 1. *Equisetinæ*
Order II. Equisetales (Horsetails).
Order I. Calamariales (Calamites).

PHYLUM III. BRYOPHYTA or Moss-plants.

Class 2. *Musci* (Mosses).
Order IV. Bryales.
Order III. Phascales.
Order II. Andreæales.
Order I. Sphagnales (Peat-moss).

Class 1. *Hepaticæ* (Liverworts).

PHYLUM II. THALLOPHYTA or Thallus plants.

C. LICHENS.
Class 2. *Basidiolichenes.*
Class 1. *Ascolichenes.*
    Sub-class 2. Discholichenes.
    Sub-class 1. Pyrenolichenes.

B. FUNGI.
Class 2. *Mycomycetes* (True Fungi).
Order III. *Basidiales* (Mushrooms, etc.).
Order II. Ascomycetes (Mildews).
Order I. Ustilaginales. (Æcidiomycetes, rusts).
Class 1. *Phyco-mycetes* (Algo-fungi).
Order II. Zygomycetes.
Order I. Oomycetes.

A. ALGÆ.
Class 3. *Rhodophyceæ* (Red algæ).
Class 2. *Phæophyceæ* (Brown algæ).
Order IV. Euphæophyceæ.
Order III. Cryptomonadaceæ.
Order II. Diatomaceæ.
Order I. Peridiniaceæ.

Class 1. *Chlorophyceæ* (Green algæ).
  Order III. Characeæ.
  Order II.   Euchlorophyceæ.
  Order I.   Conjugataceæ.

PHYLUM I. PROTOPHYTA.
  Class 3. *Myxomycetes* (Slime-molds), sometimes regarded as Protozoa (Mycetozoa).
  Class 2. *Flagellata* (more generally regarded as Protozoa).
  Class 1. *Schizophyta.*
    Order II. Cyanophyceæ (Blue-green algæ).
    Order I.   Schizomycetes (Bacteria).

TABLE II. SUBDIVISIONS OF THE ANIMAL KINGDOM.

Phylum.	Branch.	Class.	Sub-class.	Super-order.	Order.	Sub-order.
		Mammalia (mammals)	Placentalia		Primates Ungulata Sirenia Cetacea Carnivora Tillodontia Rodentia Edentata Dermoptera Chiroptera Insectivora	
			Eplacentalia		Marsupialia Monotremata	
		Aves (birds)	Ornithuræ	Euornithes	(13 orders)	
				Dromæognathæ	Crypturi Apteryges Struthiones	
PHYLUM XI. VERTEBRATA			Saururæ	Odontormæ Odontolcæ		
					Archæornithes	
		Reptilia (reptiles)			Pterosauria Dinosauria Crocodilia Chelonia Theromorpha Sauropterygia Ichthyosauria Squamata Rhynchocephalia	
		Amphibia (Amphibians)			Anura Urodela Gymnophiona Stegocephalia	

TABLE II. SUBDIVISIONS OF THE ANIMAL KINGDOM.—Continued.

Phylum.	Branch.	Class.	Sub-class.	Super-order.	Order.	Sub-order.
PHYLUM XI. VERTEBRATA (Continued)		Pisces (fishes)	Teleostei, Dipnoi, Ganoidei		many orders...... { Amioidei, Lepidostei, Heterocerci, Chondrostei, Crossopterygii }	many sub-orders
			Selachii or Elasmobranchii		{ Holocephali, Plagiostomi, Ichthyotomi, Acanthodii, Pleuropterygii }	
			Cyclostomata		{ Petromyzonetes, Myxinoides }	
		Ostracoderma (Ostracoderms)	Arthrodira		{ Antiarcha, Aspidocephali, Anaspida, Heterostraci }	
PHYLUM X. PROTOCHORDA		Cephalochorda, Tunicata, Enteropneusta (Balanoglossus, etc.)				
PHYLUM IX. ECHINODERMATA	Branch C. Echinozoa	Holothuroidea			{ Dendrochirota, Aspidochirota }	
		Echinoidea (sea urchins)	Euechinoidea		{ Spatangoida, Clypeastroida, Holectypoida, Diadematoida, Cidaroida }	
			Palaechinoidea		{ Perischoechinoida, Bothriocidaroida, Cystocidaroida }	

TABLE II. SUBDIVISIONS OF THE ANIMAL KINGDOM.—*Continued.*

Phylum.	Branch.	Class.	Sub-class.	Super-order.	Order.	Sub-order.
PHYLUM IX. ECHINODERMATA (Continued)	Branch B. Asterozoa............	Asteroidea (star fish).......	Euasteriæ.......... Encrinasteriæ (Palæasteroidea)		Cryptozonia Phanerozonia	
		Ophiuroidea..... (brittle stars)			Ophiureæ Euryaleæ	
	Branch A. Pelmatozoa.........	Crinoidea........			Articulata Flexibilia Fistulata Camerata Larviformia	
		Blastoidea........			Eublastoidea Protoblastoidea	
		Cystoidea........			Diploporita Aporita Rhombifera Carpoidea Amphoridea	
PHYLUM VIII. ARTHROPODA.......		Hexapoda (insecta)	Pterygogenea (winged insects)	Hemipteroidea Panorpoidea Neuropteroidea Ephemeroidea Libelluloidea Perloidea Embidaria Hymenopteroidea Coleopteroidea Blattæformia Orthopteroidea Palaeopterygogenea (Paleozoic insects)	2 orders 5 " 3 " 1 order 1 " 1 " 1 " 1 " 2 orders 6 " 5 " 14	
			Thysanura Campodeoidea Collembola			

TABLE II. SUBDIVISIONS OF THE ANIMAL KINGDOM.—*Continued.*

Phylum.	Branch.	Class.	Sub-class.	Super-order.	Order.	Sub-order.
PHYLUM VIII. ARTHROPODA (Continued)		Acerata (spiders, scorpions, merostomes)	Arachnida	Epectinata (True spiders) / Pectinifera	(8 orders) / Scorpionidea	
			Pantopoda (Pycnogonida) sea spiders			
			Tardigrada			
			Linguatulina (Pentastomida)			
			Merostomata		Xiphosura / Synxiphosura / Eurypterida / Limulava	
		Crustacea	Malacostraca	Arthrostraca	Amphipoda / Isopoda	
				Thoracostraca	Sympoda (Cumacea) / Stomatopoda / Schizopoda / Decapoda	Macrura / Brachyura
					Phyllocarida	
			Leptostraca / Thyrostraca (cirripedia, barnacles)			
			Entomostraca		Copepoda / Ostracoda / Branchiopoda	Branchiura / Cladocera / Phyllopoda
			Trilobita		Proparia / Opisthoparia / Hypoparia	
		Myriopoda	Chilopoda (centipedes) / Diplopoda (millepedes)			
		Protarthropoda	Onychophora (Peripatus)			

928

TABLE II. SUBDIVISIONS OF THE ANIMAL KINGDOM—*Continued.*

Phylum.	Branch.	Class.	Sub-class.	Super-order.	Order.	Sub-order.
PHYLUM VII. VERMES........	(A heterogeneous assemblage, comprising in reality a number of distinct phyla, but of little or no palæontological importance.)	Chætopoda........	Echiuroidea Haplodrili Saccocirrida Myzostomida Hyrudinæ (leeches) Oligochæta Polychæta			
		Acanthocephala..				
		Podaxonia........	Pterobranchia Phoronidea Priapuloidea Sipunculoidea			
		Rotifera Nemertina Chætognatha Nematoidea Gastrotricha				
PHYLUM VI. PLATYHELMINTHA (PLATYELMIA)...		Cestoda Orthonectida Rhombozoa Trematoda Temnocephaloidea Planaria				
PHYLUM V. MOLLUSCA.......		Cephalopoda......	Dibranchiata		Octopoda Sepioidea Belemnoidea	
			Tetrabranchiata..		Ammonoidea Nautiloidea	
		Pteropoda				
		Conularida......			Conulariidæ Hyolithidæ Torellellidæ Tentaculitidæ	
		Scaphopoda			Dentaliidæ	
		Gastropoda......	Euthyneura......		Pulmonata Opisthobranchia	
			Streptoneura....		Pectinibranchia Aspidobranchia	

TABLE II. SUBDIVISIONS OF THE ANIMAL KINGDOM—*Continued.*

Phylum.	Branch.	Class.	Sub-class.	Super-order.	Order.	Sub-order.
PHYLUM V. MOLLUSCA. (Continued)		Amphineura			Polyplacophora / Aplacophora	Chitonidæ
		Pelecypoda (Lamellibranchiata)			Teleodesmacea / Anomalodesmacea / Prionodesmacea	
		Brachiopoda	Testicardines (Articulata)		Telotremata / Protremata	
			Ecardines (Inarticulata)		Neotremata / Atremata	
PHYLUM IV. MOLLUSCOIDEA. (Prosopygia)		Bryozoa (Polyzoa)	Ectoprocta		Phylactolæmata	
					Gymnolæmata	Cheilostomata / Ctenostomata / Cryptostomata / Trepostomata / Cyclostomata
			Entoprocta			
PHYLUM III. CŒLENTERATA. (Enterocœla)		Ctenophora				
		Anthozoa	Alcyonaria		Octoseptata	Madreporaria (stone corals) / Actinaria (flesh corals) / Antipatharia (horn corals)
			Zoantharia		Hexaseptata	
		Scyphomedusæ			Tetraseptata / Aseptata / Discophora / Coronata / Stauromedusæ / Cubomedusæ	

930

TABLE II. SUBDIVISIONS OF THE ANIMAL KINGDOM—*Continued.*

Phylum.	Branch.	Class.	Sub-class.	Super-order.	Order.	Sub-order.
PHYLUM III. CELENTERATA (Enterocœla) (Continued)		Hydromedusæ (Hydrozoa)			Siphonophora Trahylinæ	{ Narcomedusæ Trachymedusæ
					Leptolinæ	{ Leptomedusæ (Campanularidæ) Sertularidæ Plumularidæ Anthomedusæ (Tubularidæ)
					Hydroidæ Eleutheroblastea	
		Graptozoa			Graptoloidea Dendroidea	Axonophora Axonolipa
		Hydrocorallina (Hydrolithozoa)			Milleporidea Stromatoporidæ Labechiidæ Beatriciidæ	
PHYLUM II. PORIFERA (Parazoa)		Calcarea Myxospongida Triaxonida (Hexactinellida)				
		Tetraxonida	{ Tetractinellida Lithistida Monaxonellida			
		Euceratosa				
PHYLUM I. PROTOZOA	Infusoria	{ Suctoria Ciliata				
	Sporozoa	{ Ectospora Endospora				
	Mastigophora	{ Cystoflagellata Dinoflagellata Flagellata				

TABLE II. SUBDIVISIONS OF THE ANIMAL KINGDOM.—*Continued.*

Phylum.	Branch.	Class.	Sub-class.	Super-order.	Order.	Sub-order.
PHYLUM I. PROTOZOA. (Continued)	Sarcodina	Mycetozoa (Myxomycetes—plants) Labyrynthulidea				
		Radiolaria			Phæodaria Nasselari- Acantharia Spumellaria	
		Foraminifera			Nummulidiaceæ Rotalidaceæ Globigerinidaceæ Lagenidaceæ Cheilostomellaceæ Textulariaceæ Miliolidaceæ Lituolidaceæ Astrorhizidiaceæ Allogromidiaceæ Nuda	
		Heliozoa Rhizopoda Proteomyxa				

BRIEF SUMMARY OF THE MORPHOLOGICAL CHAR-
ACTERS OF THE PHYLA OF PLANTS
AND ANIMALS.

A. PLANTS.

PHYLUM I—PROTOPHYTA. This division is not often employed,
the members here classed under it being referred either to the algæ
or to the fungi. It is, however, a convenient division for those
simple plants which have not the true characters of either of the
other two groups. In this group are placed organisms which combine characteristics of both plants and animals. Such are the
Flagellata, which more generally are placed among the *Protozoa,*
and the *Myxomycetes,* which are also regarded by some zoölogists
as Protozoa under the name *Mycetozoa.* The Flagellata are aquatic,
and so named from the fact that their dominant phase is a "flagel·
lula" or cell-body provided with one, few, or, rarely, many, long,
actively vibratile processes. They are attached or free and some of
them (*Volvocaceæ,* etc.) develop chlorophyll, and in this, and in
the mode of multiplication, they have the characters of undoubted
unicellular plants. Some types placed here (*Coccolithophoridæ*)
(Fig. 104) have their bodies invested in a spherical test strengthened by calcareous elements or tangential circular plates which are
variously named *coccoliths, discoliths, cyatholiths,* or rods called
rhabdoliths. These are often found in the Foraminiferal ooze
and in chalk.

Flagellates are frequently considered as forming the starting
point for unicellular plants on the one hand and Protozoa on the
other. That they have given rise to both groups is held by good
authorities. The largest species range up to 130μ in length, exclusive of the flagellum, though a large number of them rarely
exceed 20μ in length.

The *Myxomycetes* (Mycetozoa), or slime molds, are sometimes
classed with the Fungi and also with the Protozoa. They are terrestrial and devoid of chlorophyll and reproduce by spores, which
are scattered by the air, as in Fungi. The spore hatches out as a
mass of naked protoplasm, which assumes a free-swimming flagel-
late form, multiplies by division, and then passes into an amœboid
stage. By fusion of many amœboids the *plasmodium* is formed,
which is a mass of undifferentiated protoplasm without envelope and
endowed with the power of active locomotion. It penetrates decaying vegetable matter or spreads over the surface of living fungi,

and may reach an expanse of several feet, though generally small.

The *Schizophyta* form a group distinct from the preceding and unconnected with them or higher types. Bacteria are minute unicellular plants, devoid of chlorophyll, and multiplying by repeated division. In form they are spherical, oblong, or cylindrical, often forming filamentous or other aggregates of cells. The absence of an ordinary nucleus, of the ordinary sexual method of reproduction, and the manner of division, unite them with the *Cyanophyceæ,* or blue-green algæ. Some forms (Sarcina) show relationship to, or analogies with, green algæ (*Palmellaceæ*), while others suggest relationship to myxomycetes. Again, certain features suggest some flagellates and many forms exhibit a power of independent movement when suspended in a fluid. The group is no doubt a heterogeneous one, including at present primitive forms of many types of plants. Their size is commonly 1μ* in diameter and from two to five times that length, though smaller and larger forms are known. They occur fossil since Devonic and probably earlier time.

The *Cyanophyceæ* are unicellular or multicellular and contain, besides chlorophyll, a blue-green coloring matter, hence their name, though the actual color of some ranges from yellows to browns, reds, purples, or violets of all shades. Generally the single cells are held together in a common jelly. Some members of this division secrete lime (Glœocapsa, Glœothece) and serve to build up considerable deposits (see organic oölites, Chapter XI). Nearly a thousand species of Cyanophyceæ are known. No fossil representatives are known, though they must have existed in earlier ages.

PHYLUM II—THALLOPHYTA. The vegetative portion of these plants consists of one or many cells forming a *thallus,* often branched. There is no differentiation of the body into a root, stem, or leaf, while the internal structure is comparatively simple. Both sexual and asexual reproduction take place. In many classifications the *Bacteria,* the *Cyanophyceæ,* and the *Myxomycetes* are also classed here, and, besides them, the following classes are made: 1. *Peridineæ,* 2. *Conjugatæ,* 3. *Diatomaceæ* (Diatoms), 4. *Heteroconteæ,* 5. *Chlorophyceæ* (Green algæ), 6. *Characeæ* (Stoneworts), 7. *Rhodophyceæ* (Red algæ), 8. *Eumycetes* (Fungi), 9. *Phycomycetes* (Algal fungi), 10. *Phæophyceæ* (Brown algæ). The older division into the three classes of a, *Algæ,* bearing Chlorophyll; b, *Fungi,* without Chlorophyll; and c, *Lichens,* symbiotic colonies of algæ and fungi, is the most familiar and will be used here.

* One micromillimeter or 0.001 mm.

a. *Algæ.*

Algæ, or seaweeds, are thallophytes characterized by the presence of Chlorophyll, or leaf-green, though the color is by no means always green. They are largely aquatic in habitat, most of the more striking forms occurring in the sea. According to the prevailing color, three divisions are made—the Green Algæ, or *Chlorophyceæ;* the Brown Algæ, or *Phæophyceæ;* and the Red Algæ, or *Rhodophyceæ.* The *Cyanophyceæ,* or blue-green algæ, are also frequently included under the algæ.

The *Chlorophyceæ* include three forms in which the chlorophyll is not accompanied by other coloring matter. With the typical green algæ (*Euchlorophyceæ*) are generally included the divisions *Conjugataceæ* and *Characeæ,* which have a separate phyletic standing. The common green sea-lettuce, *Ulva,* is a good example of an expanded form, but in many of the green algæ (especially the *Confervales*), the thallus consists of filaments, branched or unbranched, attached at one extremity and growing almost wholly at the free end. Some forms (Halimeda, Acetabularia, etc.) are encrusted with lime and are important on "coral" reefs. The Pond-scums, or *Conjugatæ* (so named from their method of reproduction) include the Desmids, which have the power of independent movement.

Quite distinct from the others are the *Characeæ,* the most highly differentiated of the green algæ. Of these the common stonewort, *Chara,* growing in fresh water lakes, is the typical form. This is attached to the bottom of pools by rhizoids and grows upward by means of an apical cell forming a pointed axis, which gives off whorled appendages at regular intervals. Long branches occur in each whorl, and these give off secondary whorls of jointed appendages. The distance between the nodes from which the appendages arise may be several centimeters. All are encrusted with lime. The reproductive organs are also highly differentiated. Antheridia and oögonia are formed at the nodes of the appendages. The egg cells, or oögonia, when ripe are surrounded by five spirally twisted cells, and crowned by a circle of smaller ones, which afterward separate to allow fertilization. The outer cells become very hard and calcareous and are extensively preserved, in some cases contributing to the formation of limestones.

Over 1,600 species of true green algæ are known. The Pond Scums, or Conjugatæ, add nearly 1,300 species more, while the stoneworts, or Characeæ, are represented by only about 180 species, making a total of over 3,000 species.

The *Phæophyceæ,* or brown algæ, are distinguished by the possession of a brown coloring matter in addition to the chlorophyll. The *Peridiniaceæ* and *Diatomaceæ* are included here, together with the *Cryptomonadaceæ,* all of them unicellular plants with little except color in common with the true brown algæ (*Euphæophyceæ*), which are multicellular. Familiar examples of the last class are Fucus, Laminaria, and Sargassum. The kelps (*Laminaria*) develop large round "stems" which branch root-like at the base and have an oar-like expansion at the top. The rock-weeds (*Fucus*) develop air-bladders which serve for purposes of flotation. They are attached to the rock by means of a disc or root-like expansion; have a stem of rough leathery texture which forks regularly; and are expanded in a leaf-like manner with thick mid-ribs. The Gulf-weeds (*Sargassum*) have distinct stems, leaves, and stalked air-bladders, and strikingly resemble land plants.

The diatoms are microscopic unicellular plants of a yellow or reddish-brown color, and not closely related to the other algæ except perhaps to the desmids. The cell wall is impregnated with silica, so that its shape is preserved after the death of the plant. The "shell" consists of two parts, one overlapping the other like a pill-box and cover. These show great variety of form and have the power of locomotion.

Of the true brown algæ there are only about 620 species. The *Peridiniaceæ* and *Cryptomonadaceæ* comprise only about 220 species, but the diatoms, recent and fossil, include about 5,000 species.

The *Rhodophyceæ,* or red algæ, also called *Florideæ,* are so named from the presence of a red color besides the chlorophyll. Species growing near high-water mark are generally of a dark hue and may be mistaken for brown algæ. The Irish moss, *Chondrus,* is a good example. Those growing near low-water, or in the shade of other algæ, are bright colored. They are all multicellular and mostly microscopic in size, but some large species occur. Lime-secreting forms are common, the branching Corallina, the encrusting Melobesia and Lithothamnion abounding both in recent and fossil state. The total number of species of red algæ is about 1,400; this, together with the brown algæ, 840 species, the diatoms, 5,000 species, and the 3,000 species of green algæ, makes a total of over 10,200 species of algæ.

Fucoids. This is a general term applied to impressions on rocks, suposed to represent sea-weeds. In some cases land plants and even traces of inorganic structures have been included here. Ex.: *Fucoides verticalis* of the Portage, probably a land plant;

Arthrophycus harlani of the Medina, probably a trail; *Dendrophycus triassicus* of the Newark sandstone, a rill-mark impression.

b. *Fungi.*

Fungi or mushroom-plants are thallophytes devoid of chlorophyll, and growing often in the dark. They arise from spores, and the thallus is either unicellular or composed of tubes or cell-filaments (hyphæ), which may be branched, and have an apical growth, or, again, they are composed of sheets or tissue-like masses of such filaments, forming a *mycelium.* True tissue may develop in some cases by cell-division in the larger forms. Two classes are recognized: *Phycomycetes,* which are alga-like, with unicellular thallus and well-marked sexual organs, and *Micomycetes,* or higher fungi, with segmental thallus and sexual reproduction. Some of them (Polyporus, Dædelia) form resistant, more or less woody, structures growing on dead trees.

The number of species of Fungi is probably around 20,000, though some have placed it as high as 50,000 or even 150,000. Fossil forms extend back at least to the Carbonic, where they occur as hyphæ in fossil wood. Good specimens are also found in amber of Tertiary age.

c. *Lichens.*

The lichens are terrestrial thallophytes, composed of algæ and fungi living together symbiotically. The fungi are generally *Ascomycetes,* the higher class of *Basidomycetes* seldom taking part, while the algæ are either the blue-green algæ, *Cyanophyceæ* or the green algæ, *Chlorophyceæ.* The same alga can combine with different fungi to form different lichens. The fungal portion always forms the reproductive organs, though the algæ may do so when separated from the association, and growing free. Reproduction is also carried on by fragmentation, *i. e.,* the breaking off of parts capable of starting new plants. There are some thousands of existing species, but fossil forms have not been recognized except from very recent formations. It is not unlikely, however, that lichenous plants formed a chief element of the ancient land vegetation.

PHYLUM III—BRYOPHYTA. The Bryophyta include the mosses and liverworts, both terrestrial plants. In the former, and in some of the latter as well, the plant consists of a stem bearing small leaves, though in many liverworts this distinction is not present, but a *thallus* is formed closely applied to the substratum. The attachment of the bryophytes is by rhizoids, true roots being absent. These rhizoids resemble the root-hairs of higher plants. The reproductive organs are *antheridia* and *archegonia,* serving for sexual reproduction. The former are stalked and develop the spermatozoids, while the archegonia are flask-shaped, with long neck, the egg-cell lying at the bottom. From the fertilized ovum a capsule arises, generally borne on a stalk, and within this the spores are developed. There is thus an alternation of generation—the sexual stage, or *gametophyte,* developing from the spore, and the asexual, or spore stage (*sporogonium* or *sporophyte*), developing from the fertilized egg of the gametophyte, and, in turn, producing the spores. The spore-bearing generation is throughout life dependent on the gametophyte, whereas in pteridophytes it becomes an independent plant. The order *Sphagnales* contains the single genus, Sphagnum, with numerous species known as bog-mosses. The order *Andreæales* also contains a single genus, Andreæa, for the most part an Alpine and Arctic plant, growing on bare rocks. The order *Phascales* includes a few small species, chiefly of the genus Phascum. The order *Bryales,* on the other hand, contains a very large number of genera and species.

Fossil mosses, especially of the genus Hypnum, have been obtained from the Miocenic and Quaternary deposits of Europe and the Arctic region, and also from western America (Green River beds). They are doubtfully represented in Mesozoic and earlier deposits.

PHYLUM IV—PTERIDOPHYTA. The pteridophytes, or vascular cryptogams, form the highest division of the flowerless plants. Their internal vascular structure allies them with the higher plants. In them alternation of generation has been carried farthest, in that the first stage to develop from the germinating spore is the gametophyte, known as the *prothallus.* This is a small, flat, green plant-organism which carries on its under side the *archegonia* and *antheridia,* together with the rootlets or rhizoids. This sexual plant is independent of the sporophyte or asexual generation, while the latter at first draws nourishment from the prothallus but becomes physiologically independent when its roots develop. This independence of the two generations is the distinctive feature of the pteridophytes, whereas in bryophytes the sporophyte is throughout its life attached to the gametophyte, while in the spermaphytes the more or less reduced gametophyte remains enclosed within the tissues of the sporophyte.

The *Equisetales,* including the single living genus, Equisetum, with about 25 species, and the extinct Calamites, represent a range in height from a few inches in the modern forms to from 30 to 60 meters in the extinct Calamites. Equisetum arises from a subterranean rhizome, which may be a meter in length, and is jointed; the aërial shoot consists of hollow internodes, with whorls of leaves near the top of each, the leaves cohering, except near their tips. In section the aërial stem shows a hollow central cylinder, around which is arranged a circle of fibrovascular bundles, triangular in section, with the point inward. The inner end is occupied by a large air space, and outside of this again is a circle of long air tubes alternating with the fibrovascular bundles. These latter extend into the leaves, equaling in number the leaf teeth.

The stem of the extinct Calamites had essentially the same structure, but with secondary growth in thickness. In all large specimens a broad zone of wood is added, with a structure comparable in the true Calamites to that of the simplest conifers. The vascular bundles project into the pith as in Equisetum, and from their more resistant character they will remain when the pith breaks down. A rock-filling of the hollow cylinder thus made will be marked by longitudinal grooves, representing the projecting vascular bundles. In Calamites proper these grooves alternate at the nodes, while in Archæocalamites they are continuous. This shows that in the latter the leaves were superposed, while in Calamites they were alternating. In modern Equisetum both fertile and sterile branches arise from the rhizomes. The sterile are more slender than the spore-bearing ones, and bear numerous whorls of branches, which form a bushy plant, from which the name "horsetail" originated. The fertile branches bear a terminal "strobilus," or cone of sporangiophores, each of which consists of a hexagonal disk, attached by a stem to the axis and supporting on its under side six to nine large spore-cases or *sporangia*. The outer surfaces of the hexagonal plates form the solid outer surface of the cone, the sporangia extending inward toward the axis. They are not visible until the cone separates into its component parts. Some Calamites (Archæocalamites) agree closely with this mode of organization, but in others the structure of the cones was more complicated, this being brought about chiefly by the insertion of whorls of sterile bracts between those of the sporangiophores.

The *Sphenophyllineæ*, known only from the Palæozoic, and represented by the genus Sphenophyllum, had some characters of the Equisetales. The slender, little-branched, and probably clinging stem had from six to eighteen wedge-shaped or linear leaves at the swollen nodes, the leaves of successive whorls not alternating.

The structure of the stem is, however, more like that of lycopods, but the cone again suggests affinities with the Equisetales. The sporangiophores, however, spring from the bracts instead of the axis. The class combines the characters of ferns, lycopods, and Equisetales. Their nearest living relatives are probably the Psilotales (Psilotum and Tmesipteris) formerly classed with the Lycopodiales.

The *Lycopodinæ* are represented by three living and one extinct orders. The Lycopodiales are represented by two genera—Phylloglossum with one species, and Lycopodium with nearly a hundred. Selaginella with between 300 and 400 species and Isoëtes with about 50, mostly aquatic, species are each the sole representatives of their respective orders. The modern genera are small forms, but the extinct orders contained some of the largest Palæozoic trees, reaching 100 feet or more in height. A general external characteristic of these plants is the simple form of the leaves, which are generally of small size, while the sporangia are situated on the upper surface of the sporophylls. In structure the stem is a single cylinder (monostelic) with a centripetal development of woody tissue (xylem). The earliest, or protoxylem, is at the periphery of the stele. In *Selaginellales* the stem contains one, two, or several stele, while the Lepidodendrales are monostelic, as in Lycopodium. A section of a Lepidodendron stem shows the central pith, often destroyed, surrounded by a zone of primary wood, and outside of this, in most cases, a zone of secondary wood, sharply defined from the inner zone by the layer of protoxylem. In some of the smaller species the wood was solid, without central pith. The cortex or bark surrounds this and is bounded externally by the persistent leaf scars. In Sigillaria the ring of primary wood is narrower. The leaf scars are arranged spirally in Lepidodendron, but in vertical rows in Sigillaria. Both were attached to large creeping root-stocks or *stigmaria,* which were provided with numerous cylindrical "roots" which penetrated the soil on all sides.

The spores of lycopods are formed in sporangia of considerable size, which are situated on the upper surface and near the base of the sporophylls. These are arranged in definite terminal cones, or they may resemble the foliage leaves and occur in alternate zones with them. In Selaginella the sporophylls are arranged radially in the cones, these terminating the branches. A single sporangium is borne on the axis just above the insertion of each sporophyll. Large and small spores (mega- and micro-spores) occur in this genus, but in Lycopodium they are all of one kind.

In the Lepidodendrales they were heterosporous, at least in some cases. The cones of Lepidodendron and allied forms (Lepidostrobus) vary from an inch to a foot in length, according to species, and are borne on ordinary or on special branches. The sporophylls are arranged spirally upon the axis and each carries a single large sporangium on its upper surface, which in turn carries either an enormous number of minute or a small number of large spores. The upturned and overlapping laminæ from the sporophyllæ form the exterior of the cone. The Lepidodendraceæ range from the Devonic to the Permic, while the Sigillariaceæ range through the upper Palæozoic above the Devonic.

The *Ferns* are among the most varied of existing pteridophytes and exhibit a wide range in size, from the little epiphytic *Hymenophyllaceæ,* whose fronds are hardly a centimeter in length, to gigantic tree-ferns, 80 feet or more in height. The leaves or fronds vary from simple to highly compound, each pinna or pinnule being characterized by a mid-vein, and by forking lateral veins. The sporangia are borne on the under side of the frond, or on separate fronds. In the Ophioglossales a separate spike is produced. In some of the Palæozoic *Cycadofilices* (comprising most of the ferns of that period *) actual seeds instead of spores were produced, the forms also being intermediate in structure of the stems, etc., between ferns and cycads. The water-ferns or Rhizocarps (*Hydropteridiales*) produce both mega- and micro-spores. The former produce female, the latter male, prothallia. The common pepperwort, Marsilea, looking like a small four-leaved clover, is a good example.

PHYLUM V—SPERMATOPHYTA. The true flowering plants (Phanerogams), or seed-plants (Spermatophyta), comprise the gymnosperms and the angiosperms. Conifers are the most abundant representatives of the gymnosperms in the northern regions, while the palm-like cycads occur in tropical districts. They are, however, abundant in the Jurassic and other Mesozoic deposits of America and Europe. The late Palæozoic *Cordaitales* were large trees with wood of a coniferous type (Dadoxylon wood) and long strap-shaped leaves.

The angiosperms, including all the true flowering plants, are divided into the *Monocotyledons,* which include the grasses, palms, lilies, etc., with parallel-veined leaves, and the *Dicotyledons* with net-veined leaves. The latter make their first appearance in Comanchic time.

* Also classed as a separate order *Pteridospermæ* under the gymnosperms.

ANIMALS.

PHYLUM I—PROTOZOA. The Protozoa are unicellular animals either naked or enclosed in a cell membrane. In addition, many rhizopods secrete calcareous or siliceous structures, or, by cementation, form a covering of foreign substances. One or more nuclei are generally present, and reproduction is by fission. The Rhizopoda include the *Foraminifera,* which secrete shells of carbonate of lime, or build them by cementing sand grains, etc. The shells have one or more chambers (unilocular or multilocular). If many, they increase in size successively, and are arranged in various ways, including nautilian and spiral coiling. In many forms the surface is pierced by fine pores—the *foramina*—through which protoplasm is extruded in fine streamers forming the *pseudopodia.* In size the Foraminifera shells vary from minute shells to those an inch or more in diameter (Nummulites). They range from the Cambric to the present with several thousand species.

The *Radiolaria* secrete horny or siliceous internal structures, which form a much perforated latticework, ornamented by spines, bosses, etc. They also range from the Cambric to the present.

PHYLUM II—PORIFERA (SPONGES). The sponges are aquatic multicellular animals in which the body is penetrated by a complex set of canals, into which water enters, through pores in the outer wall. From the canals are given off, at intervals, digestive sacs, and these finally converge into one or more main canals, with large external excurrent openings or *oscula.* Modern sponges generally secrete a skeleton of horny substance (chitin) and, in addition, many secrete siliceous or calcareous rods or needles (spicules) which are often compound in form. In many older and some modern forms, these unite into solid structures so that the form of the sponge is preserved. They abound in all marine formations, from the Cambric to the present. The number of extinct and living species is very great.

PHYLUM III—CŒLENTERATA. The cœlenterates have a body composed of two cellular layers, the *ectoderm* and *endoderm,* the latter enclosing the *cœlomic* cavity into which the mouth opens. An intermediate non-cellular or imperfectly cellular layer is often present but no true body cavity occurs. The animals (polyps) have a simple body in the Hydrozoa—the mouth generally at the end of a proboscis-like elevation, and surrounded by tentacles. Generally they are compound, many polyps being united by hollow tubes. Special polyps for reproduction (gonopolyps) are commonly developed. and these often give rise to medusæ, or jelly-fish

—a free-swimming sexual generation, which, however, sometimes remains attached to the parent. Many Hydrozoa secrete a horny or chitinous envelope, which ends in many cases in cups or *hydrothecæ*. In the fossil graptolites these horny structures alone are preserved, as compressed carbonaceous films. In other cases (Hydrocorallines) a calcareous structure is secreted, which may be important as a reef-former (Millepora). The stromatoporoids of the Palæozoic are believed to belong to this group. They represent enormous accumulations of lime taken by minute organisms from the sea-water and built into their structures. These are often heads of great size, some attaining a diameter of ten feet.

The coral or anthozoan polyp is more complicated, there being, in addition to the parts found in the hydroid polyp, an enteric sac, or *stomodæum,* formed by invagination of the mouth area, and a series of fleshy septa or *mesenteries,* dividing the body radially. Many anthozoan polyps secrete a calcareous structure (coral) which typically is characterized by a series of radially placed calcareous plates or *septa,* variously united by transverse structures and surrounded by one or more calcareous walls. In Palæozoic time these were built mostly on the plan of four and grew into isolated horn-shaped structures on the broad septate end of which the polyp rested (*Tetraseptata*). In later times to the present the plan of six (*Hexaseptata*) or eight (*Octoseptata*) became the dominant one, and the forms became compound, so that in some modern coral heads thousands of individual polyps participate. A fourth group in which the septa were absent or represented by spines only, while the walls were provided with pores (*Aseptata*), was chiefly confined to the Palæozoic. The reproduction of the Anthozoa is carried on by fission and by ova.

PHYLUM IV—MOLLUSCOIDEA. The Molluscoidea comprise two classes which are widely different in their external adult characters but closely similar in their early life history. The *Bryozoa* are commonly compound aquatic forms, either encrusting other objects or forming solid masses not unlike in form to some early corals, with which they have sometimes been united. The colony, or *zoarium,* consists of cells (*zoœcia*) generally of lime and loosely or closely aggregated, in the latter case often becoming prismatic. They are hollow or divided by transverse calcareous partitions or *dissepiments* and have various other structures. Smaller tubes (*mesopores*) are present in some cases. Colonially the Bryozoa may constitute a solid mass or head, a flat expansion, a network, in which large open spaces are left between series of zoœcia (as in Fenestella, etc.), or a great variety of other forms. In Palæozoic time, when the number of specimens was considerably over a thousand, they often acted as important reef-formers. Mesozoic and Cenozoic Bryozoa (close to a thousand species) also contributed largely to calcareous reefs. (See Chapter X.) The animal differs from the coral polyp by the possession of a well-marked body cavity and a definite alimentary system.

The *Brachiopoda* are simple animals encased in a shell with dorsal ventral and sometimes accessory valves. In general, the ventral valve is larger and some provision is afforded for the emission through a foramen or otherwise of the fixing organ, or *pedicle*. It is, hence, called *pedicle valve*. The other valve carries supports (*crura brachidia*), from which the soft internal respiratory organs, the *brachia*, or arms, are suspended; hence the name *brachial valve* is applied. The accessory pieces are either a third shell plate (*pedicle plate, deltidial plate*) secreted by the pedicle, or a double set of plates (*deltidial plates*) meeting in the center below the foramen. These accessory plates are commonly very small and situated below the beak of the pedicle valve. Opening and closing of the valves is effected by muscular systems. Superficially the shells are either smooth or variously plicated, and sometimes spines are developed. There are about 140 living and over 6,000 fossil species.

PHYLUM V—MOLLUSCA. The molluscs are soft-bodied animals generally enclosed in a calcareous shell. The headless molluscs, or *Pelecypoda,* have a shell of two, generally symmetrical valves placed right and left and united dorsally by a *hinge,* which generally includes a series of interlocking hinge-teeth and sockets. The valves are opened either by an external ligamental structure variously arranged or by an internal compressible *resilium* which often has special supports or *resilifers* developed. The shell is closed by the adductor muscles, of which there are typically an anterior and a posterior one (*dimyarian*), or only one, situated subcentrally (*monomyarian*). Externally the shell is smooth, showing only *growth lines,* or it may be ornamented by radiating plications or striations, or by marked concentric *ribs* parallel to the growth-lines. A horny outer covering, or *periostracum,* is generally present. The animal is provided with an anterior hatchet-shaped *foot*, and with gills which hang in pairs on opposite sides of the abdomen, and with a mantle, the attachment of which to the shell is marked by the *pallial line,* and the outer portion of which secretes the shell. The remainder of the mantle secretes the inner shell layer (nacreous layer), which is often iridescent. A pair of siphons (excurrent and incurrent) is frequently formed, their presence being generally indicated by a pronounced reëntrant in the pallial line below the posterior adductor impression (*pallial sinus*).

The cephalophorous mollusca build a shell of only one part, though extra horny or shelly pieces, not secreted by the mantle, may occur. Such are the *opercula* of certain gastropods and the *aptychi* of ammonite cephalopods. In the gastropods the animal is provided with a lingual ribbon, or *radula,* beset with teeth and having a rasping function. In the cephalopods horny *jaws* are developed. In Gastropoda the shell is normally a spiral one, though in some cases the coiling is in a single plane, as is typical of coiled cephalopods. Both right- and left-handed coils occur, the former being more common, while the left-handed coils are variations in some cases, but fixed types in others. The apex of the shell is formed by the *protoconch,* generally somewhat differentiated from the conch. The latter may be smooth (except for growth lines) but is more generally ornamented by plications (spirals) and by ribs which extend across the whorl from suture to suture. The ribs may become concentrated into spiral rows of *nodes,* or *spines* (hollow emarginations of the shell-lip) may result. Temporary resting stages in shell growth are often marked by *varices* consisting of abrupt deflections of the lip, or by rows of spines (Murex). The mouth of the shell is in many cases drawn out into an anterior notch or a long canal. The inner or columellar lip of specialized types is marked by oblique plications. Old age or phylogerontic forms often have the last whorl loose-coiled or straight. The shell of primitive cephalopods is a straight cone (*Orthoceras*) divided regularly by transverse *septa,* which are pierced by the *siphuncle.* All the resulting chambers are empty, representing cut-off space as the shell became too small for the growing animal, which finally occupied only the large outer or living chamber. When the chambers are all filled with hardened mud and the shell is broken away, the edges of the septa are seen, forming the *suture.* In *Nautiloidea* this suture is generally simple, but in *Ammonoidea* it is often much fluted so as to produce a complicated pattern. The siphuncle of nautiloids is generally at or near the center, while that of the ammonoids is external. Curved forms (*Cyrtoceras*), loose-coiled (*Gyroceras*), and close-coiled (*Nautilus* and *Ammonites*) shells are progressively developed. Old age individuals, or phylogerontic groups, generally lose the power of coiling in the last whorl, which may be loose-coiled or even straight.

Baculites, one of the last survivors of the ammonoids, was straight except for the very earliest portion, which was coiled. The ammonoids are all extinct, ending with the Cretacic. Nautiloids are represented by the living Nautilus. These two groups are classed as *Tetrabranchiata*. The *Dibranchiata* are represented by the living Argonauta, the Octopus, Squid, Cuttlefish, and Spirula. The last is an internal loose-coiled shell with septa and siphuncle. A straight-coiled ancestor, the Jurassic and Cretacic Belemnites, had its shell, which was straight, protected by a heavy calcareous outer guard, often cigar-shaped, and when perfect showing the hollow at one end occupied by the shell. A modified portion of the guard alone remains in the cuttlefish, the so-called cuttlefish bone, which is embedded in the fleshy mantle of the animal.

The *Pteropoda* have thin transparent shells of various shapes, but rarely coiled. The "foot" of the animal is divided into two wing-like appendages by which these "Butterflies of the sea" keep themselves afloat on the water. The shell of the *Conulariidæ* and *Hyolithidæ* was coarser and generally rectangular in section in the former and variously shaped in the latter. The *Scaphopoda* (Dentalium, etc.) have conical, often curved, shells, open at both ends, which begin as a saddle-shaped structure growing into a ring and increasing in length. In the *Polyplacophora* (Chiton, etc.) the shell is composed of several pieces arranged serially.

Pelecypoda are rare in the Cambric but become abundant in the succeeding horizons. There are about 10,000 fossil species and about 5,000 recent ones. The Gastropoda are likewise sparsely represented in the Cambric. They appear to be at their acme of development at the present time, there being some 15,000 living species, as compared with about half that number or less of fossil ones. Only one cephalopod is known from the Cambric. They abound in the Ordovicic, at the end of which period many races died out, while new ones arose. The Ammonoidea begin in the Devonic, reach their acme in the Jurassic and die out in the Cretacic. The *Nautiloidea* and *Dibranchiata* (the latter appearing first in the Trias) have modern representatives.

PHYLUM VI—PLATYHELMINTHA, AND VII—VERMES. The platyhelminths, or flat-worms, are soft-bodied, worm-like animals without body cavity or cœlom. They have no hard parts, and nothing is known of their geological history. The great mass of animals classed together as *Vermes* is in reality a heterogeneous assemblage, many of the groups having no direct relationship with others placed here. Typical worms (chætopods) have a distinct body cavity from which the enteric and digestive tracts are separated. The body is divided into many similar segments, each of which, except the oral one, carries on each side two bundles of bristles or setæ, a dorsal and a ventral one, placed typically on elevations or *parapodia*. The head segment carries appendages varying in the different sub-classes. Aquatic worms possess gills for breathing, but these become more or less modified or even entirely lost in the mud- and earth-worms. The alimentary system consists of an anterior mouth, an intestinal canal, divisible into fore-gut, mid-gut and hind-gut, and ending in the posterior anus. In some parasitic forms, this system is much degenerated. In some chætopods a series of horny œsoph-ageal teeth is developed, and these are often preserved in great per-fection. The *conodonts* may be of this order.

Many worms build tubes of agglutinated sand, either free, or in the sand, while others secrete calcareous tubes. These are often well preserved and show the presence of these organisms in Cam-bric times. Trails left by errant worms on mud and the peculiar form of the string of sand, which has passed through the annelid body, all serve as evidence of the existence of the worms in former periods.

Phylum VIII—Arthropoda. The arthropods, or jointed-legged invertebrates, comprise a number of distinct assemblages of organisms, as indicated by the several classes included. The crus-taceans are in many respects the most characteristic, but even they comprise a number of subclasses of very diverse characters. The *Myriopoda* and *Peripatus* are worm-like. The former occur first in the Old Red Sandstone (Devonic) and are common in the Car-bonic. The oldest, and in some respects the most generalized, of the Crustacea are the *Trilobites,* which are already highly developed and very numerous in the Cambric. They do not extend beyond the Palæozoic. The organism is covered by a chitinous exoskeleton in which a head or *cephalon,* a *thorax* and an abdomen or *pygidium* are distinguishable. Each division consists of a median axis and lateral lobes and hence shows a trilobate division. The axis of the head constitutes the *glabella* and the lateral portions are com-monly divided into fixed and free *cheeks,* the latter generally carry-ing the compound eyes. The thorax is divided into a number of movable rings, but the pygidium is a single though grooved piece. The mouth is ventral and the head is provided with antennæ. Jointed thoracic legs were also present. The *Entomostraca* are modified crustaceans with a shell-like carapace. They are repre-sented in all geological horizons. The *Ostracoda,* with a bivalve shell, were especially abundant in the Palæozoic. The barnacles also had representatives in the Palæozoic but are more typical in later horizons. The animal is degenerate, attached either directly or by a fleshy stalk. In the former case a circle of shell-plates is developed, forming the corona. The *Phyllocarida* were of great importance in the Palæozoic. They generally had head and thorax enclosed in a carapace consisting mainly of two valves, with accessory pieces. The ringed abdomen and the tailpiece or *telson* (often triple) projected beyond the carapace.

The *Decapoda* have head and thorax united into a *cephalothorax,* and covered by a single carapace, or with one segment free. Each of the thirteen cephalothoracic segments has a pair of jointed appendages, some of which are modified into antennæ or mouth-parts. The abdomen consists of seven segments, the terminal one being a telson. In the *Macrura* (lobsters, crayfish, etc.) these segments are all visible, but in the *Brachiura* (crabs) they are generally turned under the carapace. Locomotor appendages (*pereiopoda*) are in five pairs, and with few exceptions each consists of seven joints. Some of the final joints are claw-like, others paddle-like, and others again merely pointed for walking purposes. Six pairs of abdominal legs occur. The claws are often found fossilized separately. Decapods first appear in the Triassic. The remaining orders show various modifications of the decapod type. They are mostly rare as fossils.

Among the *Acerata* the *Merostomata* are in many respects of greatest interest. Some *Eurypterida* in the Devonic reached a length of six feet, but were smaller in other horizons. The *Limulava* are known only from the Middle Cambric. They combined trilobite with eurypterid characters. The eurypterids had a short cephalothorax, a ringed abdomen and a telson, the body, as in Crustacea, being covered with a chitinous exoskeleton, which was repeatedly shed. A pair of compound eyes and a pair of median simple eyes or ocelli formed the chief dorsal features of the carapace. Ventrally this bore six pairs of jointed appendages, the first preoral and chelate, the others non-chelate, the last usually forming a large paddle. The first six segments of the abdomen bore broad, leaf-like appendages, referable to "gills." The posterior segment and telson were without appendages. The number of known species is over 150. The *Synxiphosura* (Cambric to Siluric, few species) had a trilobitiform abdomen, which, in the adult *Xiphosura,* of which Limulus, the horseshoe crab, is the only living example, was fused into a single piece, though still indicating the segments and trilobation. The fossil species (few in number) have been obtained from the Upper Devonic, the Carbonic, and (genus Limulus, only) from the Mesozoic and Tertiary of Europe.

The scorpions and spiders are more complex Acerata adapted

to a terrestrial life. The former are known from the Siluric (Upper), the latter from the Coal Measures on.

Altogether more than 300 fossil species of arachnids and several thousand modern species are known.

Insects are known from the Ordovicic graptolite slates of Sweden and from the Siluric of France. They are especially well preserved in the Carbonic and later terrestrial formations. The Palæozoic forms constitute a distinct group with 14 orders, all extinct. Two other orders were, however, also represented in the late Palæozoic, the cockroaches (*Blattoidea*) being especially well represented on account of the hard coriaceous character of the front wings or *tegmina*. The number of known Palæozoic insects is close to 1,000 species while the Tertiary and Quaternary have furnished over 5,800 species. There are over 384,000 living species (Handlirsch).

PHYLUM IX—ECHINODERMATA. The echinoderms or spiny-skinned animals are characterized generally by an apparently radial form, by the possession of calcareous plates or sclerites in the integument, and by an elaborate internal structure, the most marked portion of which is the highly developed water-vascular system. The oldest known forms are the *Cystoidea* (Cambric to Carbonic) in which the body was enclosed in a calyx of irregular plates, closely united by *sutures* and generally supported on a stem. Arms were rudimentary and the respiratory and water-vascular system were not pronounced. The *Blastoidea* (Ordovicic to Carbonic) were more regular in the arrangement of plates and were armless. The calyx was, however, provided with five petaloid *ambulacral areas* radiating from the mouth. The *Crinoidea* (Ordovicic to Recent) were mostly stemmed, though some had the power of separation in the adult. The calyx is composed of regular plates generally arranged in five series and terminated by branching or simple arms often of great length. The mouth of many Palæozoic forms (Camerata) was under a vaulted arch or tegmen, and the anus was often placed at the end of a tube or proboscis. The brittle-stars and starfish have the body cleft into five or more movable rays, which are supplied with branches from the water-vascular system and diverticula from the other body organs. The branch begins in the Ordovicic, but has few fossil representatives. The sea-urchins or *Echini*, on the other hand, are abundantly represented in the Mesozoic and later strata. Palæozoic forms occur as early as the Ordovicic (Bothriocidaris). In them the body is generally covered by a large number of plates, which, however, fall into ten zones, five *ambulacral*, with plates pierced for the tubed

feet or *ambulacra,* and five *interambulacral.* The whole forms a
more or less solid *corona.* In the post-Palæozoic types each zone is
generally composed of two columns of plates, so that there are in
all 20 columns, forming 5 ambulacral and 5 interambulacral zones.
The mouth and anus are generally opposite each other in the
Palæechinoidea, and in the *Cidaroidea* and *Diadematoidea.* In the
others the anus migrates toward the mouth. The *Clypeasteroidea*
and *Spatangoidea* show an elongation of form, with a pronounced
bilateral symmetry. In most of the *Spatangoidea* the mouth passes
forward, so as to lie no longer in the median axis. In the *Holothuroidea* the plates of the integument are not united, the body
thus being soft and changeable in form by inflation. The separate
plates are found fossil as early as the Carbonic.

PHYLUM X—PROTOCHORDA. These are soft-bodied animals,
some of them, as the Tunicates, degenerate, but showing affinities
with the vertebrates, in the possession of a notochord, branchial
slits, and a central nervous system. The *Cephalochorda* (Am-
phioxus) are fish-like and readily mistaken for a vertebrate, while
the *Enteropneusta* (Balanoglossus) are worm-like. While some of
these have been considered ancestral to vertebrates, it is not at all
impossible that the suggestive characters are independently developed. Vertebrates arose in the Palæozoic, and no modern form
is likely to preserve intact all the primitive characters of a class.

PHYLUM XI—VERTEBRATA. This, the most highly specialized
phylum of the animal kingdom, has its most primitive representative in the *Ostracoderma* of the early Palæozoic (Cephalaspis,
Pterichthys, Bothriolepis, etc.). Known definitely from the Devonic and Siluric, there are fragments indicating their existence
in the Upper Ordovicic of America. They retain many characters
of invertebrates and seem to unite the fish with the eurypterids, a
group of Merostomes, which flourished at the same time. (See
Patten–21; 22.) Their most striking characteristic was a well-
developed armor, or exoskeleton of bony plates, which covered the
head and anterior portion of the body. The endoskeleton was not
calcified and the mouth without hard parts. Hence all we know
of them is from the external plates and scales. The Devonic
Arthrodira have also been regarded as an independent class, differing from fishes in that their jaw elements are merely dermal ossifications and are not articulated with the skull (Dean). The head
and trunk are covered by symmetric bony plates, the head-shield
is movably articulated with the body-shield. The endoskeleton is
superficially calcified, and paired fins are rudimentary or absent.
The Devonic Coccosteus, Dinichthys and Titanichthys are examples.

Pisces.

The *Cyclostomata* (Agnatha) represented to-day by the lampreys, appear to have had some representatives in the remarkable Palæospondylus of the Old Red Sandstone. The Conodonts have been regarded as teeth of myxinoids. The elasmobranchs, or sharks, were well represented in the Devonic and later beds, the first three orders being wholly confined to the Palæozoic. The endoskeleton is more or less cartilaginous, the exoskeleton and teeth structurally identical (placoid scales). Generally only teeth, calcified vertebræ and dermal spines are preserved. The true sharks and rays (*Plagiostomi*) are mostly Mesozoic and later, but examples from the Carbonic and even the Mississipic are known. The chimæras, however (*Holocephali*), had representatives from the Devonic on.

The ganoids are remarkable in that their trunk and tail are usually covered with scales, consisting of a thick bony inner layer, and an outer layer of enamel, the scales being in some groups articulated by a peg-and-socket arrangement, and in others overlapping. The skull is covered with dermal bones, or completely ossified. The vertebral column is cartilaginous or shows various degrees of ossification. Most of the Palæozoic ganoids belong to the order *Crossopterygii* or fringe-finned ganoids. Such are the Devonic genera Holoptychius and Osteolepis—and numerous Mississippic to Permic genera. Other crossopterygians occur in the Mesozoic, and two genera (Polypterus and Calamoichthys) are still living in the rivers of tropical Africa. The cartilaginous ganoids (*Chondrostei*) range from the Mesozoic to the present time, a number of genera being still extant, such as the sturgeons and paddle-fish.

A considerable number of Palæozoic forms also belong to the *Heterocerci,* an order ranging from the Devonic (Cheirolepis) to the Upper Jurassic (Coccolepis of the Lithographic beds). Many Carbonic and Permic species (including Palæoniscus, Platysomus, etc., the common forms of the Kupferschiefer of Thuringia, etc.), belong to this order, as well as the Triassic Catopterus of North America. The *Lepidostei* include the "bony pikes" (Lepidosteus) of the North American rivers, and many Cenozoic and Mesozoic genera, but only one genus (Acentrophorus) has Permic representatives. Here belong the widely distributed Triassic Semionotus and the many common Jurassic genera (Dapedius, Lepidotus, Eugnathus, Caturus, etc.), the order being at its height at that time. The *Amioidei* also have a surviving genus (Amia) in the rivers of the southern United States and Central America, while other members extend as far back as the Lias.

The *Dipnoi,* or Lung-Fishes, range from the Devonic to the present time. Their skeleton is chiefly cartilaginous, but the upper and lower vertebral arches, the ribs and fin-supports exhibit a tendency toward ossification. They have paddle-shaped, paired fins and a highly specialized air-bladder which serves as a lung. Dental plates are common in the Devonic (Dipterus) and Carbonic (Ctenodus), while many perfect specimens also occur in these deposits.

These fish may be considered as approaching Amphibians in many respects. The Teleosts, or bony fishes, appear first in the Triassic deposits, and increase in prominence until they are the leading type to-day.

Amphibia.

The *Amphibia* are cold-blooded terrestrial vertebrates, with partly branchial respiration, in early stages, while in some forms gills remain functional throughout life. The limbs are never fins and are rarely absent. The *Stegocephalia* (Carbonic to Upper Trias) comprise the largest known Amphibians, and were protected by a dermal armor of bony scales or scutes. The teeth were sharply conical, with a large pulp-cavity, and the walls were sometimes highly complicated by infolding of the dentine (Labyrinthodonts). The *Gymnophiona* or cœcilians are vermiform amphibia, covered with scales and without limbs. They are restricted to the South American and Indo-African tropics. The *Urodeles* are naked bodied, usually with two pairs of short limbs and persistent tail. Gills often remain throughout life. The vertebræ are usually completely ossified. This group appears first in the Upper Jurassic (Wealden), and has living representatives in the newts and salamanders. The Anura (frogs, toads) are tailless and develop by metamorphosis. The oldest fossil forms are from the Eocenic.

Reptilia.

Reptilia are cold-blooded, naked, scaly or armored vertebrates of terrestrial or aquatic habit, and breathing exclusively by lungs. There is no metamorphosis during development. The *Rhynchocephalia* date from the Permic, but were most extensively represented in the Trias. A single living genus (Hatteria or Sphenodon) occurs in New Zealand. The body was lizard-like, long-tailed and sometimes scaly. The *Squamata* comprise the lizards and snakes and two extinct groups of aquatic reptiles from the Cretacic (Mosasaurus, etc.). The lizards (*Lacertilia*) have 1,925 living species but few fossil ones are known, the oldest being from the late Jurassic. Of the snakes (*Ophidia*) nearly 1,800 recent species but only about 35 fossil ones are known, chiefly from the Tertiary, though some Cretacic forms are probably referable to snakes. The *Ichthyosauria* are entirely extinct reptiles which inhabited the Triassic, Jurassic, and Cretacic seas. Their body was in general whale- or fish-like and the jaws were furnished with numerous conical teeth.

The *Sauropterygia,* also restricted to the Mesozoic, were mostly marine, lizard-like reptiles, with long necks and well-developed limbs, with five normal digits (*Nothosauridæ* Triassic) or paddle-shaped, the digits elongated by supernumerary phalanges (*Plesiosauridæ,* Trias to Cretacic). The *Theromorpha* were primitive land reptiles with many mammalian characters and often of grotesque forms and proportions (Pareiasaurus, Dicynodon, etc.). They lived in the Permic and the Triassic of North America, Europe, and South Africa.

The *Chelonians* or turtles are characterized by the possession of a more or less complete bony shell, partly composed of modified neural spines of the dorsal vertebræ and partly of dermal ossifications more or less intimately united with the former. The limbs, tail, and generally the neck and head can be withdrawn into this shell. In general a dorsal shield, or carapace, and a ventral one, or plastron, composes this shell and both are, as a rule, superficially covered by a horny or leathery epidermal layer divided by grooves or sutures into a few large scutes or shields. Their arrangement is independent of the underlying osseous plates. Turtles first appeared in the Upper Triassic (Keuper) of Europe.

The *Crocodilia* are lizard-like reptiles with the highest internal organization of the class. Their skeletal structure differs widely from that of lizards, and their respiratory organs resemble those of birds. The entire body is covered with horny scales. The most primitive groups (*Parasuchia*), resembling the Rhynchocephalia, occur in the Trias of America (Belodon or Phytosaurus, and Episcoposaurus); of Scotland (Stagonolepis); and the Gondwana formation of India (Parasuchus). There are also more specialized Triassic forms, such as the little Aëtosaurus (of which 24 complete individuals occur on a single block of Stuben-sandstone [Upper Keuper] in the Stuttgart Museum), and others from the Trias of Elgin, Scotland.

Typical marine Crocodiles occur in the Jurassic and Comanchic (*Mesosuchia*), while in the Cretacic-Tertiary and modern times these crocodiles (*Eusuchia*) again lived chiefly in fresh water and on the land. They include both long-snouted (longirostral) and broad-snouted (brevirostral) forms, the latter comprising the alligators.

The *Dinosauria* were long-necked and long-tailed reptiles with limbs adapted for support of the body. The earliest species were Triassic, the latest Cretacic. A bony exoskeleton was developed in some forms, consisting of isolated bony plates or spines, or of interlocking scutes forming a continuous shield. Most dinosaurs, however, were naked or covered by scales. The skull of most forms was extremely small in proportion to the body, while the legs in many cases were exceedingly massive.

The *Pterosauria,* or winged lizards, ranged from the Trias to the Cretacic, and their whole organization was adapted to an aërial existence. They ranged from the size of a sparrow to forms which had a spread of wing of nearly six meters. The skull was bird-like and generally fitted with sharp, conical teeth, mostly long and sharply pointed in front (Pteranodon, Nyctodactylus, Ramphorhynchus), but sometimes blunt (Dimorphoden). The neck and tail were generally long. The fifth digit of the hand consisted of four enormously elongated phalanges, which were turned backward to support the wing membrane. Three families are known: *Rhamphorhynchidæ* (Jurassic), *Pterodactylidæ* (Upper Jurassic and Cretacic), and *Ornithocheiridæ* (Pteranodon, etc.) Cretacic.

Aves.

The birds form a homogeneous and circumscribed class derived from the reptiles and partaking of their character in the Jurassic and Cretacic, where teeth and a vertebrated tail still existed. The exoskeleton consists of feathers, horny coverings for the beak, claws, etc. The endoskeleton is compact but light, the bones being permeated by air-cavities with thin but dense-textured walls, rich in calcium phosphate. The vertebræ have peculiar saddle-shaped articulations which allow great freedom of movement. The bones of the forearm are modified into wings. The oldest bird, Archæopteryx of the Jurassic, had its jaws provided with conical teeth like those of reptiles, and its vertebral column had about 20 caudal vertebræ. The Odontolcæ (with Hesperornis) and *Odontormæ* (with Ichthyornis) also had toothed jaws, but other birds were free from them. The *Struthiones,* or ostriches, rheas, cassowaries and emus are all large, flightless birds with small wings, a keelless sternum, and well-developed walking legs. They also include the extinct Æpyornis and the equally extinct moas (*Dinornithidæ*), without or with extremely rudimentary wings and pectoral arch and with massive legs. The *Struthiones* appear first in the Tertiary. The New Zealand Apteryx, a small flightless bird, represents the order *Apteryges* and the living tinamous the order *Crypturi.* Both have only fragmentary fossil representatives. The super-order *Euornithes,* with 13 orders, includes most of the existing birds. A few representatives (cormorants, etc.) occur in the Cretacic, but the great majority of types are not known before the Eocenic and many not until later.

Mammalia.

The mammals are warm-blooded animals with the body typically covered by hair, and in nearly all cases they bring forth their young alive, the monotremes alone laying eggs. All, however, suckle their young. The marsupials (opossum, kangaroo, etc.) bear their young in an immature state, and these are then placed in a pouch or marsupium. The placental mammals bear perfect young. The *Insectivora* go back to the Eocenic; they comprise the moles, shrews, hedgehogs, etc. The *Chiroptera,* or bats, also go back to the Eocenic. The *Dermoptera* are characterized by a cutaneous expansion, extending from the wrists to the ankles and forming a parachute. They are generally called flying lemurs and are unknown in a fossil form. The *Edentata,* chiefly restricted to South America, are nearly or quite toothless and include the living anteaters and sloths, the armadillos, with jointed armor, and the extinct Glyptodon with solid armor. Here also belong the giant sloths, the Megatherium, the Mylodon, and Grypotherium—all of them but recently extinct.

The *Rodentia* comprise the gnawing types with long, sharp curved incisors. They go back to the Eocenic. The *Tillodontia* are extinct forms from the North American Eocenic. They are related to the rodents. The *Carnivora,* or flesh-eaters, comprise a large number of living and extinct types, such as the *Creodontia,* of the Tertiary; the *Fissipedia,* including *Canidæ* (dogs), *Ursidæ* (bears), *Viverridæ, Mustelidæ* (otters, etc.), *Hyænidæ* (Hyænas) and *Felidæ* (cats, tigers, lions, panthers, etc.); and the *Pinnipedia,* or marine carnivores, such as seals, sealions, etc. Many of these have representatives in the Tertiary. The *Cetacea,* or whales, dolphins, etc., are aquatic (mostly marine) mammals, and occur as far back as the Miocenic. Squalodon and Zeuglodon are fossil representatives. The *Sirenia* are herbivorous aquatic mammals represented by the living manatee and dugongs, and the recently extinct sea-cow (Rhytina), etc. The Ungulates, or hoofed mammals, comprise: (1) the Eocenic *Amblypoda* (Coryphodon, Tinoceras, etc.), large, heavy creatures; (2) the *Proboscidea,* or elephants (Dinotherium, Mastodon, Stegodon, Elephas, etc.); (3) the *Condilarthra* (Phenacodus); (4) the *Perissodactyla,* or unevenly-toed ungulates (Tapir, Rhinoceros, Titanothere, and the horse family); (5) the *Artiodactyla,* or even-toed ungulates, divided into the *Bunodontia* (pigs, hippopotamus, Anthracotherium, etc.); and *Selenodontia,* (Oreodon [Tertiary], camels, deer, etc.; giraffes, antelopes, goats, sheep, cattle, etc.); (6) *Toxodontia*—Tertiary forms, including Toxodon, Typotherium, etc.

The final order of the mammals is that of the *primates,* which includes *Quadrumana* (apes, monkeys, etc.), and the *Bimana,* or man.

BIBLIOGRAPHY XXIV.

(Text-books of Palæontology, etc.)

1. BERNARD, FÉLIX. 1895. Eléments de Paléontologie. Baillière et Fils, Paris.
2. GRABAU, A. W., and SHIMER, H. W. 1909–1910. North American Index Fossils. 2 vols. A. G. Seiler and Company, New York.
3. GÜRICH, GEORG. 1908–09. Leitfossilien. 2 parts. Gebrüder Borntraeger, Berlin.
4. KOKEN, ERNEST. 1896. Die Leitfossilien. Hermann Tauchnitz, Leipzig.
5. NICHOLSON, ALLEYNE, and LYDEKKER, RICHARD. 1889. A Manual of Palæontology. 2 vols. W. Blackwood and Sons, Edinburgh and London.
6. OSBORN, HENRY F. 1910. The Age of Mammals. Macmillan Company, New York.
7. STEINMANN, GUSTAV. 1903. Einführung in die Palæontologie. Wilhelm Engelmann, Leipzig. 2nd edition, 1907.
8. STROMER, ERNST. 1909, 1912. Lehrbuch der Palæozoologie. 2 parts.
9. ZITTEL, KARL A. VON. 1881–85. Handbuch der Palæontologie. French translation, Traité de Paléontologie, by Charles Barrois, Paris.
10. ZITTEL, K. A. VON. 1895. Grundzüge der Palæontologie. 2nd Edition, 1910–11. 2 vols. Munich.
11. ZITTEL, K. A., VON. 1900. Text-book of Palæontology. Translated by Charles R. Eastman with collaboration by many specialists. 2 vols. Macmillan Company, New York.

(Classification, etc.)

12. ALLEN, J. A. 1906. The "Elimination" and "First Species" Methods of Fixing the Types of Genera. Science, N. S., Vol. XXIV, pp. 773–779.

13. AMERICAN ASSOCIATION FOR THE ADVANCEMENT OF SCIENCE. 1877. Report of the Committee on Zoölogical Nomenclature. Nashville Meeting.

14. BRITISH ASSOCIATION FOR THE ADVANCEMENT OF SCIENCE. 1842. Report of the Manchester Meeting.

15. BRITISH ASSOCIATION FOR THE ADVANCEMENT OF SCIENCE. 1865. Report of the Birmingham Meeting.

16. BUCKMAN, S. S. 1909. Yorkshire Type Ammonites, Part I.

17. ENCYCLOPÆDIA BRITANNICA. Eleventh edition. Articles on Zoöl ogy and various Phyla, Classes and Orders. Also Palæontology and Palæobotany.

18. MILLER, S. A. 1889. North American Geology and Palæontology.

19. OSBORN, HENRY F. 1912. First Use of the Word "Genotype." Science, N. S., Vol. XXXV, No. 896, pp. 340–341.

20. PALÆONTOLOGIA UNIVERSALIS. 1904. Edited by D. P. Oehlers.

21. PATTEN, W. 1912. The Evolution of the Vertebrates and Their Kin. P. Blakiston & Co., Philadelphia.

22. PATTEN, W. 1913. A Problem in Evolution. Popular Science Monthly, Vol. LXXXII, pp. 417–435.

23. SCHUCHERT, CHARLES. On Type Specimens in Natural History. Catalogue, etc., of Fossils, Minerals, etc., in U. S. National Museum, Pt. I, pp. 7–18, with bibliography of literature on type terms.

24. SCHUCHERT, CHARLES, and BUCKMANN, S. S. 1905. The Nomenclature of Types in Natural History. Science, N. S., Vol. XXI, pp. 899–901.

25. SCUDDER, SAMUEL. 1882. Nomenclator Zoologicus. Bulletin of the United States National Museum, No. 19.

26. STONE, WITMER. 1906. The Relative Merits of the "Elimination" and "First Species" Method in Fixing the Types of Genera, with special reference to Ornithology. Science, N. S., Vol. XXIV, pp. 560–565.

CHAPTER XXV.

BIOGENETIC RELATIONS OF PLANTS AND ANIMALS.*

THE CONCEPTION OF SPECIES.

A species is commonly held to comprise a group of individuals which differ from one another only in a minor degree. The degree of individual difference admissible within the species is commonly a matter of personal opinion and probably no two systematists always agree as to the precise taxonomic value of a character in different cases. In pre-modern days the idea of permanence and immutability of the species, or, in pre-Linnæan days, of the genus, dominated the minds of naturalists generally, though there were not wanting, at nearly all times, observers to whom the fixity of specific characters appeared as a dogma unsupported by facts. That variation existed within the specific limits was admitted, but the believers in the special creation and immutability of species would not admit that this variation could exceed certain limits, though what these limits were was a matter of diverse and, moreover, of constantly changing opinion. No matter how different the end members of a perfectly graded series of individuals were, if that gradation was established all those members were placed within the limits of the species. Even if some of the members of the series were originally described as distinct species or placed in distinct genera the discovery of intermediate forms, or "connecting links," caused them all to be referred to one species. The differences originally deemed amply sufficient for specific or even generic distinction at once dwindled in taxonomic value to the rank of varietal characters of a very variable species. A classic case in point is that of the Tertiary species of Paludina (Vivipara) from Slavonia. (Neumayr and Paul–29). (Fig. 252.) In the lowest members of the Paludina beds *P. neumayri* (Fig. *a*), a smooth,

* The principles here outlined will be more fully discussed in "The Principles of Palæontology" by Henry F. Osborn and Amadeus W. Grabau, to be published shortly.

round-whorled species, is the characteristic form, while the highest
beds are characterized by *P. hoernesi* (Fig. *k*), an angular-whorled,
strongly bicarinate type, which had been separated under the distinct generic name of Tulotoma. Certainly these end-forms are
widely separated, yet from the intermediate beds individuals constituting a complete gradational series from one to the other have
been obtained. This discovery led many to reconsider the classification of these forms and to group them all as varieties under one
species.

The belief in the mutability of species was gradually accepted

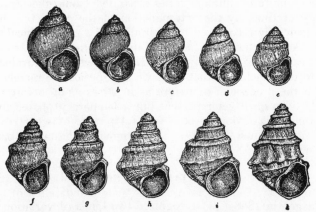

FIG. 252.   Series of Paludinas (Vivipara) from the Lower Pliocenic deposits
of Slavonia.   (After Neumayr.)   *a. Paludina neumayri, k. P.
(Tulotoma) hoernesi* from the highest beds. *b-i*, intermediate
forms, showing gradation, from the intermediate beds.

by naturalists after the publication of "The Origin of Species" in
1859. To-day there is scarcely a naturalist of prominence who does
not unhesitatingly affirm his belief in the mutability of species.
Nevertheless, we may ask, with Farlow: " . . . is our belief
in evolution merely dogmatic, like some of the theological doctrines
which we believe thoroughly but which we do not allow to inter-
fere with our daily life, or, . . . has our belief modified the
manner in which we treat what we call species?" (10)   When we
note how unwilling systematists are to-day to recognize more than
one species in a series whose end forms differ widely, when a sufficient number of members are known to bridge over all the more
striking gaps, we are forcibly impressed with the fact that, uncon-
sciously though it may be, the majority of systematists are still

influenced by the old inherited ideas of the fixity of specific limits. Palæontologists are, as a rule, no freer from the shackles of inherited ideas than are the workers in the morphology and taxonomy of living plants and animals. This may in large measure be accounted for by the fact that the very recognition of such a thing as a species carries with it the impression of an entity, and the recognition of certain characters as belonging to a species, in a measure carries with it the conception that, if those characters are modified or supplanted by others, the organism in question no longer belongs to that species.

That the Linnæan species is a fragment or group of fragments of one or more evolutional series separated from other fragments, in space or time, by the extermination of the connecting links, is pretty generally recognized by naturalists of a philosophical turn of mind. Among such the belief in the nonexistence of species is, theoretically at least, widely held. In other words, naturalists have come to the conclusion that what we call species are merely "snapshots at the procession of nature as it passes along before us, and that the views we get represent but a temporary phase, and in a short time will no longer be a faithful picture of what really lies before us." "For the procession is moving constantly onward." (Farlow–10.)

The Mutation of Waagen.

Waagen in 1868 (44) recognized two kinds of variation within the species—geographic and chronologic. To the former, which comprises the variable members appearing together in the same time period, though they may be geographically separated, he restricted the term *variation* or *variety,* while for those occurring in chronological succession he proposed the term *"mutation."* A mutation may then be defined as a slightly modified form of the species appearing in a later time-period, and in this sense it has been commonly used by palæontologists. As an example of a number of mutations appearing in successively higher horizons, the Tertiary series of Paludinas (Vivipara), already referred to, may be cited.

Palæontologists, whose business it is to study large series of forms from each successive horizon, have since recognized that what Waagen called varieties, in the belief that they had no very definite relationship to each other, are really secondary mutations or sub-mutations (Grabau–17). Thus each developing series has, on reaching a higher horizon, become modified in a certain definite way and within this horizon the derivatives of this species will become modified in certain definite directions.

As an illustration may be chosen the Linnæan species of brachiopod *Spirifer mucronatus* of the Middle Devonic of eastern North America (Fig. 253). This is represented by at least five distinct mutations in successive horizons, or in distinct basins. Each of these five mutations differs from the others in certain more or less constant characters, which, however, are the result of definite modifications of the preceding more primitive types, chiefly by the appearance of new characters.* Thus these mutations are readily

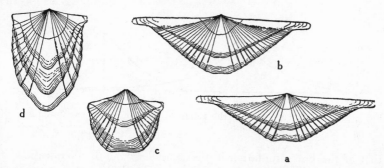

FIG. 253. *Spirifer mucronatus, a.* primitive mutation—*b.-d.* mutation *thed-fordense. b.* Long-winged retarded submutation, shell index 1.7. *c.* The most accelerated submutation (shell index 0.73). *d.* The same drawn with curvature eliminated so as to show full length. The more transverse character (higher shell index) of the younger stages is shown in each.

recognizable and separable from one another with comparative ease. Within each mutation, however, there is a long series of variants, which are modified by a progressive change in the relative proportion of width and height—a modification or change of quantitative rather than qualitative character—a type of change to which Osborn has applied the term *allometric,* while the resulting characters are *allometrons.* The change in proportion in each of these successive mutations is from broad-winged to short-winged types, or allometrons. Expressed in shell indices, derived by dividing the entire width along the hinge-line by the height measured on the curvature, the change is from a high shell index to a lower one. In each mutation the change is in the same direction, and in each a dominant type can be designated which, as a sub-mutation, represents, for the mutation to which it belongs, that index to which the

* Termed, by Osborn, Rectigradations. (See beyond.)

majority of individuals of that fauna approximate. The dominant sub-mutation of a higher mutation will be found to have a smaller index than the dominant sub-mutation of a lower mutation. In the same way, the most primitive sub-mutation of the higher mutation, *i. e.,* the one with the largest shell index, has a smaller index than the most primitive sub-mutation of the lower mutation. In like manner the most specialized sub-mutation of the higher (geologic) mutation will have a smaller index than the most specialized sub-mutation of the lower mutation. In other words, not only has the dominant sub-mutation of the higher mutation advanced beyond

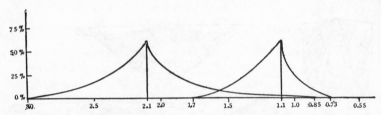

Fig. 254. Curves representing the range in shell index of two mutations of *Spirifer mucronatus.*

that of the lower mutation in the *same direction* of modification of proportions, but also the most primitive and the most specialized sub-mutation and all the intermediate sub-mutations of the later mutations are ahead of the earlier one. This may be expressed in the accompanying diagram (Fig. 254), where the height of the curve represents the percentage of individuals and the base the decline in shell index from 3.0 to 0.5.

Mutation Theory of De Vries.

In 1901 Professor Hugo De Vries published his epoch-making book "Die Mutations-theorie" (6) in which he recognized that the Linnæan "species" was in reality a compound of innumerable groups of more restricted relationship. These minor groups, which have generally been classed together as a "species," are really entities composed of very definite associations of minute characters, and to them the name *elementary species* applies. Of these elementary species there may be very many in a Linnæan species. These elementary species De Vries thinks arose suddenly by a new combination of the elements of which the characters of organisms are made up. These elements (*Einheiten*) are sharply separated from one another and the resulting combinations or elementary species are likewise distinct and definite and without transitional connecting forms. They are constant and transmit their characters truly. The sudden appearance of these new forms is a process which De Vries calls "mutation," thus using Waagen's term for a process instead of a result, as originally proposed. The "elementary species" as defined by De Vries is, in a measure, identical with the mutation of Waagen, in that the variation is a slight and definite one; but in so far as De Vries believes in the stability and immutability of the elementary species, they do not correspond to the mutation and sub-mutation (allometrons) as used by most palæontologists to-day.

ORTHOGENESIS AND THE CONCEPT OF SPECIES.

The doctrine of definite directed variation, or *Orthogenesis,* which finds many adherents, especially among palæontologists, has led to a very logical conception of the method by which species become differentiated. Though independently formulated with more or less precision by many naturalists this doctrine was most consistently and vigorously championed by the late Professor Theodor Eimer of Tübingen. Eimer's illustrations were chiefly drawn from the color patterns of recent animals, especially lizards and butterflies (9). He found that the color patterns of organisms may be reduced to four types, which always appear in the individual development in a definite succession, viz.: (1) Longitudinal stages, (2) spots, (3) cross stripes, and (4) uniform coloration. Each succeeding type is developed out of the preceding one and replaces it to a greater or less extent. When in a large number of individuals all developing in the same direction (orthogenetically) a complete cessation of development occurs in different groups at individual stages, the individuals thereafter only increasing in size, but not changing, a large number of distinct species will originate which differ from one another to the extent by which one group continued to develop beyond the other. If a number of characters develop, each in a given direction, and at a given rate in a large group of individuals, all starting from the same point, cessation of development of different characters at different times will soon result in the formation of a great number of species varying in one or more characters.

We may assume, by way of illustration, a case in which there are three structural characters, which we may designate characters (a), (b), and (c), in a given group of individuals, each changing in a definite order and at a uniform rate. A certain percentage of these individuals may, after a while, cease to develop character (a) while characters (b) and (c) continue to develop. Later in some of these, character (b) may cease to develop further and (c) continue alone, while in others (c) ceases to develop and (b) continues. In another portion of the original group character (b) may cease to develop first and (a) and (c) continue, after which character (a) may stop in some and (c) in others—the other character continuing. The combinations possible by this method will be readily recognized and the number of different types—mutations, varieties, or species, according to the rank to which they are admitted—will be readily seen. The possibilities of differentiation will be further recognized when it is considered that the length of time during which each character develops may also vary greatly. Complete cessation of development of characters has been termed *genepistasis* by Eimer, and the differential cessation *heterepistasis*.

ACCELERATION AND RETARDATION IN DEVELOPMENT (TACHYGENESIS AND BRADYGENESIS).

Another principle which is of great importance in this connection, and which was first clearly recognized by Hyatt and by Cope, is acceleration or tachygenesis.* Instead of a uniform rate of development some organisms may develop more rapidly and so are able to reach a higher stage in development. Differential acceleration may obtain between the different characters. Again, retardation (bradygenesis *), first recognized by Cope, may progressively diminish the rate of development, so that certain individuals in some or all of their characters may fall more and more behind the normal rate of progress.

Illustrations of Orthogenetic Development. Some of the most satisfactory series, showing development in definite directions, have been brought to light by the labors of palæontologists. Such series are especially well known among the ammonoids, a class of cephalopodous Mollusca which began its existence in the Devonic, culminated in the Jura, and had its last representatives in late Cretacic time.

Some of the earliest studies of the developmental changes of this group were carried on by Alcide d'Orbigny (8), who recognized a distinct succession in the form and ornamentation of the shell

* From ταχύς = fast and βραδύς = slow, γένεσις = birth. The term bradygenesis was used by Grabau in 1910 (16) as a complement of the term tachygenesis.

from rounded and smooth in youth; through ribbed, and tubercled, with angular and, later, keeled whorls; to old age, which was marked by a complete loss of all ornamentation. The late Professor Alpheus Hyatt was, however, the first to recognize the significance of these changes and to point out that they recapitulated the adult characteristics of successive ancestors. The number of recognizable characters of which the development may be studied is exceptionally large in the Ammonite shell. Thus there is the degree of coiling or involution, which varies from the condition in which the whorls do not even touch each other through whorls in contact and whorls impressed on each other to complete involution, in which the last whorl covers all the preceding ones. Then there is the form of the cross-section of the shell and the character of the outer or ventral surface of the shell, which varies from rounded through angulated to various degrees of channeled and keeled. Again the surface ornamentation varies from smooth to ribbed, noded, or even spinous, and, finally, and in many respects most significantly, there is the progressive change in the complexity of the septal sutures, from simple in the young to often highly complex in the adult. In addition to these, the form and position of the siphuncle often show a definite variation, which may be of considerable importance. To give a concrete example of the changes in the individual development of the shell and the correlation of the various stages with the adult stages of ancestral forms, we may select a closely related series of ammonites of the family *Placenticeratidæ,* all of which are characteristic of the Cretacic formations of North America. The changes here are chiefly in the form of the cross-sections and the characters of the surface ornamentations. The most advanced form of the series is *Stantonoceras pseudocostatum* Johnson, a large, robust ammonite with a broad, rounded venter and rather ill-defined, coarse, rib-like elevations on the lateral surfaces of the whorls. When this form is broken down it is found that the next inner whorl has a flattened ventral band bordered by a row of faint elongated nodes on either side and a large row of tubercles on the ventro-lateral angles. At this stage the species has the characters of the adult *Stantonoceras guadalupæ* (Roemer), which may be regarded as an immediate ancestor. A still earlier whorl shows a very narrow flattened venter, with a strong row of elongated nodes on either side of the flattening, the surface being otherwise smooth. This corresponds to more primitive species, *Placenticeras intermedium* Johnson, and *P. planum* Hyatt, one or the other of which was probably in the direct line of ancestry. At a still earlier stage in these shells the venter is hollowed and bordered by smooth ridges, while the surface is smooth—features characteristic of the adults of certain species of the genus Protengonoceras of the Lower Cretacic. In all these types the sutures show close relationship and increasing complexity with the progressive changes of the form of the shell. At a still earlier stage the venter is flattened without channel, the section of the whorl being helmet-shaped, while the earliest marked stage shows a rounded venter. The sutures of this early stage are very simple, corresponding in general to the adult suture of Devonic or Carbonic Goniatites, which the form of the shell also recalls. As

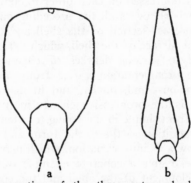

FIG. 255.   *a.* Cross-section of the three outer whorls of *Stantonoceras pseudocostatum* reduced. (After Johnson.) *b.* Cross-section of the inner whorls of *Stantonoceras guadalupæ,* enlarged. (After Hyatt.)

the form changes the complexity of the sutures increases until the complex adult suture is developed. The cross-sections of the various stages are shown in Fig. 255. The early "Goniatite" stages of *Schloenbachia aff. chicoensis* Trask, a highly developed ammonite of the Lower Cretacic of Oregon, are, according to J. P. Smith, as follows (43:*521*): The first suture (immediately succeeding the protoconch) has narrow lateral lobes and saddles * and a broad ventral saddle. The second suture has a small lobe in the center of the broad ventral saddle, which is thus divided. This corresponds to the adult suture of the Devonic genus *Anacestes,* a simple form of "goniatite" which Hyatt considers the immediate radicle of the ammonoid stock. The third and fourth sutures show

* Lobes are the backward loops of the suture and saddles the forward loops, *i. e.,* those convex toward the mouth of the shell. The ventral border is the outer border of the shell; the space between the inner margins of the whorl is the umbilicus, in which can be seen the earlier coils.

accentuation of the lobes and saddles, and recapitulate the adult sutures of such later Devonic types as Tornoceras and Prionoceras. The fifth suture is transitional to the sixth, which is characterized by a divided ventral lobe, one lateral lobe on each side, and another on each side of the umbilical border. Here, then, the lobe which complicated the original ventral saddle is itself divided by a second low ventral saddle. The shell at this stage has a low, broad, involute whorl, and in this and the character of the suture recalls the adult of the older species of *Glyphioceras*. The typical Glyphioceras condition is represented by a somewhat later suture, and still later, with the appearance of a second lateral lobe next to the umbilicus, the shell begins to resemble the late Carbonic goniatite Gastrioceras, and at a still later stage, when the diameter of the shell is 2.25 mm., a third lateral lobe appears next to the umbilicus which subsequently widens, while the whorls become higher and narrower. In this stage it recalls the genus Paralegoceras. The next stage ushers in true ammonitic ornamentation in the form of a ventral keel (2.7 mm. diam.), while the suture still remains goniatite-like. But when the shell has reached a diameter of 3.2 mm. the first lateral saddle becomes indented, a true ammonoid suture thus coming into existence. The future development is along the line of increasing complexity of suture.

A consideration of the possible mutations which may come into existence by the operation of the law of heterepistasis, or differential arrestation in development, and by the operation of the laws of differential acceleration and retardation of characteristics, will convince one that all the known types of ammonites, as well as many yet unknown types, may be accounted for in this manner. Not only all so-called species, but every individual variation will fall into its proper determinate place in the series when the method of analysis of individual characters has become sufficiently detailed.

Another example, taken from the gastropods, may serve to further illustrate the principles here discussed (Fig. 256). The modern *Fulgur caricum,* a large gastropod occurring on the Atlantic coast between Cape Cod and the Gulf of Mexico, begins its embryonic existence with a smooth shell drawn out anteriorly into a canal and not unlike in form to some smooth Fasciolarian shells (Fig. 256, *b, c*). At a very early age the shell is furnished with ribs and then an angulation appears in the outer whorl. On this angulation the ribs are soon reduced to rounded tubercles. This condition recalls the adult characters of Lower Miocenic species of this genus, which never pass beyond the tubercled stage. This stage in the modern species is succeeded by one in which strong spines occur, caused by periodic notchings or emarginations of the shell margin along the line of the angulation. The tubercles and spines pass the one into the other by what appears to be a process of enlargement of the tubercles.

When we come to consider the series of forms which lead up from the tubercled (Tertiary) species (*F. fusiformis, F. tuberculatum*) to the modern form, we find that certain intermediate characteristics have been omitted. As shown by the specimen of

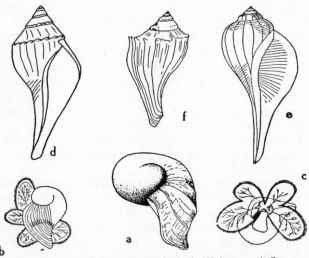

FIG. 256. Development of the gastropod shell (Fulgur and Sycotypus). *a.* Protoconch of *Sycotypus canaliculatus. b, c.* The same before hatching, showing smooth shell; animal with velum. (The early stages of *Fulgur caricum* are identical with these.) *d. Fulgur fusiformis. e. F. rapum* (representing *F. maximum). f. F. tritonis.*

F. fusiformis figured (Fig. 256, *d*), the last part of the last whorl has already lost the tubercles and has become smooth and rounded in outline. This is prophetic of the form next to be noted, *F. maximum* (Fig. 256, *e*). In this shell the tubercled stage is passed through quickly—a case of acceleration in development—and the smooth, rounded whorl stage makes up the greater part of the shell. Thus the normal characters of *F. fusiformis* have become condensed to a few whorls, in this manner making room for the smooth whorl which characterizes the shell. It is in certain advanced accelerated individuals of this type that the emarginate spines so characteristic of the modern *F. caricum* first make their appearance. In a more advanced type, *F. tritonis* (Fig. 256, *f*), the characteristic round "maximum" type of whorl has become restricted to a few earlier whorls, the adult whorl being marked by the spinous "caricum" type of whorl. Different individuals show progressive encroachment of the "caricum" type on the "maximum" type, until the latter has been completely superseded, the spines then following immediately upon the tubercles; and, in still more advanced forms, becoming telescoped with them. This is the character of the modern type, where the tubercles pass imperceptibly into the earliest spines. It is thus only by the consideration of the intermediate Tertiary

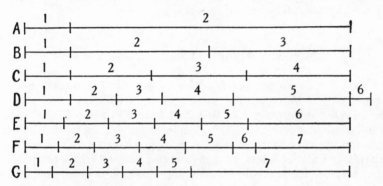

Fig. 257. Diagram illustrating the development of the Fulgur series.

Stage 1 is the protoconch which persists throughout.
Stage 2 is the smooth shell stage which in the primitive species A forms the adult, but in B is shortened.
Stage 3 is the ribbed stage, which is wanting in A, but in a somewhat more advanced species B is well developed in the adult.
Stage 4 is characterized by an angular whorl, the ribs still continuing. It is the adult character of species C, in which stages 2 and 3 are condensed.
Stage 5 is the tubercled stage characteristic of the adult of *F. fusiformis.*
Stage 6 is the smooth round-shelled stage found in the old age of species D and the adult of E.
Stage 7 (*F. maximum*) shows the caricum spines well developed in species F while in species G the modern *F. caricum*, Stage 6, has been eliminated and Stage 7 follows directly upon the tubercles (Stage 5).

types that the true history of the development of the Fulgurs is learned, the individual life history of the modern *F. caricum* being an abbreviated and incomplete recapitulation of the history of its race. Here acceleration has been so pronounced as actually to eliminate certain stages in the sequence of development. The preceding diagram (Fig. 257) will summarize this method and also give a graphic illustration of the law of acceleration.

Origin and Development of Characters the Important Question: Rectigradations and Allometrons. As pointed out by Osborn, the origin and development of individual characters or parts is the important subject for investigation, the species question being of minor significance. It has been shown in the preceding sections that characters develop more or less independently of each other, and also that they develop in recognizable directions, or orthogenetically. Such definitely developing characters when arising as new characters are termed by Osborn *rectigradations;* whereas, if they are due to a change in proportion of such characters, they are termed by him *Allometrons* (30:32).

NOMENCLATURE OF STAGES IN DEVELOPMENT.

Ontogenetic Stages and Morphic Stages. In the preceding examples it will be noted that the stages dealt with are *form stages* or *morphic stages* only, and that they have no constant relation to the actual stages in successive ontogenetic development. Thus, one and the same morphic stage, *i. e.,* stage characterized by certain morphological characters, as, for example, ribs, tubercles, or spines, etc., may be characteristic of the adult of one individual, and, of a more youthful stage, of another. In dealing with changes in form it is desirable to refer each morphic stage to the corresponding adult stage of an ancestor, and to designate it by the name of that ancestor. Thus the tubercled stage of *Fulgur tritonis* (Fig. 256, *f*) is designated the *F. fusiformis* stage, since the feature in question characterizes the adult of that species. In like manner, the smooth morphic stage of *F. tritonis* is designated the *maximum* stage, and the spinose stage the *F. caricum* stage, from the species in which these characters belong to the adult. The development of each individual (ontogeny) comprises a series of stages which develops from birth to old age. These ontogenetic stages, or *onto-stages,* are similar in time-duration for related organisms and are further characterized, in a general way, by a correspondence in the proportional rate of growth in closely related types. They are, however, independent of the morphic characters, for, as already shown, a certain morphic character may appear in one individual in the adult stage and in another more accelerated individual in a more youthful stage. (Grabau–11a.)

Simple Organisms. Hyatt and others have given us a set of

terms which are applicable to the ontogenetic stages of development of all non-colonial organisms, and hence deserve to be widely and generally used. The ontogenetic cycle, or cycle of individual development (Hyatt–20), is divided into the *Embryonic* and the *Ep-embryonic* periods, and each is further subdivided into onto-stages and sub-stages, as follows:

	Onto-stage.	Onto Sub-stage.
		Ana-prot-embryonic
	Prot-embryonic	*Meta-prot-embryonic*
		Para-prot-embryonic
		Ana-mes-embryonic
	Mes-embryonic	*Meta-mes-embryonic*
		Para-mes-embryonic
		Ana-met-embryonic
	Met-embryonic	*Meta-met-embryonic*
EMBRYONIC.		*Para-met-embryonic*
		Ana-neo-embryonic
	Neo-embryonic	*Meta-neo-embryonic*
		Para-neo-embryonic
		Ana-typ-embryonic
	Typ-embryonic	*Meta-typ-embryonic*
		Para-typ-embryonic
		Ana-phyl-embryonic
	Phyl-embryonic	*Meta-phyl-embryonic*
		Para-phyl-embryonic
		Ana-nepionic
	Nepionic	*Meta-nepionic*
		Para-nepionic
		Ana-neanic
	Neanic	*Meta-neanic*
		Para-neanic
EP-EMBRYONIC.		*Ana-ephebic*
	Ephebic	*Meta-ephebic*
		Para-ephebic
		Ana-gerontic
	Gerontic	*Meta-gerontic*
		Para-gerontic

The sub-stages *ana, meta,* and *para,* or the early, intermediate, and later sub-stages, are useful for more detailed subdivision than is possible with the stages alone. The phyl-embryonic is the only embryonic stage with which the palæontologist has to deal. It is the first stage in which hard parts capable of preservation are generally formed. The phyl-embryonic stages of the following classes of invertebrates have been definitely recognized and named:

Simple corals..............	proto-corallum.
Brachiopoda..............	protegulum (Beecher).
Pelecypoda..............	prodissoconch (Jackson).
Gastropoda..............	protoconch (protorteconch) (Hyatt and Grabau).
Scaphopoda..............	periconch (Hyatt).
Cephalopoda..............	protoconch (Owen).
Trilobites..............	protaspis (Beecher).
Echinoidea..............	protechinus (Jackson).

The *Nepionic Stage* is the babyhood stage of ep-embryonic existence. Its exact limitation cannot be defined in general terms, as it is different in different classes of organisms. In general, it may be said that, for ammonites, it covers most, if not all, of the morphic stages in which the suture is of the goniatite type. In the case of Schloenbachia, cited above, the morphic stages, up to the point where the young ammonite resembles in its sutures the genus Paralegoceras, are considered by Smith to belong in the nepionic stage. Here the neanic stage begins shortly before the suture has lost its goniatite character, but an ammonite character has made its appearance in the form of a keel. In *Fulgur caricum* and other advanced species of this group of gastropods the nepionic stage may be regarded as completed with the end of the tubercled condition (*F. fusiformis,* morphic stage).

The *neanic* is the youthful or adolescent stage, which comprises the interval during which the organism acquires all the characteristics of maturity. When this condition is reached the organism enters on the *ephebic,* or adult, stage. Long-lived individuals often show old age or senile characteristics, which consist especially in the loss of ornamentation and a degenerate change in the manner of growth. This is the *gerontic* stage in the ontogenic cycle, and it is followed by death.

Gerontic characteristics may appear early in the life of individuals of a specialized race. Thus the loss of characters and the degenerate change in growth may occur while the individual is still in the adult (ephebic) stage or even earlier. Such races are said to be phylogerontic and are approaching extinction. Thus the late Cretacic cephalopods, which lost the power of coiling either partly (Heteroceras, etc.) or wholly in the adult (Baculites), represent the phylogerontic terminals of the degenerating race of ammonoids.

It must, however, be clearly borne in mind that the existence of phylogerontic lines or races at any time does not indicate that the phylum or class as a whole is gerontic. Even within the same genus there may be found species showing a gerontic tendency. The phylogerontism here applies only to the particular branch in question, while the rest of the evolutional tree of this phylum may be perfectly sound. Many early Ordovicic nautiloids show a loss of the power to coil, and so indicate the existence of degenerating or phylogerontic branches at a time when the class of cephalopods as a whole had not yet permanently acquired the power of coiling. Gastropods with the last whorl not coiled are found throughout the geologic series, even in Lower Cambric time, where coiling had but just begun. Such senile branches are, of course, to be expected in any developing series where wrong or too hasty experiments may be made by individual genetic lines. (See illustrations in North American Index Fossils.)

Colonial Forms. These require a specially modified nomenclature since we deal not with individuals, but with groups of individuals. In these we must keep separate the individual life history or ontogeny and the life history of the colony, *i. e.,* colonial ontogeny (*astogeny or astogenesis*). The first form considered in such cases is nepionic so far as the colony is concerned. To express this fact Cumings (5) has coined the terms *nepiastic, neanastic, ephebastic* and *gerontastic,** which express for the colony what the Hyattian terms express for the individual. The first completed individual of a colony may be dignified by a distinctive term, though it cannot be considered homologous with the phyl-embryonic stage of the individual. In Hydrozoa and in compound corals the first completed individual is the prototheca (the sicula of graptolites, the initial pipe-like corallite of the Favositid corals), and in Bryozoa it is the *protœcium.* (Cumings–5.)

Intracolonial Acceleration and Retardation.

Colonial organisms may suffer differential acceleration or retardation when certain groups of individuals develop either more rapidly or more slowly than others. This leads to the formation, within the same colony, of two or more types of structure, normally characteristic of distinct species. In this manner we can explain such phenomena as the occurrence of different types of leaves upon the same plant, and different groups of individuals in the same colony of animals where some individuals retain ancestral characters, while others develop further. Among plants the tulip tree (*Lyriodendron tulipifera*) may be taken as an illustration. The two and four-lobed types of leaf are characteristic of ancestral Cretacic species. Modern trees, with normally 6-lobed leaves, also

* From ἄστυ (asty), a group of dwellings.

contain adult leaves and sometimes entire branches in which the leaves never pass beyond the four-lobed or even two-lobed type. By retardation the ancestral characters are retained side by side with the normal characters of the modern species. Eight-, 10-, 12-, and sometimes 14-lobed leaves also occur, evidencing local intra-colonial acceleration.

An example among colonial animals will further make this clear. *Favosites canadensis* of the Onondaga limestone is charac-terized by small corallites with polygonal openings, while among these are scattered at regular intervals larger ones with nearly cir-cular openings. *Favosites placenta* of the middle Hamilton of

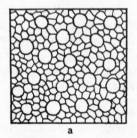 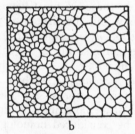

a   b

Fig. 258. Portions of the surfaces of two colonies of Favosites, somewhat enlarged, to show intracolonial acceleration. *a. F. canadensis*, showing the regular distribution of the large cylindrical corallites among the smaller prismatic ones. *b. F. placenta*, showing the *F. canadensis* condition on the left, and the large prismatic corallites on the right.

Canada when young (nepiastic) has the characteristics of adult *F. canadensis*, but when colonially adult it has retained the *F. cana-densis* type in certain portions of the colony only, other portions having developed a uniform series of large corallites with polygonal apertures. Here, then, certain portions of the colony have been retarded in their development, retaining ancestral characters, while others have continued to develop. In the upper Hamilton a species of the *F. placenta* type (*F. placentoides*) occurs with all the coral-lites uniform, large and angular in aperture (Fig. 258).

Acceleration in certain portions and retardation in others when occurring in more or less regular manner result in the formation of colonial ornamentation, such as is so characteristic of Bryozoa.

Atavism or Reversion. Not infrequently among a large number of individuals of a species characterizing a certain horizon a few will be found in which ancestral characters occur in the adult, thus recalling species of a lower geologic horizon. This atavism or reversion of the species to ancestral characters may often be seen to be nothing more than an arrestation of development at an immature morphic stage, when the characters of the young are like those of the adult ancestor of earlier geologic horizons. This arrestation of development or genepistasis is only a step removed from progressive retardation in development of which it forms the distal limit. In either case, whether complete or partial arrestation (heterepistasis) occurs, or whether development is retarded altogether or along certain lines, the resultant form will seem out of place in the horizon characterized by the more advanced species, and may sometimes lead to mistaken classification of the strata containing them.

As an example of atavistic individuals occurring in a horizon above their normal may be cited the case of the Devonic brachiopod *Spirifer mucronatus* and its derivatives already mentioned. This species, so far as known, is represented by the elongated, strongly mucronate type in the lower Hamilton beds of eastern North America. In the Upper Hamilton of Ontario occurs the mutation *S. thedfordense,* which in its younger stages has all the features of the typical lower Hamilton form, but in the adult it is proportionally much less extended, without mucronate points, without the characteristic plication in the median sinus of the pedicle and groove in the median fold of the brachial valve, and with strongly marked, regular lines of growth. With this species occur a number of individuals which have been retarded in their development and which, hence, recall the ancestral type in some of their characters— notably the strong mucronate lateral extensions. In the New York province of the Middle Devonic the chief developmental changes acquired by *S. mucronatus* consist in the relative shortening of the mucronate angles as the shell approaches the adult stage, until from a width several times its height it had changed to a form in which the width was more nearly equal to the height, and in which the mucronations were wholly obliterated. In other respects the changes were very slight. With this mutation occurs not infrequently a form showing arrestation of development (genepistasis) at an early stage, and hence it retains into the adult its youthful mucronate character, which recapitulates the ancestral condition. These arrested individuals thus recall in practically all respects the primitive mucronate type from which they are derived.

An example of a retarded individual from the Karnic limestone of the California Trias is cited by J. P. Smith. This was an immature specimen of the ammonoid genus Trachyceras which had persisted unusually long in the ancestral Tirolites stage, thus resembling the adult of that genus which belonged in a lower horizon. This occurrence threatened to cause difficulty in correlation.

PARALLELISM AND CONVERGENCE IN DEVELOPMENT.

Homœogenesis. One of the most important of the many facts brought to light by the researches of palæontologists is that many groups of organisms develop independently in similar directions,

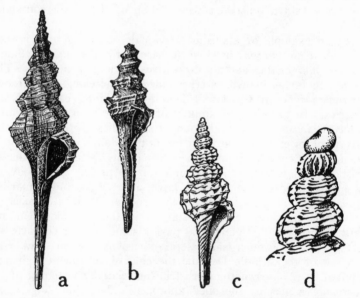

FIG. 259. Illustration of parallelism. A series of Eocenic Fusoid shells, belonging to different genera, but readily mistaken for members of the same genus Fusus under which they were originally described. *a. Falsifusus meyeri; b. Fulgurofusus rugatus. c. Fusus asper* × 1⅔. *d.* Early whorls of same, enlarged × 10.

and that hence in disconnected series species with similar adult characteristics may develop. These morphological equivalents, as Hyatt has termed them (or Homœomorphs of Buckman), are often so much alike that they have been united under the same generic or even specific name. The Eocenic fusoid shell Falsifusus, from the Gulf Coast of the southern United States, is an example of this, the adult form having all the characteristics of the genus Fusus, though, as shown by the young stages, the American form is probably derived from a Pleurotoma-like ancestor, and not a true Fusus at all.* (Fig. 252.)

The Eocenic genus Clavilithes furnishes a number of striking examples of this similar development or homœogenesis, as Eimer has termed it.† (Fig. 260.)

The typical species of this genus, *C. parisiensis,* from the Calcaire Grossier of the Paris Basin, finds its almost exact equivalent in the modern *Cyrtulus serotinus,* Hinds, of the Marquesas region in the South Pacific. Clavilithes became extinct in the Eocenic, while Cyrtulus is a derivative from the modern stock of Fusus. But by far the most interesting type of this complex series is

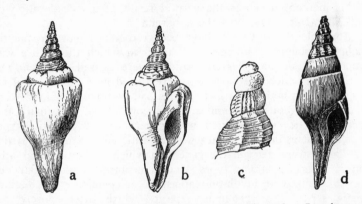

FIG. 260. Clavilithoid shells showing "convergence." *a, b. Cyrtulus serotinus.* A modern clavilithoid, being the phylogerontic terminal of the Fusus series (slightly reduced). *c.* The protoconch and early conch stages of *Clavilithes parisiensis,* an Old World Eocenic clavilithoid (enlarged). *d. Clavilithes* (*?*) *kennedyanus,* a New World Eocenic clavilithoid of independent origin (slightly reduced).

Clavilithes scalaris (Lamarck), from the Sables Moyens of France. This species is characterized by a projecting rim or flange on the shoulder of the adult whorl. This same feature is reproduced in *Clavilithes longævus* (Solander) of the Barton Beds of England, which is of wholly independent origin. Again, *Clavilithes ? chamberlaini,* Johnson and Grabau, from the Lower Claibornian of Texas, shows the same type of structure, and here, too it is independently derived. Finally, *Rhopalithes japeti* (Tournouer) represents this same feature in a genus entirely distinct from Clavilithes

---

* The distinction is not accepted by all. (Grabau–14.)

† The controversy regarding this and the other species mentioned here is dealt with by Grabau (13:622 *et seq.*) in the Studies of Gastropoda III.

Examples of such equivalents could be multiplied indefinitely. In the majority of cases, where classification has taken account only of the adult characters, such homœogenetic types have been classed together as of the same genus or species, and sometimes even as varieties of the same species.

It is hardly going too far to say that the majority of classifications of invertebrates now in vogue may be likened to a more or less warped plane passed through the crown of a tree; all the points of intersection of the branches and the plane are considered as species, while all the neighboring and some distant ones are grouped together in a genus, or family. The illogical nature of this method, which is the natural result of a consideration of adult characters only, must be apparent.

Morphologic equivalents have been recognized most frequently among ammonoids. Formerly all types in which the suture was composed of simple lobes and saddles were classed as *Goniatites.* All those in which the lobes were crenulated as *Ceratites,* and all those in which both lobes and saddles had become compound were placed in the genus *Ammonites.* It is now known that many and diverse genetic series started with genera of the goniatite type, branched out in diverse genera with ceratite sutures and that from these latter were derived the genera in which the suture was ammonitic. Again, similar types of ornamentation and similar degrees of coiling or involution appeared independently in distinct genetic series, thus producing species which often closely resembled each other in the adult type, but which had a wholly distinct ancestry.

Among vertebrates many cases of similar independent morphological equivalents have been discovered, especially in the class of mammals, and in that of reptiles. It sometimes happens that it is impossible or impracticable to separate such heterogenetic homœomorphs into their respective genera. In such cases a generic name is retained for this polyphyletic group, but it must not be considered a genus. The name *Circulus* (Bather) has come into use for such groups of homœomorphs. Platyceras is an example of a *circulus* among gastropods; it is commonly given the value of a genus, but its species are phylogerontic terminals of a number of genetic series. Many of the generic names applied to graptolites, such as Tetragraptus, Dichograptus, etc., are really circuli, for they represent similar stages in development in different genetic series. Since they occur at the same geologic horizon they have also been called "Geologic genera" (Ruedemann–39).

A distinction has commonly been maintained between cases in

which related animals or plants have developed in a similar manner but independently and those in which unrelated animals or plants have developed similar characteristics which apparently bring them more closely together. To the former the term *parallelism* has generally been restricted, while the term *convergence* has been applied to the latter case. Of course, it is understood that the use of this term does not imply that the organisms in question actually converge in their relationship, as seems to have been assumed by some, but merely that the convergence is only a morphologic one and may lead to mistaken ideas of relationship. The similar independent development of the projecting flange in the species of Clavilithes, cited above, may be considered a case of pure parallelism, while its development in Rhopalithes may be considered a case of convergence. A similar case of convergence is seen in the American Eocenic Falsifusus and the British Eocenic Fusus, already cited, both of which have adult characteristics which have led to their being classed in the same genus. That they are of independent ancestry, however, seems to be established.*

BIBLIOGRAPHY XXV.

1. BEECHER, CHARLES E. 1901. Studies in Evolution. Charles Scribner's Sons, New York.
2. BUCKMANN, S. S. 1909. Yorkshire Type Ammonites.
3. CLARK, WILLIAM B. 1910. Contributions to Morphology from Paleontology. The Paleontological Society Conferences on the Aspects of Paleontology. First Annual Meeting, Cambridge, Mass. Dec. 29, 1909. Reprinted from Popular Science Monthly, June to November, 1910.
4. CUMINGS, EDGAR R. 1903. The Morphogenesis of Platystrophia, a Study of the Evolution of a Palæozoic Brachiopod. American Journal of Science, 4th series, Vol. XV, pp. 1–48, 121–136.
5. CUMINGS, E. R. 1904. Development of Some Palæozoic Bryozoa. Ibid., Vol. XVII, pp. 49–78.
5a. CUMINGS, E. R. 1910. Paleontology and the Recapitulation Theory. The Paleontological Record, pp. 57–63, Reprinted from Popular Science Monthly. Ibid. Proceedings of the Indiana Academy of Science, 1909 Meeting, pp. 1–36.
6. DE VRIES, HUGO. 1901. Die Mutations-theorie. Leipzig.
7. DE VRIES, H. 1905. Species and Varieties. Their Origin by Mutation. Open Court Publishing Company, Chicago.
8. D'ORBIGNY, ALCIDE. 1840. Palæontologie Française. Terrains, Crétacés Cephalopodes. Paris.
9. EIMER, TH. 1898. On Orthogenesis, and the Impotence of Natural Selection in Species-forming. Open Court Publishing Company, Chicago.
10. FARLOW, W. G. 1898. The Conception of Species as Affected by Recent Investigations on Fungi. Vice-Presidential Address before the American Association for the Advancement of Science, 1898. Section of Botany.

* See the controversy above referred to.

11. GRABAU, A. W. 1902. Studies of Gastropoda. American Naturalist, Vol. XXXVI, pp. 917–945.

11a. GRABAU, A. W. 1903. Studies of Gastropoda II, Ibid. Vol. XXXVII, pp. 515–539.

12. GRABAU, A. W. 1904. Phylogeny of Fusus and Its Allies. Smithsonian Miscellaneous Collections, part of Vol. XLIV.

13. GRABAU, A. W. 1907. Studies of Gastropoda III. On Orthogenetic Variation in Gastropoda. American Naturalist, Vol. XLI, No. 490, pp. 607–651.

14. GRABAU, A. W. 1910. Studies of Gastropoda IV. Value of the Protoconch and Early Conch Stages in the Classification of Gastropoda. Seventh International Zoölogical Congress, Proceedings, Boston, 1907. Advance sheets.

15. GRABAU, A. W., and REED, MARGARET. 1910. Mutations of *Spirifer mucronatus*. Seventh International Zoölogical Congress Proceedings, Boston, 1907. Advance sheets, 1910.

16. GRABAU, A. W. 1910. Palæontology and Ontogeny. The Palæontologic Record, pp. 54–57. Reprinted from Popular Science Monthly.

17. GRABAU, A. W. 1913. An Illustration of Waagen's Theory of Mutations. American Naturalist (*in press*).

18. HUSSAKOF, L. 1910. Vertebrate Paleontology and the Evidences for Recapitulation. The Paleontologic Record, pp. 63–66. Reprinted from Popular Science Monthly.

19. HYATT, ALPHEUS. 1889. Genesis of the Arietidæ. Smithsonian Contributions to Knowledge, 673. 238 pp., 14 pls.

20. HYATT, A. 1894. Phylogeny of an Acquired Characteristic. Proceedings of the American Philosophical Society, Vol. XXXII, pp. 349–647, pls. 1–14.

21. HYATT, A. 1897. Cycle in the Life of the Individual (Ontogeny) and in the Evolution of Its Own Group (Phylogeny). Science, Vol. V, pp. 161–171. Proceedings of the American Academy, Vol. XXXII, pp. 209–224.

22. JACKSON, ROBERT T. 1912. Phylogeny of the Pelecypoda; the Aviculidæ and Their Allies. Memoir of the Boston Society of Natural History, Vol. IV, No. 8.

23. JACKSON, R. T. 1912. Phylogeny of the Echini, with a Revision of Palæozoic Species. Memoirs of the Boston Society of Natural History, Vol. VII.

24. JACKSON, R. T. 1913. Alpheus Hyatt and His Principles of Research. American Naturalist, Vol. XLVII, pp. 195–205.

25. JOHNSON, DOUGLAS W. 1904. Geology of the Cerrillos Hills, New Mexico. School of Mines Quarterly, 1903–04, Part II, Palæontology.

26. LOOMIS, F. B. 1910. Ontogeny: A Study of the Value of Young Features in Determining Phylogeny. Paleontologic Record, pp. 51–53. Reprinted from Popular Science Monthly.

27. LULL, RICHARD S. 1910. Relation of Embryology and Vertebrate Palæontology. Ibid., pp. 47–50.

28. MORGAN, THOMAS HUNT. 1903. Evolution and Adaptation. Macmillan Company, New York.

29. NEUMAYR, MELCHIOR, and PAUL, C. M. 1875. Congerien und Paludinen-schichten Slavoniens. Abhandlungen der königlich-kaiserlichen geologischen Reichsanstalt. Bd. VII, Heft 3.

30. OSBORN, HENRY F. 1907. Evolution as It Appears to the Paleontologist. Seventh International Zoölogical Congress Proceedings. Boston

Meeting, 1907. Advance sheets, 1910. Also Science N. S., Vol. XXVI, No. 674, pp. 744–749, Nov., 1907.

31. OSBORN, H. F. 1908. The Four Inseparable Factors of Evolution. Science N. S., Vol. XXVII, No. 682. Jan., 1908, pp. 148–150.

32. OSBORN, H. F. 1908. Coincident Evolution through Rectigradations. Ibid., Vol. XXVII, No. 697, pp. 749–752.

33. OSBORN, H. F. 1910. Paleontologic Evidences of Adaptive Radiation. The Paleontologic Record, pp. 34–38. Reprinted from Popular Science Monthly.

34. OSBORN, H. F. 1911. Biological Conclusions drawn from the Study of the Titanotheres. Science N. S., Vol. XXXIII, pp. 825–828.

35. OSBORN, H. F. 1912. The Continuous Origin of Certain Unit Characters as Observed by a Palæontologist. American Naturalist, Vol. XLVI, pp. 185–206, 249–278.

36. OSBORN, H. F. 1912. First Use of Word "Genotype." Science N. S., Vol. XXXV, pp. 340–341.

37. OSBORN, H. F. 1912. Tetraplasy, the Law of the Four Inseparable Factors of Evolution. Journal of the Academy of Natural Sciences, Philadelphia. Vol. XV, second series, pp. 273–309.

37a. OSBORN, H. F. Assisted by Grabau, A. W. 1911. Article on Palæontology. Encyclopædia Britannica, 11th Edition, Vol. xx, pp. 579–591.

38. PENHALLOW, D. P. 1910. The Relation of Paleobotany to Phylogeny. The Paleontologic Record, pp. 67–72. Reprinted from Popular Science Monthly.

39. RUEDEMANN, RUDOLF. 1904. Grapholites of New York. Memoir VI of the New York State Museum, Part I, Vol. I.

40. RUEDEMANN, R. 1910. Anatomy and Physiology in Invertebrate Extinct Organisms. Paleontologic Record, pp. 39–42.

41. SHIMER, H. W. 1906. Old Age in Brachiopoda. American Naturalist, Vol. XL, pp. 95–121.

42. SHIMER, H. W. 1908. Dwarf Faunas. Ibid., Vol. XLII, pp. 472–490.

43. SMITH, JAMES PERRIN. 1897. Development of Schloenbachia. Journal of Geology, Vol. V, pp. 521 et seq.

44. WAAGEN, W. 1868. Die Formenreihe des *Ammonites subradiatus*. Beneckes Geognostisch-Palæontologische Beiträge, Bd. II, pp. 179–256 (185–6).

CHAPTER XXVI.

PHYSICAL CHARACTERISTICS OF THE INHABITABLE EARTH.— BIONOMIC CHARACTERS OF THE ENVIRONMENT.*

A comprehensive survey of the inhabitable world shows its divisibility into three great bionomic realms, each of which has its peculiar characteristics and its specially adapted forms of animal and plant life. The essential character of each is determined by the nature of the medium in which the organisms live, *i. e.,* whether salt water, fresh water, or air. We have, accordingly:

1. The Marine, or *Halo-biotic* realm.
2. The Fresh Water, or *Limno-biotic* realm.
3. The Terrestrial, or *Atmo-biotic* (also called *Geo-biotic*) realm.

While each of these is distinct from the others, they also grade into one another to a greater or less extent along their lines of intersection. Thus the marine and fresh-water realms intergrade in the estuaries of rivers, where the water is brackish. The marine and terrestrial realms intergrade at the shore, where organisms are periodically exposed between tides first to the one and then to the other medium. Again, the terrestrial and fresh-water fluvial, lacustrine, etc., realms intergrade along the margins of streams and the shores of lakes.

Each one of the bionomic realms may be further subdivided into a light, or *photic region,* and a dark, or *aphotic region.* Between these two may frequently be determined a dusk, or *dysphotic region.* Schimper (6) has defined these regions in the marine realm on the basis of plant life as follows:

The photic region extends over such depths wherein the intensity of sunlight is sufficient for the normal development of macrophytes. The dysphotic region is insufficiently lighted for the

* This and the succeeding two chapters are in part a reprint, with additions and emendations, of a paper published by the author in 1899 under the title *Relation of Marine Bionomy to Stratigraphy.* Bulletin of Buffalo Society Natural Sciences, Vol. VI, pp. 319–365.

normal development of macrophytes, which exist there but scantily or not at all, while certain moderately assimilating microphytes, especially diatoms, still exist. The aphotic region comprises that part of the sea where only the non-assimilating vegetable organisms can exist. The depth at which these regions pass into one another varies with the locality and the purity of the water. In the open sea the dark region begins at a depth of about 200 fathoms. In the fresh water realm the aphotic region is not often found, though deep lakes, like Lake Superior and Lake Geneva, extend to depths not penetrated by sunlight. Such cases are, however, comparatively uncommon. A *limno-aphotic* region is further found in the streams and lakes of caves where the sunlight is shut out by the roof of the cavern. Caverns, too (natural and artificial), constitute the only aphotic region of the terrestrial realm, and they are often peopled with a well-adapted fauna and flora.

The final division into *life districts* depends on the absence or presence of a substratum, and this division can be equally well carried out in the marine, fresh water, and terrestrial realms. The absence of a substratum compels the organism to float or swim in the medium, and for this purpose special organs and a specially modified body-form commonly exist. The substratum may be visited for food or other purposes, but the organism is perfectly at home in the medium.

Each realm may, then, be divided into the following life-districts, the medium being salt water, fresh water, or air, according as the marine, fluvio-lacustrine, or terrestrial realms are considered:

1. Littoral district: Light; substratum present.
2. Pelagic district: Light; substratum absent.
3. Abyssal district: Dark; substratum present.
4. Abysso-pelagic district: Dark; substratum absent.

I. The Littoral Districts.

A. *Marine.* The marine littoral district extends from the shore at high-water mark to the edge of the continental shelf, where it quickly merges into the abyssal district. The depth to which the littoral district extends is approximately 200 meters, though the hundred-fathom line is commonly taken as the seaward boundary of this district. Around oceanic islands and young continents the littoral district is very narrow, the ocean floor soon falling off to deep water. The origin of this district is to be sought in the activities of various geologic agencies, chief among which are the inland cutting of waves and currents, thus extending the sea landward; and the deposition of the land-derived detritus on the edge of the continental shelf, thus pushing this edge seaward and widening the submarine platform. Subsidence of the land permits the advance of the sea over the low country, and broad epicontinental seas are formed, which fall entirely within the littoral life district. In mediterraneans, too, the littoral belt is generally a broad one, only the central portion descending to abyssal depth. (See further, Chapter III.)

The conditions become more favorable for the development of littoral life as the continent grows older, provided, of course, that no important oscillatory movements occur. As time progresses the breadth of the submerged continental shelf increases, both by landward cutting and by seaward building, and the surface of the land becomes more and more reduced, thus causing a decrease in the amount of detrital material which can be carried into the sea, and a concomitant increase in the purity of the water. When peneplanation, or the reduction of the land to base-level, has been accomplished, the amount of detritus carried into the sea is practically *nil;* and any organisms, like corals, adapted only to pure water, can flourish close to the continental shore, and deposits of a purely organic nature, such as extensive deposits of pteropod or foraminiferal shells, may form in comparatively shallow water.

The epicontinental sea and the littoral belt of the mediterraneans are especially adapted for the development of local or provincial faunas. Such provincializing of faunas is most marked if, by some oscillatory movement of the land or some other physical change, the basins of these intracontinental seas become separated from the littoral district of the ocean sufficiently to prevent intercommunication between the organisms of the two provinces. A barrier is thus formed, which need not necessarily be a land barrier, and a great diversity of faunas may result. A rather marked diversity of fauna existed in early Tertiary time between the Mississippi embayment and the Atlantic coast, and in Palæozoic time between the Bay of New York and the central interior sea. Recent provincial faunas are frequently met with. It requires only a comparatively slight elevation of the sea-floor, or a moderate deepening of the abyssal oceanic basins, to draw off the water from the shallower regions and lay dry large portions of the littoral district. Such a change would, of course, result in an almost complete extinction of the littoral flora and fauna thus exposed and force the survivors to accommodate themselves to a narrower field. Revival of stream activities, consequent upon elevation of the land, would result in carrying a large amount of débris into the sea and thus produce conditions unfavorable to the existence of many organisms.

Landward the littoral district interlocks with the corresponding districts of the terrestrial and fluvial realms, the faunas and floras of all more or less intermingling. It is in this portion of the littoral district that an important subdivision must be considered; namely, the shore. The shore, as already noted (*ante,* Chapter XV), is that part of the littoral district which lies between the highest water mark (often considered as including even the highest point of the wave mark) and the lowest line drawn during the lowest ebb. In the greater part of this division of the littoral district there is a change of medium twice every twenty-four hours, and a change of the consequent physical conditions attendant upon the character of the medium. Organisms living in this portion of the littoral zone must be capable of withstanding the effects of the partial or complete removal of their normal medium for a greater or less time. It is here that the interlocking of the terrestrial and marine floras and faunas becomes most marked, and an intermingling and a migration from one district into the other occur. Migration from the land to the sea is exemplified by the whales, seals, and other aquatic mammals, which have become marine in so far as their mode of locomotion is concerned. Owing however, to the inability of air-breathing animals to adapt themselves to a water-breathing habit, all terrestrial animals passing into the sea must assume a pelagic life, where they can retain their normal method of respiration.

Among other animals which have exchanged their normal terrestrial habit for a prevailingly marine one may be mentioned several birds, such as the Penguins and the Albatross; certain snakes, turtles, and crocodiles, and a number of insects. The birds and insects here considered represent a passage from the aerial to the marine pelagic district; while the reptiles, like the mammals, illustrate a passage from the land to the pelagic district of the sea.

While thus the land fauna, in advancing into the sea, naturally takes to a pelagic life, the land flora can adapt itself to the conditions of the littoral district. This is well shown by the eight species of phanerogams, which have acquired a wholly marine habit, and are now known as eel grasses or sea grasses. In the case of these plants the adaptation is so complete that they can no longer live out of their adopted habitat. The mangrove plants, on the other hand, are only partially accommodated to the conditions of the marine littoral district, for it is necessary that their crowns of leaves should be above water.

Marine animals and plants, likewise, attempt migrating from the sea to the land. In their adaptation to the new habitat the animals are the more successful, just as the plants are the more successful in migrating the other way. Thus two genera of fish, Periophthalmus and Boleophthalmus, are able to pass the greater part of their lives out of water. They "skip along close to water-line on the seashore, where they hunt for molluscs (Onchidium) and insects." (Semper–7:*189*.) The large branchial cavity of these fishes is not completely filled by the gills, but serves in part as an air cavity or primitive lung. In a number of fishes, such as *Anabas scandens* of the Philippines, this gill-cavity is further modified into a "labyrinthine organ," or much prolonged cavity, the mucous membrane of which is thrown into complicated folds, thus greatly increasing the surface. These fish can exist for days out of water and are able to make long overland excursions. Semper holds that these fish may be regarded "as Amphibians with quite as much reason as toads and frogs, or even better, since they are capable of changing the nature of their respiration—of air, that is, or of water—at will, and suddenly without any interruption." Several of our littoral gastropods, *e. g.,* Littorina, Ilyanassa, etc., are capable of existing out of water for a considerable time. In Brazil Littorina climbs the trees of the mangrove high above water and oysters and other bivalves are attached to the roots of these trees and are laid bare at low tide. Ampullaria forms a connecting link between sea and land snails, for it not only breathes by means of a gill but also has a pulmonary sac like that of the land snails into which air is carried by means of a long breathing-siphon.

The possibility that related species of marine gastropod Mollusca may leave the sea in different parts of the world and give rise to terrestrial forms, which, though differing from their marine ancestors, may be very similar to each other, deserves attention. In this way some of the puzzling problems of distribution of terrestrial gastropods on widely distant oceanic islands may be accounted for.

Among the Crustacea there are several species of crabs (*e. g., Birgus latro,* etc.) which live in damp woods far from all water and whose respiration is carried on chiefly without the intermediation of their normal medium.

The advent of marine vegetation on the land has occurred only up to the limit of the salt spray on exposed shores, and here the number of species is small. But at, or just below, high-tide limit a number of algæ find a congenial abode, and grow there in luxuriant masses. Chief of these in our northern latitudes are the Fuci, with *Fucus vesiculosus* and *Ascophyllum nodosum* predominating. At low-tide these hang like a wet fringe over the exposed rocks and give shelter to numerous species of the smaller littoral animals, as well as other algæ.

The littoral districts of the marine and fluvial realms also interlock along the shores where streams mouth into the sea or expand into broad estuaries. Here marine animals will venture up into the fresh water littoral district, while, similarly, fresh water animals pass into the littoral district of the marine realms. The common meeting-ground of the two approaching floras and faunas is in the estuarine or brackish water facies of the littoral districts.

The neritic zone, "Flachsee," or thalassic zone, is that portion of the littoral district which is never uncovered. It is separated as a distinct district by Walther, Haug, and others, who restrict the term littoral to the shore zone. It is, however, so intimately connected with the shore zone in all its physical and bionomic characteristics that a separation is not natural. The bottom of the neritic zone of the littoral district is less diversified than that of the shore zone. In its upper portion and in its shoals it may partake of the character of the shore zone, but in its deeper portions the character of the bottom is usually more uniform, being either rocky or, what is more common, composed of fine detrital material mingled with organic matter in various stages of dissolution. According to the character of the bottom, plant life will vary and with it, to a greater or less extent, animal life.

Taken as a whole, the littoral district is the most important portion of the sea, both from a bionomic point of view and from its bearing on palæontology. "The littoral region," says Lovèn (4 :*86*), "comprises the favored zones of the sea, where light and shade, a genial temperature, currents changeable in power and direction, a rich vegetation spread over extensive areas, abundance of food, of prey to allure, of enemies to withstand or evade, represent an infinitude of agents competent to call into play the tendencies to vary which are embodied in each species, and always ready, by modifying its parts, to respond to the influences of external conditions." This district may perhaps be regarded as the cradle of organic life, from which were peopled the abyssal and pelagic districts, on the one hand, and the terrestrial and fluvial realms and their various districts, on the other.

B. *Fresh Water.* The littoral district of the fresh water realm is almost coextensive in area with that of the streams and fresh water lakes and ponds of the world. The only exception to this is found in those portions of very deep lakes where sunlight does not penetrate to the bottom and in the subterranean streams and lakes. The fauna of the limno-littoral district is much less diverse than that of the corresponding district in the sea. Whole classes of animals, like those of the Echinodermata, the Anthozoa, the Brachiopoda, Cephalopoda, Pteropoda, Scaphopoda, etc., are normally absent from fresh water, while most of the remaining ones are poorly represented by genera and species, though often prolific in individuals. Plant life, on the contrary, is abundantly represented, not only by desmids, diatoms, and fresh-water algæ, but also by the large number of swamp plants which grow partly submerged and represent the transition zone between the terrestrial and limno-littoral districts.

C. Terrestrial. The terrestrio-littoral district is coextensive with the surface of the land. No other life district comprises such a range of physical characteristics, and no other district is inhabited by such a variety of highly specialized types of animal and plant life. Here we pass from the cold of the arctic snow-fields to the burning sands of the tropics, from the land of nearly continuous rains to the rainless desert regions, parched by the continued drought of years, and from the region of plentiful food supply to the stony, arid wastes, where the nature of the soil is hostile to practically all forms of plant life. It is to be expected that under such widely varying conditions a fauna and flora should develop which in its variety outruns that of any other life district, and which in its own extremes reflects the range of its environment.

II. The Pelagic Districts.

A. Marine. The marine pelagic, or halo-pelagic district, is the common meeting-ground of most of the life districts. It touches all shores and communicates with the corresponding districts of both the terrestrial and fluvial realms. It has direct communication with the littoral district, many inhabitants of which leave the bottom at times to lead a temporary existence in the pelagic district; while many pelagic animals, in turn, visit the bottom or shores for food. Occasionally inhabitants of the pelagic district enter for a time the corresponding district of the terrestrial realms, *i. e.,* the aerial; as, for example, the so-called flying-fish; and, in turn, as already noted, many aerial animals spend a part of their lives in the marine pelagic district, or at least show a decided preference for a pelagic life. The passage of land animals to the halo-pelagic district has already been noted. Similar intermingling of fresh water, or limno-pelagic, and salt water pelagic types occurs in the estuaries and stream mouths, and it is notorious that halo-pelagic fish will enter the limno-pelagic district in breeding time. It is quite probable, as Sir William Flower suggests, that the Cetacea, in their transition from a terrestrial to a marine life, passed through a stage in which they lived in fresh water. A similar transition for the sea-grasses is not improbable, though they can no longer live in fresh water. Intercommunication between the abysso-pelagic and pelagic districts also occurs, as well as between the abysso-pelagic and abyssal.

B. *Fresh Water.* The pelagic life of ponds, lakes, and rivers is much less varied than that of the sea, though, as will be seen later, the number of individuals of a given species may often be very great. In ponds and lakes no very distinctive characteristics not found in shallow seas exist, aside, of course, from the distinctions due to the difference in degree and kind of salinity. In rivers, on the other hand, we must consider the importance of currents, which vary greatly in strength, but are essentially constant in direction. It is this constancy which, as Chamberlin has pointed out, favors the development of a special body form, the resistance of which to the current is at a minimum. Such a body form is found in fish and in the ancient Eurypterida, and it is a possibility not to be lightly set aside that both fish and eurypterids originated in the rivers of the Palæozoic and earlier lands. Indeed, this is all but definitely proven for the *Eurypterida* (O'Connell–5) and seems to be indicated for the fish as well. Significant in this connection is the fact that the early remains of fish as of eurypterids are not found in normal marine deposits, but in those which are at least open to the suspicion that they are formed by rivers or at least at the mouths of rivers, while the best preserved remains, and the most abundantly represented in the Palæozoic, are found in river flood-plain deposits and in deltas. This subject will be more fully discussed in the next chapter (Grabau–3).

C. *Terrestrial.* The pelagic life of fresh water is, as we have seen, much less abundant than that of the sea, and, again, the aerial life, or that of the pelagic district of the land, is much less prominent than that of the streams and lakes. This gradation is in direct correspondence with that observed in the gradation in the density of the medium. Moreover, in the terrestrial realm the pelagic district is only temporarily inhabited, few, if any, terrestrial animals or plants spending their entire existence suspended in the air. The most familiar examples of animals spending a part of their lives at least in the atmo-pelagic district are : insects among invertebrates, pterosaurs among reptiles, the birds, and, among mammals, the bats.

III. The Abyssal Life District.

A. *Marine.* The marine abyssal districts comprise the lightless depths, or generally those depths exceeding two hundred fathoms. (Chapter III.) As assimilating plant life is absent in these districts the food supply of the organisms existing in them must be wholly derived from the districts in which such assimilating vegetation exists. A large proportion of the food of the abyssal animals is contained in the organic oozes and sediments which constantly settle down in a more or less decomposed state from the lighted districts. The abysso-pelagic district is frequently invaded by organisms from the pelagic district, which descend into the dark regions during the day.

B. *Fresh Water and C. Terrestrial.* In the non-marine realms the lightless districts are sparingly represented. Lakes of great depth, whose bottom is in perpetual darkness, do exist, but the life of these dark regions is mostly unknown. Cave life, on the other hand, both fluvio-lacustrine and terrestrial, has been made the subject of much study, and its characteristics are known to harmonize with the peculiar conditions which give these districts their especial stamp.

BIBLIOGRAPHY XXVI.

1. CHAMBERLIN, THOMAS C. 1900. The Habitat of the Early Vertebrates. Journal of Geology, Vol. VIII, pp. 400–412.
2. GRABAU, A. W. 1899. The Relation of Marine Bionomy to Stratigraphy. Chapter III in the Geology and Palæontology of Eighteen-mile Creek. Bulletin of the Buffalo Society of Natural Sciences, Vol. VI, pp. 319–365.
3. GRABAU, A. W. 1913. Ancient Delta Deposits of North America. Bulletin of the Geological Society of North America, Vol. XXIV pp. 498–526.
4. LOVÉN, SVEN. 1883. On Pourtalasia, a Genus of Echinoidea. Stockholm.
5. O'CONNELL, MARJORIE. 1912. The Habitat of the Eurypterida. Paper presented before the New York Academy of Sciences. Also in Grabau (2), pp. 499–515.
6. SCHIMPER, A. F. W. 1898. Pflanzengeographie auf physiologischer Grundlage. Jena. English translation by W. R. Fisher. Plant Geography, Oxford, 1903.
7. SEMPER, KARL. 1881. Animal Life as Affected by the Natural Conditions of Existence. Appleton International Scientific Series, Vol. XXX.

CHAPTER XXVII.

BIONOMIC CLASSIFICATION OF PLANTS AND ANIMALS.

A bionomic classification, or one based on the relationship of the organism to its environment, cannot agree with one based entirely on anatomic characteristics. It is a more primitive classification, but a very useful one from many points of view.

SUBDIVISIONS.

Primary Divisions. The primary divisions of the organisms agree with the primary divisions of the life districts, *i. e.,* the marine, fresh water, and atmospheric or terrestrial. We have, accordingly, *halo-bios, limno-bios,* and *atmo-bios (geo-bios),* each of these including the plants and animals of the respective realms.

Secondary Divisions. The next division is based on the relation of the organism to the substratum, where we have floating types or *plankton,* swimming types or *nekton,* and bottom types or *benthos.* The first two belong to the pelagic and abysso-pelagic districts, the third to the littoral and abyssal. Their further subdivisions and relationships are as follows:

A. Plankton (floating organisms)..........

1. *Holoplankton:* organisms spending all their lives as plankton (ex., jelly fish).
2. *Meroplankton:* organisms leading a planktonic life during larval stages only (ex., Crustacea, echinoderms, cœlenterates).
3. *Pseudoplankton:* organisms normally attached but floating through accident, as the Sargassum, leaves and trunks of trees, or parts of dead organisms, such as shells of molluscs, etc.
4. *Epiplankton:* organisms living upon or attached to floating objects (ex., Crustacea and hydroids of the pseudoplanktonic Sargassum; *Lepas* attached to floating logs, etc.

B. Nekton (swimming or flying organisms)....

1. *Holonekton.*
2. *Meronekton.*
3. *Epinekton:* organisms parasitically or otherwise attached to swimming or flying animals.

Pelagic and Abysso-pelagic.

C. Benthos (bottom or-ganisms)............ {
1. *Vagrant:* with power to walk, crawl, or creep over the bottom.
2. *Sedentary:* Attached to the bottom.
} Littoral and Abyssal.

According to the realm in which the organism lives we have, therefore:

    I. *Marine* or *Halobios,* including
        A. Haloplankton
        B. Halonekton
        C. Halobenthos
    II. *Freshwater* or *Limnobios,* including
        D. Limnoplankton
        E. Limnonekton
        F. Limnobenthos
    III. *Terrestrial* or *Atmobios* (Geobios), including
        G. Atmoplankton
        H. Atmonekton
        I. Atmobenthos

With reference to depth, we may further subdivide marine plankton, etc., into *anoplankton* (from ἄνω, upward [*]) or that occurring above the 100 fathom-line; this may be divided into anoholoplankton, anomeroplankton, anopseudoplankton and anoepiplankton. Below 100 fathoms we have the *mesoplankton* (from μέσος, middle), and again, just above the abyssal depths may occur the *hypoplankton* (from ὑπό, under), anonekton, mesonekton and hyponekton, as well as anobenthos (littoral district), mesobenthos (bathyal district) and hypobenthos (abyssal district) may also be recognized.

Each of these divisions may now be considered in detail.

A. *Haloplankton.*

1. *Holoplankton.* The term *plankton* was introduced by Victor Hensen in 1887. It is derived from the Greek πλαγκτός, which means wandering or drifting about aimlessly. The true plankton, or *holoplankton,* is most typically developed in the sea. It comprises those organisms which spend their lives in the sea drifting about from place to place, without power to direct their own

---

[*] The term epiplankton was proposed for this by George H. Fowler in 1911 (Encyclopedia Britannica, 11th ed., vol. xxi, p. 721), but was preoccupied by Grabau in 1909 as above defined (3). Hence the names anoplankton and anobenthos are here proposed. The names mesoplankton, mesobenthos, hypoplankton and hypobenthos, also proposed by Fowler, are, however, acceptable.

course. These organisms range in size from creatures of microscopic dimensions to medusæ 50 cm. in diameter. While some of the larger animals of this group have power to propel themselves through the water, they nevertheless are subject to the force of strong waves or currents, which render them helpless. Holoplanktonic organisms are wholly pelagic, and are characterized by a more or less transparent body and by the absence of opaque skeletal structures, only a few forms retaining delicate calcareous shells, inherited from their benthonic ancestors. In its horizontal distribution the holoplankton of the sea is dependent chiefly upon the marine currents, as the organisms composing it are practically unable to carry on independent migrations, though many of them can dart about in quiet water. Hence they fall an easy prey to actively predaceous animals. The occurrence of holoplanktonic animals in swarms is also accounted for by their lack of independent locomotion, for the eggs, liberated by the floating parent, commonly develop without separating far from the parent, with which they are carried along by the currents of the sea. These animals have, however, the power to rise and descend in the water, and during the day many of them live at a depth of from fifty to one hundred and fifty fathoms, coming to the surface only on quiet nights. The animals of this class also occur in the abyssopelagic district.

2. *Meroplankton.* This term (from μέρος, a part) was introduced by Haeckel in 1890 (4) and is applicable to the larvæ of benthonic animals which lead, during the larval stages, a truly planktonic existence and which occur with and suffer the same vicissitudes as the true or holoplankton. The upper levels of the ocean are usually crowded with such meroplanktonic organisms, and to them is due the horizontal distribution of benthonic species. Floating about in the sea in perfect clouds or swarms these meroplanktonic organisms pass their short existence a sport of the waves and currents. Sooner or later, however, they sink to the bottom, a veritable rain of seedling organisms; and, if they fall on a fertile soil, if they reach the proper facies of the substratum, they develop into the benthonic adult; but, if they fall upon an unfavorable bottom, or if the food supply is scarce, they perish. Thus, other things being favorable, wherever the facies of sea-bottom normal to a particular species of benthonic organism exists, the bottom may be peopled with that species by the larvæ which reach it from the upper waters, where they were carried by waves and currents during their meroplanktonic wanderings. As Walther says, should unfavorable circumstances temporarily destroy a whole fauna, its depopulated home would at once be surrounded by swarms of

delicate larvæ, and, as soon as the old conditions are reëstablished, this fauna will again appear with countless individuals. This explains the sudden reappearance in later strata of the fauna of an earlier bed, even though it was absent from the intervening strata.

From a stratigraphic point of view the meroplankton is of vast importance, for to it is due the wide dispersal of the benthonic organisms, which of all marine life forms are the best indices of the physical conditions of the sea bottom. It is during the larval period that benthonic marine invertebrates spread in all directions from their center of occupancy, and that they have an opportunity to enter and occupy distant regions.

3. *Pseudoplankton.* This term was introduced by Schütt (8) for such organisms which, like the Sargassum, are normally or in early life benthonic, but continue their later existence as plankton. Walther has extended the meaning of the term so as to include those organisms which are carried about by floating objects, to which they are either attached as sedentary benthos or which serve them as a substratum on which they lead a vagrant benthonic existence. This group, however, is distinct, and is separated here under the name of *epiplankton*.

Under pseudoplankton may, however, be included those benthonic or nektonic organisms which become planktonic only after death; *i. e.*, that portion of the plankton which consists of the floating parts of dead organisms, such as the leaves and trunks of trees, dead insects and carcasses of vertebrates, and, above all, the shells of molluscs, which, on the death of the animal, are distributed more or less widely, according to the nature of the shell. Thus the shell of Spirula is widely distributed and embedded in contemporaneous sediments where the organism never lived, and leaves of terrestrial plants are found in sediments far from land. Tree trunks from tropical America are carried to the northeast coast of Iceland, where they become embedded in contemporaneous sediments.

4. *Epiplankton.* This term (from ἐπι, upon) was proposed (Grabau–3) for those organisms which live upon a floating substratum, to which they are either attached or upon which they lead a vagrant existence. The substratum may be holoplanktonic or pseudoplanktonic, the latter being the most frequent. Examples of epiplankton are the algæ, hydroids, and bryozoans attached to the floating Sargassum and other algæ; and the Crustacea, molluscs, and other animals living among their branches; and the organisms attached to floating tree trunks and other pseudoplankton.

A large number of algæ, especially the shallow-water forms,

have attached to them sedentary animals as well as other species of algæ. Among the animals, hydroids and bryozoans are the most common, though other sedentary animals, such as Spirorbis, are frequently abundant. Animals belonging to the vagrant type of the benthos are by no means rare. The large fronds of the Laminaria cast up on our northern shores during every storm are frequently veritable menageries of invertebrate life, which, under favorable conditions, may float about for days. These fronds, for example, are commonly covered with a dense growth of the delicate littoral hydroids Obelia and Campanularia, while Bugula and other Bryozoa and Spirorbis are usually common. The hollow stem is commonly surrounded by an extensive growth of Membranipora, while not infrequently tubularian and other hydroids find this a suitable resting place. The root-like base of the stem often embraces the shell of Modiola or Cyprina, which in turn is overgrown with coralline algæ. Sponges are also found among the "roots" of the Laminaria, and Acmæa, Chiton, Crepidula, Anomia, and other molluscs are attached to the shell, or to the stone which frequently takes its place. Finally, worms and crustaceans are not rare inhabitants of the sheltering space between the branches of the "roots"; and sea anemones, small star-fish, brittle-stars, and sea urchins also occur, both on the basal portion of the stem and on the frond itself. Such floating menageries may be carried far out to sea or, what is perhaps more frequent, may be driven ashore. Not infrequently they are carried far up into the estuaries and, becoming stranded, are buried in the mud; or else they are cast up on mud flats behind some sheltering bar or ledge.

While these cases illustrate an epiplanktonic existence due to accident, the cirriped Lepas illustrates a habitually epiplanktonic existence; this barnacle rarely occurring except attached to floating objects. Many of the animals found on the Sargassum seem to be characteristic of it in its floating condition, not occurring on it in its native haunts. (Ortmann–7.) Walther has adduced evidence which goes to show conclusively that many of the larger fossil Pentacrini, and perhaps other crinoids, occurred with their stems wound around floating timbers, and he explains the occurrence of these marine animals in fresh water coal strata as due to stranding in estuaries of species leading an epiplanktonic existence.

The marine or haloplankton forms one of the chief sources of food for many marine animals and is everywhere devoured in vast quantities. Dead organisms which sink to the sea-floor in an incomplete state of decomposition form the chief element of the organic oozes which furnish food to many littoral as well as abyssal animals. The skeletal portions of the dead plankton often accumulate in vast quantities on the bottom, and, in the greater depths where terrigenous sediments are absent, they usually form diatomaceous, radiolarian, globigerina, pteropod, and other oozes. The purity of such oozes, i. e., their freedom from clastic sediment, is usually an index of the purity of the water in which they were deposited, but from this we cannot always decide that such oozes, when found in fossil state, indicate deep sea. The absence of clastic sediment may be due to the low relief of the land, which may have been worn down to base-level, thus allowing water of moderate depth near shore to be free from detrital material.

B. *Halonekton.*

The term *nekton,* derived from the Greek νηκτός, which means swimming, was introduced by Haeckel in 1890 (4), for those animals which lead an actively swimming life. The group is typified by the class of fishes. A torpedo-like form, terminating anteriorly in a head, and perfect bilateral symmetry are the chief characteristics of these animals. A strong musculature for propulsion is usually situated in the posterior portion of the body, while appendages for balancing and steering are also usually present. The body is non-transparent and a calcareous supporting skeleton is ordinarily developed. Typical nektonic animals of the modern sea are: the squids, the fish, and the degenerate mammals—whales, porpoises, etc. Besides holonektonic forms there are in the sea epinektonic ones, i. e., sessile forms more or less pemanently attached to a swimming host. The whale barnacle, attached to the under side of whales, and the ship's barnacles are examples among invertebrates, while the Pilot-fish attached by suckers to sharks represent this type among vertebrates.

C. *Halobenthos.*

The term *benthos,* from βένθος, the depths of the sea, was likewise introduced by Haeckel in 1890 (4). It covers those organisms which inhabit the sea-bottom. We may divide the benthos into sedentary and vagrant (*vagile*) benthos, the former attached to the bottom, the latter moving over it. Living in such intimate relation with the sea-bottom, halobenthonic organisms are to a high degree dependent upon its facies, and their remains are generally entombed in the region where they have lived, instead of being deposited anywhere else, as in the case with planktonic and nektonic organisms. The sedentary benthos is, to a large degree, dependent for food on those organisms which are swept within its reach by the currents, while the vagrant benthos is more actively engaged in seeking out its food. Large numbers of sedentary benthonic animals have assumed a radial structure, especially well typified in corals and crinoids, and also shown in the corona of the barnacle; while others, such as brachiopods, have a bilateral symmetry of high degree. Some of the lower vagrant benthonic animals, *e. g.,* the Echinoidea, are also built on the radial plan, but the majority of the free benthonic animals are bilaterally symmetrical. Among the vagrant benthos the struggle for existence is most intense, and, as a result, the variety of adaptations and the wealth of form and color are almost unlimited. Transitions from the vagrant benthos to the nekton are numerous, and it sometimes becomes difficult to decide if an animal belongs to the vagrant benthonic or to the nektonic type. The gradation is just as complete as between nekton and plankton. In general, a radial form may be said to be characteristic of the sedentary benthos, while a bilaterally symmetrical form is as characteristic of the vagrant benthos. Examples of change of form with change of habit occur in many classes. Both plants and animals, themselves belonging to the sedentary benthos, may lead, secondarily, a vagrant life by being attached to vagrant benthonic forms. These may be regarded as vagrant epibenthos. Among plants, algæ are the most familiar examples, while among animals hydrozoa (Hydractinia on shells inhabited by hermit crabs), actinians, and bryozoans furnish the most characteristic examples.

D. *Limnoplankton.*

Fresh water plankton is met with in all fresh water lakes, ponds, and streams. It not infrequently occurs in surprising amounts. Thus studies of the Illinois River and its tributaries have shown that it averages 2.7 parts per million of the water in the stream, and that the total average moving down stream past any given point aggregates 75,000 tons per annum, or about 8.5 tons per hour (6). The holoplankton here is largely composed of minute plants, while the meroplankton, consisting both of larval plants and animals, constitutes a very large percentage of the mass. Finally, the pseudoplankton makes up a not inconsiderable portion of this mass. The term limnoplankton has been restricted to the plankton of the larger fresh water seas by a number of writers, notably O. Zacharias, who uses the term *heleoplankton* for the plankton of shallow ponds and *potamoplankton* for that of rivers.

E.   *Limnonekton* (*Heleonekton, Potamonekton*).

The nekton of fresh water, like that of the sea, is typically represented by the fish, though other classes of animals, such as the aquatic mammal, are also represented. The merostomes of the Palæozoic also appear to belong here. An interesting example of a meronektonic life is evidenced by the tadpole, while an epinektonic condition exists in the larval fresh water mussel (Unio) which attaches itself to the gills of fishes.

F.   *Limnobenthos* (*Heleobenthos, Potamobenthos*).

Both sedentary and vagrant benthos occur in fresh water; the former is chiefly represented by plants, but a number of invertebrates also belong here. Such are the sedentary infusoria, rotifers, and bryozoa, and the fresh water sponges and hydrozoa, though the principal members of the latter class are only temporarily attached and may move about at will. The vagrant benthos, on the other hand, is well represented by molluscs, worms, and crustacea, though the crawfish also leads at times a benthonic life.

G.   *Atmoplankton.*   H. *Atmonekton.*   I. *Atmobenthos.*

Among the air-breathers permanent planktonic and nektonic types are unknown, though many unicellular plants, especially bacteria, live in the atmosphere for a considerable period of time, and must during that period be classed as atmoholoplankton. The meroplankton, however, is well represented, chiefly by the spores and seeds of plants, which are wafted about by the winds, and so become widely dispersed. Terrestrial nekton is represented by insects, birds, flying reptiles, and bats. None of these lead a permanently nektonic life in the air, for all return, more or less frequently, to the substratum. Nevertheless, during their period of flight, which often is very long, they must be considered as nekton of the air. The benthos of the earth's surface is pretty sharply divided into sedentary benthos, or plants, and vagrant benthos, or animals, though some exceptions occur among the lowest plants, while some animals lead a temporary or permanent (parasitic) attached existence.

BIBLIOGRAPHY XXVII.

(See also Bibliographies XXVI and XXVIII.)

1. CHUN, CARL. 1890. Die pelagische Thierwelt in Grossen Tiefen. Verhandlungen der Gesellschaft deutscher Naturforscher und Aerzte. Bremen.
2. GRABAU, A. W. 1899. The Relation of Marine Bionomy to Stratigraphy. Chapter III in Geology and Palæontology of Eighteen-mile Creek. Bulletin of the Buffalo Society of Natural Sciences, Vol. VI, pp. 319–365.
3. GRABAU, A. W. 1909. Some New or Little Known Geological Terms and Their Application in Stratigraphic Writing. Abstract: Science, N. S., Vol. XXIX, p. 750.
4. HÆCKEL, ERNST. 1890. Planktonstudien. Vergleichende Untersuchungen über die Bedeutung und Zusammensetzung der pelagischen Fauna und Flora. Jena.
5. HENSON, VICTOR. 1887. Ueber die Bestimmung des Planktons, oder des im Meere treibenden Materials an Pflanzen und Thieren. (V. Bericht der Commission zur Wissenschaftlichen Untersuchungen der deutschen Meere.)
6. ILLINOIS STATE LABORATORY OF NATURAL HISTORY. Bulletin, Vol. VI, Art. II.
7. ORTMANN, ARNOLD. 1895. Grundzüge der marinen Thier-geographie. Jena.
8. SCHÜTT, F. 1893. Das Pflanzenleben der Hochsee. Plankton Expedition, Vol. I. Leipzig.
9. WALTHER, JOHANNES. 1894. Einleitung in die Geologie als historische Wissenschaft. I. Bionomie des Meeres. II. Die Lebensweise der Meerestiere. Jena. Gustav Fischer.

CHAPTER XXVIII.

BIONOMIC CHARACTERISTICS OF PLANTS AND ANIMALS.

A bionomic consideration of the different classes of modern plants and animals is of the utmost importance to the stratigrapher, since it is from such studies that he is enabled to interpret the conditions of the past, in so far as they are indicated by organisms. The present chapter will, therefore, deal somewhat at length with the bionomic characters of the various classes, special stress being laid on those types which are capable of fossilization.

BIONOMIC CHARACTERS OF PLANTS (Schimper–25).

Protophyta.

The majority of these primitive plants are not adapted for preservation, and hence are unknown in the fossil state. The slime molds, or Myxomycetes, occur on decaying logs, in damp wood, on rotting leaves, etc. The Schizophytes or bacteria are everywhere present. They are abundant in the plankton of the shallower portions of the sea, but rare in the open sea. In fresh water, in the air, and in the soil, as well as in all decaying substances, they occur, themselves forming the principal agents of decay. Their work in the formation of iron ore deposits has elsewhere been referred to. The Cyanophyceæ occur in the sea, in fresh water, on moist earth, on damp rocks, and on the bark of trees. They enter the intercellular spaces of higher plants, and may enter into the structure of the lichen thallus. Some species flourish in hot springs with a temperature as high as 85° C. Volvox and other flagellates, most of which are generally regarded as animals, are especially at home in stagnant water, and amidst putrefying organic matter in the sea or in fresh water. Many flagellates are also parasitic and the spores of some may survive a temperature of 250° to 300° F. for ten minutes, though the adults are killed at 180°.

Thallophyta.

ALGÆ. The lowest of the green algæ (Protococcaceæ) constitute, with the diatoms, the Cyanophyceæ, and the bacteria the chief holoplanktonic plants, though many of them also have a benthonic habit, being attached chiefly to other plants, or encrusting stones, as in the case of some fresh water Cyanophyceæ. They are mainly inhabitants of fresh water, though diatoms are also abundant in the sea. Protococcus itself is terrestrial. The Charophycea, often classed with the green algæ, secrete lime. This is especially true of Chara, which occurs in fresh water lakes from two meters down, and which is probably an important factor in the formation of fresh water limestones. (See *ante,* page 471.) The majority of the green algæ belong to the benthos, being equally abundant in the marine and fresh water realms. The red algæ are benthonic and chiefly marine, though some species occur in fresh water. Lime-secreting types also occur in this class, constituting the nullipores or coralline seaweeds which inhabit the littoral district of the sea, chiefly in tropical regions but to some extent also in temperate climates. They occur as jointed fronds of a red color (Corallina), as crusts on other algæ (Melobesia), or as extensive pink incrustations on stones or shells (Lithothamnion). They are especially characteristic of depths between 15 and 35 (or 50) fathoms, where they constitute the "coralline zone" of the littoral district. The brown algæ are mainly marine benthonic types, usually attached to a rocky substratum. The common brown algæ of the northern coasts (Fucus, Ascophyllum) have already been referred to as clothing the rocky ledges and forming a substratum for Hydrozoa, Bryozoa, sponges, etc., as well as other algæ. Though typically attached, some forms, like the Sargassum, will continue to grow and multiply, even after they have been torn from their anchorage and carried into mid-ocean. The Sargassum is thus typically pseudoplanktonic, as are also all the other algæ attached to it. Many of the brown seaweeds grow to great size. A familiar example is the common kelp (Laminaria) of the Atlantic coast, which generally grows to ten or more feet in length, while the giant kelp of the Pacific (Macrocystis) is said sometimes to reach a length of three hundred meters. The Laminarians are typical of the littoral district down to fifteen fathoms, this interval being known as the zone of Laminarians. The large species all grow in the deeper portions of this zone, where they are anchored by their "roots" to stones, shells, or other objects of support. They often hold on to objects small enough to be carried away with the seaweed during a violent storm; and since the stipe and frond of the seaweed are commonly covered with sedentary benthonic animals, this seaweed forms a ready agent for the wider dispersal of such organisms.

In general the larger algæ are attached to a rocky or other hard substratum or to other algæ (epiphytic). On muddy or sandy bottoms algæ are rare, though stranded algæ may be buried in numbers in mudflats. The large algæ (macrophytes) are mostly restricted to the photic region, where they are distributed in the two belts, the perpetually submerged (*i. e.,* below low tide) and the periodically emerging belt (between tides). Marine algæ are found to the height of the salt spray on the shore, while terrestrial algæ are known from the tropics, where they live as epiphytes on leaves, especially in the rainy districts. In the temperate regions they are associated symbiotically with fungi to form lichens, which increase in numbers and importance as the climate becomes cooler. They and the mosses constitute the chief epiphytes and epiliths in the temperate and cooler climates. Lichens sometimes form structures which under favorable conditions may be preserved. In the arctic regions microscopic red and brown algæ (Sphærella, etc.) often color the snow and ice and, together with many other microphytes, form a characteristic element of the vegetation of these regions.

Diatoms are important rock-builders, since their siliceous skeletons or frustules are readily preserved. They occur both in fresh and salt water, no ditch, pond, or pool being without them, and they form a characteristic member of the marine plankton. A great many types, however, are benthonic, forming yellowish-brown films on the mud in shallow pools, or growing attached by slender stalks to other plants. They commonly possess the power of motion found also in desmids and other unicellular plants. Fossil diatoms are abundant in the Tertiary of many localities, often forming extensive beds of nearly pure frustules, generally of fresh water origin. Underlying the city of Richmond, Virginia, is a bed of these organisms eighteen feet thick, while other extensive deposits occur in the coastal plain of Maryland and New Jersey, as well as in many other parts of the world. In Mesozoic deposits they are less abundant, and they are not known positively from Palæozoic deposits, probably owing to alteration of the frustule. Diatomaceous deposits are often erroneously spoken of as infusorial earth.

FUNGI. The members of this group are destitute of chlorophyll and, consequently, are dependent upon organic matter for food, being either parasites (growing upon living organisms) or saprophytes (growing upon dead organic matter) or both parasitic and saprophytic. Fungi can thus grow in the dark regions of the earth, sunlight not being essential. They are mostly terrestrial (when not living within their host), though some marine representatives are known, and certain of the molds (phycomycetes) form on decaying animals in fresh water or sometimes on living fish or crustacea. The large terrestrial fungi are most characteristic of the temperate zones, the tropical species being mostly small.

LICHENS. Lichens are terrestrial plants growing chiefly upon the bark of trees, rocks, the ground, mosses, and, more rarely, upon perennial leaves. In large forests they hang as a dense growth from the trees (Usnea), but in other cases they encrust the rough bark of the trees. They may also occur on the smooth bark of young trees or shrubs, and sometimes on decayed or decaying wood. All of these are classed as *corticolous* lichens. Saxicolous lichens grow on rocks and stones, which they disintegrate. They comprise the *calcicolous* forms, growing on limestones, or other calcareous rocks, on the mortar of walls, ets., and *calcifugous* forms which grow on rocks of non-calcareous character. *Terrestrial* lichens grow on all kinds of soil, some preferring peaty, some calcareous, some sandy, and some granitic soil, but none grow on cultivated soil.

Muscicolous lichens grow on decaying moss, such as the dead peat mosses, while *epiphyllous* species grow on perennial leaves, whose vitality they do not affect. The distribution of lichens is greater than that of any other class of plant, occurring from the poles to the equator, practically wherever land exists. Lichens may be dried so thoroughly that they can easily be reduced to powder, yet their vitality is only suspended, and moisture will restore them to renewed activity. Their growth is extremely slow, and the life of the plant seems to be very long, in some cases many hundreds of years.

BRYOPHYTA AND PTERIDOPHYTA.

These are wholly absent from the sea, but in fresh water a few bryophytes are known. The peat-moss (Sphagnum) grows abundantly in wet woods or in bogs. The growing ends increase while the old portion dies off. Among the pteridophytes the class of Filicinæ has an aquatic group in the rhizocarps, or water ferns (Hydropterideæ), which grow partly submerged or floating. The spores of these plants are widely distributed by flotation and may become enclosed in the finer lutaceous sediments. Spores referred to rhizocarps (Protosalvinia) are found in abundance in the black Devonic shales of North America, and it has been held that the black color and petroliferous character of these shales are wholly due to the spores of these plants. If the spores are, indeed, those of rhizocarps, they would be an indication of the formation of the black shales in the estuaries of rivers, since these plants are found only in fresh water.

Ferns are most abundant in the tropics, where they develop an extraordinary wealth of form, and vary in their dimensions from small moss-like plants to trees. They are especially characteristic of humid forests.

Equisetinæ, or horse-tails, are represented by the living Equisetum and by the extinct Calamites, which latter often grew into large trees. Equisetum to-day grows in low moist ground and in the sand and gravel of railroad embankments, and along road sides. Much silica is present in the epidermis of the plants, giving to it a rough, harsh feel.

Lycopodiaceæ, or club-mosses. These are to-day represented by small prostrate plants found mainly in the deeper woods. In late Palæozoic time, however, they were represented by forest trees (Lepidodendron, Sigillaria, etc.) A few aquatic lycopods exist (quill-worts, Isoetæ). These plants grow either partly or completely submerged, and in general resemble the smaller club-mosses.

Both Equisetæ and Lycopodiaceæ are characteristic of the tropic and temperate zones, the Lycopodiaceæ being more prominent in the tropics.

Spermatophyta.

By far the greater mass of spermatophytes or phanerogamous plants are terrestrial in habitat, though a not inconsiderable number live in fresh water. Certain members of the pondweed family (Potamogetonaceæ) and the frog's-bit family (Hydrocharitaceæ), comprising about twenty-five species in all, have become wholly adapted to a marine benthonic habit and are known as sea-grasses. The pondweed family is represented on the Atlantic coast by the eel-grass (*Zostera marina* L.) and the ditch-grass (*Ruppia maritima* L.), both of which are extremely common, and both of which are concerned in the gradual choking of the marshes. A number of species are partly marine, as the marsh-grass (Spartina) growing within the limit of tide-water. The mangrove, as already noted, is partly adapted to a marine habitat, all of it but the leaves being periodically submerged.

All degrees of freshwater phanerogams are found, from those having only their roots in the water, as many of the larger swamp plants, to those nearly or entirely submerged. Parasitic, saprophytic, and epiphytic phanerogams are further characteristic types adapted to peculiar habitats. In short, the variety and adaptability of the spermatophytes are as multitudinous as the variation in the character of the terrestrial realm.

The coniferous gymnosperms are almost wholly confined to temperate climates, especially the colder belts, but cycads are most characteristically tropical plants. Both monocotyledons and dicotyledons are more commonly represented by trees in the tropical than in the temperate zone, the number of trees diminishing toward the colder belts, where the conifers increase in number.

Arboreal vegetation is characteristically unknown in regions where the sub-soil is permanently frozen, *i. e.,* where the mean summer temperature is below 10° C. Such is the character of the treeless plains of northern Canada, the coldest part of the North American continent, where the mean annual temperature is below —8° C. and the mean summer temperature below 10° C. Here sedges, grasses, and lichens predominate, while trees and sphagnum-bogs are conspicuously absent.

The present northern extent of the forest regions of Canada is limited by the mean summer temperatures of 10°-15° C. Here the poplar (*Populus tremuloides* and *P. balsamifera*), the birch (*Betula alba*), spruce (*Picea alba* and *P. nigra*), pine (*Pinus banksiana*), and larch (*Larix americana*) occur, while beneath them the ground is often an extensive sphagnum swamp. "Poplar, birch, and pine extend northward as far as the heavy forest extends, while larch and the true species of spruce extend northward to the northern limit of trees, becoming small and dwarfed before they finally disappear." (Tyrrell–*28:389-91.*)

South and west of the forested area are the grassy plains, which, because of their dryness, do not support trees or sphagnum bogs. As these plains were in the condition of the frozen tundra after the retreat of the ice, and with the amelioration of the climate became dry, no trees or sphagnum bogs ever developed there.

Ecology and Ecological Adaptations of Sphermatophytes.

Modern spermatophytes, as a whole, are divisible into a number of habitudinal types, among which the following are the most important:

1. *Hydrophytes and Hemihydrophytes*. Aquatic plants are marine, or brackish, or fresh water. The marine types comprise the grass-wracks or eel-grasses (*Zostera marina*, and *Z. nana*). A few plants are confined to a brackish-water habitat (*Ruppia maritima*, etc.), while others are adapted to both fresh and brackish water. The aquatic vegetation of ponds and lakes may be divided into types with: (a) submerged leaves, (b) submerged and floating leaves, (c) floating leaves, (d) submerged leaves and erect leaves or stems, (e) erect leaves or stems, and lastly (f) marsh plants.

2. *Xerophytes*. This group includes the plants which have devices for procuring or for storing water, or for limiting transpiration, adaptations related to dry habitats. They have frequently long tap roots which, in some cases, reach down to a subterranean water supply. There is also often a superficial root system. Xerophytes of the deserts often have succulent stems, like the cacti of southern and central America. In other deserts, such as the Sahara, succulents are not prominent. A spiny character also characterizes many Xerophytes.

3. *Bog Xerophytes*. These are plants living in the peaty soil of fens and moors, which, though physically wet, are physiologically dry. Such plants can survive a partial or complete drying up of the bog.

4. *Tropophytes*. These are plants with a xerophytic character during the unfavorable season. Thus deciduous trees are xerophytic during the leafless period of winter while other plants survive the unfavorable period by means of their bulbs, rhizomes, or other special structures.

5. *Hygrophytes*. These are intermediate between Xerophytes and hydrophytes and are sometimes called *Mesophytes*. Assimilation goes on throughout the whole year, except during periods of frost or when buried by snow.

6. *Sciophytes*. These are plants growing in the shade of forests. They may be hygrophytes or they may be herbaceous tropophytes.

7. *Halophytes*. These are plants growing in saline soils, and they are characterized by xerophytic adaptations. Many of them are succulent, their leaves and, to some extent, their stems having much water-storing tissue.

8. *Calcicole and Calcifuge Plants*. Plants invariably inhabiting calcareous soils are said to be calcicoles, while calcifuge species are rarely or never found in calcareous soil. They are sometimes termed *silicicoles*.

BIONOMIC CHARACTERISTICS OF ANIMALS.*

I. PROTOZOA.

FORAMINIFERA. The Foraminifera are typically marine organisms, though a considerable number of species has become adapted to brackish water, living in estuaries and near the mouths of streams, while many species, commonly placed in this class, live entirely in fresh water. Their distribution is so great that scarcely any marine sediments are wholly free from the shells of these animals. Most Foraminifera belong to the vagrant benthos, though sedentary benthonic forms also occur. Only something over twenty living planktonic species are known, these belonging chiefly to the genera Globigerina, Orbulina, and Pulvinulina (Figs. 101-103), the first predominating. The small number of species is, however, counterbalanced by the enormous number of individuals. The benthonic Foraminifera are confined chiefly to the littoral district, where the character of the bottom and the temperature of the water exert important influences on the distribution of these organisms. A muddy facies of the sea-bottom seems to be conducive to the existence of a large number of species, but the rocky bottoms are not without their types; while algæ and sea-grasses commonly form the home of vast numbers of these organisms. The coarse, sandy and gravelly bottoms are not generally inhabited by these animals, though their dead shells are not uncommon in the sands along our beaches; while along some shores, they are so abundant as to constitute the greater portion, if not the whole, of the deposit. Dana (9) states that in the Great Barrier-reef region of Australia the shells of Orbitolites are so abundant that . . . "they seemed in some places to make up the whole sand of the beaches, both of the coral islets and of the neighboring Australian shore."

The vertical range of the benthonic Foraminifera is very great, species sometimes passing through a range of several thousand fathoms. In such cases there is often a change in the size or thickness of the shell with the change in depth. Although the planktonic Foraminifera comprise so few species, the number of their individuals is enormous. From their shells the Globigerina oozes form in deep water, where no sediment is carried; but it is evident that, in a region where the land is reduced to near base-level, so that little or no sediment is carried into the sea, pure accumulations of such shells will occur near shore, thus, forming a

* Only those represented by fossils are taken into account here.

foraminiferal ooze in shallow water. But not only planktonic shells but the benthonic species as well may form a pure accumulation of foraminiferal shells, as has been the case in the chalk, in which the planktonic species are practically wanting. (Walther–29:215.) Reproduction of the Foraminifera is carried on by fission, budding, and spore formation. In the first two cases, the resulting part and the buds have the characteristics of the parent, except its size, and there are no special structures which serve for the greater distribution of the species. When spores are formed, these may be provided with a flagellum, whereupon the organisms pass through a mero-planktonic stage.

While the geographical distribution of the benthonic species is very restricted, and influenced by the facies of the sea bottom, the geographical distribution of the pelagic species is prevented from being world-wide only by the changes in the temperature of the water and by the ocean currents. The pelagic species are extremely abundant in tropical regions, and their shells form vast accumulations on the sea-bottoms over which they live. In the great depths these shells are absent, for they may be completely dissolved while they sink to the bottom, or shortly after reaching it.

RADIOLARIA. The Radiolaria are marine planktonic Protozoa. They inhabit principally the open sea, where they occur at the surface or at various depths below it. In regions of terrigenous sedimentation, or where an influx of fresh water occurs, these animals are seldom met with. Hence their siliceous shells occur in abundance only in the deposits found at a distance from shore, and in deep water, where they may constitute as high as seventy per cent. of the mass. The greatest abundance of radiolarian skeletons was found by the *Challenger* expedition at a depth between 2,000 and 4,475 fathoms—the greatest depth sounded. In many places in the Pacific the bottom ooze is almost entirely composed of radiolarian shells with some intermixture of sponge spicules. The celebrated Barbados earth, a Tertiary deposit, is likewise composed of radiolarian remains, to the exclusion of almost every other organism.

Fission, budding, and spore formation constitute the methods of reproduction in Radiolaria. The spores may be provided with flagella, constituting "swarm spores," which, like their progenitors, lead a planktonic existence.

II. PORIFERA.

The sponges are marine or fresh-water animals, of a sedentary benthonic habit. In general only such species as secrete a calcareous or siliceous skeleton—either continuous or consisting of separate spicules—are capable of preservation in a fossil state. The vertical distribution of marine species ranges from the shore zone down to the greater depths of the sea. Not infrequently species are found which regularly undergo an exposure of several hours between tides, though most littoral species occur below low-water mark, or in tide pools from which the water is never drained. Sponges will grow wherever a suitable surface for attachment is found, the most usual substratum chosen being cliffs, boulders, shells, or the stems and "roots" of the larger algæ. In deeper and quieter water, the sandy and gravelly bottoms are inhabited by sponges, and in the great depths they occur on the oozes and other soft deposits. A pseudovagrant (epi-vagrant) benthonic habit is assumed by a number of species, which attach themselves to the carapaces of Crustacea. Certain sponges bore into shells and other calcareous substances, forming extensive galleries and commonly destroying the shell. *Clione sulphurea,* common on our Atlantic coast, completely riddles shells, and then forms large irregularly rounded masses of a sulphur yellow color, often entirely enveloping the shell.

The reproduction of the sponges is either asexual or sexual. In the former case, buds are formed, which, growing larger, without detaching themselves, put out buds of their own, thus forming a colonial aggregation. Sponges torn into several pieces will frequently form as many new individuals, and sponges which were placed in close juxtaposition by Bowerbank in a relatively short time united into one. A method of internal gemmation occurs, in which groups of cells, or gemmulæ, become detached and after a time develop into complete sponges. Sexual reproduction, from either hermaphrodite or sexually distinct parents, leads to a free swimming blastula. This develops into a gastrula, which attaches itself and develops into the adult. Thus a mero-planktonic stage occurs in sponges, which serves as a means of extensive distribution.

III. Cœlenterata.

Hydrozoa. The Hydrozoa are typically marine Cœlenterates, though a few species occur in fresh water, *e. g., Hydra viridis* and *H. fusca, Cordilophora lacustris* and the fresh water medusa of Lake Tanganyika: *Limnocnida tanganyikæ.* Some Scyphomedusæ (Aurelia, Cyanea), according to Moseley, seem to prefer to float near the mouths of fresh water streams; while in New South Wales these medusæ were observed floating in shoals where the water was pure enough to be drinkable. The majority of species have a sedentary benthonic stage, the hydriform stage, which is generally colonial, the compound polyp stock being attached to rocks, algæ, shells, timbers, or other objects of support, by means of a thread-like branching root-stock or hydrorhyza, which spreads out over the object of support and from which the individual polyparia arise, each with a distinct stem or hydrocaulus. A few forms, like *Hydractinia polyclina* and some Podocoryne, are pseudo-vagrant benthos, being attached to the shells of gastropods carried about by hermit crabs. Some species, like *Bougainvillia fruticosa*, prefer an epi-planktonic habit, becoming attached to floating timbers, a similar habit being assumed by those hydroids which live attached to the floating Sargassum. An epi-nektonic manner of life may perhaps be considered the habit of Hydrichthys, which lives parasitically upon a fish. *Corymorpha pendula*, though not attached, lives partly buried in the mud of the shallow sea; while Hydra leads, at times at least, a kind of vagrant benthonic life, though its journeyings are probably never very great.

Many, if not most Hydrozoa have a distinct medusiform person which, when perfect, is perhaps the best type of a holo-planktonic organism. In a few Hydrozoa—Hydra Sertularidæ—the medusi-form stage is wanting, in others it is degenerate, never becoming free (Clava); but in a large number of species it is a free individual. Again, in the Narco- and Trachymedusæ, as well as in some others, only the medusa occurs, the hydroid being suppressed. Compound medusæ occur as well as compound hydroids. The former are the Siphonophora in which, by budding from the parent medusa, a compound colony is formed which leads a holo-planktonic existence. Lucernaria is an example of a medusa attached to foreign objects. The medusæ, whether free or attached, produce the sexual products which give rise to new hydroid colonies or directly to new medusæ. The egg develops into a ciliated planula which leads a mero-plank-tonic existence before it settles down to become a benthonic hydroid, or before it develops into the medusa. A number of hy-droids grow attached to rocks and sea-weeds, or to bridge piles, in such a position as to become regularly exposed for several hours each day during ebb tide. Even the delicate and unprotected Clava of our northern shores delights to live under such conditions, and is rarely found in deeper water or in tide pools. Most hydroids, however, can not withstand such exposure, and hence they are found only in the deeper waters or the deeper tide pools.

The majority of hydroids are inhabitants of the littoral district, and they usually occur in the more moderate depths. The tubularian hydroids probably never extend to any considerable depths, the deep-water forms belonging chiefly to the Plumularidæ. (Agassiz–1, ii:35.) One of the abyssal Plumularians was obtained by the *Blake* at a depth of 1,240 fathoms, which exceeded by more than 300 fathoms that at which Plumularians were obtained by the *Challenger*. (Agassiz–1.)

The Palæozoic class of graptolites or Graptozoa is the most important group of the Cœlenterata from a stratigrapher's point of view, for it constitutes one of the most important classes of index fossils known.

Lapworth (Walther–29) holds that the majority of dendroid graptolites (Dendroidea) undoubtedly grew attached to sea-weeds, rocks, or other supports, in the manner of most modern hydroids, but some were attached to floating algæ, leading an epi-planktonic existence. Cases of such attachment have been observed among these fossils.

Lapworth argues that, if the sicula was attached by means of the slender basal thread, the *nema,* to floating objects of support, whether disc or sea-weed, the second and succeeding hydrothecæ, growing in the same direction as the sicula, would open downward. This suggests that the earlier graptolites were not planktonic, but grew attached to sea-weeds and rocks after the manner of modern hydroids. This view is taken by Hahn (16) with reference to Dictyonema. In later genera of graptolites, however, which may have been attached to floating objects (epi-plankton), the branches either bent backward, so as to cause the later hydrothecæ to open in an opposite direction from the sicula and early hydrothecæ; or the direction of growth was reversed, the second and succeeding hydrothecæ growing backward along the nema, which became the supporting rod or virgula.

Some of the graptolites appear to have led a holoplanktonic existence, the nema being attached to a central organ or disc, which probably served as a float. This was long ago demonstrated in a number of species by Professor Hall, and lately has been shown in great detail in Diplograptus by Ruedemann. This observer holds that this mode of attachment was characteristic of the virgulate graptolites (Axonophora) as a whole, while the Axonolipa he thinks were attached to seaweeds. (Ruedemann–25:515.) Whether holo-planktonic or epi-planktonic, either method of life accounts for the wide distribution of the graptolites. The fact that they are almost universally found in carbonaceous shales suggests that floating algæ may have been the principal carriers of these organisms, the decaying vegetable matter furnishing the carbon for coloring the muds in which the organisms were buried. On the other hand, it is not improbable that much of the carbonaceous material was derived from the graptolites themselves. The general slight thickness of these beds, and the fact that in successive beds the species change, indicate a slow accumulation of the deposits in relatively quiet water.

According to Ruedemann's observations (23), the young Diplograptus, on leaving the gonophore, has already advanced into the sicula stage, so that a free-swimming planula stage appears not to exist. It is probable that this is true of most, if not all, graptolites, and that hence the distribution of these animals is such as will be accounted for by the vicissitudes which they met with as a floating colony.

ANTHOZOA. The Anthozoa are typically marine sedentary benthonic animals, inhabiting the warmer waters of the oceans. A large number are without hard supporting parts, and consequently leave no remains, while others, probably the majority of Anthozoa, secrete a calcareous or horny corallum, which is capable of preservation. Among the Actinaria, or fleshy polyps, a certain amount of locomotion of a creeping or gliding nature is often observable (Metridium, etc.), the individuals possessing this ability thus passing from a normal sedentary to a vagrant benthonic life. A few forms are also met with among the plankton. Occasionally epi-planktonic individuals are met with, attached to floating algæ or timbers; and epi-vagrant benthonic individuals attached to moving crustaceans are not unknown. The Madreporaria, or stone corals, are normally sedentary forms, though they are not necessarily attached, but may rest upon the sands. (Fungia, some Porites.)

Though the normal medium of the Anthozoa is salt water, a few are known in brackish and even in tolerably fresh water. *Cilicia rubeola* is reported by the *Challenger* (Vol. XVI, pt. II; 36) in the river Thames in New Zealand; and Dana (9:*120*) states that " . . . upon the reefs enclosing the harbor of Rewa (Viti Lebu), where a large river, three hundred yards wide, empties, which during freshets enables vessels at anchor two and a half miles off its mouth to dip up fresh water alongside, there is a single porous species of Madrepora (*M. cribripora*), growing here and there in patches over a surface of dead coral rock or sand. In similar places about other regions species of Porites are most common." Several species of corals grow at the mouth of the Rio de la Plata.

Porites limosa flourishes in muddy water, and *Astrea bower-*

banki does not seem to mind mud or sediment, or even muddy brackish water, growing on, and encrusting the stones at the mouth of the Mangrove Creek, Australia, these stones being covered with mud and slime, and being washed over twice in the twenty-four hours by muddy, brackish water. (Tenison-Woods.)   A common Red Sea coral, *Stylophora pistillata*, is recorded by Milne-Edwards and Haime from the intensely salt and dense waters of the Dead Sea.

The simple corals (Caryophyllia, etc.) are chiefly found on muddy bottoms, often attached to a shell or other object resting on the mud. The bathymetric distribution varies from shallow water to a thousand fathoms or more. This method of life corresponds well with what is known of the Palæozoic Tetraseptata, which commonly lived on a muddy bottom, with their bases not infrequently showing signs of attachment to shells or other foreign objects. The compound corals build heads or stocks often of great size and weight. They are generally attached to stones, shells, or to the rock bottom and, through rapid increase by budding or division, masses of great size may be formed over a small object of support. Even on muddy bottoms a small object of support may serve as the nucleus around which a coral mass will grow, which, as it increases in size and weight, will sink to a greater or less depth into the mud on which it rests.

The typical compound or reef corals are very restricted in their bathymetric distribution. They do not normally occur below fifty fathoms, and the majority live in less than twenty fathoms of water. Very many, indeed, live so close to the surface as to be exposed at the lowest tides. A minimum annual temperature of twenty degrees centigrade marks the regions in which most reef-building corals occur, though in a few cases colder regions are known to be inhabited by true reef-builders. In all seas, however, which are subject to freezing, or are regularly invaded by floating ice, reef-building corals cannot thrive, and hence the occurrence of modern or ancient coral reefs is a reliable indication of a minimum winter temperature above freezing.

The reproduction of the Anthozoa is both asexual and sexual. The asexual method is carried on by fission and budding, the new-formed corallites usually remaining united with their parents, thus producing colonial forms. In some cases, however, the buds become free and begin an independent life (Fungia, Balanophyllia, etc.). New colonies, however, are mostly begun by sexually generated individuals. From the fertilized egg develops a meroplanktonic ciliated embryo, in appearance not unlike the planula of the hydrozoa. After attachment this develops into the polyp, which early begins to secrete its horny or calcareous corallum.

IV. Molluscoidea.

BRYOZOA. The Bryozoa or Polyzoa are marine or fresh water, chiefly colonial, benthonic animals. A few occur parasitic on a living substratum, but the majority of species are epiphytically attached to algæ, to hydroids, etc. (epizoön), or to inorganic objects (epilith), either basally or in an encrusting manner. The majority of species are marine; and their bathymetric distribution ranges from the shore zone, where they are exposed at low tide, to the abyssal depths, a species of Bifaxia having been obtained below 3,000 fathoms. The majority of species, however, live in moderate depths. While the Bryozoa normally lead a strictly sedentary benthonic life, a few species may drift about with the sea-weed to which they are attached, thus assuming an epi-planktonic habit. Holoplanktonic forms are, however, unknown.

Many of the Palæozoic species resembled and had a habitat similar to that of certain corals, often forming extensive beds or even reefs composed of few species but of an enormous number of individuals.

The egg of the bryozoan develops into a meroplanktonic ciliated larva, which later on settles down, becomes attached, and develops into a full-grown individual which, by budding, produces the colony.

BRACHIOPODA. The brachiopods are marine benthonic organisms, of exceptional stratigraphic importance, since they are to a high degree dependent on the facies of the sea bottom. Some species of Terebratula and Lingula can withstand a considerable exposure, the former having been noted out of water for hours together at low tide. Lingula is buried, by means of its long fleshy peduncle, in the sand near shore; Crania is attached to rocks and shells by one of its valves; but the majority of brachiopods are attached by their fleshy pedicles to rocks, shells, corals, or to one another. They seldom live on muddy or sandy bottoms, but are readily embedded in these, by becoming detached, after death, from the rocks or other objects to which they adhered.

The bathymetric distribution of the Brachiopoda ranges from shallow water to 2,900 fathoms (in one case); the majority of species occurring, however, above the hundred-fathom line, while a goodly number have been obtained in depths of ten fathoms or less. A number of species have an individual range of several hundred fathoms, this range in one of two cases being nearly 800 fathoms.

The mero-planktonic larva of brachiopods is known as the cephalula, and consists of a ciliated umbrella-like anterior end, carrying four eyes; a middle portion carrying the mantle lobes; and a posterior portion. When the larva becomes attached by the posterior end, which develops into the pedicle of the adult, the anterior end becomes enveloped by the forward-turning mantle lobes and develops into the body of the brachiopod.

V. MOLLUSCA.

PELECYPODA. The pelecypods are marine or fresh-water benthonic molluscs, which lead either a sedentary or a vagrant life. The majority of species live in the sea, but of these some can adapt themselves to brackish or even fresh water. Thus species of Cardium, Solen, Mya, and other marine pelecypods have been obtained in fresh, or nearly fresh, water; while Unio, on the other hand, has been found in the Brisbane river within reach of the flood tide. In the neighborhood of Rio Janeiro, Solen, and Mytilus, were found living with fresh-water Ampullaria in brackish water (Darwin–10).

A number of pelecypods inhabit the shore zone, but the majority of these live buried in the sands and muds, and so are protected from desiccation at low tide. *Mytilus edulis,* however, is a good example of a shore pelecypod, for it habitually grows in positions where it will periodically be exposed at low tide; while *Modiola plicatula* is especially common in salt marshes, where it is covered only for a short period at high water. The closely related *Modiola modiola,* which occurs on our northern shores, is, however, seldom exposed, growing either in deep water or in tide pools which are never drained.

Ostrea arborea is another striking shore mollusc, growing in vast quantities on the free roots of the mangrove, and withstanding a periodic exposure under a tropical sun. *Ostrea borealis,* on the other hand, is at home only in water of several fathoms' depth.

The bathymetric range of the pelecypods is very great, and even a single species may have a range of considerable magnitude. Thus, while *Mytilus edulis* does not occur below fifty fathoms, another species, *M. phaseolinus,* ranges from the shore to a depth of 3,000 fathoms. In the greater depths, the pelecypods are commonly characterized by exceeding delicacy of shell and sculpture, the shell being often quite transparent. Some deep-water species show bright colors, but the majority are pale. Altogether there are to be found among these deep-water species "innumerable illustrations of beauty, adaptation, or unusual characteristics . . ." (Agassiz). In the littoral district, on the other hand, the thick-shelled pelecypods predominate, and this is especially true of the shore zone.

Pelecypods, like brachiopods, are excellent facies indicators, for, though they live on all kinds of sea bottom, the species, or at least the faunal combinations, are dependent on, and characteristic of, the particular facies on which they live. The majority of pelecypods are free animals, a few, such as the oyster, mussel, and the like, being attached to foreign objects—either by direct cementation or by a byssus. The free pelecypods often have the power of locomotion, Unio, Mactra, and others traveling occasionally for considerable distances. Generally, however, these molluscs lie buried wholly or partially in the sand, and never change their location except when disturbed by storm waves. Some few pelecypods (Pecten, Lima) have the power of swimming short distances by the opening and closing, in rapid succession, of their valves, and the forcible ejection of water. Even Solen, though normally a burrowing animal, will swim for some distance in search of the proper bottom, and it may often be seen circling around in an aquarium, by a series of jerks, due to the periodic ejection of the water from the siphons. A number of pelecypods bore into wood or stone (Teredo, Lithodomus, Saxicava, etc.), leading a sedentary life within the habitation thus formed.

The bivalve molluscs have many enemies which prey upon them. Not the least of these are the carnivorous gastropods, whose depredations are usually marked by the vast number of shells with round holes bored into them, scattered along our beaches. Boring sponges will riddle the shells of littoral species, and corallines, Bryozoa, worms, and hydroids will attach themselves to the shells. There is abundant evidence in the riddled and punctured shells that even the Palæozoic molluscs were subject to similar attacks of boring sponges and carnivorous gastropods. When the animals die, their valves usually fall apart; and from their position, and the character and direction of the waves and currents, one valve may be carried shoreward, the other, seaward. This explains the frequent predominance, along the shore and in certain local portions, of fossiliferous beds of one valve, the other being entirely absent or at least very rare.

The marine pelecypod normally passes through a mero-plank-tonic larval stage—the trochophore—in which the young is provided with a velum, furnished with vibratory ciliæ (veliger stage). At certain seasons of the year these ciliated embryos swarm in the pelagic district, especially in the neighborhood of the shores, where they become the sport of the currents, which distribute them far and wide. When they finally settle down upon the sea bottom, on the loss of the velum, they develop further if they reach the proper substratum, other conditions being favorable. Vast numbers of the larvæ are destroyed before they reach the bottom, serving as food for all kinds of animals, or succumbing to unfavorable conditions; and vast numbers of others die from falling on an unfavorable bottom. That most species nevertheless develop to the fullest extent is due to the enormous fecundity of most pelecypods. As an extreme example may perhaps be mentioned our common northern oyster, *Ostrea virginiana,* which, according to Brooks (2: xxviii), produces nine millions of eggs. In fresh-water pelecypods the mero-planktonic veliger larva exists in one species only (*Dreissensia polymorpha*), which is believed to have migrated from salt to fresh water in recent geologic times. (Lang–19.) In the other freshwater pelecypods the development proceeds in a different manner, special adaptations to special modes of life being met with. In some cases (Pisidium, Cyclas) the eggs develop in special brood-capsules in the gills of the mother, which they leave with shell fully formed, as young bivalves. In these genera the velum remains rudimentary, the animal passing through the trochophore stage within the gills of the mother. In the Unionidæ the embryo passes through its several stages in the gill of the mother, leaving it with a bivalve shell, which is, however, furnished with a triangular process on the ventral border of each valve, by means of which the embryo attaches itself to the fins (Anodonta) or gills (Unio) of fishes. In this manner the animal leads an epinektonic existence, becoming enclosed by the rapid growth of the epithelium of the part where the embryo is attached, and leading then a truly endo-parasitic life. After several weeks the embryo has become transformed into a young mussel, which, breaking through the enclosing tissue of its nest, falls to the bottom of the water, there to develop into the adult.

SCAPHOPODA AND AMPHINEURA. The first of these classes is represented by the Dentalidæ; the second by the Chitonidæ, which alone are important palæontologically. Both are marine, being of a sedentary benthonic habit, though not permanently attached. Dentalium lies buried in the mud and sands usually at great depths, while Chiton and its allies cling to stones, shells, etc., and are rare in deep water, where only their more archaic representatives occur. A few species of Dentalium occur in moderately shallow water, but most of them live below the hundred fathom line, some reaching a depth of 2,000 fathoms or more. Chiton seldom extends below 500 fathoms. In both groups a mero-planktonic larva occurs.

GASTROPODA. The gastropods are typical benthonic animals, inhabiting the sea, fresh water, and the land. They almost invariably belong to the vagrant benthos, though the degree of locomotion varies greatly among the different species. Among the exceptions to the general vagrant habit are Vermetus and some other genera, which lead a truly sedentary benthonic life, being attached to rocks or shells. Some genera, like Capulus, adhere continually to shells and the tests of echinoderms and Crustacea; while the limpets, though adhering powerfully to rocks and shells by the muscular foot, are, nevertheless, in the habit of crawling about in search of food. Swimming and floating gastropods are also known, the latter (Janthina, Glaucus, etc.) belonging to the true plankton.

The number of species living on land and in fresh water is relatively small, though the individuals often occur in great numbers. The sea is the home of most gastropods, though some marine forms can live in fresh water, while conversely fresh-water forms have been found in water temporarily salt. Thus Limnæa was found by Darwin (10) in Brazil, in a fresh-water lake to which the sea had access at least once a year.

Among the normally fresh-water gastropods several occur which have become adapted to a marine life. Thus *Planorbis glaber* was found at a depth of 1,415 fathoms at Cape Teneriffe, and two species of Nerita have been found in the sea. Limnæa and Neritina live in the Baltic, where the water contains from 10 to 15 permille of salt.

The variety of form and coloration is exceedingly great among the gastropods, a fact which can easily be correlated with their high degree of cephalization and actively vagrant life. They occupy all parts of the sea, being much less dependent on the facies of the sea bottom than the pelecypods are. The division into carnivorous and herbivorous forms is also much more strongly emphasized than in the pelecypods, which live largely upon the plankton.

The shore zone is occupied by a number of species, which can withstand periodic exposure. Many of them require this exposure and will invariably crawl to the surface if kept in confinement, even if the water is kept cool and well aerated. Other species, again, live in shallow water, even if stagnant, and will not stand a long exposure.

Various species of Neritina (*N. dubia, N. ziczac,* etc.) live habitually high up on the trees of the mangrove swamps, depositing their eggs, however, on the surface of the water. Others occur on the dry land, far from any water. (Semper–26.)

Nassa obsoleta covers the gentle muddy beaches at low tide, where dead organisms remain for it to feed upon, and it also abounds on every exposed mud flat on our northern coast. *Littorina rudis* and *L. palliata* are commonly found on the New England shore clinging to rocks or to the stems of the marsh-grass (Spartina), high up, where they are exposed to the air for half the day. The lack of a siphon forces these animals to live above the mud (12:*168*). On the marshes of Cold Spring Harbor, these species of Littorina occur in places where they are "submerged for only a short time at high tide, and then under water that is nearly fresh." (Davenport–12:*169*.) In the Mississippi sound Davenport found nearly all of the individuals of *Littorina irrorata* "living on the stems of the short marsh-grass twenty to thirty centimeters above the water level and exposed to the sunlight." *Littorina rudis* lives prevailingly where it is much exposed. On the English Channel it has been found two meters above the other marine animals, where it is moistened only by the highest tides (Fisher–13:*182*); and on the New England coast it is sometimes found in similar positions. Species of Littorina are reported as passing the winter out of water, with their gill chambers full of air. (Simroth–27:*84*.)

The majority of gastropods are shallow-water forms, though a number of them range to depths of between 1,000 and 2,000 fathoms. The deep-sea gastropods are characterized by faint colors, though often this is counterbalanced by the brilliancy and beauty of the iridescence, and even the non-iridescent abyssal species give out "a sort of sheen which is wanting in their shallow-water allies." (Agassiz–1, ii:*63*.) The coarse ornamentation by knobs, spines, etc., so common in shallow-water species, does not occur in the deep-sea forms, where the ornamentation is more delicate, and often of exquisite richness and beauty. Gastropods feeding on vegetable matter are wanting in the deep sea, where no vegetable matter occurs, except what is brought down as sediment. The food of deep-sea molluscs is largely confined to soft-tissued animals, since thick shells and other hard armors are generally absent in these depths. Agassiz states that the Pleurotomidæ outnumber any other group of molluscs in the abyssal fauna. These gastropods are characterized by a notch in the outer lip near the suture, which serves for the discharge of the refuse, thus preventing fouling of the water used for respiration. Some of these molluscs are provided with hollow barbed teeth and poison fangs, which they use to kill their prey. This apparatus "is even more fully and generally developed in the related group of the Conidæ, few of which reach any great depth." (Agassiz–1, ii:66.)

A few gastropods are viviparous (*Paludina vivipara, Littorina rudis*), producing their young in advanced state of development.

In nearly all the marine gastropods a veliger larva occurs, the velum being generally large, wing-like, and fringed with cilia. This velum may be retained until the shell is long past the protoconch stage. While in most marine gastropods the veliger larva leads a mero-planktonic existence, some marine forms (Fulgur, Sycotypus), and the oviparous, land, and fresh-water gastropods pass through their veliger stage within the egg capsule, losing the velum and other larval organs before passing from the capsule, which they leave as young gastropods with well-developed shells.

In the case of the marine forms cited, the velum, though of no use to the animal as a locomotor organ, is very large, and is lost only just before the embryo leaves the egg capsule. In terrestrial and fresh-water forms, on the other hand, the velum is reduced to a single ring of cilia or to two lateral ciliated streaks. (Lang–19, ii:257), while in some terrestrial species it is wanting entirely. It is obvious that the distribution of species thus deprived of a temporary pelagic life must be more restricted, other things being equal, than that of species having a free veliger stage of greater or less duration.

Land snails generally require a considerable amount of moisture in the atmosphere in order to be able to live an active life. Hence they are found most abundantly near streams and in damp woods and ravines, where they live on the ground or on the vegetation. Nevertheless they can withstand a considerable amount of desiccation by burying themselves in the soil or closely clinging to rocks or trees. Even the deserts have their species, which obtain their required moisture chiefly from the dew, and from the succulent plants on which they feed. Hence the presence of snail shells in loess deposits is not necessarily indicative of deposition by water. Some remarkable cases are recorded by Woodward (31:14), of the suspension of vitality in snails and their subsequent revivification. Thus a specimen of a desert snail which had been affixed to a card in the British Museum for a period of four years (1846-1850), again came to life upon being immersed in tepid water.

PTEROPODA. The pteropods are marine planktonic molluscs

which live in vast numbers in the pelagic district, usually some distance from shore. While able to swim about in the water, they are, nevertheless, at the mercy of the waves and currents. Their food consists of pelagic organisms, and not uncommonly one species of pteropod will prey upon another. They shun the light, descending during the day to the regions of perpetual twilight or even darkness, some descending as far as 700 fathoms. Nearly all the shelled pteropods of the present time are confined to warmer waters, and are especially abundant in the warm ocean currents. Their shells often accumulate in vast numbers on the ocean bottom. A veliger larva, similar to that of the gastropods, occurs.

CEPHALOPODA. The cephalopods are marine nektonic or benthonic molluscs inhabiting water of moderate depths. Swimming is accomplished by the forcible ejection of water from the hyponome, and probably also by the use of the arms. Among the dibranchiata the majority of Sepioidea (Squids, Calamaries) are active swimmers, usually inhabiting the open sea, but appearing periodically on the coasts in great shoals. They live mostly on small fish. The Octopoda are less adapted to active swimming, lying usually in wait for their prey on the sea-bottom or in crevices and hollows. The Argonauta is, however, a partial exception to this, for, though it crawls about on the sea-bottom like other octopods, it is often met with swimming at or near the surface, by the ejection of the water from its hyponome. Argonauta is, therefore, like other cephalopods, at times a vagrant benthos, at others a nekton, inclining perhaps more to the latter, as do the decapods; while other octopods are commonly benthonic. Among the less active decapods, Sepia may be mentioned as more normally a vagrant benthonic form, crawling about on the sea-bottom, though able to swim as well. A sedentary benthonic cephalopod is also known. This is Spirula, which attaches itself to rocks like an actinia (Agassiz, Walther), or lies partly buried in the mud, with its beautiful coiled and chambered shell wholly concealed by the fleshy parts. A perfect specimen was dredged off Grenada in the Caribbean by the *Blake,* from a depth of 950 fathoms. (Agassiz–1, ii:61.)

Spirula would seem to be a widely distributed form, judging from the occurrence of its shell in almost all parts of the tropical and temperate seas. The animal is very rare, however; only one specimen with soft tissues preserved having been obtained by the *Challenger* expedition. This was taken close to the island of Banda in 360 fathoms (Challenger Narrative). Altogether perhaps only half a dozen animals with the soft parts preserved have been obtained. The wide distribution of the shell of Spirula is due to the fact that after the death of the animal the shell ascends to the surface, owing to the air-filled chambers, and then becomes a part of the plankton. It is carried hither and thither by the currents and waves, and finally may reach the sea-bottom in regions remote from its original home, and be buried in sediments of every description, and under conditions in which the animal never existed. Thus the shell of Spirula becomes an excellent index fossil, being widely distributed and buried in all kinds of sediment.

To a more restricted degree this method of pseudo-planktonic distribution of the shell, after the death of the animal, occurs also in Nautilus, the only modern representative of the tetrabranchiate cephalopods. The animal belongs to the benthos, living in shallow water in the tropics. Occasionally it swims near the surface, but before long it returns to the bottom, where it crawls about with its shell uppermost, feeding on crustacea and other animals. On the death of the animal the shell may float for a considerable time on the surface, buoyed up by the air in the chambers, and thus it may be carried for a greater or less distance before it settles to the bottom, where it will be buried in all kinds of sediment (Walther). The verity of such statements has, however, been questioned by Ortmann and others, who believe that the Nautilus shell is seldom carried far from the region inhabited by the living animal.

What is true of the shells of Nautilus and Spirula is true of the shell of Sepia, and was undoubtedly true of the shells of Ammonites as well. (Walther–29:509; 30:258 et seq.) In fact, we may even believe that the shells of the Ammonites were better floaters than either those of Spirula .or Nautilus, for these two genera are retrosiphonate, the siphonal funnels passing backward and thus giving more ready access to the water; while the shells of the Ammonites were prosiphonate, their siphonal funnels bending forward like the neck of a bottle, and thus making the entrance of water more difficult. This conception of the planktonic wanderings of the shells of cephalopods after the death of the animal furnishes a satisfactory explanation of many anomalies observed in the occurrence of these animals in the geologic series. It accounts, especially, for the sudden appearance and disappearance of the same species in widely separated localities, irrespective of the character of the rock, and of its normal faunal contents. This widespread distribution of these shells makes them excellent index-fossils, so that even small formations may readily be correlated by their species of Ammonites, even though widely separated.

It does not follow, of course, that ammonoid shells must always be regarded as strangers which have drifted to their present position; in fact, it is often easy to see that such has not been the case in any particular locality, from an examination of the shells themselves, as well as from the extraneous evidence. Thus, according to Clarke (5:*135, et seq.*), the ammonoids of the Naples beds of western New York " . . . bear sufficient demonstration in themselves that they have lived and died in these sediments." Many of the most delicate shells retain their apertures unbroken, and their suface ornamentation uninjured, a fact which is not consistent with transportation by waves and currents. The presence of the young in all stages of development further argues for an indigenous occurrence. "On the other hand," says Clarke, "there are excellent reasons for regarding the prenuncial Intumescens fauna, that of the Styliola [Styliolina] limestone, as due to transportation from some adjoining province not yet known to us." The Goniatites of this fauna are associated with the millions of holo-planktonic Styliolina, with floated logs, and probably other pelagic organisms, and the sediment in which they were embedded was such as probably was not conducive to the well-being of such animals, so that their occurrence is best explained by the hypothesis of flotation.

Of the embryology of Nautilus, and hence of the whole group of Tetrabranchiata, nothing is known. The Dibranchiata develop directly within the egg capsule, no veliger stage occurring.

VI. Platylelmintha.   VII. Vermes.

These worms are marine, fresh-water, or terrestrial animals. They belong chiefly to the benthos, though some marine forms lead a partially nektonic existence, while others are typically planktonic. Several oligochætous annelids have become adapted to a marine life, though the group is normally fresh-water or terrestrial. Among the benthonic species all grades of a sedentary life are observable, from the tube-building orders, which live permanently in attached tubes, to those which only temporarily occupy a given area. Tubicolous worms, which, like Spirorbis, attach their tubes chiefly to algæ, may often lead an epi-planktonic existence when the algæ are torn from their anchorage and washed away by currents.

A muddy bottom seems to be the favorite haunt of the littoral species, except such forms as build attached tubes (*e. g.*, Serpulidæ, etc.), which occupy stony and shelly bottoms. These latter often build extensive reefs of interwoven calcareous tubes.

Besides calcareous tubes, many worms build tubes of aggluti-nated sand grains or shell particles, and worms living in the shells of dead molluscs are frequently met with. These agglutinated sand tubes are often very resistant, sometimes, with the castings, covering the mud flats and beaches in great numbers, and not infrequently being heaped together in windrows. The dredge brings large numbers of these tubes, together with numerous castings, from the deeper water. The bathymetric distribution of the worms is varied. The majority are undoubtedly littoral species, but deep-sea forms are also common. Beyond the hundred-fathom line the tubicolar annelids are the most characteristic, specimens having been ob-tained from a depth of 4,000 fathoms off Teneriffe (*Challenger*). Other worms also occur. Even species of the same genus have a widely varying distribution in depth. Thus the tubicoloid genus Spirorbis has its littoral species growing within the shore zone; while another species, *S. nautiloides,* has been dredged at a depth of 700 fathoms. Similarly, the Sipunculid Phascolosoma is repre-sented along our northern shores by a species living in mud and sand above low tide, while the *Blake* brought up a species in a Den-talium shell from a depth of 1,568 fathoms. (Agassiz–1, ii:*53.*) The Myzostomidæ are parasitic on living Comatula, and also have been found on the column segments of Jurassic crinoids (Graff).

Among the annelids, the family Eunicidæ is of particular in-terest, in that its several members are characteristic of different bathymetric zones, thus furnishing, in a measure, an index to the bathymetric position of the fauna which they characterize. This family is well represented in the lithographic shales of Bavaria. (Ehlers.)

Among the worms regeneration of lost parts and generation of new individuals from fragments of old ones are not uncommon. Thus, in one of our common halo-pelagic worms, Autolytus, swim-ming buds carrying the sexual products are periodically constricted off, each regenerating a new head, with highly developed eyes at the anterior end. The oligochæte Lumbriculus in autumn falls into pieces, all of which are able to regenerate into complete ani-mals. (Lang–19; i:*267.*)

A mero-planktonic ciliated larva, the trochophore, is character-istic of worms, this being the product of a sexual mode of repro-duction. These larvæ are often obtained in vast numbers in the tow-net, together with other mero-planktonic and many holo-plank-tonic forms.

The œsophageal teeth of annelids are abundantly represented in many bituminous shales, from the Palæozoic on. Some of these objects, known as conodonts, were formerly regarded as the teeth of mixinoid fishes or as radulæ of gastropods.

VIII. Arthropoda.

Crustacea.

Trilobitæ. The trilobites are extinct Palæozoic Crustacea of an undoubted marine habitat, probably able to swim as well as crawl, and so belonging at one time to the nekton, at another to the vagrant benthos. Whether or not a mero-planktonic larva existed is not known, but it might be assumed from the wide distribution of some species. Since trilobites cast off their exoskeletons, as does Limulus, some of these may have floated a considerable distance, coming to lodge where trilobites never lived. It is certain that from the number of fossil trilobites we cannot judge the number of individuals existing at a given place, since a number of specimens may represent the cast-off exoskeletons of one individual. Trilobites, like many modern Crustacea, probably turned on their backs while sinking to the sea-floor, this accounting for the frequent overturned position in which their remains are found.

Phyllopoda; Copepoda. These belong largely to the plankton, the phyllopods occurring mostly in fresh water, the copepods having fresh water (Cyclops) and marine representatives. The copepods further comprise commensal forms, which live in the branchial cavity of Ascidians (Notodelphus) or on the carp (Argulus) ; and a large number of parasitic types. Some of them, however, are only occasionally or temporarily parasitic. Some phyllopods have a bivalve shell (Estheria, etc.), which is frequently preserved in the finer fresh water sediments of continental formations. A planktonic nauplius larva occurs. The eggs of some phyllopods have the power to withstand desiccation for years. In fact, the eggs of Apus do not develop unless they have been subjected to desiccation for some time (Semper). This accounts for the periodic reappearance of these organisms in the temporary water bodies of desert regions. The occurrence of such types (Estheria) in otherwise unfossiliferous deposits thus indicates that these deposits may be of desert origin.

Ostracoda. The ostracods are marine or fresh-water, planktonic or vagrant benthonic Crustacea whose imperfectly segmented body is enclosed in a bivalve shell. The majority of the marine forms are holo-planktonic, living in shallow water or in moderate depths, though a few species were found by the *Challenger* at depths exceeding 2,000 fathoms. Some species are cosmopolitan and the order is represented in nearly all waters, their shells occurring in nearly all the bottom deposits. The animals are also abundant on algæ, over which they crawl slowly. The fresh-water Cypris swims about, subject, however, to the influences by which other members of the plankton are affected; or it crawls about on the vegetation. Cypris is also represented in brackish and salt water. Its eggs have the power to withstand desiccation for a long time, and hence the species can continue in water bodies which become periodically dried up, as in desert regions. The larva of the ostracods is a pelagic nauplius.

Cirripedia. The cirripeds, or barnacles, are marine sedentary benthonic Crustacea which have degenerated much from the true type of crustacean, owing, no doubt, to their attached mode of life. The body is covered with calcareous plates variously arranged, which fall apart after the death of the animal; after which, from single pieces, it is quite impossible to determine the species, owing to the great variation of the skeletal parts. (Darwin.) Balanus and its congeners are sessile, being attached to the rocks and other solid supports along the shore, seldom venturing into water of great depth. Some species are periodically exposed for many hours at low tide, some, in fact, never being covered more than one or two hours at flood tide, so high up on the shore do they attach themselves. Balanus has been found at a depth of 500 fathoms, but it usually lives in lesser depths. *Balanus improvisus* occurs also in brackish water, and some species of this barnacle have been reported from fresh water (Tscherniansky). *Coronula diadema* leads an epi-nektonic life, attaching itself to the body of whales. *Verruca incerta,* a common West Indian type, occurs in the Globigerina ooze. Lepas and its congeners are pedunculate, attaching themselves by a fleshy peduncle, which represents the elongated head end. The majority of the Lepadidæ are pelagic, leading an epi-planktonic existence, attached to floating logs, pumice, or other objects. Three species of Lepas were found by the *Challenger* attached to the Sargassum. Some members of this family descend into deep water, *Scalpellum regium* having been dredged by the *Challenger* from nearly 3,000 fathoms. These abyssal cirripeds are usually attached to nodules, dead or living shells, corals, large Crustacea, to spines of sea urchins and other objects. (Agassiz—1, ii:50.) The cirripeds, upon hatching from the egg, pass through several larval stages, the first of which is the nauplius stage. In this the body is unsegmented, with median frontal eyes, dorsal shield, frontal sensory organs and three pairs of limbs. After a series of moults the Cypris stage is reached, in which the larva is enclosed in a bivalve shell, like that of the Ostracoda. During these stages the larva belongs to the mero-plankton. When it settles down and becomes attached it passes through a pupa stage, during which the transformation of the larva into the cirriped takes place.

Phyllocarida. These are mostly extinct forms, represented in all the divisions of the Palæozoic. Several living genera (Nebalia, etc.) are regarded as belonging here, and these are marine. They are swimmers, and their development is direct, without metamorphosis. Some of the Palæozoic forms referred to this class were undoubtedly marine (Stenotheca, Ribeiria), but the majority seem to have been fresh water forms living in the rivers of the Palæozoic lands. This is inferred from their peculiar occurrence in sediments which could only have been formed at the mouths of streams and in playa-like basins. At any rate, they did not seem to be normal inhabitants of the open sea, but, if marine at all, lived near the mouths of great streams.

Schizopoda, Stomatopoda, Sympoda. These are marine Crustacea, capable of swimming about by the use of their abdominal legs and caudal fin. Larval stages are often wanting.

Decapoda. The decapods belong chiefly to the benthos, inhabiting either fresh or salt water, rarely the land. Pelagic species also occur, some of which are good swimmers; while a few belong to the plankton and others to the epi-plankton, living on the Sargassum. They commonly feed on living or dead animal matter. The bathymetric distribution varies greatly, though the majority of species are confined to comparatively shallow water, generally not exceeding fifty fathoms. A considerable number, nevertheless, are abyssal. The range of individual species is often great; *Alpheus avarus,* for example, is said to range on the Australian coast from less than ten to about 2,500 fathoms (*Challenger*), though this is questioned by Ortmann (21:75). Among the hermit crabs occur some forms which have left their native element and have taken to the land. The *Challenger* found some of them in the mountains of the Antilles, up to 300 meters. They sometimes inhabit the shells of land snails and have been seen climbing trees. Among the true crabs, or Brachyura, shallow-water species predominate, comparatively few occurring below 400 fathoms. A number of species live in fresh water or on land. The majority of decapods leave the egg in the zoëa stage, in which the abdominal region is perfectly segmented, though still without appendages, except perhaps the rudiments of the sixth pair. The compound eyes are stalked. Other larval stages follow until the adult is reached. These larvæ often occur in vast quantities in the plankton.

Arthrostraca. This super-order includes mostly marine forms, though the order Isopoda comprises marine, fresh water, and terrestrial types. The latter occur in damp woods, under moss, stones, or logs, and are also abundant in the crevices of rocky cliffs. The marine Isopods are common in shallow water, on algæ, or swimming about in tide pools. *Chiridotea cœca* lives on sandy shores, moving about just below the surface of the sand, and leaving a meshwork of curious trails in its wake. Some of the lower sand flats are often found covered with these markings. The animal is usually found at the end of the trail, its whereabouts being indicated by a little lump of sand. *Limnoria lignorum* eats its way into driftwood or bridge piles, often completely riddling and destroying the wood. Caprella clings to hydroids and slender seaweeds. Though chiefly found in the littoral district, some abyssal species are known, several having been obtained at a depth of over 3,600 meters. Sometimes different species of the same genus range from shallow water to great depths. Blind species are common in the Mammoth and other caverns. A number of types are parasitic on fishes. The Amphipods are chiefly marine, though fresh and brackish water species also occur in marine genera (Gammarus). Cyamus is parasitic on the skin of whales. Several species live on the beach just above the reach of the ordinary tide, where they hide under the dead seaweed or burrow in the sand (Orchestia). They generally move about by leaps and hence are commonly known as beach fleas. Talorchestia lives in a similar manner just a little below high-water mark and the beach at low tide is often completely riddled by its burrows. A number of Orchestidæ can live wholly out of the water in damp woods or in the dry stream beds.

Acerata.

Merostomata. The Xiphosurans are represented by the single living genus Limulus, which is a marine vagrant benthonic animal, though often swimming on its back when young. The usual habitat of this animal is in shallow water, where it is often partly buried in the mud or sand. Portions of the coast are often strewn with the cast-off exoskeletons of Limulus, which usually lie on their backs, a position which these structures will naturally take on sinking to the bottom.

The young Limulus on hatching is a trilobitiform, free-swimming, commonly meroplanktonic organism without caudal spine (J. S. Kingsley).

Modern Limulus is restricted to the eastern shores of America and Asia. A Tertiary species (L. decheni) is known from the Oligocenic brown coal of Teuchern, near Merseburg, in Saxony, an occurrence scarcely suggestive of marine habitat. A marine species (L. walchi) is abundant in the lithographic slates of Bavaria, associated with land forms, however. A small species occurs in the Bunter Sandstein of the Vosges, a formation chiefly of terrestrial (river) origin, and suggesting that Limulus in the Trias was still a river animal. This was most probably true also of Protolimulus, which occurs in the Chemung delta deposits of Pennsylvania. The Carbonic Xiphosurans, Prestwichia, and Belinurus were undoubtedly fresh-water (river) organisms, occurring in the non-marine coal deposits. Cyclus, on the other hand, is found in the interbedded limestone of the Coal Measures, as well as in the Coal Measures themselves. The habitat may have been marine, but not necessarily so, since these carapaces could easily have been washed from the land.

Altogether it seems as if the early Xiphosurans were river-living animals, venturing perhaps occasionally into the sea (euryhaline) and assuming their marine habitat in the Mesozoic and modern times.

The Synxiphosurans may have been partly marine and partly fresh water. The Upper Cambric Aglaspis suggests their derivation from the trilobites. This occurs in the St. Croix sandstone of Wisconsin, a terrestrial deposit reworked by the sea. The Siluric genera Neolimulus, Bunodes, Hemiaspis, and Bunodella occur in deposits which are partly marine and partly of delta type. It is not improbable that most of them were derived from the land-waters and buried in the sea margin deltaic deposits. The possibility of a marine character for some can, however, not be denied. Pseudoniscus, on the contrary, in America occurs in the Pittsford black shale deposits, which are most suggestive of influx of fresh water, and hence a non-marine habitat is indicated. The European species are from Oesel and their real habitat is doubtful. (O'Connell—20.)

The Eurypterida have generally been considered marine, but the elaborate study of the habitat of these organisms made by Miss O'Connell (20) points unmistakably to a non-marine habitat of these merostomes since pre-Cambric time. The majority of forms occur in rocks not explainable as normal marine sediments, but as delta or as playa-lake deposits without direct connection with the sea. Individuals are occasionally found in marine deposits which cannot be interpreted as deltas, but in such cases the remains are of single individuals or are fragments. Since all known specimens of this kind represent merely the exoskeleton (Clarke and Ruedemann–6), it is easy to see that they may have reached their resting place as pseudoplankton. A characteristic mode of occurrence of these organisms is in the black muds intercalated in torrential conglomerates and sandstones. The geographic distribution, too, is of such a character as to indicate a river rather than a marine habitat. For further discussion of this problem see page 1043 and the references there cited.

The *Limulava* are known only from the Cambric, where they are found in a remarkable state of preservation in black bituminous shales (sapropellutytes), together with trilobites, worms and other animals suggesting a marine habitat.

Arachnida; Pantapoda. The spiders and scorpions are typically terrestrial animals, breathing by means of trachæa. The Pantapoda (Pycnogonida), or sea-spiders, however, constitute a class of marine organisms, resembling in many characters the Arachnida, of which class they are often considered relatives. There is also a true spider, *Argyroneta aquatica,* which leads an aquatic life in fresh water. Scorpions first appear in the Siluric, where they are associated with eurypterids, from which they may have been derived. Spiders are known from the Coal Measures, but insects date from the Ordovicic graptolite slates of Sweden (Protocimex).

Myriopoda and Insecta.

These are also terrestrial tracheates, but with marine·representatives.

Larvæ of insects also live in the sea, and a number of adult insects are marine in habit, though continuing to breathe air. Many insects and spiders have been met with in the open sea, far from land, swimming in great numbers on the surface, while others have been found creeping between rocks under water by the shore. The bug Halobates comprises some fourteen species living on the surface of the sea, running about like the fresh-water bug Hydrometra, often hundreds of miles from land. In the Upper Siluric of France a primitive cockroach, *Palæoblattina,* has been obtained. Myriopods have been found in the Devonic, but more abundantly in the Carbonic. The Palæozoic myriopods, like the Palæozoic insects, were distinct from the Mesozoic and recent forms. The modern *Chilopoda* date from the Tertiary; the *Diplopoda* from the Cretacic.

ECHINODERMATA.

CYSTOIDEA AND BLASTOIDEA. These classes are entirely extinct, being confined to the Palæozoic. They were undoubtedly marine organisms like all the echinoderms.

CRINOIDEA. The crinoids are without exception marine organisms, though *Antedon rosacea* has been taken in water containing only 25 permille of salts, or nearly a third less than in normal seawater. The majority of crinoids belong to the sedentary benthos, being anchored or attached to the sea-bottom either by a stem or by the base of the calyx. Antedon must be classed with the vagrant benthos for, although it ordinarily rests on the sea-bottom or other stationary objects of support, it is able to walk about on the bottom by means of its arms; and also to swim with graceful movements through the water. Planktonic crinoids appear to have existed in the Mesozoic seas (Saccocoma, Uintacrinus), and, as already noted, Walther has furnished evidence which indicates that some of the stemmed Pentacrini of the Lias led an epiplanktonic life, growing attached to floating timbers with which they were carried about, calyx downward.

Kirk (18) has recently brought forward evidence to show that many Palæozoic as well as later crinoids separated from their stems late in life and assumed secondarily a planktonic existence, the crowns floating away, while the dead stems remained behind to separate into their component ossicles and form a bed of crinoidal limestone.

The bathymetrical distribution of the modern crinoids ranges from shallow water to 2,000 fathoms, rarely more. One species of Antedon (*A. abyssicola*, Carp.) has been obtained at a depth of 2,900 fathoms, but most of the species of this genus live in shallow water, *A. loveni*, occurring in three to four fathoms. This genus is perhaps the most cosmopolitan of the modern crinoids, its geographic range being between eighty degrees northern and fifty-two degrees southern latitude. The following modern stalked crinoids have been obtained in less than ninety fathoms of water (Walther—29:*298-300*):

Eudiocrinus indivisus Semp., 30 fathoms (54 meters).
Metacrinus rotundus Carp., 70 fathoms (128 meters).

Pentacrinus asterius L., 80 fathoms (range 80-320 fathoms equals 146-584 meters).

P. decorus Wy. Th., 84 fathoms (range 84-667 fathoms equals 153 to 1,219 meters).

P. mülleri Oerst, 84 fathoms (range 84-531 fathoms equals 153 to 970 meters).

Promachocrinus kerguelensis Carp., 28 fathoms (range 28-120 fathoms equals 51-218 meters).

Rhizocrinus lofotensis Sars, 80 fathoms (range 80-1,900? fathoms equals 146-3,474 meters).

R. rawsoni Pourt., 73 fathoms (range 73-1,280 fathoms equals 133-2,340 meters).

The egg of Antedon develops into an egg-shaped mero-planktonic larva, which has a tuft of long flagella on the anterior end and five ciliated rings surrounding it; no mouth or anus is present. This embryo swims about for a period of time, varying from a few hours to several days, and, on settling down to a benthonic life, attaches itself at a point on the ventral side between the first and second ciliated rings. The whole anterior part, as far as the third ciliated ring, becomes the stalk, the posterior part developing into the calyx. In Antedon the stem is retained only during the early stages of development, the adult animal being free.

ASTEROIDEA; OPHIUROIDEA. These belong to the marine vagrant benthos, living mainly in shallow water or in moderate depths, though some species descend to depths of 2,000 fathoms or over. Some littoral starfish can undergo an exposure for several hours in regions laid bare by the tide. A muddy or sandy bottom seems to be the most characteristic facies for these animals, and from such bottoms hundreds are often brought up in a single haul of the dredge. Their relative scarcity in beds in which they are known to occur is probably due to the fact that, after the death of the animal, the skeleton quickly falls apart into its component plates, which become separately embedded in the sediments. In the majority of the Asterozoa meroplanktonic, bilaterally symmetric, ciliated larvæ occur, which in the Asteroidea are known as bipinnaria and brachiolaria, and in the Ophiuroidea as pluteus. These are often found in great numbers in the pelagic fauna.

ECHINOIDEA. The Echinoids, or Sea Urchins, are without exception marine vagrant benthonic animals, living usually in large numbers in moderate depths. A few species descend to depths between 2,000 and 3,000 fathoms, but the majority prefer the shallow portions of the littoral districts. On the coast of Maine thousands of *Strongylocentrotus dröbachiensis* are exposed at very low tides, lying among stones and covered with fragments of shells and small pebbles. The Echinoidea delight in a sandy bottom, from which they are brought up in vast numbers at each haul of the dredge. Some species prefer fine mud, in which they are often buried to some extent. When living on rocks they commonly excavate holes for themselves, and even the solid granite has been known to be thus attacked by the animal. If corners and crannies are available, these are often occupied by the animal in preference to the drilled hole.

The larva of echinoids is known as a pluteus, and is a mero-planktonic, bilaterally symmetrical, usually more or less ciliated organism, with a number of processes or arms. It is often carried by marine currents to great distances, remaining in some cases afloat for several weeks before settling down.

HOLOTHUROIDEA. The holothurians, like the echinoids, are marine benthonic organisms, but their habit of life is often more sedentary than vagrant, the animals being buried in the sand and mud, though never attached. Their bathymetric range is from the shore zone, where they may be dug out of the sand at low tide, to the depths of the abyssal district. Sandy or muddy bottom is usually preferred by these animals, though many live among coarse blocks, and vast numbers occur among the coral masses of every coral reef. The ciliated larva, or auricularia, of the holothurians is a mero-planktonic organism with definite mouth and anal opening.

From the fact that only isolated plates occur in the skin of the holothurians, they do not constitute any important part of marine deposits.

X. PROTOCHORDATA.

These animals are all marine and unknown in the fossil state.

XI. VERTEBRATA.

OSTRACODERMA. These extinct fish-like animals appear to have led primarily a fluviatile and lacustrine existence, if we may judge by the strata in which they occur. The earliest remains are fragments from an Upper Ordovicic sandstone (Harding sandstone) of Colorado, which was probably deposited as a terrestrial sediment and subsequently in part reworked by the advancing sea. The late Siluric transition beds of Great Britain and eastern North America, and the beds of the Old Red Sandstone type of the same countries, show the best preserved representatives, these beds being strictly non-marine deposits. Some of the best preserved specimens of Bothriolepis are from the fresh water (river, flood-plain and delta) deposits, which constitute the Gaspé sandstone of eastern Canada.

The Upper Siluric bone-bed (Ludlow) of England also furnishes these remains, and this deposit may have been formed in an estuary, or an enclosed basin near the sea. A few fragmentary remains have been obtained from marine Siluric and Devonic strata, but these, like the similar occurrences of eurypterids, are not satisfactory evidence of the marine character of these fishes. In Pennsylvania, remains occur in sandstone beds, most probably of river origin, belonging in the Upper Siluric (Monroan) horizon.

PISCES. The earliest true fish appear in the Siluric, but are more typical of the Devonic. Here the Arthrodires were especially abundant, many of them still inhabiting the rivers of the continent. They began to migrate into the sea, however, judging from the more numerous remains found in open sea deposits, such as the Onondaga limestone. The abundant fish fauna of the Upper Devonic shales of Ohio is associated with tree trunks, spores of land plants, etc., in sediments suggesting a river delta rather than open sea. These Upper Devonic fish did, however, live in the seas of that time as well, for their remains are also found in undoubted marine strata. The Cyclostomi (or Lampreys) seem to be first represented by the remarkable Palæospondylus of the Old Red Sandstone of Caithness, Scotland. The Elasmobranchs, or sharks, also lived in the rivers of Old Red Sandstone time, and their remains are found in the semi-terrestrial deposits of the Upper Siluric in Europe and America. These fish, however, entered the sea in Devonic, if not in Siluric, time, and thereafter became chiefly marine organisms, continuing so down to the present time.

The living ganoids either inhabit fresh water rivers exclusively, or, as in the case of the sturgeons, enter the rivers from the sea. In Palæozoic and Mesozoic time they were marine and fluviatile. The living Dipnoi inhabit the tropical swamps of South America (Lepidosiren) and of Africa (Protopterus) and also the rivers of Queensland (Ceratodus). Ceratodus also occurs in the Bunter Sandstein of Württemberg, the Keuper of Austria, the Stonesfield slates of England, and the fresh water Jurassic of Colorado. It also occurs in the Kota-Maleri beds of India and in the Karoo formation of South Africa. All of these formations represent river deposits. With few exceptions the other Dipnoans (Ctenodipterini) also occur in fresh water (chiefly river) deposits, such as the Old

Red Sandstone, the Devonic sandstones of Canada, the Coal Measures and the continental Permic deposits. The living Protopterus of Africa regularly spends the dry season of several months in its crust of dried mud, leading a latent existence or summer sleep until the rains again soften the crust and release the fish.

The various species of mud-fish are examples of fishes leading an amphibious life, for these have been transported in their "nest" of dried mud halfway round the world without suffering. Dean believes that the vitality of these fish becomes exhausted by being kept in water all the time, which deprives them of their periodic summer rest. Many fresh-water fish regularly swallow air and will die if prevented from doing so, even more quickly than frogs which have been similarly placed, although the latter are provided with true lungs.

A few other types of fish are able to live in the air for a certain length of time, as, for example, the tropical fish (Periophthalmus and Boleophthalmus), referred to in the preceding chapter, which spend a good part of their existence on the beach, and *Anabas scandens* of the Philippines is able to exist for days out of water.

Many fresh-water fish periodically visit the sea, while marine fishes as frequently ascend fresh-water streams.

AMPHIBIA. The amphibians are cold-blooded, aquatic or terrestrial vertebrates, usually without dermal covering, which, however, is present in some forms as a corneous or osseous structure. These animals breathe by gills and by lungs, the former remaining functional throughout life in some species. True limbs are generally present in the Amphibia, and are used for swimming or walking.

The Carbonic and Triassic Stegocephalia were mostly armored, especially on the ventral side. They lived on land or possibly in fresh water. The larger forms were predatory and probably fed on other amphibians, fishes, and Crustacea. The Cœcilians (Gymnophiona) are worm-like, legless amphibians confined to the tropics. They are unknown in the fossil state. The Urodeles are naked-bodied types with generally two pairs of limbs and persistent tail. They inhabit fresh water (newts), where the gills remain permanent; or damp, shady places on the land (salamanders), where they lose their gills. They subsist on worms, gastropods, small aquatic animals, and fish spawn. Permanent larval forms (Axolotl) of the land form, Amblystoma, inhabit the lakes and ponds of Mexico and other countries. These have the form of large tadpoles about to be transformed, with legs and external gills. They reproduce in this state, some of them never reaching the Amblystoma stage. The Urodeles began in the Cretacic and continue to the present.

The Anura (frogs and toads) pass through a tadpole stage, during which they breathe by means of gills and lead an aquatic life. On transformation they lose the gills and the tail and become air-breathers, though frogs can remain under water for a very long period of time, absorbing oxygen through the skin. The Anura are wholly post-Mesozoic in age. No marine amphibians are known.

REPTILIA. The Rhynchocephalia comprised terrestrial and aquatic forms, often of great size. The Squamata include two Cretacic groups of marine reptiles, some of which, like the mosasaurs, were of large size. The lizards (*Lacertilia*) and snakes (*Ophidia*) are chiefly terrestrial reptiles, though some of the latter (*Hydrophidæ*) live in the water. Some Pleistocenic species attained a length of 10 meters, but modern forms are all small. The lizards are mostly provided with legs, while the snakes are legless. At the present time, lizards are chiefly restricted to the warmer regions of the earth's surface. Comparatively few forms pass beyond the fortieth parallel, while above the sixtieth parallel lizards are practically absent; though *Lacerta vivipara,* a species ranging over nearly the whole of Europe, extends northward to the seventieth parallel in Norway, and, together with the blind-worm (*Angius fragilis*) occurs in Lapland but is absent from the New World. Both groups probably appeared in the Cretacic. The fish-lizards (*Ichthyosauria* and *Sauropterygia*) were wholly nektonic in habit, living in the sea, but breathing by means of lungs. They were, therefore, neither true holo-nekton nor atmo-nekton, but a transitional type between the two, as are other vertebrates which lead a permanently nektonic life (*e. g.,* whales, etc.). Some species inhabited fresh or brackish water.

The Theromorphs were habitually walking animals. It is believed by many that the mammals have arisen from these reptiles.

The Chelonia or turtles are terrestrial or aquatic in habit, but, like all other reptiles, are air-breathers. A few types are exclusively marine, but the larger number live in fresh-water lakes or rivers. It has been supposed that the ancestral species were aquatic, living in swamps and shallow water, like modern crocodiles; and that from these descended the fluviatile types, from which in turn were derived the early marine types, on the one hand, and the terrestrial, on the other.

The modern crocodiles are aquatic reptiles living in fresh water, swamps and streams. The oldest Triassic crocodiles (Parasuchia and Pseudosuchia) are all found in terrestrial—partly fluviatile and partly eolian—deposits, such as the Newark beds of eastern North America, the Stuben Sandstein of Germany, the Elgin sandstone of Scotland, and the Gondwana beds of India. They appear to have been land and river forms. The Mesosuchia in Jurassic and Comanchic time had taken to a marine life, but in the Cretacic and later periods, the crocodiles were chiefly fluviatile or terrestrial. In the Pliocenic alligators and crocodiles became extinct in Europe, but in America they continued in the tropical and sub-tropical districts. The crocodiles inhabit, further, nearly all the larger streams and many lakes of Africa, India, and the north coast of Australia (Heilprin). The Dinosaurs are wholly confined to the Mesozoic, where they were represented by a wealth of types. They comprise three groups: 1st, carnivorous land forms (*Theropoda*), varying in size from that of a cat (*Compsognathus*) to that of an elephant (*Megalosaurus,* Trias to Cretacic), and mostly very grotesque in appearance. They walked upon their hind limbs, the shorter fore limbs being lifted from the ground and the body being further balanced and supported by a huge tail. Some leaping or kangaroo-like forms likewise occurred (Trias to Cretacic). 2d. Massive herbivorous quadrupedal forms without dermal armor (*Sauropoda,* Middle and Upper Jurassic and Lower and Upper Cretacic), and comprising some of the most prodigious land animals known; Brontosaurus having a length upward of 18 meters, and Diplodocus upward of 20 meters. 3d. (*Predentata*). Large herbivorous unarmored bipedal (Iguanodonts), and armored quadrupedal forms with small skulls (*Stegosauridæ*), or with large horned skulls (*Ceratopsidæ*). The carnivorous dinosaurs were frequenters of the estuaries and deltas of rivers, and roamed about the low, flat, and muddy flood plains of rivers, as shown by the countless footprints preserved in the rocks of the Newark system, the Bunter Sandstein, and other non-marine deposits of early Mesozoic age. The Pterosauria or Ornithosaurs (Jurassic and Cretacic) were a remarkable group of bird-like lizards, with hollow bones and fore limbs adapted for flight, after the manner of bats; some forms being strong and others weak flyers.

AVES. Birds are essentially aerial nekton. A number of living and extinct forms (*Dromæognathæ,* with the Struthiones, the New Zealand Apteryx and the South American Tinamous), are either nearly wingless or have wholly or to a considerable extent lost the power of flight, even though possessing small wings. To compensate for this loss the legs are generally powerfully developed, especially in the Struthious birds (ostriches, rheas, cassowaries, emus, and the extinct Æpyornis and the Moas). The majority of birds have the power of flight to a greater or less extent, some forms being able to remain in the air for a long time (gulls, petrels), though flightless forms exist in several orders of the Euornithes. Some are especially adapted to a natatory existence (penguins, ducks, etc.), while others spend much of their life wading in streams and ponds (herons, storks, ibises, cranes, snipes, etc.).

MAMMALIA. This, the highest class of vertebrates, is primarily adapted to a terrestrial life, though volatorial or atmonektonic types (*Chiroptera,* or bats) and natatorial or halo- and limnonektonic (hydronektonic) types (*Cetacea,* or whales, and *Sirenia,* or sea-cows) are also known. Among the terrestrial mammals, climbing or arboreal types, running and walking or cursorial types, leaping or saltatorial types, and burrowing or fossorial types are distinguishable.

BIBLIOGRAPHY XXVIII.

1. AGASSIZ, ALEXANDER. 1888. Three Cruises of the *Blake.* 2 vols. Bulletin of the Museum of Comparative Zoology, Vols. XIV, XV.
2. BROOKS, W. K. 1881. Développement de l'huitre Américaine. Archives de Zoologie Expérimentale et Générale, T. IX. Notes et Revue, pp. xxviii–xxix.
3. CHAMBERLIN, THOMAS C. 1898. A Systematic Source of Evolution of Provincial Faunas. Journal of Geology, Vol. VI, pp. 597 *et seq.*
4. CHUN, CARL. 1888. Die pelagische Thierwelt in grösseren Meerestiefen und ihre Beziehungen zu der Oberflächen Fauna. Bibliotheca Zoologica, Heft 1.
5. CLARKE, JOHN M. The Naples Fauna, Pt. I. Fifteenth Annual Report of the New York State Geologist.
6. CLARKE, J. M., and RUEDEMANN, RUDOLF. 1912. The Eurypterida. Monograph of the New York State Museum, No. XIV, and plates.
7. CONN, H. W. 1885. Marine Larvæ and Their Relation to Adults. Studies of the Biological Laboratory of Johns Hopkins University, Vol. III, pp. 165–192, pls. VIII, IX.
8. DALL, WILLIAM H. 1890. Deep Sea Molluscs and the Conditions Under Which They Live. Presidential Address. Biological Society, Washington. Proceedings, Vol. V, pp. 1–27.
9. DANA, JAMES D. 1872. Corals and Coral Islands.
10. DARWIN, CHARLES. 1841. Voyage of the *Beagle.*
11. DAVIDSON, TH. 1886. A Monograph of the Recent Brachiopoda. Transactions of the Linnæan Society of London. Zoology, IV.
12. DAVENPORT, C. B. 1903. Animal Ecology of the Cold Spring Sand Spit. University of Chicago, Decennial Publication, X.
13. FISCHER, PAUL. 1887. Manuel de Conchyliologie. Paris.
14. FUCHS, TH. 1882. Ueber die pelagische Flora und Fauna. Verhandlungen der königlich-kaiserlichen geologischen Reichsanstalt in Wien, pp. 49–55.

15 HÆCKEL, ERNST. 1893. Planktonic Studies. Translated from the German by George W. Field. Report of United States Fish Commission, 1889–1891, pp. 565–641.

16. HAHN, F. FELIX. 1912. Dictyonema Fauna of Navy Island, New Brunswick. New York Academy of Science, Annals, Vol. XXII, pp. 135–160, pls. xx–xxii.

17. HENSEN, VICTOR. 1890. Einige Ergebnisse der Plankton Expedition der Humboldt Stiftung. Sitzungsberichte der Berliner Akademie der Wissenschaften, von 13 ten. März, 1890, pp. 243–253.

18. KIRK, EDWIN. 1911. Some Eleutherozoic Pelmatozoa. United States National Museum Proceedings, Vol. XLI, pp. 1–137. Contributions from the Geological Department of Columbia University, Vol. XXI, No. 6.

19. LANG, ARNOLD. 1891–1896. Text Book of Comparative Anatomy. Translated by H. M. and M. Bernard, Vols. I, II. London, Macmillan.

20. O'CONNELL, MARJORIE. 1912. The Habitat of the Eurypterida. Paper presented before the New Academy of Sciences, November meeting.

21. ORTMANN, ARNOLD E. 1896. Grundzüge der Marinen Tiergeographie. Jena, Gustav Fischer.

22. ORTMANN, ARNOLD E. 1896. An Examination of the Arguments Given by Neumayr for the Existence of Climatic Zones in Jurassic Times. American Journal of Science, 4th series, Vol. I, p. 257.

23. RUEDEMANN, RUDOLF. 1895. Development and Mode of Growth of Diplograptus. McCoy. Fourteenth Annual Report New York State Geologist, pp. 219–249, pls. 1–5.

24. RUEDEMANN, R. 1904. Graptolites of New York, Part I. New York State Museum Memoirs, Vol. VII.

25. SCHIMPER, A. F. W. 1898. Pflanzengeographie auf Physiologischer Grundlage. Jena, G. Fischer. English Translation (Plant Geography) by W. R. Fischer, Oxford, 1903.

26. SEMPER, KARL. 1881. Animal Life as Affected by the Natural Conditions of Existence. International Scientific Series, Vol. XXX.

27. SIMROTH, HEINRICH. 1891. Die Entstehung der Landtiere. (See also Die Pendulations-theorie, 1907.)

28. TYRRELL, J. B. 1910. Changes of Climate in Northwestern Canada Since the Glacial Period. In Veränderung des Klimas, etc. Stockholm, pp. 389–391.

29. WALTHER, JOHANNES. 1897. Ueber die Lebensweise fossiler Meeresthiere. Zeitschrift der deutschen geologischen Gesellschaft. Band XLIV, Heft II, pp. 209–273.

30. WALTHER, J. 1894. Einleitung in die Geologie als historische Wissenschaft. I. Bionomie des Meeres. II. Die Lebensweise der Meeresthiere.

31. WOODWARD, S. P. 1880. Manual of the Mollusca.

CHAPTER XXIX.

CHOROLOGY, OR THE PRINCIPLES OF THE GEOGRAPHICAL DISTRIBUTION OF ANIMALS AND PLANTS.

Having briefly considered the life districts of the habitable earth, and the bionomic characters of plants and animals, we may now enquire into the laws which govern the geographical distribution of organisms. It is clear that, whatever the present distribution of plant and animal life, it has not always been so. Even the most cosmopolitan species had its circumscribed center of origin, for it is extremely unlikely that the same species originated in more than one locality.* From this locality, its center of dispersion, it spread to occupy whatever territory was available. Occupancy of new territory, however, is possible only if this territory corresponds in facies to that from which the species is derived, in the degree in which the species is dependent upon the facies. Hence the exodists from their land of birth are not always able to find a suitable place of settlement, and, though their numbers may be vast, a large proportion is sure to perish.

The factor of greatest importance in determining whether or not an area is to be permanently occupied by the members of a newly arrived species is the organic factor, or the question of food supply and protection from enemies. If the food supply is insufficient, or if contending species hold the ground, the new arrivals may be prevented from occupying the territory, even though the facies is otherwise adapted to their needs.

* Strictly speaking, of course, a species is monophyletic and can arise only in one locality. But types so similar that they may easily be mistaken for the same species may arise in different localities. Thus, what appears to be the same species of Fusus (*F. closter*) occurs in the West Indies and in the Red Sea, but they are most probably of independent origin. Organisms of such similar characteristics that they are commonly mistaken for members of the same genus are frequently met with in widely separated localities, where they have arisen independently. The independent origin of horses in America and in the Old World was advocated by Cope but rejected by others. Some widely separated pulmonate gastropods, placed in the same genus, may have arisen independently from marine ancestors.

DISPERSAL AND MIGRATION.

It will help us to realize the dependence of organisms on their environment if we distinguish two modes of distribution, the involuntary and the voluntary. The former may be called *dispersal;* the latter, *migration.*

Dispersal is the distribution of animals and plants by causes not primarily involving the activities of these organisms, as the carrying of the seeds of plants by the wind, the carrying of marine or fresh water planktonic or meroplanktonic organisms by currents and the like. Migration, on the contrary, is accomplished by active movements in search of food, or to escape from enemies, and is confined chiefly to animals, though stolonal propagation of plants may also be classed as a species of migration. Migrants are composed of the nekton and the vagrant benthos, while dispersants comprise the holoplankton, the epiplankton, and the meroplankton. Sedentary benthonic organisms cannot migrate, but they may be carried by a floating sub-stratum, and their mero-planktonic young may be dispersed and thus settle in other districts. Migrating organisms require a continuity of the conditions of existence in space, such as continuous shores for the marine vagrant littoral benthos, or a more or less uniform medium for pelagic migrants. The involuntary dispersal of organisms, on the other hand, may often go on in spite of barriers which migrants could not surmount. Thus, as already pointed out, the meroplanktonic young of the vagrant benthos may have a much wider distribution than could ever be brought about by the migration of the adults, who are often restricted by barriers not present in the pelagic district. Fresh-water molluscs, for example, are dispersed widely in streams, lakes, and ponds which are discontinuous, and to which the adults could not migrate. Again, plants may, by the dispersal of their seeds, surmount streams or other barriers, which root or stolonal migration could never bring about. The wide dispersal of cocoanut palms, by flotation of the nut, is a good example.

Littorina littorea may be instanced as a type which has migrated down the Atlantic coast within the space of a few years. Originally introduced from England, it characterized Halifax harbor in 1852 and slowly made its way southward and northward. In 1855 it was noted at Bathurst, Bay of Chaleur; in 1868 on the coast of Maine, appearing at Portland in 1870. At Salem, Massachusetts, it was first noted in 1872, and at Barnstable, Cape Cod, in 1875. It was rare at Woods Hole in 1875, common in 1876, and appeared at New Haven, Connecticut, in 1880 (Morse–*33*). In 1898 *Littorina rudis* and *L. palliata* were still the predominant types on the Long Island coast, but by 1901 *L. littorea* had gained a marked predominance (Balch–3), and it is still rapidly advancing. (Davenport–11:*168.*) Since the opening of the Suez Canal in 1869 many Mollusca of the Mediterranean have migrated into the Red Sea.

BARRIERS TO MIGRATION AND DISPERSAL. Under barriers to migration and dispersal we may place topographical barriers first, such as northward and southward stretching continents for marine organisms, desert tracts for fresh water organisms, and great bodies of water for terrestrial organisms. But topographical barriers are not the only ones, nor in many cases the most important. Differences in temperature, character, and direction of winds and ocean currents, improper facies of the substratum, and insufficient food supply, as well as hostile species, constitute some of the chief barriers to distribution. If by some means or other a barrier is surmounted, and a new colony is established, the new colony may become more or less isolated, the barrier proving too effective for all but a few individuals. "Migration," says Ortmann (38:*186*), "is often slow or only possible under peculiar circumstances, often it is accidental, and only a few individuals can transgress the original limits on rare occasions; then even migration acts as a means of separation. The few individuals occupying a new locality are afterward practically separated from the original stock remaining in their native country, and thus they may develop separately into a different species, even in the case that immigration from the original stock is not altogether impossible, since any rare individuals of the latter reaching the new colony from time to time are soon absorbed by the new form and their characters disappear by the continuous crossing with the modified individuals and by the transforming power of the external conditions."

Where barriers are numerous, the number of species of a given group of animals or plants is, as a rule, much greater than where barriers are few. Thus in the eastern United States, where important barriers are wanting, only one true species of chipmunk occurs; while in California, where barriers are numerous, a dozen or more species and sub-species are found (Jordan–25). On the other hand, the fauna and flora of a region with few barriers are likely to show a greater variety of organisms of types which do not interbreed than is found in a region with many barriers, since immigration of many different types is possible into an open region, but prevented by the barriers of a closed region. Where separation by barriers has brought about the formation of distinct species, nearly related species are normally found in adjoining districts, and not generally in the same or in widely separated districts. It is universally true that in such cases the species of a genetic series within the same *chronofauna,* or fauna of the same geological time division, differ more widely the further they are removed in space, and are closely related in immediately adjoining *locofaunas.* This is beautifully illustrated by the mutations of the Hawaiian Achatinellidæ, a group of brilliantly colored tree snails, different species of which inhabit the different rugged valleys incised in the margins of the extinct volcanic craters of these islands. The most nearly related mutations of these snails live in adjoining valleys, where, nevertheless, they are almost wholly isolated from the inhabitants of the neighboring valleys. Here the amount of divergence in characters between the occupants of two valleys can, as Gulick says, be roughly estimated by measuring the number of miles between the valleys. Recently Gulick has formulated this in the following law: "Forms that are most nearly related, and are, therefore, the least subject to sexual and impregnational isolation, are distributed in such a manner that their divergence is directly proportional to their distance from each other, which is also the measure of the time and degree of their geographical isolation; while those most manifestly held apart by sexual instincts and impregnational incompatibilities do not follow this law." (Gulick–19:*221.*) The trout of the modern (Holocenic) chronofauna furnishes a good illustration of this law. Thus *Salmo clarki,* the cut-throat trout of the Columbia and Missouri rivers—which interlace at their headwaters—has its nearest relatives in the basin of Utah (*S. virginalis*) and in the Platte (*S. stomias*). "Next to the latter is *Salmo spilurus* of the Rio Grande, and then *Salmo pleuriticus* of the Colorado. The latter in turn may be the parent of the Twin Lakes trout, *Salmo macdonaldi.* Always the form next away from the parent is onward in space across the barrier." (Jordan–25 : 547.) The distribution of the fossil eurypterids of the American Siluric in such a manner as to parallel the distribution of the trout above mentioned has been cited as a proof of the river habitat of these organisms. (Grabau–18.) It should be emphasized, however, that isolation cannot always be determined to be a factor in the production of species, and, indeed, if variation is orthogenetic, the development of new mutations in a progressive series can very well go on within one area. Thus many of the pronounced mutations of Planorbis in the Steinheim strata occurred within the same Tertiary locofauna. In the Eocenic locofauna of the Paris basin a large number of successive mutations in each of a number of genetic series of molluscs occurred side by side, and the same is also true to some extent of the corresponding molluscan fauna of the Gulf States of America.

FAUNAL GROUPS. The fauna of any area may be considered as belonging to one or more of the following groups: endemic species, immigrants and erratics, and relics. Endemic species are those which originated in the locality in which they are found. Immigrants have invaded the region, and erratics have been carried there accidentally, and both have established themselves in the new region. Relics are remnants, in favored places, of a once widely distributed fauna, which, by the breaking up of the area which they occupied, became resolved into a number of local remnants, which remain separated.

FACTORS GOVERNING DISPERSAL AND MIGRATION. In all cases when considering the laws which govern the distribution of organisms it is necessary to consider two phases of the subject: first, the chemical, physical, and organic characters of the localities; and, second, the nature and habits of the organisms—their bionomic characteristics. If the two are harmonious in a given case, it is evident that the locality considered can be inhabited by the organism in question. Under chemical characters we must consider the composition of the medium and its variation; and under physical characters we comprise climate and topography of the substratum; while under organic characteristics we include the presence of suitable food in sufficient quantity, and absence or paucity of competing organisms.

Inorganic Factors. The Medium.

Composition of Medium. Under this heading we include the salinity of the sea; the inclusion of air and other gases in the water, and of water and carbon dioxide in the air. The salinity of the sea is its most characteristic bionomic feature. On the whole, salinity is a pretty constant factor, varying but slightly in surface extent or in depth in the open sea. Along the continental margins, however, in the bays and marginal seas, a great variation is observable. The question of variation has already been discussed at length (Chapter IV), but a few salient points may here be repeated Thus in the Red Sea, where the supply of water is scanty, and the evaporation great, the salt constituent is 4.3 per cent. or 43 permille while in the Baltic, where the supply of fresh water is abundant and evaporation is small, the surface-salinity is very low, averaging 7 permille. The decrease in salinity eastward is very striking; thus it is 34 permille in the Skagerak, 22 permille in the Kattegat, 6 permille at Riga and 3 permille at the northern end of the Gulf of Bothnia (Uleåborg). The vertical range is also greater than in the open sea, the salinity in the "Great Belt" of the Baltic increasing downward from 10 permille on the surface to 30 permille at the bottom (66 meters).

Stenohalinity and euryhalinity. Many animals cannot live in water with less than 30 or 35 permille of salts; *i. e.,* that of the normal open sea. These stenohalic * types will die when the salinity is lowered or raised. Euryhalic † types, on the other hand, can suffer a considerable freshening of the water, and will live as long as any salt remains. Brackish-water organisms are adapted to a small amount of salt and will suffer if the amount is increased. The brackish state of water has never been definitely delimited, but probably a salinity of 2 or 3 permille (.2 to .3 per cent.) would be the upper limit. Of other mineral matter besides the normal salts iron in the form of ferrous carbonate ($FeCO_3$) may sometimes be present in considerable quantity, especially in more or less land-locked portions. Such excess of iron or of other minerals in solution appears to have a distinct effect on the growth of the fauna living in the water, resulting in its dwarfing, as has been repeatedly found by experiments. As an example may be mentioned the fauna of the Clinton iron ore layer of Rochester, which consists of individuals having "an average of about one-third the diameter of the same species in the beds just above and below" (Loomis–28 : *895*). The fauna of the Tully pyrite layer of western New York, consisting of upward of forty-five species, is composed of individuals "on an average only one-fifteenth the size of the same species in the normal and preceding Hamilton fauna." (Loomis–28 :*920.*) In this case the dwarfing was undoubtedly in part effected by the H_2S liberated by sulpho-bacteria from decaying organic matter. The reaction of this upon the iron carbonate produced the pyrite which enclosed the fauna. ($FeCO_3 + 2H_2S + O = FeS_2 + CO_2 + 2H_2O$.)

Quantity of Air. The quantity of air in the water, both salt and fresh, depends upon the depth and the amount of agitation. Deeper strata of water have necessarily less air than those nearer the surface, while agitated water will include more air than still water. It is upon the oxygen of this included air that all animals are dependent, and when it is present in insufficient quantity the animals generally perish, though some will come to the surface for more air. In partially enclosed bodies of water where the density

* From στενός = narrow and ἅλς = the sea, (salt).
† From εὐρύς = broad.

of the bottom layers is greater than that of the surface, vertical currents are slight, and hence the lower strata are poor in oxygen and unable to support animal life. Thus in the Black Sea animal life is practically absent below a depth of 125 fathoms, though dead planktonic organisms sink to the bottom, where they are decomposed by anærobic bacteria. The great depths of the Black Sea are covered by a layer of black mud, from which H_2S is abundantly separated and which is rich in pelagic diatoms and fragments of very young pelecypods from the meroplankton. The presence of abundant H_2S in these depths is characteristic. It is separated by the sulphobacteria from the dead organic matter and the sulphates of the sea water. Accompanying it is the formation of iron sulphide and the separation of carbonates, especially $CaCO_3$. Pure atmospheric air contains almost 21 per cent. of oxygen and about 79 per cent. of nitrogen (see *ante,* Chapter II). There is always, however, some carbon-dioxide and water vapor present, the quantity varying with the temperature and the movements of the air, besides being very variable in different localities.

Carbon-dioxide, while necessary to plant life, is injurious to the higher types of animals, if the proportion is above 1 to 2,000 of volume. A somewhat larger quantity, however, has no serious effect on some lower forms of terrestrial animals, and in some cases it may even be beneficial to them. The moisture in the air is necessary to the existence of most terrestrial organisms, many, indeed, being unable to exist in a region where the percentage of water vapor in the air is low. Nevertheless, some animals are found in extremely dry regions, and these are not infrequently types which belong normally to moist climates. Land snails, for example, generally require much moisture, and large numbers of such animals perish during the dry summers, or survive only by burying themselves in the earth or in crevices of rocks, and closing the mouth of the shell with a membranous operculum. In deserts these snails can obtain moisture only during the night or early morning from the heavy dews which result through excessive radiation, and it is only during these times that they lead an active life.

In the saturated atmosphere of the tropical forests are found many types of animals which are normally aquatic. Thus a type of leach, allied to the medicinal leach of the fresh water ponds, lives on trees in the moist forests of India and the Indian islands; and a number of species of land planarians are known, mostly from the tropics. Many amphipod Crustacea of the family Orchestidæ, or beach fleas, live exclusively on land, though they have the gills of the true water species. These require a very moist atmosphere.

Numerous other types of normally aquatic animals can live on land in a moist atmosphere. Some of these animals which have become adapted to a terrestrial life can be drowned by being kept under water; and this is true even of a number of fish, which habitually come to the surface to swallow air.

Volume of Water. The volume of water has in many cases a direct effect upon the size of the animals living in it, the controlling factor being the amount of water allotted to each individual. Thus in experiments on the common fresh water snail, *Limnæa stagnalis,* Semper found that if a large number of individuals developed in a given quantity of water, the size of their shell will be smaller than that of a smaller number occupying the same amount of water. Again, a number of individuals developing in a limited amount of water will have smaller shells than the same number of individuals developing in a larger amount of water. This would be noticeable in a gradually filling lake basin, where the shells in the lower strata would be larger than those of the upper strata. Here the diminishing food supply, which may be supposed to characterize a shoaling lake, would be another factor contributing to the same result. In Semper's experiment it was found "that the favorable effect of an increase of volume of water is highest between 100 and 500 cubic centimeters for each individual, and that it then gradually decreases, till, at 5,000 cubic centimeters, it would seem to cease entirely; *i. e.,* an increase of volume above this maximum has, as it appears, no further effect whatever upon the rapidity of growth." Fouling of a limited quantity of water by the excretions of the animals also causes dwarfing. The number of eggs produced under unfavorable conditions is also smaller.

Climate.

Climate and Temperature. The climate of the sea is much more uniform than that of the land. It is true that, in the very shallow parts of the sea, the water is often heated to such a degree as to make these regions uninhabitable for most animals. Ordinarily, however, the continual change of water, due to tidal and other currents, is sufficient to keep the temperature at a moderately low, and more or less uniform, degree. The daily range of temperature in the sea is of less importance to organisms than the total amount of heat received; for daily changes affect chiefly the upper strata of the water, which are directly influenced by the heat of the sun. At a moderate depth below the surface, the stratum of mean temperature is reached; this, where not affected by oceanic currents, varying mainly with the change in latitude. It is to this region of unvarying temperature that many of our littoral vagrant benthos descend on the approach of winter; so that, as every collector knows, many tide pools and sandy bottoms of moderate depth become deserted during the colder months. Many marine organisms are eurythermal, *i. e.*, able to bear a considerable range of temperature. Others, again, are stenothermal, a comparatively slight deviation from the normal temperature of their medium being fatal to them. The larvæ or eggs of stenothermal animals are often able to resist very great changes of temperature which would destroy the adult animal. Thus the winter eggs of some of the lower Crustacea, the germs of Bryozoa and of fresh water sponges, resist any degree of cold, while the full-grown individuals perish in the autumn. Many insects cannot survive the winter, though the eggs and the embryo within the eggs commonly withstand the severest cold. On the other hand, the young may be more susceptible to changes in temperature than the adult. Brooks found that, in the case of the oyster, the difference of 2° or 3° F. in the temperature of the water was sufficient to kill the whole larval brood. Thus, as Dall says, "By inhibiting natural increase . . . a species may be as sharply limited in its permanent range as if material barriers interposed." (Dall–9:*218*.)

Cold-blooded animals can usually withstand a lowering of temperature better than warm-blooded animals. Thus frogs and toads can be frozen into the ice and survive, and so can certain fishes (*e. g.*, Salmon, etc.).

In all cases a rapid change of temperature is more fatal to organisms than is a gradual one; for many normally stenothermal types can by degrees adapt themselves to a higher or lower temperature. When once acclimatized it is the change from the normal temperature of the new habitat which affects the organism. Thus members of a species acclimatized to more tropical regions will be affected by a fall of temperature to a point where members of the same species in more northern regions are wholly unaffected.

Currents. One of the marked features of the media characterizing the three organic realms is the frequent presence of currents within them. These may be temporary or fixed, and, according to this characteristic and their strength, they become powerful factors in the influence which they exert upon the distribution of organisms in the realms in question. In the air, currents are most numerous and also more variable, though certain air currents, as the "trade winds," have a great constancy within certain limits. Irregular and variable air currents often greatly influence the migration of aerial organisms, even the strongest flyers being carried away by them. But the greatest influence exerted by air currents on organisms is in the dispersal of seeds of plants, which thus may become widely scattered. Air currents are the chief cause of the persistent ocean currents, which are of such importance in the distribution of life. In fresh water lakes temporary currents may be set up by the winds, but these are of minor significance. The important currents in fresh waters are those due to gravity, as exemplified in every stream and river. That river currents are of great importance in the distribution of fluvial life, as well as in the transportation of terrestrial animal and plant life, is a matter of common knowledge.

By far the most important currents affecting the life districts of the earth are the ocean currents, for they not only aid in the distribution of organisms, but they are also instrumental in imparting to sea and land characters which they would not otherwise possess.

The characteristics of the ocean currents of the present geologic period (Holocenic) may be taken as an illustration, especially since it is highly probable that similar conditions prevailed throughout most of Tertiary time. The depth of the moving bodies of water constituting the oceanic currents is from 50 to 100 fathoms; and the direction of motion corresponds to that of the prevailing winds. As already discussed at length in Chapter V, each of the great oceans has its own eddy-like current, moving slowly around it and leaving the central portion in a relative state of quiescence. In the northern hemisphere the currents move in the direction of the hands of a clock, *i. e.,* clockwise; in the southern hemisphere, counter-clockwise. As a result, the motion of the waters is westward at the equator, both north and south of it, and eastward in the polar ends of the north and south oceans, respectively. Hence dispersals of organisms dependent on ocean currents would be from east to west in the equatorial regions, as from the west coast of Central America to the east coast of Asia, and from the west coast of South America to Polynesia and Australia. It is true that the equatorial counter-current sets eastward between the north and south equatorial currents, but this is a relatively weak current. The comparatively warm drift across the north Pacific (Kuroshiwo drift) is an aid to eastward migration and dispersal across the north Pacific, and this would probably be much more effective if the cold water from the Arctic were shut off by the closure of Behring strait. Such conditions existed during part of Tertiary time, and thus may have greatly aided migration of marine organisms in this direction. The cold west-wind drift or

Antarctic stream of the South Pacific, together with the cold Peruvian current of the west coast of South America, acts as a barrier to migration of warm water animals and plants from Australia to South America, and probably did so throughout Tertiary time.

In the Atlantic the peculiar conformation of Africa and South America results in the splitting of the South Equatorial current into the Brazilian current, flowing southward along the east coast of South America, while the main current crosses the equator into the Caribbean Sea and the Gulf of Mexico. Here again the cold west-wind drift and the cold Benguela current on the west coast of South Africa prevent dispersion between the southern portions of these continents of all warm water types. The presence, however, in the modern fauna of gastropods on the east coast of South America, which appear to be derived from species inhabiting Indo-Pacific waters, suggests that migration of tropical animals up the west coast of Africa is possible under certain conditions, in spite of the cold Benguela current. In the North Atlantic, the Gulf Stream, with its northeastward drift, favors dispersal of species from the east American to the west European coast; while the return Canary and North Equatorial currents may well be effective in carrying planktonic organisms from the northeast African coast and the Mediterranean to the West Indian waters of tropical America.

A factor which must be taken into consideration is the varying rapidity of flow of the currents. Thus the Gulf Stream, as it issues from the Florida straits, has an average velocity of 80 or 90 miles a day,* while the drifts, like that crossing the middle North Atlantic, may have a velocity of only from ten to fifteen miles per day. If the meroplanktonic stage of a normally benthonic animal is passed through very quickly it is evident that before the creature can be carried very far it will end its pelagic existence and sink to the bottom. In the case of such larvæ carried by the transoceanic currents, the depths to which they will settle after having been carried for a few days is likely to be such as to prove destructive to the organism. Thus organisms taken up by the Gulf Stream as it leaves the Florida coast would, even if the stream retained its maximum velocity, have to travel considerably over a month before they could reach the European coast, while with the actually diminishing velocity of the drift in the North Atlantic the time required will be many months. Before that time most meroplanktonic organisms will have completed their metamorphosis and have perished on an uncongenial bottom. Holoplanktonic types, however, and even nektonic animals are widely dispersed by these cur-

* It varies from 1.5 to 2.5 meters per second.

rents. Thus even Middle and South Atlantic fish are carried by the Gulf Stream to the Norwegian coast, though these do not generally propagate themselves in these northern waters.

One mode of dispersal that must not be overlooked is that effected by the epiplankton. The transportation of the Crustacea, Hydrozoa and other organisms, with the Sargassum, from the Bahamas to the middle North Atlantic, is an example. Trunks of trees from the forests of the Mississippi and the Orinoco are carried northward by the Gulf Stream, past the coast of Norway, as far as Spitzbergen, whence they are again carried southward and cast ashore on the northeast coast of Iceland. Sea-weeds, molluscs and other organisms are frequently found attached to these trees, having made the long journey on their floating substratum. Seeds of land plants commonly accompany these woods.

The warm ocean currents also have an important influence on the relative abundance of the benthonic life in the regions traversed by them. Being rich in plankton, and thus supplying an abundance of food to the animal life inhabiting the sea-bottom below it, it is not surprising to find that here the bottom life is developed in the greatest luxuriance, and that vast accumulations of organic limestones occur in the littoral regions thus affected. This is true, however, only of those portions of the littoral district which lie at a sufficient depth below the surface to escape the motion of the streaming water, which might otherwise prevent the attachment of the benthos as it settles down. Thus, off Charleston, South Carolina, in depths from 100 to 350 fathoms, the sea-floor is but sparsely settled beneath the Gulf Stream.

Topography. Next to the climate of the sea the topography of the sea-bottom, and that of the adjacent land, are the most powerful factors in determining the distribution of marine organisms. The facies of the ocean floor, or the material of which it is composed, is perhaps the most significant part of sea-bottom topography, though submarine ridges and barriers are of great importance, especially when such barriers cut off marginal bodies of water, the inhabitants of which may be prevented from intermingling. The separation thus produced may lead to the development of local faunas and floras. The importance of the greater inequalities of the sea-bottom and the submarine continental shelves and deep oceanic basins that result from them, as well as the conformation of the coast-line, with its varying facies, has already been considered. (See Chapter III.)

Of all topographical features which influence the distribution of marine organisms, northward and southward stretching bodies of land, like the continents of North and South America, are perhaps the most important. For since they form a continuous barrier across the warmer portions of the ocean, extending into the cold regions, the migration of the warmer-water species from one side to the other is prevented. Thus the marine faunas on the opposite sides of North or South America differ widely.

By the application of this principle to the Cambric faunas of North America and Europe, it has become apparent that a more or less continuous land mass, sufficient to prevent intermingling of faunas, separated the Atlantic and Pacific oceans in Cambric time. This land barrier must have extended from New England northeastward, joining this land-mass to the Scottish highlands, and southward, forming the Appalachian old-land, which was joined with the continent of South America. On opposite sides of this land-mass different faunas flourished; in the lower Cambric the Olenellus fauna on the west and the Holmia fauna in the Atlantic; in Middle Cambric time the Olenoides and Paradoxides faunas flourished in these respective basins (see the maps in Grabau–17). (See also Figs. 264a-c.)

The only topographic element of importance in lakes and other bodies of standing fresh water is the enclosing land mass, which prevents direct migration from one lake into another. In rivers the presence of rapids and falls may become a barrier to all but the most agile of swimmers. Here, however, the barrier is most effective against upstream migration. The banks likewise constitute barriers.

Terrestrial animals and plants are often prevented from migrating or becoming dispersed by the existence of topographic barriers in the form of mountains of great height and consequent range in climate; by large bodies of water, deep river gorges and impassable streams; and by extensive desert tracts; the last being produced by a combination of the topographic and climatic factors. For animals of a more limited range of habitat, minor topographical barriers become restrictive, as shown by the distribution of the Hawaiian tree snails (*Achatinellidæ*), already referred to, for which the exposed ridges separating adjoining ravines form almost impassable barriers.

The Organic Factors.

The organic conditions of the three realms likewise exert an important influence on the distribution of animal and plant life.

By organic conditions is meant the nature and abundance of food supply and the relative importance of competing organisms. Since plants primarily furnish the food supply of animals, those regions rich in plant life are, in general, well adapted for the existence of animal life. Yet even in regions where plant life is wholly absent, as in the deep sea, an abundant fauna exists, the food supply of which, however, is derived from the illuminated regions where plants grow.

Closely related to the food supply is the struggle for a living among species and individuals. It is a well-known fact that most of the lower animals have such an enormous offspring that, supposing none were destroyed, in a short time all the space in a given region would be occupied by the progeny of a single pair; and the number would be such as to exceed enormously that permitted by the food supply. Migration to new regions is therefore a necessity, and emigrants are continually sent out in all directions from the mother country. If no other occupants were in the region, an intraspecific struggle for existence would be witnessed in every locality settled by these migrants—members of the same species fighting among themselves for a living. Such a struggle would, of course, result in the destruction of vast numbers and in the emigration of others. But, when the newly opened area is entered simultaneously by several species, or if the area is already occupied by other species, an interspecific struggle occurs, the outcome of which depends on the relative ability of the contending species to hold their own. The resident species may be driven out by the newcomer, or it may hold its own and prevent the intruder from settling; or, again, what is perhaps more common, the two species may accommodate themselves side by side and jointly occupy the disputed area.

An example of a struggle between resident and invading species is found in the faunas of the Portage beds of New York State. The resident fauna was the Ithaca fauna, derived by modification from the preceding Hamilton fauna. The invading fauna came from Eurasia, invading the New York area from the northwest. The interspecific, or interfaunal, struggle continued throughout Portage time, the invading species gradually acquiring the mastery.

Biogeographical Provinces.

At each period of the earth's history, zoögeographic and phytogeographic provinces existed which were more or less distinctly separable from one another and which varied from period to period. Even within the same period the geographic provinces are not constant for all animals or plants, because some groups of animals and plants are not affected by barriers which are restrictive to others. Nevertheless a general division of the earth's surface into biotic provinces is possible, up to a certain extent; at least within the marine and terrestrial realms. Within these two realms the distribution of organisms is the resultant of migration and dispersal, not only of the organisms themselves, but also of their ancestors in preceding geologic periods. Thus the problem of geographic distribution of a given group of organisms resolves itself into a study of the migrations and dispersions of the ancestral types of these organisms from the point of their origin in past time. From the point of origin or *center of distribution* a process of *adaptive radiation* has carried the organism outward and onward in space and time. Barriers arising across the path of distribution break the continuity of the range; and from these separated remnants, or *relicts*, arise new diversified types, along a number of distinct lines radiating from the central stock, the resultants being in general well adapted each to a particular phase of the environment. In other distinct provinces similar lines of evolution may give rise to parallel series of modifications; so that, in provinces widely separated, similar lines may arise independently, the closeness of the resemblance seemingly indicating a close geographic connection between the provinces. The species of the gastropod genus Clavilithes are an excellent example of this phenomenon. This genus is represented by a number of very marked species in the Eocenic strata of the Paris Basin. A parallel series occurs in the London-Hampshire Eocenic basin, but there are scarcely any identical species. Another parallel series occurs in the Gulf Eocenic of the United States, a province entirely distinct from, and without communication with, the European provinces, which themselves were closely circumscribed. Nevertheless, the American series has the same specific types as the Paris series, corresponding species of the two generic stocks being scarcely distinguishable, so far as the specific characters are concerned; though it is an easy matter to separate them generically—that is, to place each species in its proper genetic series. If, as seems highly probable, these two groups of Clavilithids had a common ancestor, in early Eocenic, Palæocenic, or late Cretacic time, they became entirely separated in mid-Eocenic time, and the parallel specific types arose independently.

Marine Provinces.

The following are the marine zoögeographical regions of the present geologic epoch, as given by Ortmann (*38: 66*):

    I.   Littoral life-district
            1. Arctic region
            2. Indo-Pacific region
            3. West American region
            4. East American region
            5. West African region
            6. Antarctic region
    II. Pelagic life-district
            1. Arctic region
            2. Indo-Pacific region
            3. Atlantic region
            4. Antarctic region
    III, Abyssal life-district
            No regions distinguishable.

Marine geographical provinces have been distinguished for several classes of organisms by different authors. Among these the following may be mentioned:

I. *Corals.* Dana recognized three principal regions: (1) Red Sea and Indian Ocean; (2) the whole of the Pacific Islands and the adjacent coasts of Australia; (3) the West Indies. The last region is the most isolated and it contains the largest proportion of peculiar forms.

II. *Higher Crustacea.* Prof. J. D. Dana also proposed to divide the oceans into the three main areas, based on the distribution of the Crustacea. These are: (1) the Occidental; (2) the Africo-European, comprising the western shores of the Atlantic, both African and European; and (3) the Oriental, which includes the vast area from the east coast of Africa to the Central Pacific. Each region is subdivided into local and climatic provinces.

III. *Barnacles.* Darwin, considering the distribution of the species of barnacles, divided the oceans into the following regions: (1) The North Atlantic, comprising North America and Europe down to N. lat. 30°; (2) the West American, from Behring Strait to Tierra del Fuego; (3) the Malayan, from India to New Guinea; (4) the Australian, comprising Australia and New Zealand. The third and fourth regions are the richest in species.

IV. *Mollusca.* S. P. Woodward (61) divided the oceans into three main divisions or regions: (1) The Atlantic; (2) the Indo-Pacific, corresponding to Dana's Oriental region for crustacea; and (3) the West American. The following is the modified system of Woodward (Lydekker–*29:1016*):

Molluscan Regions.

| A. Atlantic and Circumpolar regions....... | 1. Arctic sub-region
2. Boreal " "
3. Celtic " "
4. Lusitanian   sub-region
5. West African " "
6. South African " " |

| B. Indo-Pacific regions.................. | 1. Indo-Pacific sub-region.

2. Japanese sub-region |

| C. Australian regions................... | 1. Australian sub-region

2. Neozealandian sub-region |

| D. American regions.................... | 1. Aleutian   sub-region
2. Californian " "
3. Panamic " "
4. Peruvian " "
5. Magellanic " "
6. Argentinian " "
7. Caribbean " "
8. Trans-Atlantic " " |

V. *Fishes.* Günther (20) recognized the following marine zoölogical regions based on the distribution of shore-haunting fishes:

1. *Arctic ocean.* 2. *Northern temperate zone* divided into: (a) the temperate North Atlantic and (b) the temperate North Pacific with further subdivisions of each. 3. *Equatorial zone,* divided into: (a) Tropical Atlantic, (b) Tropical Indo-Pacific, and (c) Pacific coast of tropical America with further subdivisions. 4. *Southern temperate zone* with several subdivisions, and 5. *Antarctic ocean.*

VI. *Marine Mammals.* The following marine geographic regions based on the distribution of seals, sea-cows, and cetaceans have been recognized by Sclater (43):

1. *Arctatlantica* (seals of the sub-family Phocinæ).

2. *Mesatlantica* (monk seal and manatis).

3. *Philopelagica* (Indian ocean, etc.), characterized by the presence of dugongs and absence of seals.

4. *Arctirenia* (North Pacific) with *Phoca,* and sea-bears and sea-lions, formerly the northern sea-cows (Rhytina) now also the gray whale (Rhachianectes).

5. *Mesirenia* (Mid-Pacific) without sea-cows, but with the elephant-seal (Macrorhinus).

6. *Notopelagica* (Southern ocean) with four peculiar genera of seals, numerous sea-bears and sea-lions, and two peculiar whales, the pigmy whale and Arnoux's beaked whale.

Former Marine Geographic Provinces.

The most elaborate attempt to divide the world into marine zoögeographical provinces for one of the past geological periods of the earth's history is that of the late Victor Uhlig of Vienna, in his "Die marinen Reiche des Jura und der Untern Kreide" (52). He recognizes at least four large faunal districts, based mainly on the distribution of fossil cephalopods, namely:

1. The boreal.
2. The Mediterranean—Caucasian.
3. The Himamalayian.
4. The Japan Province.
5. The South Andine realm.

The boreal realm of the Jurassic time originally defined by Neumayr was circumpolar in the arctic region with extensions into the heart and the northern region of Russia to the east of the Urals and westward to Greenland, including the Urals and Scandinavia as probable islands. A narrow southward extension included the region of the Lena River and the lower Amur. The Pacific extension of this realm comprises Alaska and the western coast of America (California, Nevada, etc.) to the head of the Gulf of California and with an epicontinental lobe extending into Montana, Wyoming, Idaho and eastward to the Black Hills (Logan Sea). This region has been separately named the North Andine Province. On the whole, the boreal was a shallow sea, with a peculiar and uniform fauna. Coral reefs were conspicuously absent.

The Mediterranean-Caucasian realm comprised the expanded Mediterranean area, which extended eastward to the borders of India and northward to the Caucasus Mountains. It included the Jurassic formations of the Alps. Between it and the Boreal realm of Russia lay the mid-European province of Neumayr, which, by Haug, Uhlig, and others, is regarded as a neritic border zone of the deeper Mediterranean sea. The characteristic genera of ammonites of the Mediterranean realm (Phylloceras, Lytoceras) are regarded by Haug as stenothermic and able to live only in the deeper waters where temperature changes are slight; while the other genera were eurythermic and so had a wider distribution.

The Himamalayian realm comprised northern India and the Himalayan region, and extended thence to the Malay archipelago. In it are recognizable an argillo-arenaceous and a calcareous facies, a part of the latter being often considered as abyssal. Two related provinces are recognized: (a) the Ethiopian, comprising the east coast of Africa and part of Madagascar; and (b) the Maorian, in Oceanica. The Japan Province is a small one limited to the Japanese archipelago and Korea. It is characterized by a commingling of boreal and Malayian features, though less markedly related to the latter. The South Andine realm comprised Central America and the whole west coast and the southern end of South America, and appears to be likewise represented in the southern coast of Africa.

Considering these realms as a whole it appears that the faunas of the last four are more closely related to each other than they are to the boreal. Haüg has united the Mediterranean-Caucasian, the Himamalayian, and the North Andine realms into a single broad equatorial faunal and climatic belt which is sharply contrasted with the Holarctic-Boreal belt. Such a broad zonal division is favored by Uhlig.

On the whole, it appears, as Koken (27:330) pointed out, that the distribution of marine faunas is less dependent on climatic differences than on the distribution and development of coast lines.

Present and Former Biogeographic Provinces of the Land.

The terrestrial provinces of the present time are generally comprised within three great divisions or sub-realms, as first proposed by Blanford, and under these are included a number of distinct regions. As commonly accepted, these are:

I. Arctogæa, or northern sub-realm, with
  1. Arctic, or circumpolar region.
  2. Ethiopian, or African region (south of the Sahara).
  3. Indo-Malayan, or Oriental region (including southern Asia and the Malayan islands).
  4. Malagasian, or Madagascar region.
  5. Nearctic, or North American region.
  6. Palæarctic, or Eurasiatic region.

II. Notogæa, with four regions:
  1. Austro-Malayan.
  2. Australian.
  3. Polynesian.
  4. Hawaiian.

III. Neogæa, comprising South America, with one region:
  1. Neotropical.

To these may be added the Antarctic continent, or *Antarctogæa,* the former existence of which, connecting most of the other regions, seems to be demonstrated by a number of independent lines of evidence, as developed in the study of the distribution of a great variety of types of organisms.

Fresh Water Biotic Provinces.

Simpson (47) has proposed the following regions as subdivisions of the fresh water realm, based on the distribution of the fresh water mussels or Unios in the present chronofauna.

1. Palæarctic.
2. Ethiopic.
3. Oriental.
4. Australian.
5. Neotropic.
6. Central American.
7. Mississippian.
8. Atlantic.

The *Palæarctic* region comprises Europe, North Asia, and western North America; the Oriental includes the Malaysian Islands to New Guinea. Simpson holds that the mussels originated in North America in the Triassic, whence they migrated or dispersed into South America, from which region they passed by an old Antarctic land bridge to New Zealand and Australia, thence to southern East Asia, whence they entered the remaining part of Asia, Europe and Africa. In early Tertiary time they migrated across northeast Asia to northwest America.

It should be noted in this connection that the active migration of the adult is a comparatively slow process, and is, of course, confined to streams. The young are attached to the gills of fishes and so are much more rapidly distributed. Here, too, of course, continuous water bodies are required. But there are other methods of dispersal by means of which these shells can transgress land barriers often of considerable extent. Notable among these are the dispersal of the eggs and young shells by water birds, to whose feet they become attached, and by large water beetles and other insects. Thus, while large bodies of sea water cannot be traversed in this way, narrow straits could easily be covered.

Perhaps a better index to the former land connections is found in the distribution of the fresh water crayfish. Their migrations were traced to a certain extent by Huxley (24), later by Faxon, and most recently by Ortmann (39).

The distribution of the family *Potamobiidæ* Huxl., comprising two genera, Cambarus and Potamobius, may be briefly considered. The first of these genera includes 67 species, and is found only in the eastern parts of North America, Mexico, and Cuba. The genus is divisible into five groups, the smallest of which contains three species and the largest twenty-six. The first group of sixteen species is restricted chiefly to the southern parts of the United States and Mexico. The most primitive species belong chiefly to the southwest; and in fact this is also true of the primitive species of the second and fifth groups. This fact points to an origin of the genus in the southwest, its starting point being apparently in Mexico. The second genetic group, with eight species, shows a striking discontinuity of distribution, isolated representatives being found in Mexico, the Gulf States, the southern Atlantic States, and Cuba; all of them separated from the members of the group found in the southwestern and central States. This indicates that, after the migration of the species of this group from Mexico into the United States, unfavorable physical conditions at intermediate points broke up the former continuous range. The third group, with thirteen species, has a continuous distribution in the Alleghany mountains and in the east; a single species reaching north to the Gulf of St. Lawrence region. It also extends northward in the Mississippi region, but is less prominent, and is represented at only one station in the southwest, and there by a single species. The fourth group, with twenty-six species, is also scarce in the south and southwest, but is abundant in the Upper Mississippi-Missouri-Ohio basin. Eastward it extends up the Ohio into Pennsylvania, Virginia, Maryland, New Jersey, and New York, its northeastern limit being near Montreal. In the central region it extends northward to Lake Winnipeg and the Saskatchewan River, the most northerly locality known for this genus. Westward it extends to Wyoming. The fifth group consists of three species, one occurring near New Orleans, the other two in Mexico. On the whole, the most primitive species are in the Mexican region, the probable birthplace of the genus, as has already been suggested. Here also has remained a rather primitive side branch, group 5. The other groups advanced northward and northeastward, the most specialized becoming discontinuous on account of adaptation to a changed environment.

Cambarus appears to be derived directly from a less specialized fresh water crayfish, Potamobius, which has a strikingly discontinuous distribution, one group of seven species occupying a continuous area in Europe and western Asia, and another in western North America. A third group, separated as the subgenus Cambaroides, occurs in northeastern Asia; this group, according to

Ortmann, forming a morphologic equivalent (homœomorph) of Cambarus, though not closely related to it. Ortmann believes that the three groups originated from a common ancestor whose home was in eastern Asia. A branch was sent out westward, which finally reached Europe; while another branch migrated eastward, reaching western America by means of a land area connecting Asia and America. Of these migrants a single species has remained behind in Unalaska. When finally, by geographical changes, the European and American branches became separated from the Asiatic one, each developed independently, the result being three distinct groups, as above stated. From members of the American group, which had reached Mexico, the genus Cambarus developed, in a remote period, becoming differentiated into five groups, through processes of geographical isolation.

From the distribution of these and other fresh water decapods Ortmann concludes that the following land connections must have existed in the near past.

1. Northeast Asia with Northwest America across the Behring Sea.
2. East Asia with Australia.
3. South Asia with Madagascar and Africa.
4. New Zealand with Australia.
5. Australia with South America.
6. West Indies with Central and South America.
7. South America with Africa.

Ortmann holds that the above connections were necessary; for, while a few species of fresh water crayfish or crabs have been found in brackish or even salt water, this occurrence is very exceptional, the animals being preëminently dwellers in fresh water, so that a migration across oceans or parts of oceans is practically precluded. Furthermore, since these animals cannot live out of water for any great length of time, deserts or waterless tracts form absolute barriers for them. The eggs of these creatures are carried under the abdomen of the female, and the young hatch in a state similar to the parents. While water fowl or other agents may occasionally effect a passive transport, such cases are rare and have never been observed. "The whole character of the distribution of the different species is *against the assumption of exceptional means of dispersal.*" (Ortmann–39.) The connection of Asia and northwest America by way of Behring Sea is also indicated by the distribution of mammals and other land animals. The connection continued probably through the whole of Tertiary time. The connection between eastern Asia and Australia is also indicated by the distribution of the snails (Helix). This bridge appears to have existed before the Upper Cretacic. The connection between Africa and India demanded by the distribution of the fresh water decapods seems to have been in mid-Cretacic time or earlier. Other facts show that this union continued through Eocenic time. The connection between New Zealand and Australia is believed to have been by way of New Caledonia and New Guinea, and belongs to pre-Eocenic time; while that between Australia, New Zealand and South America, generally assumed by students of zoögeography, is believed by Ortmann to have been across the Pole, and to have continued to the end of Mesozoic time. There are indications that the West Indies, Central America, and the northern margin of South America formed the "Antillean continent" during Jurassic and Cretacic time, a remnant of and successor to Appalachia; after this was broken up, the northern remnant, consisting of the Greater Antilles and parts of present Central America, probably remained a unit up to the Eocenic, after which it was dismembered, to be once more established in Pleistocenic time, and finally destroyed in the present. Finally, the connection between South America and Africa is believed to have existed in Jurassic and early Cretacic time, but was severed in subsequent periods.

Terrestrial animals, especially mammals, are even better indices of former land connections than the fresh water animals cited, inasmuch as even moderate dividing straits form absolute barriers to the majority of types. For an extensive account of this subject the student is referred to Lydekker's "Geographical Distribution of Mammals."

RELICTS.

RELICT FAUNAS AND LAKES. The occurrence of halo-limnic organisms or animals or plants normally of marine type in continental seas or lakes has been a matter of great scientific interest ever since Lovén, in 1860, announced the presence of Crustacea closely related to marine types in the great fresh water lakes of Sweden, and showed by the geological structure of the region that these organisms entered the lakes at a time when they were connected with the sea. They, therefore, constituted the relics of a former marine fauna, which had mostly become extinct by the gradual freshening of the waters of the lakes after the connection with the sea was broken. Similar left-over marine faunas or relicts were discovered in many other continental seas, both fresh and salt; some of these occurrences, like that of the sea-dog, or harbor seal, Phoca, in the Caspian and other seas, had been known previously, and used by Pallas and V. Humboldt to demonstrate the former connection of these lakes with the oceans. Oscar Peschel (41) in 1875 applied the name relict seas (*Reliktenseen*) to these bodies of water, which he regarded as derived from the sea by the growth of enclosing land. He and most authors since his time regarded all continental seas containing marine organisms as relicts, even though some of these seas are far inland. Credner (8), however, strongly opposed this view, evidently believing, with Penck, that a distinction should be made between a relict fauna and a relict sea. The former may enter the lake by a process of migration, as is believed to be the case in many instances where the seals (Phoca) are found in fresh water lakes the geologic surroundings of which show that they never were a part of the ocean; or where a marine fauna has entered a lake basin of independent origin through a temporary connection with the sea. Such is the case with the Great Lakes of North America, some of which are known to have been temporarily invaded by the sea by way of the Hudson-Champlain depression during early Pleistocenic time, but the origin of which was wholly independent of the sea (16). Thus Lake Ontario was a fresh water lake before it became temporarily connected with the sea. Credner classes as true relict seas all those which at one time were a part of and connected with the oceans. He makes the following divisions:

I. Relict seas due to damming and isolation of parts of the sea, through a growth to above the sea-level of enclosing rock masses.

II. Relict seas due to isolation of basin-like depressions in the sea-floor, owing to a negative change in the sea-level. Emersion lakes.

III. Relict seas due to shrinking of former mediterraneans.

The first division includes (a) coastal lakes due to damming of bays and inlets, by growth of deltas (Lake Akiz), or by the enclosure of bodies of water between the growing delta and the open coast (Lake Pontchartrain and others in the Mississippi delta); (b) coastal lakes or lagoons (barachois) due to the growth of sand-bars (Kurische Haff) and barrier reefs; (c) atoll seas or coral island lagoons, and others.

Under the second division are comprised the marginal lakes of the fjord type, as on the coast of Norway, Scotland (Loch Lomond), Iceland (Lagarfljöt), and others. Credner classes Lake

Champlain in this group, but this basin can hardly be said to have been a part of the sea in the sense that the marginal fjord lakes are. It is an ancient erosion basin of truly continental origin, as is the case with most of the Great Lakes. The Champlain valley was temporarily invaded by the sea, as was Lake Ontario, both being primarily continental basins due to erosion and damming. For this group a separate division—that of relict seas due to invasion—might be erected. In this category may belong Lake Venern and Lake Vettern of Sweden, both of which are old erosion basins and may have been lakes before the marine invasion. This group of relict seas is more nearly related to the true lakes which contain a relict fauna.

Among other lakes containing a pronounced relict fauna, Lake Baikal of central Asia and Lake Tanganyika of central Africa are perhaps the best known. The relict nature of the former basin has been much questioned (Credner–8, ii:*25*), but the relict nature of a part of the fauna is commonly conceded (Hoernes–22). Besides the seal *Phoca baikalensis*, B. Dyb., and a number of fish, among them *Salmo migratorius* Pallas, planarians, and sponges are represented by types more closely related to marine than to fresh water forms. One of the sponges especially (*Lubomirskia baikalensis*, W. Dyb.) is a truly marine type, occurring in Behring Sea. The molluscan fauna of Lake Baikal is especially peculiar. Of the twenty-five described species of gastropods only three are found elsewhere, but none outside of Siberia (Dybowski, W.–13). There is a marked resemblance, however, between this fauna and that of the Tertiary fresh water lakes of eastern Europe, which most probably were the source whence the Baikal fauna migrated.

The relict fauna of Lake Tanganyika is a most interesting and remarkable one (Moore–32). It includes the fresh water medusa *Limnocnida tanganyicæ*, the first and almost the only jelly-fish found outside of the sea; and a number of molluscs which can be traced back to ancestors probably in the Jurassic seas of that region. Some of these would unhesitatingly be classed as marine types if found in a fossil condition, which is particularly true of the Fulgur-like genus Holacantha, of which four species inhabit this lake; and of the trochoid genus Limnotrochus, also represented by four species (Bourguignat–4). This association, with Planorbis, Physa, Vivipara, and other normal fresh water forms, would, if found embedded in the strata, lead to some interesting speculations regarding the conditions of deposition.

The relict fauna of the Scandinavian and Finnish lakes, of which there are no less than thirty-one, comprises seven Crustacea three fish, and one seal (*Phoca annellata* Nilss). The Crustacea are especially interesting. *Mysis oculata* Fabr. var. *relicta* is the most widely distributed type. It is a variety of a true marine form which occurs in the northern seas on the coast of Labrador and Greenland. The same variety occurs in lakes Superior, Michigan, and Ontario, in the Gulf of Bothnia, and in the Caspian Sea. The other marine Crustacea of the Scandinavian-Finnish seas are three amphipods; one isopod, one phyllopod, and one lophyropod.

Relict seas derived from the shrinking of former mediterraneans are found in the Caspian and Aral seas, which are still shrinking. These seas are fragments of a once extensive southeast European-Asiatic mediterranean of later Tertiary time (Sarmatien). The relict fauna of the Caspian includes, besides the seal (*Phoca caspica*), sixteen species of molluscs, including Cardium, Adacna, Venus, etc.; two Crustacea, four sponges, and a number of fish. These seas are further characterized by having salty or brackish, instead of fresh, water.

MARINE RELICTS—BIPOLAR FAUNAS. "Bipolarity in the strict sense," says Ortmann, "*i. e.,* the presence of an identical species at the North and South Poles, while it is absent in the intermediate regions, is extremely rare, and there are hardly any well-established cases. Bipolarity in a wider sense—presence of closely allied species at the poles, while in the intermediate regions allied forms are absent—is a well-established fact." The known cases are chiefly of pelagic animals. Ortmann thinks that, in some cases, as medusæ, pteropods, and tunicates, the ancestors lived in the tropical seas of Tertiary time, and their descendants migrated both north and south, the tropical forms subsequently becoming extinct. The difference between the north and south polar types in other cases is explained by Ortmann as due to different sources of the migrants, the Arctic faunas being derived from the old Mesozoic Mediterranean waters, and the Antarctic from Pacific waters. Other examples of marine relicts, or the occurrence of faunas in basins of the sea, while they have become extinct in the neighboring region, is shown by the fauna of Quahog Bay near Portland, Maine; and in the southern parts of the Gulf of St. Lawrence, as about Prince Edward's Island, and the opposite coast of Nova Scotia, where the water is shallow and much warmer than on most parts of the Maine coast. Here *Venus mercenaria* is found in some abundance, associated with oysters and other southern species which are absent from the New England coast. They constitute "a genuine southern colony, surrounded on all sides, both north and south, by the boreal fauna." (Verrill and Smith–54:*360.*)

TERRESTRIAL RELICTS. These are faunas and floras which have migrated into certain regions during a period of different climatic conditions, and then became stranded in certain spots where the environment remained uniform, while the surrounding area changed. The Arctic plants and butterflies of Mount Washington in New Hampshire are examples. These occupied the region during the general refrigeration of the climate in the last glacial period, and on the retreat of the ice were left stranded on the higher points where these conditions were more nearly normal for them. According to Professor Asa Gray, 37 northern species of plants still remain and thrive on the summits of the White Mountains of New Hampshire, and part of them also on the Adirondack and Green Mountains. A number of these species were found on a Greenland nunatak by the Jensen expedition of 1878.

DWARF FAUNAS AND MICRO-FAUNAS.

These are faunas in which all the individuals are of much smaller size than their norm, and which therefore clearly lived under conditions preventing the organisms from reaching their full size. That such conditions are primarily environmental is indicated by the fact that all the organisms are affected, whereas, if individuals only were dwarfed, or only members of one species, this might be considered as more likely an individual response. Micro-faunas are associations of small species determined by the peculiarity of physical conditions and not due to dwarfing of normally large species. While dwarfed forms of known larger species are readily enough recognized, it is not always easy to say whether a given fauna—not known elsewhere—is dwarfed or is a micro-fauna due to selection.

Shimer (45) has listed the chief agencies of dwarfing noted in recent and fossil marine invertebrate faunas, as follows:

1. A change in the normal chemical content of the sea water.
    (a) Due to freshening of the sea water.
    (b) Due to a concentration of the salt, iron, etc.
    (c) Due to an increase in H_2S and other gases.
2. Presence of sand and other mechanical impurities in the water.
3. A floating habitat.
4. Variation in temperature.
5. Extremes in depth of water and variation in amount of water per individual.

As an illustration of the dwarfing due to the freshening of sea water Shimer cites the organisms of the Black and Caspian Seas, which are freshened by the influx of stream water (see tables of salinity, pp. 146, 154). As shown by Forbes (14), the species of molluscs in the Black Sea are all smaller than those same species in the British seas. *Cardium edule,* the common cockle of the British coast, is dwarfed when it lives in the brackish water of the estuaries. The shell is not only reduced in size, but becomes thin and has its external character less strongly marked. The cockles of the Caspian Sea are small, thin, and smooth, with lateral or central teeth or both suppressed. The cockle of the Greenland estuaries is likewise thin, smooth and almost edentulous, the rudiments of hinge-teeth occurring in the young but disappearing in the adult. This species is abundant in the Pliocenic Crag deposits of Suffolk and Norfolk, especially in the fluvio-marine portion. Among other species dwarfed by brackish water are *Mya arenaria* and *Littorina littorea.*

Shimer described a diminutive Pleistocenic? fauna from the estuarine clays of the Hudson bottom opposite Storm King, 40 feet below the bed of the river. This fauna consisted mainly of large numbers of *Mulinia lateralis* (Say) and a lower development of *Trivia trivittata* Say. These species live at present off the New England and New Jersey coasts in normal marine or but slightly freshened water, where their size is almost twice that of the Hudson estuary specimens.

Dwarfing due to concentration of salt, *i. e.,* increase in salinity, is shown to some extent in the Mediterranean, which, with a salinity of 39 permille, has many of its species smaller than their representatives in the open water of the British and Spanish coasts. The dwarfed faunas of the European Permic have in part been ascribed to such concentration of the water. The possibility of dwarfing of faunas through an excess of iron salts has been shown by experiments upon fishes and tadpoles, which in eight months were retarded in growth from 3 to 5 mm. Fossil examples are found in the Pyrite layer, which in the Genesee Valley and westward in New York replaces the Tully limestone of the Upper Devonic. In this the fauna of 45 species was found by Loomis (28) to be on the average only one-fifteenth the size of the normal form. The dwarfing was apparently due to presence of much iron in solution, in the form of ferrous carbonate, and this was precipitated as pyrite by sulphuretted hydrogen derived from the decaying organic matter ($FeOCO_2 + H_2S = FeS + CO_2 + H_2O$). The

Clinton iron ore also contains a somewhat dwarfed fauna which may have been due to the presence of much iron in the sea water.

Dwarfing effects due to an abundance of H_2S in the water are shown in the Black Sea, where, owing to the slight vertical currents, much stagnation occurs, and much H_2S is separated out (see *ante,* Chapter IV). Here life below a certain depth is practically absent, while the bottom deposits are strewn with young shells from the plankton. The dwarf faunas of the Palæozoic Black shales have been considered as produced by conditions such as now exist in the Black Sea, but the depth during the formation of most of them was probably slight, though stagnation was no doubt marked.

The presence of mud or other mechanical impurities likewise exerts a dwarfing effect on many organisms. This is illustrated by the fauna of the eastern part of the Mediterranean, where a large quantity of fine mud brought in by the Nile is held in suspension. (De Lapparent–12:*132.*) Shimer thinks that the dwarfed faunas of the late Siluric rocks of eastern New York (Rosendale, Cobleskill, Rondout, Manlius) are due to the presence of an abundance of lime-mud, of the same kind of which the strata are composed. This is a general characteristic of Palæozoic calcilutytes.

Dwarfing of organisms due to a floating habitat is seen in the case of a California coast Pecten (*P. latiauritus*), which when growing near the coast is large and more strongly sculptured than when fastened to floating kelp far from the coast (var. *fucicolus*). The molluscs, living on and among the sea-weed which crowds the eastern shallower part of the harbor of Messina, are throughout of smaller forms, but are present in enormous number of individuals. (Fuchs–15:*204.*) Walther (56) remarks upon this that the physical conditions of a special type of plant life here cause indirectly the origin of the micro-fauna. The micro-fauna here is not so much a dwarf fauna as one due to selection of small species by the peculiar characteristics of the habitat.

The influence of variation in temperature on the size of the individuals is illustrated by the experiment of Semper (44) on *Limnæa stagnalis,* in which he found that growth began at a temperature of 12° C., but that a lower temperature retarded or completely arrested growth, though not affecting the life of the animal. "If," says Semper "a Limnæa came to be placed in a pool or stream where for only two months of the year the temperature is higher than the minimum (12° C.), growth will be checked throughout the greater part of the year, and a diminutive race result, since sexual maturity cannot be reached with a lower temperature." Excessive temperature also causes dwarfing, for polar species entering waters the temperature of which is higher than their optimum will remain smaller than normal. Thus northern species of Pecten never reach the same size in warmer southern waters. The same rule holds for mammals and birds. The dwarfing of the faunas of the Black and Caspian seas may be in part caused by the extremes of temperature in these waters.

Variation in the amount of water supplied likewise affects the size of aquatic animals. Thus Semper found, in experimenting with *Limnæa stagnalis*, that "the smaller the volume of water which fell to the share of each animal the shorter the shell remained." (Semper–44:*161*.) With the same number of whorls, the average length of shell for a given number of animals in 100 c.c. of water was ¼ inch, while the same number of animals in 2,000 c.c. of water had an average shell length of ¾ inch.

Deep-water individuals are also, as a rule, smaller than the shallow-water forms, various factors, such as difference in temperature, density and salinity of water, of food supply, etc., being operative here.

The dwarf faunas of the Windsor limestone (Mississippic of Nova Scotia) and of the Magnesian limestone or Zechstein of Europe, is probably due to several causes, notably the decrease in volume of water and the accompanying increase in salinity of the water, these deposits being intercalated between continental sediments. Similar dwarfed faunas are obtained from the Cretacic of New Mexico and southern Colorado. (Stanton–49; Shimer and Blodgett–46:*67*.)

BIBLIOGRAPHY XXIX.

1. AGASSIZ, ALEXANDER. 1888. Three Cruises of the *Blake*, 2 vols· Bulletin of the Museum of Comparative Zoölogy, Vols. XIV, XV.

2. ANDRÉE, KARL. 1912. Probleme der Ozeanographie in ihrer Bedeutung für die Geologie. Naturwissenschaftliche Wochenschrift, No. 16, pp. 241–251.

3. BALCH, FRANCIS NOYES. 1901. List of Marine Mollusca of Coldspring Harbor, Long Island, with descriptions of one new Genus and two new Species of Nudibranchs. Proceedings of the Boston Society of Natural History, Vol. XXIX, pp. 133–162, pl. 1.

4. BOURGUIGNAT, J. R. 1890. Histoire Malacologique du Lac Tanganyika. Annales des Sciences Naturelles, série 7ᵐᵉ Tome X.

5. CHUN, CARL. 1886. Ueber die geographische Verbeitung der pelagisch lebenden Seethiere. Zoologischer Anzeiger, Nr. 214, 215.

6. CLARKE, JOHN M. 1897. The Stratigraphic and Faunal Relations of the Oneonta Sandstone and Shales, the Ithaca and Portage Groups in Central New York. Fifteenth Annual Report of the New York State Geologist, pp. 27–82; also, Sixteenth Annual Report, 1898.

7. CLARKE, J. M. 1910. Paleontology and Isolation. Paleontologic Record, pp. 72–75. Reprinted from Popular Science Monthly.

8. CREDNER, RUDOLF. 1887–88. Die Reliktenseen. Petermann's Mittheilungen, Ergänzungs-Band XIX, Nos. 86 and 89.

9. DALL, W. H. 1911. Nature of Tertiary and Modern Marine Faunal Barriers and Currents. Proceedings of the Palæontological Society. Bulletin of the Geological Society of America, Vol. XXII, pp. 218–220.

10. DARWIN, CHARLES. 1841. The Voyage of the Beagle.

11. DAVENPORT, CHARLES B. 1903. The Animal Ecology of the Cold Spring Sand Spit. University of Chicago, Decennial Publication X.

12. DE LAPPARENT, A. 1900. Traité de Géologie. 4th edition, Vol. I.

13. DYBOWSKI, W. 1875. Die Gastropodenfauna des Baikal Sees. Mémoires de l'Académie impériale-de St. Petersbourg. T. XXII, No. 8.

14. FORBES, EDWARD. 1859. Natural History of the European Seas, edited and continued by R. A. C. Godwin-Austen.

15. FUCHS, TH. 1871. Verhandlungen der königlich-kaiserlichen geologischen Reichsanstalt.

16. GRABAU, AMADEUS W. 1901. Geology and Palæontology of Niagara Falls and Vicinity. Bulletin of the New York State Museum of Natural History, No. 145.

17. GRABAU, A. W. 1910. Ueber die Einteilung des Nordamerikanischen Silurs. Compte Rendu du XIᵐᵉ Congrès Géologique International, pp. 979–995.

18. GRABAU, A. W. 1913. Ancient Delta Deposits. Bulletin of the Geological Society of America, Vol. XXIV, pp. 339–528.

19. GULICK, JOHN T. 1905. Evolution, Racial and Habitudinal. Publication 25, Carnegie Institution of Washington.

20. GÜNTHER, A. C. L. G. 1880. The Study of Fishes. London.

21. HEILPRIN, ANGELO. 1887. The Geographical and Geological Distribution of Animals. International Scientific Series, Vol. LVII.

22. HOERNES, RUDOLF. 1897. Die Fauna des Baikalsees und ihre Relicktennatur. Biologisches Centralblatt, XVII, pp. 657–664.

23. HOLLICK, ARTHUR. 1893. Plant Distribution as a Factor in the Interpretation of Geological Phenomena, with Special Reference to Long Island and vicinity. Contributions from the Geological Department of Columbia College, No. X. Transactions of the New York Academy of Sciences, Vol. XII, pp. 189–202.

24. HUXLEY, THOMAS. 1879. The Crayfish. London.

25. JORDAN, D. S. 1905. The Origin of Species through Isolation. Science, N. S., Vol. XXII, Nov. 3, pp. 545–562.

26. KIRCHOFF, ALFRED. 1899. Pflanzen und Tierverbreitung. Hann, Hochstetter und Pokorny, Allegemeine Erdkunde, 5th edit., Vol. III. Leipzig.

27. KOKEN, ERNST. 1893. Die Vorwelt und ihre Entwickelungsgeschichte. Leipzig.

28. LOOMIS, F. B. 1903. The Dwarf Fauna of the Pyrite Layer at the Horizon of the Tully Limestone in Western New York. New York State Museum. Bulletin 69, pp. 892–920.

29. LYDEKKER, RICHARD. 1911. Zoological Distribution. Encyclopædia Britannica, eleventh edition, Vol. XXVIII.

30. MARR, J. E. 1892. Life-zones in Lower Palæozoic Rocks. Natural Science, pp. 124–131.

31. MERRIAM, JOHN C. 1910. The Relation of Palæontology to the History of Man, with Particular Reference to the American Problem. The Palæontologic Record, pp. 88–92. Reprinted from Popular Science Monthly.

32. MOORE, J. E. S. 1903. The Tanganyika Problem. Hurst and Blackett, London.

33. MORSE, E. S. 1880. The Gradual Dispersion of Certain Molluscs in New England. Bulletin of the Essex Institute, Vol. XII, pp. 3–8.

34. MOSELY, H. N. 1882. Pelagic Life. Address at the Southampton Meeting of the British Association. Nature, Vol. XXVI, No. 675, pp. 559 et seq.

35. MOSELY, H. N. 1885. The Fauna of the Sea Shore. Nature, Vol. XXXII, pp. 417 et seq.

36. MURRAY, JOHN. 1885. Narrative of Cruise of H. M. S. Challenger, with a General Account of the Scientific Results of the Expedition. Challenger Report, Vols. I, II.

37. ORTMANN, ARNOLD E. 1895. Grundzüge der Marinen Tiergeographie. Jena. G. Fischer.

38. ORTMANN, A. E. 1896. On Separation and Its Bearing on Geology and Zoögeography. American Journal of Science, 4th series, Vol. II, pp. 63–69. Also: On Natural Selection and Separation. Proceedings of the American Philosophical Society, Vol. XXXV, pp. 175–192.

39. ORTMANN, A. E. 1902. The Geographical Distribution of the Fresh-water Decapods and its Bearing upon Ancient Geography. American Philosophical Society Proceedings, Vol. XLI, pp. 267 et seq.

40. ORTMANN, A. E. 1910. The Double Origin of Marine Polar Faunas. Seventh International Zoological Congress, 1907.

41. PESCHEL, OSCAR. 1875. Entwickelungsgeschichte der Stehenden Wasser auf der Erde. Ausland, March 15, 1875.

42. REED, F. R. COWPER. 1910. Pre-Carboniferous Life-Provinces. Records of the Geological Survey of India, Vol. XL, pt. I, pp. 1–35.

43. SCLATER, P. L. and W. L. 1899. The Geography of Mammals. London.

44. SEMPER, KARL. 1888. Animal Life as Affected by the Natural Conditions of Existence.

45. SHIMER, HERVEY W. 1908. Dwarf Faunas. American Naturalist, Vol. XLII, No. 499, pp. 472–490.

46. SHIMER H. W. and BLODGETT, M. E. 1908. The Stratigraphy of the Mount Taylor Region, New Mexico. American Journal of Science, XXV, pp. 53–67.

47. SIMPSON, C. T. 1900. Synopsis of the Najades or Pearly Fresh-water Mussels. Proceedings of the United States National Museum, Vol. XXII, pp. 511–1044.

48. SMITH, JAMES PERRIN. 1895. Geologic Study of Migration of Marine Invertebrates. Journal of Geology, Vol. III, pp. 481–495.

49. STANTON, TIMOTHY W. 1893. The Colorado Formation and its Invertebrate Fauna. Bulletin of the United States Geological Survey, 106.

50. STANTON, T. W. 1910. Palæontologic Evidences of Climate. Palæontologic Record, pp. 24–27. Reprinted from Popular Science Monthly.

51. THOMSON, WYVILLE. 1873. The Depths of the Sea. An Account of the General Results of the Dredging Cruises of H. M. S. S. Porcupine and Lightning.

52. UHLIG, VICTOR. 1911. Die Marinen Reiche des Jura und der Kreide. Mittheilungen der geologischen Gesellschaft in Wien. IV Jahrgang, Heft 3, pp. 329–448, with map.

53. VAUGHAN, T. WAYLAND. 1910. The Continuity of Development. The Palæontologic Record, pp. 81–84. Reprinted from Popular Science Monthly.

54. VERRILL, A. E. and SMITH, S. J. 1873. Report upon the Invertebrate Animals of Vineyard Sound and the Adjacent Waters, with an Account of the Physical Characters of the Region. United States Commission of Fish and Fisheries Report, pp. 295–747.

55. WALLACE, ALFRED RUSSELL. 1876. The Geographical Distribution of Animals. London.

56. WALTHER, JOHANNES. 1894. Einleitung in die Geologie als historische Wissenschaft. I. Bionomie des Meeres. II. Die Lebenweise der Meeresthiere. Jena. Gustav Fischer.

57. WELLER, STUART. 1895. A Circum-insular Palæozoic Fauna. Journal of Geology, Vol. III, pp. 903–927.

58. WELLER, S. 1898. The Silurian Fauna Interpreted on the Epicontinental Basis. Journal of Geology, Vol. VI, pp. 692–703.

59. WILLIAMS, HENRY S. 1910. The Migration and Shifting of Devonian Faunas. Palæontologic Record, pp. 27–34. Reprinted from Popular Science Monthly.

60. WILLISTON, S. W. 1910. The Birthplace of Man. Palæontologic Record, pp. 85–88. Reprinted from Popular Science Monthly.

61. WOODWARD, S. P. 1880. Manual of the Mollusca.

CHAPTER XXX.

FOSSILS, THEIR CHARACTER AND MODE OF PRESERVATION.

DEFINITION AND LIMITATION OF THE TERM FOSSIL.

Fossils are the remains of animals and plants, or the direct evidence of their former existence, which have been preserved in the rocks of the earth's crust. By direct evidence is meant the impressions left by animals in transition, the structures built by them, etc. Beds of iron ore and deposits of apatite or of crystalline limestone must be considered indirect and not always reliable evidence of the former existence of organisms, since, in these cases, organisms were only the agents active in their formation. Under remains preserved in the earth's crust must be included those formed in the northern ice fields, for we have seen that these ice masses are to be regarded as a portion of the rocky crust of the earth, though in most respects the least permanent one.

It has been a common custom to limit the term fossil to those remains which were buried prior to the present geologic period. This will be seen from the common text-book definitions of this term. A few of them may be quoted. *Fossils:* "All remains or traces of plants and animals which have lived before the beginning of the present geological period, and have become preserved in the rocks." (Zittel, Eastman's translation.) "Remains of animals and plants which have existed on the earth in epochs anterior to the present, and which are buried in the crust of the earth, are called fossils." (Bernard's Elements, adapted from the English translation.) "All the natural objects which come to be studied by the palæontologists are termed 'fossils' . . . Remains of organisms . . . found . . . in those portions of the earth's crust which we can show by other evidence to have been formed prior to the establishment of the existing terrestrial order . . ." (Nicholson and Lydekker, Manual of Palæontology.) "Of those animals and plants which have inhabited the earth in former times, certain parts, decomposable with difficulty, or not at all, have been preserved in the strata of the earth, and these we call fossils, or petrefactions." (Steinmann, Einführung in die Paläontologie, translated.) This definition in terms of past geologic time is an arbitrary one, and is not based on any distinction in character between the remains which were buried before and those which were buried during the present geologic epoch. Thus the marine shells in the post-glacial elevated clays of northern New England and Canada (Leda, Saxicava, etc.) differ in no wise from those of the same species buried in the modern deposits off the present coast. "In the former case the strata have been elevated several hundred feet; while in the latter case they still retain their original position, or, at least, have experienced no appreciable disturbance. In like manner many of the Miocenic and Pliocenic shells are not only of the same species as those recently buried on neighboring shores, but the changes which they have undergone since burial are frequently not greater than those experienced by shells buried in modern accumulations. The difference in the alteration is merely one of degree, and with proper discrimination specimens can be selected which show all grades of change, from the unaltered state of shells in modern mud-flats to the crystalline condition of an ancient limestone fossil, in which the original structure has been completely lost." (Grabau–13:97, 98.) It is thus seen that it is far more logical to extend the term "fossil" so as to include all remains of animals and plants preserved from the time of the earliest fossiliferous strata to the present. This is the position taken by Lyell, who defines a fossil as: "Any body or the traces of the existence of any body, whether animal or vegetable, which has been buried in the earth by natural causes." In this definition made by the geologist the time element is entirely omitted and in this respect it contrasts markedly with the definitions quoted above from palæontologists. Of the latter, however, D'Orbigny forms an exception, for he considers the term "fossil" to comprise "all bodies or vestiges of bodies of organisms buried naturally in the rocks of the earth and found to-day, except when actually in the living state." (Cours Élémentaire de Paléontologie, Vol. I, p. 13.) Geikie, too, neglects the time element in his definition of a fossil. He says: "The idea of antiquity or relative date is not necessarily involved in this conception of the term. Thus, the bones of a sheep buried under gravel and silt by a modern flood and the obscure crystalline traces of a coral in ancient masses of limestone are equally fossils." (Text-book of Geology, 3d ed., p. 645.) This general definition of a fossil is the one insisted upon by Grabau and Shimer in "North American Index Fossils" (Volume I, page 1.)

FOSSILIZATION.

"Geologic time is continuous, and the development of life is progressive. No break divides the present from the past, and the geologic phenomena of the present epoch are controlled by the same laws which governed those of past time. Fossilization is a mere accident by which some animals and plants are preserved, and it resolves itself into a process of inhumation, neither the nature of the organism nor the time or mode of burial being of primary significance. These are of first importance in determining the degree of preservation which the fossil is to experience, and, consequently, the nature of the record which is to remain; but they do not affect the process of fossilization, which is merely the burial of the dead organism. Thus the idea of change is not necessarily involved in the concept of a fossil, although it is true that few organisms long remain buried without undergoing some chemical change. Examples of the preservation of organisms in an almost unchanged condition are nevertheless known, the most conspicuous being the mammoths frozen into the mud and ice of Siberia, and retaining hair, skin, and flesh intact; and the insects and other animals included in the amber of the Baltic, where they have remained unchanged since early Tertiary time. Ordinarily, however, the flesh of the buried animal soon decays, and, consequently, no record of the soft parts is retained. In plants the decay is less rapid, and the buried vegetable remains may be indefinitely preserved in the form of carbonaceous films.

"The hard parts of animals are best preserved as fossils. Such are the shells and other external skeletal structures secreted by a variety of animals, as crustaceans, molluscs, echinoderms, corals, and so forth; and the bones, teeth, and other hard structures of the vertebrates. Besides the actual remains of animals and plants, any evidence of their existence, which is preserved, is commonly included under the name of fossil. Thus impressions made by living animals and plants in the unconsolidated rock material, and structures built by animals from inorganic material, are fossils if properly buried. Examples of the first are the footprints of vertebrates; the tracks and trails of jelly-fish, worms, molluscs, or Crustacea; the burrows of worms, borings of animals in stones or shells. and the impression made by sea-weeds in motion. Among the second class are worm tubes built of sand grains; foraminiferal shells, built of foreign particles; flint implements and other utensils of primitive man; and the relics of the Swiss Lake dwellers . . .

(Grabau–13:*98, 99*.)   Here belong, further, ancient buried cities, like Pompeii; the Roman coins, weapons, etc., buried in the peat bogs of Flanders and the north of France; and, in fact, all artificial productions of early man or other animals which have been preserved.   Finally, coprolites, or the characteristic excrementa of animals, have frequently been preserved, and these constitute a class by themselves.   Thus four distinct types or classes of fossils may be recognized, viz.:   (Grabau and Shimer–14:*3*.)

1. Actual remains and their impressions.
2. Tracks, trails, and burrows of organisms.
3. Artificial structures.
4. Coprolites.

These may now be discussed more fully.

Types of Fossils.

1. *Actual Remains.*

Preservation of Soft Tissues.   As has already been noted, a number of cases are known where the fleshy portions of animals have been preserved.   The mammoth (*Elephas primigenius*), and the rhinoceroses frozen into the mud and ice of Siberia are classical examples.   Insects, spiders, and myriopods have been preserved in great perfection in the Oligocenic amber of the Baltic provinces.   This fossil resin was produced by a species of pine (*Pinus succinifer*) and its quantity was so great that the deposits, though they have been worked since very ancient times, have not yet been exhausted.

Remains of man and other animals have been found perfectly preserved in peat-bogs where they had been entombed for hundreds of years.   Mummification, or the preservation of the flesh in dried condition, must also be noted in this connection, for in this manner many remains of the human period have been preserved.   Natural mummies have been found in saline soil at Arica in Chile (South America), and they have also been found occasionally in dry caverns and in crypts, notably in Bordeaux, France. In the desert region west of the Peruvian Cordillera in South America climatic and other conditions have proved particularly favorable to the natural preservation of human remains.   "The tombs and graves [of the Incas] are usually found on elevated places outside of the valleys where the extreme dryness of the air

combines with the nitrous character of the sand, into which moisture has seldom found its way, to desiccate and preserve the bodies
of the dead, thus mummifying them naturally. The same factors
have caused the clothing and objects placed with the dead to be
preserved for many centuries." (Mead–17:8.) Bodies of animals
have been similarly mummified, particularly those of household
pets, such as dogs and parrots; and foods, such as corn and beans,
have been perfectly preserved. In the Atacama desert in Chile, in
the Chuquicamata copper mining district, was found the body of a
miner who had been caught, while at work, by a cave-in of the roof
of a mine in a side hill. "The stone and earth surrounding the
mummy were impregnated with anhydrous sulphate of copper
(brochantite), and sulphate of copper (blue vitriol). This mineral
prevented the organic matter from decomposition." "The skin
has not collapsed on the bones, as in the mummies found usually
in the region, but the body and limbs preserve nearly their natural
form and proportions, except for the crushing . . ." which
took place on the caving-in of the mine. The age of the mummy
is unknown, but it is probably several hundred years old, as indicated by the primitive character of the implements embedded with
the body.

Preservation of animal tissue by impregnation with mineral
matter also occurs. As an example may be mentioned the well-
preserved body of a negro woman which had been buried for fifty-
seven years and was found near Tuskegee, Macon county, Alabama,
in 1894. The body lay in a sandy soil where the water from a near-
by spring kept it continually wet. In this water, silica, lime, and
magnesia were held in solution, and silica, lime, and oxide of iron
in suspension. About 50 per cent. of the substance of the body
had been replaced by mineral matter. Lead was also found present
in the body and might have been active in its preservation. (Sted-
man–23.) All told, however, the complete preservation of the animal body is of rare occurrence, and probably never dates back
very far in geologic history. A remarkable exception to this rule
is found in the muscle fibers of Devonic and later fish, and in
Mesozoic reptiles, which have been so perfectly preserved by a
process of replacement that their structure can readily be determined under the microscope. These will be noted again in
the discussion of modes of preservation.

Impressions of the soft parts in rocks, or even a carbonaceous
film representing them, are found under favorable conditions. The
most familiar examples of this kind are ferns and other plant remains, but those of animals are not unknown. In the fine litho-

graphic lutytes of the Solnhofen district in Bavaria have been found the impressions of medusæ and of naked cephalopods with the inkbag still containing the sepia in a solidified state, while the beautiful impressions of insect wings and the membranous wings of pterosauria are among the most noted preservations obtained from this rock.

Even more perfect examples of the preservation of soft parts have recently been obtained by Walcott from the Stephen shale (Cambric) of western Canada (26). Here worms, holothurians, and other soft-bodied animals occur in a wonderful state of preservation, so that, in many cases, even the internal anatomy can be ascertained. The appendages of trilobites and other organisms are also well preserved. The rock in which these fossils occur is an exceedingly fine-grained sapropellutyte. Other remarkable preservations of soft tissues in rock of this type are known from the Lias of Württemberg, where, at Holzmaden, the impression of the skin of the Ichthyosaurians has been obtained.

Preservation of Hard Structures and of Petrified Remains. The hard parts of animals are best adapted for preservation. This is particularly the case where these parts are either calcareous or siliceous. Such are the shells of Protozoa; the spicules of sponges; the coral of the coral-polyps; the test of the echinoderm; the shell of brachiopod or mollusc; the calcareous structure of Bryozoa; the exoskeleton of Crustacea; and the bones and teeth of fishes, amphibians, reptiles, birds, and mammals. But hard parts of a purely organic origin are also commonly preserved. These are the structures composed of chitin and conchiolin. *Chitin,* or *entomolin,* as it is also called, is the substance of which the elytra and integuments of beetles and other insects are composed, and which, commonly with an admixture of calcium carbonate or phosphate, forms the carpace and other exoskeletal parts of Crustacea, etc. Its composition is probably expressed by the formula $C_{15}H_{26}N_2O_{10}$. Chitinous structures of other animals are the perisarc of Hydrozoa and the similar network of horny fibers in the Ceratospongiæ. *Conchiolin* is the organic matter of shells which, on solution of the lime by acids, remains as a soft mass. The young shells, particularly the protoconch, consist wholly of this material. It is generally strengthened by subsequent deposition of calcium carbonate, but in some cases, as in the nautiloids, it seems to remain in the original chitinous condition, and is occasionally preserved.

These structures, whether of chitin or conchiolin, are preserved either as impressions, or, more generally, as carbonaceous films.

Sometimes various minerals, as pyrite, or chlorite, or even talc, replace them. The same thing may be said of the cellulose composing the tissues of plants, where decomposition is a slower process than in the fleshy tissues of animals. The cell structure of plants may thus be conserved for a long period, and this is especially the case where there is a nearly complete exclusion of air, as in fine sediments or in peat bogs.

The first requisite in fossilization is the burial or inhumation of the remains. Even the hard parts of animals will be destroyed if exposed too long to the atmosphere. Thus the bones of the American bison, which, during the process of extinction that this animal was undergoing on the western plains, were abundantly scattered about, are fast disappearing by decay, so that shortly no traces of them will remain except where they have been buried.[*] This fact must be borne in mind in considering the remains of earlier mammals. Those found can constitute but a small portion of the skeletons once scattered about but which disintegrated before the slow process of burial by continental waste or by dust saved them. The soft tissues of animals and the tissues of plants decay, of course, rapidly, and even inhumation, except in the cases noted above, will not check the process of decay. Immersion in water likewise results in the decay of organic matter, for bacteria here become an active agent in the dissolution of tissues. Hard structures, such as shells or bones, will also suffer destruction by solution, especially if the waters are rich in carbon dioxide. Thus, as already noted in an earlier chapter, the shells of many Protozoa are dissolved after the death of the animal before they settle down to the abyssal portions of the sea, and hence deposits of these shells are generally absent from the greater deeps, though abundant in regions of lesser depth. Solution may continue even after burial if the beds are raised above the sea-level, and if they are permeable.

The buried hard parts of animals generally undergo a process of petrifaction, which most commonly is either *calcification* or *silicification,* or sometimes the first followed by the second, *i. e.,* a replacement of the lime by silica, or, more rarely, the reverse. Pyritization, or the replacement of the remains by iron pyrites (or, more frequently, by marcasite) and replacement by iron oxide, sphalerite, barite, vivianite, glauconite, or other minerals, also occurs. The process of replacement differs in different groups of organisms.

[*] A certain percentage of these bones, however, has been picked up and burned for commercial and other purposes.

Petrifaction of non-mineral substances.

(a) *Replacement of soft animal tissue.* As stated above, the muscle tissues of a number of groups of vertebrates have been known to be preserved in a most remarkable manner. In the upper Devonic shales (Cleveland shales) of Ohio the muscular tissue of cladodont sharks has been mineralized in such a perfect manner that in places "they suggest in color, distinctness, and texture the mummified tissue of recent fish." (Dean–10:274.) Similarly, well-preserved muscular tissue has been found in fishes of the lithographic stone (Reis–20, pl. II), and in other deposits both finer and coarser. The muscular mass thus preserved is pure mineral, composed of about 80%+ of calcium phosphate. Reis holds that the muscular tissue was in a semi-decomposed condition, that mineralization took place quickly, and that the remains must have been so effectively enclosed that decomposition was checked. The phosphate, he thinks, is derived from the body of the animal and precipitated on contact of the decomposing material with the calcium carbonate of the surrounding sediment. Dean, on the other hand, favors the view that the phosphate was deposited from solution within the undecomposed tissue of the shark, which thus became mineralized before it had time to decompose. The partial replacement of human bodies mentioned above is analogous to the more ancient case here cited.

(b) *Petrification of plants.* (Roth–22:605.) Aside from the unicellular diatoms, in which the cell walls of the living plant are impregnated with amorphous silica, and the unicellular to multicellular lime-secreting algæ, the tissues of plants may in general be regarded as free from mineral matter. But plants immersed in mineral waters, or buried where such waters have free access, are saturated and completely impregnated with the mineral matter. Colloidal silica is most favorable for the preservation of the delicate cell structures, while calcite or other minerals of high crystallizing power will cause deformation if not disruption and complete destruction of the cell walls.

A mass of wood completely penetrated by and saturated with silica still shows its original form and structure, even to the ornamentation of the cell walls, which, in a properly prepared slide, will not appear very different from the fresh or dried tissues. Even in appearance the impregnated wood resembles the unaltered wood, being fibrous and splintery, and the change is often noticeable only from the difference in weight and hardness. The silica of wood thus saturated may be dissolved in concentrated hydrofluoric acid, when the woody tissue will be left behind unattacked. This shows, according to Göppert, a cellular structure which in most cases is sufficient for the generic determination of the wood.

Replacement of the cell walls themselves generally follows impregnation, and thus the wood becomes wholly changed to silica. Under these circumstances the finer structure is often destroyed and the mass becomes uniform and breaks with a conchoidal fracture. Illustrations of this are found in the brilliantly colored, agatized woods of Arizona, fragments of which are hardly distinguishable from agates of wholly inorganic origin.

Opalized woods are not uncommon. Here, as in the case of woods replaced by quartz, the structure of the wood is generally retained, and in some cases the interior has been found to be but slightly impregnated with the opal, or even to be unaltered wood, thus showing the progress of opalization from without inward. (Blum–4:*197*.)

Calcified woods are not uncommon, occurring in all formations, from the Devonic up. They have been found in limestones, sandstones, shales, basaltic conglomerates, volcanic ashes and tuffs, and other deposits. Daubrée found at Bourbonne-les-Bains, in the department of Haute-Marne, France, piles of red beechwood, in places so completely impregnated with transparent calcium carbonate that on solution in hydrochloric acid only 3.1 per cent. of insoluble matter, showing plant structure, remained. The piles supported an ancient Roman canal, and when found were buried about 8 meters below the surface.

Aragonite is also known to have replaced wood. Even gypsum has been found replacing wood in some Tertiary beds, and phosphate, as well as fluorite of lime, is likewise known in this connection. Barite also has replaced wood in some limestones of the Lias, and a talc-like, complex silicate, probably pyrophyllite, has been found replacing fronds of Neuropteris and Pecopteris and the leaves of Annularia in Carbonic rocks in the Piedmont district. Chlorite has been found occurring in a similar manner. So delicate is the replacement that the venation is easily recognizable, although no part of the original organic matter remains. Wood largely replaced by sulphur and devoid of structure has been found in Cesena, Italy, and plant remains replaced by sulphur have also been obtained from the Tertiary beds of Aragon. (Blum–7:*170*.)

In the Carbonic and later coal-bearing horizons wood replaced by siderite, often with considerable iron oxide, or wholly by limonite or hematite, is not uncommon in various parts of the earth; while sphalerite, galenite, and marcasite are also known. Galenite has been reported as replacing the fronds of ferns in some Coal Measures of Saxony. Malachite, azurite, and chalcocite are found in carboniferous marls, probably of Jurassic age, in the district of Angola, West Africa, in the Urals, and in other regions. Even modern cedar wood has been found coated with and, in some cases, largely replaced by malachite, as reported by Dr. A. F. Rogers from Brigham, Utah (21). From a tuff bed enclosed between basaltic flows below the Limburg (Germany) wood of *Prunus nadus* (?) replaced by a kaolin-like substance has been obtained in abundance. This still retains the structure and occasionally carbonaceous remnants of the wood occur.

Where the actual plant remains have been removed by decay an impression or mold often remains, in which a cast of the plant may be formed by infiltrating foreign material. Such casts are common in the Carbonic sandstones of the Joggins region of Nova Scotia, in western Scotland and elsewhere. Trunks of Calamites, Sigillaria and Lepidodendra, together with their rootstalks, Stigmaria, are abundant in these strata as sandstone casts, resulting from the filling of the cavities left by the decaying wood.

Decaying wood or other delicate parts of plants may leave a record behind in the rocks in the form of a film of colored mineral matter, precipitated by the decaying organic matter, or by the removal of the coloring matter of that portion of the rock covered by the decaying plant. This process of self-inscription upon the rock by the plant has been termed *autophytography* (White–28), the first mode producing a *positive* picture, and the second a *negative* one.

Petrifaction of mineral structures.

(a) *Protozoa.* The shell of the Foraminifera is typically composed of carbonate of lime, either in the form of calcite (vitreous species) or of aragonite (porcellaneous species). The skeletal structures of Radiolaria are mainly of silica, though horny types (of acanthin) also occur. Both types of Protozoa are well adapted for preservation and extensive deposits of them are known, such as the Radiolarian beds of Barbados (Miocenic) and the chalk of western Europe (Cretacic).

(b) *Sponges and hydrozoans.* These organisms are generally capable of preservation on account of the chitinous material which composes the network of many sponges and forms the perisarc of the Hydrozoa. They are most commonly preserved as carbonaceous films, but cases of pyritization among the graptolites are not uncommon. Such pyritized specimens stand out in relief and afford good material for sectioning. (Wiman–27.) Pyrophyllite also has been found replacing these organisms, which thus became outlined in white on the dark shales in which they occurred. (Blum–5: *126*; *7:175.*)

In a considerable number of sponges siliceous or calcareous spicules occur, frequently uniting into a solid network, and then preserving the form of the sponge. The siliceous spicules of sponges are sometimes replaced by calcite in the process of fossilization.

(c) *Silicification of corals.* Most corals are composed of calcium carbonate in the form of aragonite, with the exception of the *Alcyonaria,* which are calcite. Often a small percentage of magnesium carbonate is present. The structure of the corals is frequently very porous, but it is most probable that these pores are first filled by calcium carbonate, and that silicification is a process of replacement pure and simple. While silicified corals preserve the form well, the finer structure is commonly destroyed. The ringed structure, known as Beekite rings and more fully described under the section on molluscan shells, occurs rarely in corals; the rings seldom occur so abundantly or of such size as in molluscs or brachiopods. Corals are occasionally replaced by other minerals, sphalerite having been most frequently observed.

(d) *The brachiopod shell.* In a number of inarticulate brachiopods the shell consists chiefly of chitin, and here the preservation is similar to that of other chitinous structures. In Lingula, alternating layers of chitinous and calcareous matter make up the shell, but in the majority of species the shell is wholly composed of calcium carbonate. This is present in the form of calcite. The greater portion of the shell is composed of a layer of fibers or prisms of calcic carbonate which constitutes the inner layer of the shell. Outside of this is a thin lamellar layer of calcic carbonate, covered in turn by the periostracum, or outer corneous film. In a large number of species the shell is traversed by vertical canals or tubules which expand upward and terminate in the lamellar layer, not piercing the periostracum.

Calcification and silicification occur in the brachiopods as in the mollusc shells, the tubules, when present, forming additional spaces for the infiltration of lime or silica. Details will be mentioned in the description of molluscs. Nearly all the minerals mentioned under molluscs have been found replacing brachiopod shells; *i. e.,* pyrite, galenite, sphalerite, the various iron oxides, barite, etc.

(e) *Shells of molluscs*. These are composed of calcareous salts, either carbonate of lime or mixed carbonate and phosphate of lime, penetrated and bound together by an organic network of conchiolin. In the Pelecypoda the shell consists of three layers: (1) the outer or periostracum, a horny integument without lime; (2) the middle prismatic or porcelaneous layer, consisting of slender prisms perpendicular to the surface and closely crowded; and (3) the inner or nacreous layer, which has a finely lamellate structure parallel to the shell surface. Many pelecypod shells consist entirely of aragonite. In Ostrea and Pecten the whole shell is calcite, while in some others (Pinna, Mytilus, Spondylus, etc.) the nacreous layer is aragonite, while the prismatic layer is calcite. In the gastropod and cephalopod shell the inner or nacreous layer is often wanting, while the periostracum is generally present. The structure of the middle layer differs much from that of the pelecypods. The shells are mostly aragonite, except those of a few gastropods (Scalaria and some species of Fusus) and a few cephalopods (*e. g.*, the guard of Belemnites), which are of calcite.

The first process of alteration in the shells is the removal by decay of the horny periostracum covering the shell and of the conchiolin which penetrates the calcareous mass. As a result the shell is rendered porous, which can be proved by applying it to the tongue, when it will be found to be adhesive. This porous condition may be observed in many Miocenic and later shells. The aspect of a shell which has thus undergone the first change is more or less chalky, instead of firm and often shiny, as in the fresh shell. Frequently shells composed of aragonite are entirely destroyed, while in those in which both calcite and aragonite occur the latter is dissolved away while the calcite remains unimpaired. Water carrying salts in solution will enter the pores and there deposit its mineral matter, until the pores are filled. If the matter in solution is carbonate of lime, this process of infiltration will result in the complete calcification of the shell, whereby the finest structural details will be fully preserved. Those portions of the shell which originally were aragonite may be changed to calcite. In some cases, however, the whole shell is converted into crystalline calcite, and then the finer structure is destroyed. At other times granular limestone replaces the shells. If, however, the infiltrating substance is silica, the process of fossilization does not stop with the filling of the pores, but from the greater insolubility of the silica it becomes the dominating substance and gradually replaces the more soluble lime. This process is frequently most active around certain centers, and is then indicated by the formation of concentric rings of silica

(*Kieselringchen*), which have been named *beekite rings*, after Dr. Beek, sometime Dean of Bristol, who first called attention to them. These rings often form a regular ornamentation of the surface of shells and have been mistaken for original features. According to T. M. McKenny Hughes (15:*265 et seq.*), these rings form in a layer ⅛ to ¼-inch thick, just beneath the outside film of lime. Blum (4:*190*) records cases where the calcium carbonate of the shell is still largely retained, while at many places single tubercles of silica project, surrounded each by one or two rings, but seldom more. This was especially noted in brachiopods. In some cases the shell was changed to chert with only scattered rings. A shell of *Orthis rectangularis* from the Carbonic limestone was wholly silicified, the silica appearing in the form of small spheres which are arranged in place of the former radial striations of the shell. A shell of Gryphæa contained several layers of silica in the form of beekite rings. A *Plicatula armata* had its inner surface preserved in compact yellowish-brown chert; while its outer surface, with all its original roughnesses, was composed of beekite rings. *Pecten vagans* showed the reverse, with a layer of stalactitic quartz between the two layers. Arca had both outer and inner surfaces made up of beekite rings, while between these layers appeared a porous mass of chert. A specimen of *Exogyra reniformis* from the Oxford Oolite was replaced by beekite rings, while *Trigonia costata,* to which it adhered, was replaced by chert only. Belemnite guards had their surfaces covered with beekite rings, while the interior was still fibrous calcite. Others had been changed entirely to beekite. The rings here had become concentric cylinders, the axes of which coincided with the original calcite fibers. In other cases the guard was composed of a number of concentric layers or funnels, each of which was composed of beekite rings.

So far as present observation goes, there seems to be no inherent character within the organism or the formation within which it is embedded which determines whether silicification is to be accompanied by the formation of beekite rings or not. Both cases have been found within the same formation at the same locality and within the same genus.

Silicified shells are among the most acceptable fossils, for they will readily weather out in relief or even become entirely free, or they may also be easily separated from the enclosing matrix by the use of weak acid.

A great variety of minerals besides silica replaces the calcium salts of mollusc shells. The chambers of ammonites often contain ankerite (Quenstedt), others again are chiefly filled by strontianite (Sandberger). In the Zechstein of Altenburg shells of Schizodus have been found replaced by malachite, which fills the space between external and internal mold. Gypsum has also occasionally served as replacing substance of pelecypods and gastropods. Barite is not an uncommon replacing agent of molluscan as well as brachiopod shells and other hard structures. In the Lias of Whitby, England, the ammonites are commonly replaced by barite, colored brownish by bituminous matter. Celestite or anglesite more rarely takes the place of barite. Vivianite not uncommonly replaces the guards of Belemnites in the New Jersey Cretacic, as well as shells of other molluscs. Even wulfenite has been recorded as replacing the shell of an Isocardia. Iron pyrite or marcasite is a common replacing agent of mollusc shells, especially those of ammonites. This substance often becomes altered to limonite, and not infrequently disintegrates altogether, where not protected from the air; and thus beautiful fossils are destroyed. Blum records the case of an Avicula in which the outer surface was pyrites and the inner calcite. Sphalerite, and, rarely, smithsonite, galenite, and other metallic salts, replace the shells of pelecypods and gastropods and, more rarely, of cephalopods. In the Côte-d'Or, a Liassic pelecypod has been found completely replaced by specular hematite, while ordinary red hematite is not infrequently found replacing mollusc shells. Chlorite has been found replacing shells in several cases. In the Tertiary beds of Aragon, Spain, Planorbis has been found replaced by native sulphur (Blum—7:*171, 176*); and Tertiary Helix from near Madrid has been reported replaced by meerschaum or sepiolite.

(f) *Crustaceans, Merostomes, Insects, etc.* As has been noted above, the exoskeleton of Crustacea is composed of chitin impregnated with calcium carbonate and phosphate. Sometimes the chitin carbonizes and a black mass of carbon mixed with lime remains, which is susceptible of a high polish. Again, the organic matter may be entirely removed and replaced by calcium carbonate or other minerals. Thus trilobite tests are sometimes changed entirely to crystalline calcite. Pyrite not infrequently replaces the tests of trilobites, as in the famous specimens of *Triarthrus becki* from near Rome, New York, discovered by Valiant, in which Matthew and Beecher have found the antennæ and legs beautifully preserved, the whole test having become pyritized. The exoskeletons of merostomes correspond closely to those of Crustaceans. The insect body is rarely preserved, except the wings and the elytra of beetles, owing to the absence of mineral matter.

(g) *Echinoderms.* This class of animals is characterized by the possession of calcareous dermal plates wholly composed of calcite, which in many groups form a solid test or enclosure for the main mass of viscera within. The plates are not firmly united with each other, but they have the power to grow and change form during the life of the individual. A characteristic feature of all the skeletal parts is their extreme porosity. This is true of the test and the spines of the sea-urchin as well as of the calyx, arms, and stem of the crinoids. The porosity shows in section, and it is also indicated by the fact that the specific gravity of a recent Cidaris spine, with its pores unfilled by water, is only 1.46, while the completely calcified spine has a specific gravity of 2.7. The hollow spaces constitute about 43 per cent. of the spine. (Haidinger, Blum–4:*161*.) During the life of the animal the pores in the calcareous tissue are occupied by organic matter (chitin), which is removed by decay after death. Furthermore (Haidinger), each skeletal element of the echinoderm test is composed of an individual crystal, the crystalline axis of which is coincident with the organic axis; and the new lime which fills the pores crystallizes in continuity with the calcite of the original structures. As a result, perfect cleavage is obtained in the skeletal parts, each plate or spine having virtually become a perfectly cleaving calcite fragment. The axis of the crystal coincides with the organic axis of the part. (Hessel, Blum.) In crinoid stems the cleavage often shows a rotation of axis in the successive joints, so that corresponding cleavage planes make an angle with each other. (Blum–4:*161*.) According to investigations carried on by Dr. A. F. Rogers (21) the twisting is sometimes such as to place the crystals composing the successive joints into a twinning position. At other times it is irregular, and again in some species there is no twisting at all.

Silicification of echinoderms occurs more rarely. When it does occur, beekite rings, while present, are often less pronounced and abundant than in molluscs or brachiopods. (Blum–4:*192*.)

Pyrites occasionally replaces echinoderm structures. Thus pyritized crinoid stems are not uncommon in some formations. Pyritized spines of Cidaris have been recorded from the Oolite of Helgoland. (Blum–4:*202*.)

Entire specimens of Liassic Pentacrinites are found in the sapropellutytes of Holzmaden, Württemberg, replaced by iron disulphide.

Cerussite (lead carbonate) has been found as a frequent replacing agent of crinoid remains in the lead-bearing formations of the department of Kielce, southwestern Russia. These replaced remains commonly have the aspect of crystals of this mineral, with which they occur loose in the gange of the ore-beds. (Blum–4:*209.*)

(h) *Vertebrates.* The bones of vertebrates contain much calcium phosphate with the calcium carbonate, the whole being bound together by the organic *ossein,* or bone-cartilage. According to Berzélius, the bones of mammals consist of: bone cartilage 32.17 per cent.; ducts 1.13 per cent.; basic phosphate of lime with a trace of fluoride of calcium, 54.04 per cent.: carbonate of lime, 11.30 per cent.; phosphate of magnesia, 1.16 per cent.; and carbonate of sodium with a trace of the chloride, 1.20 per cent. The organic substance is replaced by the mineralizer, which is commonly calcium carbonate. Sometimes complete crystallization takes place. Among the bones found in the gypsum beds of the Paris basin and other regions many had been more or less impregnated with gypsum.

Pyritized skeletons of Ichthyosaurs, Plesiosaurs and other reptiles, as well as higher types, are common. Where marcasite is the replacing agent decomposition readily sets in and, if the matrix is a clay slate (argillutyte), alum efflorescence marks the progress of this decay.

Chalcopyrite is common as a coating of fish remains in Thuringia and Hessia, though seldom wholly replacing them. Bornite occasionally performs the same office. Native copper sometimes results from the alteration of these coatings. Cinnabar sometimes occurs in the same manner as the copper ores, seldom completely replacing the fish remains.

The teeth of mammals are rich in phosphate of lime, 60 per cent. or more of this salt being present. To the large proportion of this substance the durability of the teeth is attributable, they being among the most frequently preserved parts of mammals. The enamel of the teeth contains a somewhat larger percentage of phosphate of lime than the dentine, a difference which is expressed in the diverse degrees of preservation of these parts. (D'Orbigny–11:*37.*)

Eggs of vertebrates have not infrequently been found well preserved. Examples are: the eggs of the Moas of New Zealand, Chelonian eggs from the Tertiary of Auvergne, France, in which the shell was filled with mud which subsequently hardened; the Miocenic egg from South Dakota described by Farrington (12), which was completely silicified, and the fossil egg of Quaternary age from Arizona, described by Morgan and Tallmon (18), in which the shell is perfectly preserved, showing the same structure found in modern hen's eggs, the shell agreeing in composition with that of the egg of the wild goose. The interior with the exception of a small space near the periphery was filled solidly with a beautiful crystalline mass of the mineral colemanite. "In several places next the shell a semi-fluid layer of bitumen occurs, which probably represents the original organic matter within the shell."

Excessive silicification.

In some cases, notably in the Carbonic strata of the Mississippi Valley region, it has happened that silica has been deposited to excess in crinoids, shells or corals, with the result that the original form has been wholly destroyed, the fossil at the same time swelling out enormously. This excessive deposition goes on more particularly along lines of fracture, or, as in the crinoid calices, between the component plates. These become more and more separated as the deposition of silica goes on, and they also become sunken below the level of the network of silica. Eventually they are probably buried in the accumulation of silica which closes over them. Thus from a small fossil in which all the plates are discernible, a large mass of structureless silica is formed, which seldom gives a clue to its origin. (Bassler–1.)

Molds and Casts. Whenever organisms are buried in material of sufficient plasticity to adapt itself to the contours of the buried bodies, molds of the exteriors of these bodies will be made. Such molds may be temporary or they may be persistent ones. Lutaceous material generally furnishes the most perfect molds. Even soft tissues, when encased in a matrix which solidifies rapidly enough, may leave a mold behind after decay. Thus the bodies of human beings buried in the volcanic mud which overwhelmed Herculaneum and Pompeii left behind a perfect mold of their exterior. Again, the calcareous tufa, forming constantly in many portions of the earth, encloses leaves, mosses, or even fish and other animals and covers them with a crust of lime. On the subsequent decay of the enclosed body a perfect mold of its exterior is commonly preserved from which an artificial cast could be made. Viscous lava also may flow around and enclose a foreign body, which, if it is able to withstand the heat of the molten mass, may leave a distinct mold or impression. Impressions of medusæ are known from the Cambric of the southeastern United States (Walcott–25). When two valves of a bivalve mollusc become buried in juxtaposition, the space between them is filled with mud and thus an internal mold is produced. The same occurs in gastropods, in cephalopods and in other shelled animals, and may also be found in trilobites and other Crustacea. This mold of the interior is commonly spoken of as a "cast," which is wholly erroneous, since the cast reproduces the original in a new substance, whereas the mold is a reverse copy. Between the external and internal mold a cast may be formed by infiltration of mineral matter or by artificial means. Not uncommonly the removal of the shell by solution is followed by a closing of the cavity between the external and internal mold, owing to the pressure to which the enclosing rocks are constantly subjected. In such cases, the more strongly marked surface features will be impressed upon the smoother surface, or, in general, the features of the exterior will be impressed on the mold of the interior, which thus shows the normal external features, though weakened, together with a reversed impression of the interior. This, as shown by J. B. Woodworth, is illustrated by many Palæozoic mussels, which are represented by internal molds (*Steinkerne*). These show the lines of growth and other features of the exterior of the shell, and, on the same specimen, may be seen the mold of the scars marking the former attachment of the mussel.

In the Tampa beds of Florida natural casts of corals occur. The original corals have been removed by solution, but have left behind hollow molds in which afterward geodes of chalcedony were formed, the exterior of which accurately reproduces in silica the form of the corals. On the whole, while natural molds—both external and internal—are common, and characteristic of nearly all porous rocks, natural casts are correspondingly rare. It should, however, be noted that pseudomorphs are closely akin to casts as here defined, since in them the replacement is *pari passu* with the removal of the original substance of the shell or other hard structure, while in normal casts complete removal of the original substance precedes deposition of the new material.

2. *Tracks, Trails and Burrows of Animals.*

Tracks. These are made by vertebrates walking or hopping along the soft sand or mud, which will register their footprints. If the mud is very soft the footprint will be closed again by the flowage of the mud, but, if it is viscous, or so nearly dry as to remain permanent, the footprints may readily be preserved. Numerous reptilian footprints are known from the Newark sandstones of the Connecticut Valley and the related district of New Jersey. Lull (16) believes that these may have been partially hardened by the heat of an underlying lava sheet, which was only recently covered by sediments and had not yet cooled completely. This is not necessary, however, since, as shown in an earlier chapter, footprints may be preserved for a long period by mere drying of the mud. Even the delicate impressions of the web membranes of the foot were frequently preserved, which seems to indicate that the arenaceous mud must have been fairly hard and resistant before the next layer of sand was spread over it. This later layer on its under side furnishes accurate impressions in relief of the footprint, which, though rudely reproducing the form of the foot which made the impression, reproduces the *impression* in reverse. Since the original fossil is the impression (of which there may be many made by one individual) and not the animal's foot, the relief impression of it must be considered a *mold* and not a *cast*.

Trails. These are made by animals crawling over the mud and dragging their bodies along. Jelly-fish floating in shallow water may have their tentacles dragging along over the bottom, thus leaving distinct impressions. Plants are not infrequently dragged along over the shallow sea-bottom, with the result that a certain type of trail is made on the mud which may be indistinguishable from similar trails made by floating animals. Even attached plants, like the beach grass on the sand-dunes, may have a very characteristic semi-circular trail when swung about by the wind. Sea-weeds partly buried on an uncovered mud flat may be moved by the wind and so produce similar markings. These may, in some instances, be preserved, as appears to have been the case in the structures described as Spirophyton from the Palæozoic rocks of North America and elsewhere.

Burrows. While tracks and trails are made by animals in transit, burrows are the temporary or permanent abodes of animals. At the end of many trails of molluscs or crustacea a mound is found which marks the place where the creature has temporarily buried itself in the sand. This type of burrow is not generally well preserved, though under favorable conditions it may be found. At the end of a peculiar trail on the Potsdam sandstone of New York, known as Climactichnites, Woodworth (29) has discovered an oval impression which he considers to have been made by the animal in resting. This may possibly represent the collapsed burrow.

The remarkable structures known as Dæmonelix which occur in the Miocenic deposits of the Nebraska region and which were first described as sponges and have often been considered as plants, are probably the burrows of some species of burrowing mammal. The strata in which they occur are of the continental type of deposit and the skeletons of rodents have been found in the expansion at the base of the erect spiral. The material which has filled the burrow has solidified and now forms a solid core or mold of the original burrow. It should, however, be said that sections of the core disclose what appears to be a cellular structure, which has led to the supposition that the Dæmonelix is not a burrow but a plant, which grew around the skeleton and has been preserved in the attitude of growth.

The borings of sponges in shells (Clione) and the excavations made by molluscs and echinoderms in wood and stone represent

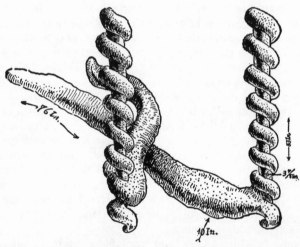

FIG. 261. Two views of a typical example of *Dæmonelix circumaxilis,* from the Miocenic beds of Nebraska. (After Barbour.)

permanent lodgments of the organisms, and are more nearly of the grade of artificial structures than is the case with the burrows before mentioned, which are more transient, and more nearly related to trails made in transit. For illustration of the burrows of echinoids of limestone in Brazil, see Branner (8).

Burrows like the Devil's Corkscrew, above described, if, indeed, they are burrows, and like the borings of aquatic animals, are preserved by reason of the character of the material in which they were excavated. Worm-tubes, on the other hand, so characteristic of the sandy and muddy beaches, are maintained by a lining or cement of mucus, secreted by the animal. These, therefore, carry us a step further into the class of undoubtedly "artificial structures."

3. *Artificial Structures.*

Beginning with the worm-tubes already mentioned, or even with the excavations made by some animals, we have this type of fossil increasing in importance as we rise in the scale of organic being. Even as far down as the group of rhizopods we find many types building shells by cementing foreign particles with the aid of a secretion. This type of habitation is analogous to the worm-tube already mentioned. Though represented in most classes of animals, it is not until we reach man that these artificial structures assume any great importance.

Thus the implements of stone, shell, bone or metal, the pottery and the copper, bronze and iron vessels; the beads and other ornaments; the coins and the habitations of man from the rude excavation in the rock to the buried cities of historic time, with all their accessories, belong to this type of fossils. This group, therefore, falls largely in the province of Anthropology, or the science which is concerned with man in all his relations, including his palæontology.

4. *Coprolites.*

The excrements of certain animals have a definite and recognizable form, and so become valuable indices to the former presence of such animals. Most important among these are the coprolites of fishes and reptiles, the latter constituting important fossils in the Mesozoic rocks. Very much concerning the food of the animal can often be learned from the remains found within the coprolite. The excrements or "castings" of worms also belong here. They generally consist of cord-like masses of molded sand which have passed through the intestine of the worm and from which the nutrient organic matter has been abstracted. They cover some modern beaches in great quantities, and are not infrequently preserved. Certain echinoderms, particularly holothurians, have recognizable excrements. Rothplotz has found an abundance of calcareous rods in the bottom deposits of Great Salt Lake, which he regards as excrements of Artemia, an abundantly represented crustacean in this body of water. They closely resemble known excrements of Artemia, but are calcareous, since the species of the Salt Lake are supposed to feed on calcareous algæ.

MECHANICAL DEFORMATION OF FOSSILS.

Wherever rocks containing fossils have been under pressure, or have, through other means, suffered mechanical disturbances, the fossils commonly show a more or less pronounced deformation. Two types of deformation may be considered: (1) that due to the normal desiccation and consequent shrinking of the rocks in otherwise undisturbed regions, and (2) that due to orogenic disturbances. The first type is especially marked in shales, and is due to the vertical pressure exerted by the overlying rock and the vertical shrinking of the shales upon the loss of water. Shells of brachiopods and pelecypods are commonly flattened out, while gastropods, cephalopods and trilobites are most frequently distorted by this vertical pressure. The amount of compression can sometimes be estimated by noting the sagging of the strata on either side of a concretion enclosed by them. Again, it may be estimated from a comparison of the compressed shell with uncompressed examples from the same formation, but preserved in limestone bands or lenses. The latter have suffered little or no vertical compression on account of the fact that the component grains of the rock were already as firmly packed when the rock solidified as they were ever likely to be.

The second group begins with the deformations due to horizontal slipping within a stratum, owing to the pressure of a superincumbent mass. Under such circumstances slickensides are frequently produced within a given formation, and fossils may readily be affected by such movements. Lateral compression of the strata, either slight or sufficient to produce foldings, will distort the fossils embedded in them and not infrequently alter their form so that they are no longer recognizable. A brachiopod, for example, by compression may assume the outline of a pelecypod, and may readily be mistaken for one. When, through strong compression, cleavage is induced in a given stratum, the fossils of that bed may become largely or entirely destroyed. The same is true if metamorphism affects the strata, though occasionally, as in the Palæozoic of Scandinavia, fossils are found in schists and other metamorphic rocks.

INDEX FOSSILS.

Fossils which serve to indicate definite geological horizons are called Index Fossils (German, *Leitfossilien*). The best index fossils for marine formations are furnished by invertebrates, though marine vertebrates, when well preserved, are also good horizon markers. The very detailed knowledge of vertebrate anatomy required, however, to determine the genera and species makes vertebrate remains available only to the trained specialist. Plants furnish good and reliable index fossils for terrestrial or delta formations, although their distribution is much more subject to limitations, owing to climatic influence. The same may be said to be true of land vertebrates. The subject is further discussed under correlation, in Chapter XXXII.

BIBLIOGRAPHY XXX.

1. BASSLER, R. S. 1908. The Formation of Geodes with remarks on the Silicification of Fossils. Proceedings of the United States National Museum, Vol. XXXV, pp. 133-154.
2. BASSLER, R. S. 1910. Adequacy of the Paleontologic Record. The Paleontologic Record, pp. 6-9, reprinted from Popular Science Monthly.
3. BERNARD, FÉLIX. 1895. Éléments de Paléontologie.
4. BLUM, J. REINHARD. 1843. Die Pseudomorphosen der Mineralogie, and First Appendix (Erster Nachtrag) 1847. Stuttgart.
5. BLUM, J. R. 1852. Pseudomorphosen, Second Appendix.
6. BLUM, J. R. 1863. Pseudomorphosen, Third Appendix.
7. BLUM, J. R. 1879. Pseudomorphosen, Fourth Appendix.
8. BRANNER, JOHN C. 1905. Stone Reefs on the Northeast Coast of Brazil. Bulletin of the Geological Society of America, Vol. XVI, pp. 1-12, pls. 1-11.
9. CALVIN, SAMUEL. 1910. Adequacy of the Paleontologic Record. The Paleontologic Record, pp. 2-6. Reprinted from Popular Science Monthly.
10. DEAN, BASHFORD. 1902. The Preservation of Muscle Fibers in Sharks of the Cleveland Shale. American Geologist, Vol. XXX, pp. 273-278, pls. VIII and IX.
11. D'ORBIGNY, ALCIDE. 1849. Cours Élémentaire de Paléontologie et de Géologie Stratigraphiques. 3 vols. Victor Masson, Paris.
12. FARRINGTON, OLIVER C. 1899. A Fossil Egg from South Dakota. Field Columbian Museum. Publication 35, Vol. I, No. 5, Geol. Series pp. 192-200, pls. XX-XXI, figs. 1-2.
13. GRABAU, A. W. 1899. Palæontology of Eighteen Mile Creek. Bulletin of the Buffalo Society of Natural Sciences, Vol. VI.
14. GRABAU, A. W. and SHIMER, H. W. 1909. North American Index Fossils, Invertebrates. Vol. I.
15. HUGHES, T. McKENNY. 1889. On the Manner of Occurrence of Beekite and Its Bearing upon the Origin of Siliceous beds of Palæozoic Age. Mineralogical Magazine, Vol. III, No. 40, pp. 265-271.
16. LULL, RICHARD S. 1904. Fossil Footprints of the Jura-Trias of North America. Memoirs of the Boston Society of Natural History, Vol. V, 97 pp., 1 pl.
17. MEAD, CHARLES W. 1907. Peruvian Mummies. American Museum of Natural History. Guide Leaflet No. 24.

18. MORGAN, WILLIAM C., and TALLMON, MARION C. 1904. A Fossil Egg from Arizona. California University, Department of Geology, Bulletin, Vol. III, pp. 403–410, 2 pls.

19. NICHOLSON, H. ALLEYNE, and LYDEKKER, RICHARD. 1889. Manual of Palæontology. 2 vols. Third edition.

20. REIS, OTTO M. Die Cœlacanthinen, mit besonderer Berücksichtigung der im weissen Jura, Bayerns Vorkommenden Arten. Palæontographica XXXV, pp. 1–96, pls. I–V.

21. ROGERS, AUSTIN F. Private Communication.

22. ROTH, J. 1879. Allgemeine und chemische Geologie, Vol. I. Especially literature on fossilization of plants.

23. STEDMANN, J. M., and ANDERSON, J. T. 1895. Observations on a so-called petrified man, with a report on chemical analysis by J. T. Anderson. American Naturalist, Vol. XXIX, pp. 326–335.

24. STEINMANN, GUSTAV. 1903. Einführung in die Palæontologie. Wilhelm Engelmann, Leipzig.

25. WALCOTT, CHARLES D. 1898. Fossil Medusæ. Monograph of the United States Geological Survey. XXX.

26. WALCOTT, C. D. 1911. Cambrian Geology and Palæontology. Smithsonian Institution Collections, Vol. 57.

27. WIMAN, C. 1895. Ueber die Graptolithen. Geol. Inst. Upsala, Bull., Vol. II, No. 2.

28. WHITE, C. H. 1905. Autophytography: a Process of Plant Fossilization. American Journal of Science, 4th series, Vol. XIX, pp. 231–236.

29. WOODWORTH, JAY B. 1903. On the Sedentary Impression of the Animal whose trail is known as Climactichnites. New York State Museum Bulletin 69, pp. 959–966, 2 pls., 3 figs.

G. PRINCIPLES OF CLASSIFICATION AND COR-RELATION OF GEOLOGICAL FORMATIONS.

CHAPTER XXXI.

NOMENCLATURE AND CLASSIFICATION OF GEOLOGIC FORMATIONS.

DEVELOPMENT OF CLASSIFICATIONS.

The history of the earth is written in the strata of the earth's crust. Like all histories, it is a continuous succession of events, but the record of these events is never complete and seldom even un-broken in any given region. It is of the first importance to the chronographer of earth history that he should find a continuous record, in order that he may have a measure by which to judge the partial records of any given region and to discover the breaks and imperfections in the local records thus presented. (Grabau–5.) The question then arises: under what conditions may we expect to obtain a continuous record and how are we to guard against the introduction of errors?

•We have, in the first place, to deal with the time element in the history of the earth. In human history the time element is a mea-surable factor, its duration being recorded in years and centuries. No such precise measurements are possible in earth history, al-though several attempts have been made to reduce geologic time to units of human chronology. (For methods and results, see beyond.) But while we cannot now, and probably may never, hope to divide geologic time into centuries and millenniums, we can divide it into periods, each of which has its own special significance in the his-tory of the earth. The basis for such subdivision was long ago found in the succession of organic types from relatively simple to highly complex forms. As long as the doctrine of special creation of organic types was held, and with it the belief in successive acts of creation, and more or less complete extinction of the faunas and floras preceding, it was a comparatively simple matter to divide the earth's history into periods or eras characterized by these successive changes in the ancient inhabitants of the earth. That there was much apparent justification for this belief in the characters of the faunas and floras found in the strata of the earth cannot be questioned. Thus, trilobites are even to-day unknown from strata later than Palæozoic, nor until recently have strata containing ammonites been recognized as older than the Mesozoic. That sudden disappearances of whole organic assemblages, and the equally sudden appearance of others of a different type occur repeatedly are matters of common observation; but it was not always recognized that such sudden changes are seldom universal in extent, though generally traceable over wide areas. While abrupt changes in organic content of the strata have come to be generally regarded as marking the lines between the greater divisions in the earth's history, they are correlated with, and, in fact, dependent on, widespread physical breaks in the continuity of the strata which compose the earth's crust. Such physical breaks were, indeed, taken as the planes of division by the pioneers in stratigraphy, who considered stratigraphic succession rather than geologic chronology. Thus, about the middle of the 18th Century Lehman, a German miner (11) proposed a threefold division of the rocks of the earth's crust into (1) "Primitive" (*Primitiv*) or *"Urgebirge,"* including all the igneous and metamorphic rocks in which there was no sign of life and which showed no evidence of having been derived from the ruins of preëxisting rocks, and, therefore, of chemical origin, antedating the creation of life; (2) *Secondary,* comprising the fossiliferous strata, and largely composed of mechanical deposits, produced after the planet had become the habitation of animals and plants; and (3) *Alluvial* deposits, due to local floods, and the deluge of Noah. Füchsel, a contemporary of Lehmann, recognized that certain groups of strata belonged together and constituted a geologic *formation.* He held that each formation represented an epoch in the history of the earth, and thus he brought into consideration the time element in the earth's history. Half a century later Werner introduced his "transition formations" between the primitive and secondary rocks, comprising a series of strata, first found in northern Germany, which were intermediate in mineral character between the crystallines and sedimentaries and partook in some degree of the characters of both. This *Uebergangsgebirge,* or transition formation, consisted principally of clay slates, argillaceous sandstones or graywackes and calcareous beds, which, in the region studied by Werner, were highly inclined and unconformably overlain by the horizontal Secondary strata. The latter, including formations up to the top of the chalk, were called by Werner the *Flötzgebirge* formation, on account of their horizontality, and because they were the stratified rocks *par excellence*. The term *Flötz* signifies "a level floor," and had been generally used since the time of Agricola for stratified rocks. With the Flötz were included the trap rocks of the Secondary strata, as subordinate members, these being held by Werner and his followers to be the result of aqueous precipitation. All deposits above the chalk were referred by Werner to alluvial deposits under the designation *Angeschwemmtgebirge*. Werner's followers later on distinguished a series of strata between the chalk and the alluvium, and applied to this the term *Newer Flötz* (*Neues Flötzgebirge*). These are the rocks subsequently named "Tertiary" by Cuvier and Brongniart. In the Wernerian terminology, the characters of the strata themselves rather than their time relations were considered, and Füchsel's term "formation" was applied by Werner and his followers to groups of strata of similar lithic composition. Thus he spoke of limestone formation, sandstone formation, slate formation, etc. The term "transition" strata soon began to take on chronologic meaning, and it was widely applied to rocks older than those designated as Secondary. It was still retained even after it was shown that these strata are not always transitional in mineral character and that strata belonging to the Secondary or even later series had sometimes the mineralogical character of the original Transition rocks.

At the time of Lyell, the strata of the earth's crust were generally divided into Primary, Transition, Secondary, Tertiary and post-Tertiary. It had become recognized that crystalline and metamorphic rocks were not all of one age, but that some were even newer than the Secondary formation. As a chronologic term, Primary had come to be applied by some to the fossiliferous rocks older than the Secondary, while it had become a matter of some question whether any of the crystalline rocks really antedated the oldest fossiliferous deposits. Lyell, to avoid confusion, used the term *Primary Fossiliferous* formation "because the word primary has hitherto been most generally connected with the idea of a nonfossiliferous rock." About this time the terms *"Palæozoic,"* * *"Mesozoic,"* † and *"Cænozoic"* † were introduced to replace the terms Primary Fossiliferous (the former Transition), Secondary and

---

* Proposed by Sedgwick, 1838. From παλαιός, *palaios*, ancient, and ζωή, *zoë*, life.

† Proposed by Phillips, 1841, from μέσος, *mesos*, middle; καινός, new, recent. The latter was also written Kainozoic.

Tertiary, but they met at first with little favor. Palæozoic was the first to be adopted, while Secondary and Tertiary were still retained. Later Mesozoic gradually replaced Secondary, but Tertiary has still retained its hold in geologic literature to the present day. To it the Quaternary * has been added, which comprises the formations designated by Lyell as Post-Pliocene, together with his Later Pliocene or Pleistocene. These have frequently been included with the Tertiary under the term Cænozoic (=Kainozoic), but they have also been separated under the term Psychozoic, introduced by Le Conte, but limited by him to the most recent formations, which in-include abundant remains of man.

It is thus seen that the classification at first proposed as a rock classification became a chronologic one, as geologists began to perceive that all kinds of rock may be formed during each period of the earth's history. When the fossils of each of these four divisions became better known, it was found that each was characterized by its peculiar assemblage of organisms. It was further found that in most regions the strata of each of these larger subdivisions were separated from those above or below by a marked unconformity, so that records of disturbances of widespread occurrence were looked upon as generally marking the dividing lines between the greater subdivisions of the earth's history. The use of unconformities in defining limits of geologic formations was also extended to the further subdivision of the larger units, and, in fact, such breaks have frequently been advocated as the best available criterion. But geologists have pretty generally recognized the fact that a classification based on unconformities is an incomplete one, and that a complete record of geologic time can be expected only in a series resulting from continuous deposition. Such a series is, however, nowhere obtainable, since in no known region of the earth has there been continuous and uniform deposition. Stratigraphers are thus compelled to construct their typical section from fragments of overlapping sections from all parts of the world. Each fragment thus used in the building up of the typical scale must be complete in itself, and its relationship to the next adjoining fragments of the scale must be determined.

Selection of the Type Section.

What, then, are the criteria which must guide us in the selection of our typical section? First and foremost, the section must show

* Proposed by Morlot in 1854.

continuous deposition. No sharp break either lithic or faunal should occur between the members, but all should be transitional. The character and origin of the strata composing the section must be carefully considered, since all rocks are not of equal value as indices of continuous deposition.

Hydroclastic rocks are by far the most reliable indices of deposition, since none other are formed under so uniform an environment. Marine sediments, further, are more reliable than those of fresh water lakes, since the latter are only temporary features of the earth's surface and are preceded and succeeded by conditions which will of necessity destroy the continuity of formation of strata. Thus marine formations alone will serve for the erection of a standard scale, all formations of a continental type, whether of fresh water or of atmo-, anemo-, or pyroclastic origin, must be ruled out of the standard scale. Hence the Old Red Sandstone of Britain, the non-marine Carbonic formations, the Newark, Potomac, Dakota and Laramie formations of North America, are all to be discarded in the making of a true geologic formation scale. Even among marine strata, there are some which must be ruled out, as not furnishing a reliable account of the progress of rock deposition. Thus sandstones and conglomerates, either as basal members or intercalated between a series of clay or lime rocks, are almost sure to introduce an element of uncertainty, if not error, into the section, even if the gradation above and below is a perfect one. As has been pointed out in an earlier chapter, shore-derived siliceous clastics of coarse grain, when not forming a basal sandstone or conglomerate, can become widespread only by an oscillatory movement of the land, which results in a temporary retreat and re-advance of the sea. Such a change involves almost certainly a time interval unrecorded in the section, but represented rather by an unrecognizable break within the terrigenous member itself. An example of such a formation is found in the St. Peter Sandstone of central United States, a formation which in itself represents a disconformity, constantly increasing in magnitude toward the north, where it includes an unrecorded interval elsewhere represented by from 2,000-3,000 feet of limestones. Shore deposits of all kinds should be ruled out in the establishment of a typical section, for they represent local conditions and, therefore, cannot furnish reliable evidence of the general progress of development.

Deposits formed in an enclosed basin, whether marine or continental, are likewise unsatisfactory for purposes of establishing a general scale. Such deposits at present included in the standard scale of North American strata are : the Medina and Salina formations of New York, which were formed under local and in part continental conditions, and cannot, therefore, represent a standard by which the more widespread marine conditions existing elsewhere can be measured. Wherever possible, such local formations should be taken out of the standard scale of strata and replaced by formations of purely marine origin. These may, of course, not exist within the limits of the territory for which the scale is made, in which case the old terms, perforce, have to be retained.

The best example of a truly representative classification of the divisions of a larger formation, which has yet been devised, is that of the Triassic system. In no one region of the world is there a complete representation of marine Triassic strata; in fact, the best known divisions of this system are to a large extent non-marine. But, by a careful study of all the widely dissociated marine members and their relation to each other, a standard classification, more nearly perfect than that of most other similar formations, has been devised. By its use the various dissociated marine members of each region, as well as the non-marine members, may be measured and the time relation of each to the others and to all may be ascertained.

Time Scale and Formation Scale.

While the time scale is thus of primary importance as a standard of comparison, a formation scale is also needed. A formation is a stratigraphic unit, composed in general of similar or closely related strata and characterized by a particular assemblage of organisms (fauna or flora). Sometimes a formation may consist of a single stratum—more frequently it comprises many strata. The rules recently promulgated by the United States Geological Survey for the government geologists in the preparation of the geologic folios of the United States (18:23) make the formation the cartographic unit, and define it among sedimentary rocks as follows: "Each formation shall contain between its upper and lower limits either rocks of uniform character or rocks more or less uniformly varied in character, as, for example, a rapid alternation of shale and limestone." It is further suggested that, "As uniform conditions of deposition were local as well as temporary, it is to be assumed that each formation is limited in horizontal extent. The formation should be recognized and should be called by the same name as far as it can be traced and identified by means of its lithologic character, its stratigraphic association, and its contained fossils."

Subdivisions of Time and Formation Scales.

The primary divisions of the geologic time scale are, as we have seen, based on the changes in life, with the result that fossils alone determine whether a formation belongs to one or the other of these great divisions. The primary divisions now generally recognized are as follows:

Present name.	Definition.	Old Equivalent.	Corresponding formation as generally used.
Psychozoic	Mind-life	Quaternary*	Quaternary
Cenozoic	Recent-life	Tertiary	Tertiary
Mesozoic	Mediæval-life	Secondary	Mesozoic
Palæozoic	Ancient-life	Transition or Primary Fossiliferous	Palæozoic
Eozoic (or Proterozoic)	Dawn of life (or First life) } Primary		{ Algonkian†
Azoic	Without Life }		{ Archæan‡

Corresponding to each time division we have a formational division, which represents the rock material accumulated during the continuance of that time. As will be seen from the above table, the formation scale now generally in use is made up partly of the old names in vogue during Lyell's time, partly of the newer names, and in part of distinct names applied to the rocks of these divisions by American geologists and adopted by workers in other countries as well.

A number of terms have been proposed by which the subdivisions of the time and formation scale are to be known, but at present there is no unanimity in the usage of these terms. The following are the most important of the proposals made, the numbering being in the order of magnitude of the categories:

* In many text-books the Quaternary is included with the Tertiary under Cenozoic, which is not the historic sense of the term. Post-Tertiary time is essentially characterized by the presence of man and may be separated as Psychozoic.

† Walcott, 1889. From a tribe of North American Indians.

‡ Proposed by Dana.

I. *International Geological Congress.* At the first meeting of the Congress in Paris in 1878 a commission was appointed to frame a plan of procedure for the unification of geologic classification and naming. The recommendations of this Commission, adopted at the Bologna Congress in 1881, as far as they affect the point in question, are as follows. (1) Era—Group; (2) Period—System; (3) Epoch—Series; (4) Age—Stage; (5) . . . —Assize. No time equivalent for (5) (Assize) was designated.

During succeeding Congresses proposed modifications of this scheme were discussed until in 1900 the 8th Congress, convened in Paris, accepted the following scheme:

Chronologic.	Stratigraphic.
1. Era (Erès).	1. (No stratigraphic term).
2. Period (Période).	2. System (Système).
3. Epoch (Époque).	3. Series (Séries).*
4. Age (Âge).	4. Stage (Étage).†
5. Phase (Phase).	5. Zone (Zone).

Periods, and the corresponding systems, have a worldwide value, and are characterized by the development of the organisms during the *period,* and their entombment in the strata of the *system.* Pelagic faunas, where available, are especially characteristic, owing to their wide distribution and independence of local environments. The termination of the names of periods and systems adopted is *ic, ique* (French); *isch* (German); *ico* (Spanish, Italian, Portuguese, Roumanian); Ex. Cambric (Cambrique, Kambrisch, Cambrico); Devonic (Devonique, Devonisch, Devonico); also Carbonic (Carbonique, Karbonisch, Carbonico); Cretacic (Cretacique, Kretacisch, Kreide Formation), etc.

Periods are generally divisible into three epochs each, which are designated by the prefixes *Palæo-, Meso-,* and *Neo-*. For *Palæo-* the term Eo may be used, wherever the name is long and the name itself further abbreviated. (Williams—19.) Thus, while Palæocambric, Mesocambric and Neocambric are used, Eodevon, Mesodevon and Neodevon, or, Eocret, Mesocret and Neocret, may be used for these longer terms. Locally, series are commonly given names derived from typical localities, these ending in *ian* (*ien,* Fr., etc.), as the following example will show:

---

* German, Abtheilung.   † German, Stufe; Italian, *piano;* Spanish, *piso.*

Epoch.	Local name of series. Eastern United States.		Western Europe.

Neodevonic..............	{ Chautauquan { Senecan	}	{ Famennien { Frasnien
Mesodevonic.............	{ Erian { Ulsterian	}	{ Givétien { Eifélien
Eodevonic..............	{ Oriskanian { Helderbergian	}	{ Coblentzien { Taunusien { Gedinien

The values of these local series are not always uniform nor equivalent. In practice it is often more convenient to speak of *Lower, Middle* and *Upper Siluric, Devonic,* etc., series (German: *Unterdevon, Mitteldevon, Oberdevon,* etc.; French *Dévonien inférieur, Dévonien moyen, Dévonien supérieur, etc.*). These terms are commonly employed in a general discussion of the strata of a series.

Ages and their corresponding stages receive local names. Stages are relatively restricted in areal distribution and different countries have different stages corresponding to the same age.

Stages end in *ian* (*ien,* Fr.; *ian,* Germ.*; *iano,* Spanish, Italian, Portuguese, Roumanian). Thus we have Bartonian, Bartonien, etc.; Portlandian, Portlandien, etc., stages.

The stratigraphic division of the fifth order, the zone, is often needed, and this division is named wherever possible after a particular species of organism which characterizes it. Thus we have in the Lias of England the following 17 zones characterized by particular species of ammonites. (Geikie–4:*1133*.)

Upper Lias or Toarcian
{ 17 zone of *Lytoceras jurense*
{ 16 zone of *Dactylioceras commune*
{ 15 zone of *Harpoceras serpentinus,* etc.
{ 14 zone of *Dactylioceras annulatum*

Middle Lias or Liassian
{ 13 zone of *Paltopleuroceras spinatum*
{ 12 zone of *Amaltheus margaritatus*

* The German terms are often contracted, instead of Astian Stufe, Astistufe is used.

Lower Lias or Sinemurian

11 zone of *Liparoceras henleyi*, etc.
10 zone of *Phylloceres ibex*
9 zone of *Ægoceras jamesoni*
8 zone of *Deroceras armatum*
7 zone of *Caloceras raricostatum*
6 zone of *Oxynoticeras oxynotum*
5 zone of *Arietites obtusus*, etc.
4 zone of *Arietites turneri*, etc.
3 zone of *Arietites bucklandi*
2 zone of *Schlotheimia angulata*
1 zone of *Psiloceras planorbe*

In the Trias, too, a number of distinct zones marked by species of ammonites or other fossils are recognized.

II. *Dana's System.* In the last edition of his Manual (3:406), Professor James D. Dana gives the following classification:

Chronologic.	*Stratigraphic.*
1. Aeon (Ex.: Palæozoic).*	1. Series (Ex: Palæozoic).
2. Era (Ex.: Siluric).	2. System (Ex.: Siluric).
3. Period (Ex.: Palæo-Siluric).	3. Group (Ex.: Niagaran).
4. Epoch (Ex.: Clinton).	4. Stage (Ex.: Clinton).

III. *United States Geological Survey.* The United States Geological Survey in its ruling of 1903 makes the *period* the unit of the time scale and correlates with it the *system* of the formation scale, thus following the usage of the International Congress. The systems recognized are: "Quaternary, Tertiary, Cretaceous, Jurassic, Triassic, Carboniferous, Devonian, Silurian, Ordovician, Cambrian, Algonkian, and Archæan." No complete scheme is formulated, only the following terms being used:

Chronologic.	*Stratigraphic.*
1.	1. ....
2. Period.	2. System.
3.	3. Series.
4.	4. Group.

As far as this scheme was developed it is thus seen to correspond to the one promulgated by the International Congress, with the exception that *group* is used for the division of the fourth order

---

* Examples added by the author.

instead of *stage*. The terminations of the names of the systems are not altered to correspond to that adopted by the Congress.

Unification of Terminology.

In the development of the classification of the geologic formations, the systems were gradually introduced either by intercalation of a previously unknown system between two well-established ones, as the Devonian between the Silurian and Carboniferous; or by the separation of the new system from an older one with which it was formerly included, as Ordovician from Silurian. No uniform method of derivation of these names was followed, though the majority of names had a geographic origin. Neither was uniformity of termination considered, though among the later-formed names *ian* was generally selected. This heterogeneous terminology has become so firmly embodied in the framework of stratigraphic classification that it probably will be a long time before we can hope to replace it by a more homogeneous one. Such terms as Carboniferous are wholly out of harmony with the majority of other terms and ought to be discarded. But the adoption of a uniform termination of these names, as suggested by the Congress, and as is widely practiced, particularly in Europe, will do away with the most objectionable part of this terminology and bring it into harmony with the remaining portion of the scheme. In the table on p. 1108 the systems used in this work are given with the termination used by the International Congress, and with it the old heterogeneous termination. The author and derivation of each term is given. (See also table on page 22.)

A tendency toward splitting up some of the larger systems and uniting others has been shown by many stratigraphers. The Palæocenic has been introduced in the Cenozoic and united with the Eocenic and Oligocenic as Palæogenic; Miocenic and Pliocenic have been united as Neogenic; and Pleistocenic and Holocenic as Cenogenic. The Liassic has also been separated as a distinct system by some European stratigraphers. Recently this method of subdivision has been carried to great extremes in the works of Schuchert and Ulrich, to which the student is referred (14; 17). The subdivisons advocated by Ulrich are more extreme than the facts seem to warrant, and they have not generally been adopted.

Local Stages and Substages. Generally, detailed study of a given region will show the occurrence of numerous local forma-

Eras.	Systems Chiefly according to recommendation of International Congress.	Systems Old usage.	Founder.	Origin or derivation of name.
Psychozoic or Quaternary	Holocenic	Recent	Portuguese Committee I.C. (1885)	Wholly recent.*
	Pleistocenic	Pleistocene	Lyell (1839)	Most recent.*
Cenozoic or Tertiary	Pliocenic	Pliocene	Lyell (1833)	More recent.*
	Miocenic	Miocene	Lyell (1833)	Less or intermediate recent.*
	Oligocenic	Oligocene	Beyrich (1854)	Few recent.*
	Eocenic	Eocene	Lyell (1833)	Dawn of recent.*
Mesozoic or Secondary	Cretacic	Cretaceous	Omalius d'Halloy (1822)	Creta chalk (chalk bearing)
	Comanchic	Comanchean	R. T. Hill (1893)	Comanche Indians
	Jurassic	Jurassic	Alexander von Humboldt (1795)	Jura Mountains
	Triassic	Triassic	F. von Alberti, (1834)	Original three-fold division
Palæozoic or Primary Fossiliferous	Permic	Permian	Murchison (1841)	Government of Perm, Russia
	Carbonic	Carboniferous (Pennsylvanian)	Conybeare (1822) H. S. Williams (1891)	Coal-bearing Pennsylvania
	Mississippic	Sub-Carboniferous (Mississippian)	D. D. Owen (1852) A. Winchell (1870)	Below the coal-bearing strata Mississippi valley
	Devonic	Devonian	Sedgwick and Murchison (1839)	Devonshire, England
	Siluric	Silurian (Upper Silurian)	Murchison (1835)	Ancient tribe of Silures inhabiting South Wales, etc.
	Ordovicic	Ordovician (Lower Silurian)	Lapworth (1879) Murchison (1835)	Ancient tribe of western England
	Cambric	(Up'r Cambr'n) Cambrian	Sedgwick (1835) Sedgwick (1835)	Old Roman Province of Cambria, N. Wales

Thus names were derived, in part, from the age of the formation, in part, from their lithic character and contents, in part from typical localities, and in part from former inhabitants of typical localities.

tions of the value of stages or substages, as in the following case:

	Hiatus and disconformity	
	Detroit River Series	Lucas dolomite Amherstburg limestone Anderdon limestone Flat Rock dolomite
Upper Siluric or Monroan. (Neosiluric)	Hiatus and disconformity	
	Sylvania sandstone	
	Hiatus and disconformity	
	Bass Island Series	Raisin River series Put-in-Bay series Tymochtee shale Greenfield dolomite
	Hiatus—disconformity	

* Referring to the percentage of modern organisms present.

Where fully developed most formations include several zones. Thus, in Maryland and West Virginia, the Oriskany formation, which belongs to the Oriskany stage of the Lower Devonic series of eastern North America, contains at least two zones, the upper, or *Hipparionyx proximus,* zone, 258 feet thick, and the lower, 90 feet thick with *Anoplotheca flabellites* and other fossils. In some cases, however, what has been considered a single formation may represent an aggregation of apparently uniform lithic character, of such great stratigraphic range as not only to transgress the limit of a series, but even that of a system. An example of this is found in the Arbuckle and Wichita sections of Indian Territory and Oklahoma, where the following pre-Mississippic formations were formerly recognized: (Ulrich–16.)

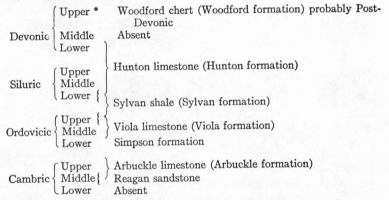

Devonic	Upper *	Woodford chert (Woodford formation) probably Post-Devonic
	Middle	Absent
	Lower	
Siluric	Upper	Hunton limestone (Hunton formation)
	Middle	
	Lower {	Sylvan shale (Sylvan formation)
Ordovicic	Upper {	Viola limestone (Viola formation)
	Middle	
	Lower	Simpson formation
Cambric	Upper	Arbuckle limestone (Arbuckle formation)
	Middle{	Reagan sandstone
	Lower	Absent

It has since been found that the Hunton formation is not a unit, but represents fragments of several distinct formations separated by large breaks and unrepresented time intervals (13).

Principles Governing the Naming of Formations.

A formation may retain its name only so far as its essential unity is retained, though change in lithic character does not necessarily require a change of name. Thus, when a shaly formation in one locality can be traced into, and can be shown to be the exact depositional equivalent of, a limestone formation in another

---

* The classification is by the author, and is made in harmony with the present classification of the formations supposed to be included in the divisions given.

locality, both should be called by the same name. Such exact equivalency, however, seldom obtains. The following figures copied from Willis' paper (20) show the case mentioned and the far more common cases in which such depositional equivalency is not complete. In Diagram II the *m* (shale) formation grades into the *n* (limestone) formation, but with a prolonged overlap. In this case neither formation is the exact equivalent of the other, and both may occur together. Hence, each should receive a different name. An example of this kind is furnished by the

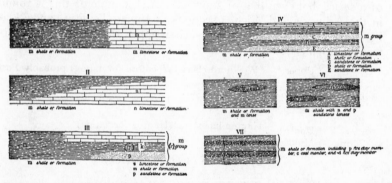

FIG. 262. Diagrams showing horizontal variation in sediments. (After Willis.)

Catskill and Chemung formations, which grade into each other by overlap, the Catskill alone being present in eastern New York and the Chemung alone in western New York, while between these points parts of both are present. In the diagram cited, the near shore overlapping the offshore deposits, the overlap is regressional and a replacing one and due to shoaling of the water. In the Catskill-Chemung case, a continental formation overlaps a marine one.

Diagram III represents three formations on the right equivalent to the shale formation (*m*) on the left. This shale formation (*m*) is represented on the right by its middle portion, while the lower is replaced by a sandstone formation and the upper by a limestone formation. Each of the two new formations receives a distinct name, as *p* sandstone formation and *s* limestone formation. If the name "*m* shale" is retained for the middle member, a new name (*x*) for the entire group *p m s* must be given, the *x* group being then equivalent to the *m* shale of the left hand locality, but including the *m* shale at the right hand locality. A better method, however, is to give the shale on the right hand a new name (*k*) and call the group *p k s* the *m* group, this being equivalent to the *m* shale. While a difference of opinion exists as to whether or not the name *m* should be applied in the above case to the middle member, it is generally agreed that, when the shale formation *m* breaks up into a number of units, as in diagram IV, none of which can absolutely be identified with the original mass *m*, each of the smaller members should receive a distinct name, while collectively they may be called the *m* group, being the exact equivalent of the *m* shale. If lenses of sandstone or conglomerate of importance are present in a formation these should receive distinct names, as *n* and *p* lenses in *m* shale. (Diagram VI.) If only one lens is present, however, this may be known by the same name as the enclosing formation, though it may be better to give even a single lens a distinct name. Thus, in the Cattaraugus formation of southwestern New York and adjacent areas in Pennsylvania, three conglomerate lentils occur, the Wolf Creek, near the base, the Salamanca higher up, and the Kilbuck still higher up. In some localities only one of the upper two lentils is present: in others both are absent. The desirability of distinct names, even where only one of these lentils occurs, is apparent.

Where the main mass is of uniform character, but contains thin beds of another character, the whole may be classed as one formation (*m*), while the minor strata are spoken of as distinct members. (Diagram VII.) Thus the Waldon sandstone formation of the southern Appalachians contains the Sewanee coal member besides shale and other coal members and conglomerate lenses.

Names of sedimentary formations are derived from localities where the formation is best developed or where it was first studied. "The most desirable names are binomial, the first part being geographic and the other lithologic (*e. g.*, Dakota sandstone, Trenton limestone, etc.) The geographic term should be the name of a river, town, or other natural or artificial feature at or near which the formation is typically developed. Names consisting of two words should be avoided. Names taken from natural features are generally preferable, because less changeable than those of towns or political divisions. When the formation consists of beds differing in character, so that no single lithologic term is applicable, the word "formation" should be substituted for the lithologic term (*e. g.*, *Rockwood formation*)." (18:*24*.)

SELECTION OF NAMES FOR SYSTEMS, SERIES AND STAGES (GROUPS). These divisions, as already noted, are of much wider distribution than formations. The names of systems are mostly uniform throughout the world, as Devonic, Triassic, Cretacic, etc. American terms have in some cases been proposed where the original European names seemed less desirable. Thus, Taconic has been used for Cambric, Champlainic for Ordovicic, Ontaric for Siluric, Guadaloupic for Permic. Where names proposed originally for series became those of systems, on the raising of the original series to the rank of a system, they naturally differed in different countries. Thus the original Subcarboniferous is known as the *Mississippic* in America and is now regarded as a separate system, while in eastern Europe it is the *Donjetic* and in western Europe the *Dinantic*. The old Lower Cretacic or Infra-Crétacée * is the *Neocomic* of Europe, in its broader sense, and the *Comanchic* of America. The names of series generally differ in different countries, and those of stages in the different sections of the same country. The name in either division is derived from a typical locality and the appropriate ending (*ian, ien*) is affixed. When the name itself is not adaptable in its original form, the practice generally has been to substitute the Latin form (Turonien from Touraine, Campanien from Champagne and Carentonien from the Charent). Sometimes the name is derived from the original name of the locality, as Cambrian from Cambria, the old Roman name for North Wales, and Cenomanien from Cœnomanum, the old Latin name of the town of Mans in the Department of Sarthe and Rothomagien from Rothomagus, the Roman name of Rouen.

MAPPING.

The question is often asked: Should geologic maps express primarily formations or geologic horizons? In other words, should the mapping be based on lithic formations or on time units? The decision generally has been in favor of the mapping of lithic units or formations. Generally the units have been small enough to allow a grouping into systems, and these have then been referred to their proper time period. This method is apparently the most satisfactory, since all mappable features, such as the outcrops themselves, as well as the topography of the region, are the direct consequence of the lithic formations, and have no regard whatever to time relations. The present outcrops show only the present extent of the formations, and give no clue to the former extent of the strata deposited during a given time interval, except in so far as the lithic character of the formation indicates this.

Mapping on Formational Basis. The United States Geological Survey has adopted the formation as its cartographic unit, mapping

---

*In recent classifications this term is discarded. See Haug Traité, p. 1170.

being hence conducted on a lithic basis. "As uniform conditions of deposition were local as well as temporary it is to be assumed that each formation is limited in horizontal extent. The formation should be recognized and should be called by the same name as far as it can be traced and identified by means of its lithologic character, its stratigraphic association and its contained fossils." (18:73.) In mapping it is often impossible to draw a sharp line when two contiguous formations grade into each other. In such cases the boundary has to be more or less arbitrarily established. An example of this is the Siluro-Devonic boundary of the Helderbergs. Here in some places the Manlius or uppermost Siluric member is found to grade up into the Coeymans or lower Devonic member both lithically and faunally.*

Mapping on Faunal Basis. When two formations of the same lithic character are separable by their faunal content only it is often found practicable to map them separately on a purely faunal basis. In such a case it is frequently necessary to represent the transition portion by a commingling of colors of the two series. Sometimes the faunal change is a horizontal one, where two distinct faunas occupied different portions of the province at the same time, there being no change in lithic character. An example of this is seen in the two Portage faunas of New York, the Ithaca and the Naples, which existed side by side throughout Portage time. This is expressed on the map by two colors, or two shades of the same color, which horizontally pass into each other or overlap along the line of interlocking of the faunas. (Clarke–2.)

Mapping of Discontinuous Formations. It is a matter of common experience that formations change in passing away from the shore line, certain more terrigenous ones (as sandstones, etc.) coming to an end and others of more truly marine origin (such as limestones) appearing. As a result, detailed maps of adjoining areas, not parallel to the old shore line, may exhibit considerable diversity of formations, and it may even happen that quadrangles not so far removed from each other may exhibit scarcely any formations of the same name. Thus the Columbia quadrangle of Central Tennessee (Hayes and Ulrich–9) and the McMinnville quadrangle of eastern Tennessee (Hayes–8) have no formations in common, though they are separated by an interval † of only

---

* This is not always the case, however, and this close relationship has been denied by Ulrich. But there can be no question of this gradation in the Schoharie region of New York (see Grabau–6).

† The Chattanooga formation which appears on both maps is not of the same age, being younger in the more eastern quadrangle.

two quadrangles. This distinctness is partly due to the fact that formations represented in one are wanting in the other, owing to discontinuity of sequence (represented by either unconformities or disconformities). It would, however, be just as true if the formations were complete in both. The greater number of subdivisions is found in the more western nearer shore phase of the lower (Ordovicic) system, while the Siluric and Mississippic systems have their nearer shore phase in the eastern sections. The following dia-

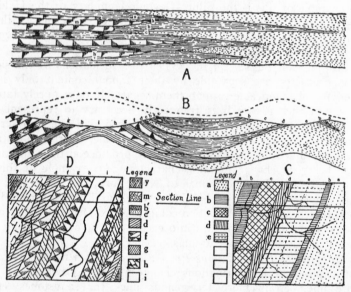

Fig. 263. *A*. Section showing variation of strata from shore seaward. *B*. The same section after folding and erosion. *C, D*. Maps of the same region, representing the two end quadrangles which have scarcely any formations in common.

grams (Fig. 263) illustrate the change in formations away from shore, and the resultant differences in the cartographic units of two quadrangles separated by an interval of one quadrangle only. In the eastern portion of the section only sands were deposited, constituting but one formation. Owing to repeated oscillation during the deposition of these sands, a series of intercalations of the more off-shore clays and the still more distant limestones occurred. Two anticlinal folds were formed which subsequently suffered erosion and exposed the succession of beds. The strike of the eroded strata is northeasterly, though the section is due east and west at right angles to the original shoreline. The two quadrangles mapped have only formations *b, c,* and *d* (called b^1, c^1, d^1) in common. Formation b^1 of the western quadrangle is, however, more nearly equivalent to the upper part of *c,* as it appears in the eastern quadrangle. The bed c^1 of the western quadrangle is only a part—the lower—of bed *c* as it appears in the eastern quadrangle, while d^1 and *d* are almost exact equivalents. In the eastern quadrangle occur the formations *a* and *e,* which are not found in the western one, while the latter shows formations *f, g, h, i, m* and *y,* not found in the eastern quadrangle. In the eastern quadrangle, furthermore, the formations differ on opposite sides of the valley, *b* being thin on the eastern and thick on the western side, while *c* and *d* of the western side are represented by *e* on the eastern side.

Types of Geological Maps.

Formation and System Maps. Two kinds of geological maps are in vogue in most countries. These are the *formation map* and the *system map.* The first takes account of the geological formations, and is illustrated by the folio sheets of the Geological Atlas of the United States, already referred to. In these each formation is given a distinct color, or pattern, all the formations of a system generally being grouped together under a similar tint, such as pink, brown, etc. For the production of such maps, large scale basemaps are needed, those used by the United States Geological Survey being mostly on the scale of 1 to 62,500, or approximately 1 inch to a mile. As the scale of the map is increased, smaller units can be mapped, and structural details not representable on the smaller scale map may be introduced. The *system* map aims to represent in distinctive colors only the geologic *systems,* each of which receives a distinct color pattern. The new geological map of North America, issued by the United States Geological Survey, may be taken as an example of this type. Here eighteen distinct color shades are used to represent the systems from the Cambric to the Quaternary, though for convenience the boundary in a few cases is not drawn precisely at the dividing line between the systems.

The International Geological Map of Europe is also a system map, though the attempt has there been made to differentiate by distinctive shades the lower, middle and upper portions of some of the systems (*e. g.,* Triassic, Jurassic, etc.).

Intermediate Maps. Maps intermediate between the system and formation map are also known. The best examples are the complete maps of New York State, on the scale of 5 miles to 1 inch, while the map issued with the summary final report of the Second Geological Survey of Pennsylvania may serve as another example. These maps represent *series* rather than formations, though in many cases the series consist practically of one formation only, such as the Onondaga limestone. In other cases the unit mapped includes what, on a map of larger scale, would be represented as several distinct formations. Such, for example, is the Clinton series which on the New York State map is shown by one color only, while on the map of the Rochester quadrangle it is shown as five distinct formations. The Portage group, represented as a single unit on the State map, is divided into eleven formations on the Canandaigua-Naples map (1/62,500), exclusive of the Genesee shale and the Tully limestone.

Notation of Formations on Map. In addition to the color and pattern used in the representation of the formations or larger units, a conventional sign, which may be a letter, or combination of letters, or a number is used. This insures greater ease in identifying the formation on the map. The United States Survey, in its folios, has adopted a group of letters as the symbol, the first letter representing the horizon, the other the name of the formation. Thus, on the Hancock quadrangle, where the Siluric is represented by five formations some of the symbols are: Sc, *Clinton shale;* Smk, *McKenzie formation;* Stw, *Tonoloway limestone.* The S in each case signifies Siluric (Silurian). In the Geological Map of North America, above referred to, numbers are used to further differentiate the systems from one another.

Legend. In order that the proper superposition of the formation may be ascertained, a legend is added consisting of small rectangles colored to correspond to the color pattern which it represents on the map, and furnished, moreover, with the corresponding symbol and the name of the formation. These rectangles are arranged in the order of superposition or sequence. As a rule, the oldest formation is put at the bottom and the youngest on top. The New York State Survey has, however, adopted in some of its larger maps the reverse arrangement, the oldest being on the top. This is done, apparently, to bring the color pattern of the legend into harmony with that of the map; in which the successive older formations crop out in belts of decreasing age from the north southward.

Continuous and Discontinuous Mapping.

Since rock outcrops are, as a rule, scattered over a considerable area with intervening portions in which the rock is covered by glacial or other loose soil deposits, two modes of mapping on the same scale have come into usage. The first is the mapping of outcrops only, forming what may be called *outcrop maps.* The intervening covered spaces may be left blank or may be colored for the superficial deposits. The result will be a map very difficult to read and to follow, while the structure of the region is not readily ascertainable from such a map. The practice of printing the pattern, representing the superficial unconsolidated deposit, over the color pattern of the formation is adopted in some quarters, as in the case of the International Geological Map of Europe. American maps, as a rule, represent rock formations only, without the overtint for superficial unconsolidated deposits. These deposits are either entirely omitted or represented on a separate map. It is, of course, understood that in such cases the map does not represent an accurate picture of the surface features of the lithosphere, but is hypothetical so far as the covered portions are concerned. In a region of simple structure no appreciable errors are likely to arise from such a mapping, but in a complicated region this may readily be the case.

SECTIONS.

Types of Sections. Geological sections are of three kinds: (1) the *natural cross-section,* (2) the *columnar section,* and (3) the *ideal section.* The natural cross-section represents structure (in so far as it is ascertainable) and surface features, and is the one most generally employed in connection with geological representation. It gives the third dimension of the land form, the other two being furnished by the map. Cross-sections should, whenever the scale permits it, be drawn to the natural scale, *i. e.,* vertical and horizontal scales should be alike. In some instances this is not possible, owing to the smallness of the scale and the large number of structural features to be represented. In such cases an exaggeration of the vertical over the horizontal scale is necessary, but this should not be over five times, or, in rare cases, ten times, the horizontal. It must be borne in mind that vertical exaggeration of the scale always involves an increase in the steepness of dip of the strata and a corresponding distortion of other characters.

Columnar sections are designed to show the superposition and relative thickness of the strata of the region which they represent, provided they are drawn to scale. They serve their main purpose in giving a quick and comprehensive view of the stratigraphy of a region and in making comparison with other regions possible. If a uniform set of scales, each a multiple of the others, could be adopted, ready comparisons of published sections for different regions would be possible, and would greatly facilitate the work of correlation.

Ideal sections are attempts to restore the conditions as they were before deformation or erosion has taken place. The term is also sometimes used for generalized cross-sections, but this is better avoided. In so far as structure is eliminated, the columnar section is an ideal section, but sections to which the term is best applicable should show a wider relationship than is possible in a columnar section. Fig. 152, page 739 and Figs. 157 and 158, page 743, are examples of ideal cross-sections.

THE LENGTH OF GEOLOGICAL TIME.

Various estimates of the actual length of geologic time have been attempted, the basis of most of such estimates being the rate of deposition, ascertainable in modern river systems, or the rate of erosion of river canyons, such as the Niagara, the Yellowstone, Colorado, etc., and the rate of retreat of the Falls of St. Anthony. (See Williams–19.) If it can be ascertained that the beginnings of erosion have a definite relation to some other event which itself is of definite value in geochronology, a basis for a rational estimate of the actual time duration is furnished. Such a relationship seems to have existed between the beginnings of the Falls of Niagara and of St. Anthony, and the end of the Pleistocenic glacial period. So many questionable factors, however, enter into the problem, that it is scarcely worth while, with our present incomplete knowledge, to attempt much more than the most general estimate. Thus Cambric, Ordovicic and Siluric time has been estimated at 10,000,-000 years; Devonic time at 2,000,000 years; Mississippic to Permic time at 5,000,000 years, making a total of 17,000,000 years for the Palæozoic. Mesozoic time has been estimated at 7,000,000 years, Cænozoic at 3,000,000 years and Psychozoic at 50,000, marking a total of 27,050,000 years since the beginning of Cambric time. This estimate is conservative, others having made a much larger one. Thus Dana's estimate of the age the earth was at least 48,000,000 years. Geikie's estimate ranges from 100,000,000 to 680,000,000 years, while McGee has suggested a possible age of 7,000,000,000 years for our earth. Since we have not as yet ascertained the actual thickness of the stratified rocks of the earth, and since we know so little about the rate of erosion, we must conclude that all such estimates are premature and almost valueless, and that even the estimates of the proportional length of duration of the various divisions are extremely hypothetical. Geological time was long, very long, as measured in terms of human chronology—long enough to permit the development of the multifarious forms of life upon the earth. Only a part of this time is recorded in the known rocks of the earth's crust—for there are probably many lost intervals, the duration of which we cannot even estimate.

BIBLIOGRAPHY XXXI.

1. CLARKE, JOHN M. 1896. The Stratigraphic and Faunal Relations of the Oneonta Sandstone and Shales, the Ithaca and Portage Groups in Central New York. New York Geological Survey, Fifteenth Annual Report, pp. 27–82, map.

2. CLARKE, J. M. 1903. The Naples Fauna in Western New York. New York State Museum, Memoir 6, pp. 199–454, 26 pls., 16 figs.

3. DANA, JAMES D. 1895. Manual of Geology. Fourth Edition. American Book Company, New York.

4. GEIKIE, ARCHIBALD. 1903. Text-book of Geology. Fourth edition. Macmillan and Co., London.

5. GRABAU, A. W. 1905. Physical Characters and History of Some New York Formations. Science, N. S., Vol. XXII, pp. 528–535.

6. GRABAU, A. W. 1906. Guide to the Geology and Paleontology of the Schoharie Valley in Eastern New York. New York State Museum Bulletin 92 (58th Annual Report, Vol. III), pp. 77–386, 24 pls., 216 figs.

7. GRABAU, A. W., and SHIMER, H. W. 1910. Summary of North American Stratigraphy. North American Index Fossils, Vol. II, pp. 604–663. A. G. Seiler & Co. New York.

8. HAYES, C. WILLARD. 1895. McMinnville Folio, Tennessee. United States Geological Survey, Geological Atlas of the United States, Folio 22.

9. HAYES, CHARLES W., and ULRICH, EDWARD O. 1903. Columbia Folio, Tennessee. Geological Atlas of the United States, Folio No. 95. United States Geological Survey.

10. LE CONTE, JOSEPH. 1902. Elements of Geology. D. Appleton and Co., New York.

11. LEHMANN, JOHANN G. 1736. Versuch einer Geschichte von Flötz-gebirgen.

12. LYELL, CHARLES. 1856. A Manual of Elementary Geology. Sixth Edition.

13. REEDS, CHESTER A. 1911. The Hunton Formation of Oklahoma. American Journal of Science, 4th series, Vol. XXXII, pp. 256–268.

14. SCHUCHERT, CHARLES. 1910. Paleogeography of North America. Geological Society of America Bulletin, Vol. XX, pp. 427–606, 56 pls.

15. SINCLAIR, W. J. 1910. Interdependence of Stratigraphy and Paleontology. The Paleontologic Record, pp. 9–11. Reprinted from Popular Science Monthly.

16. ULRICH, EDWARD O. 1904. In Taff's Preliminary Report on the Geology of the Arbuckle and Wichita Mountains in Indian Territory and Oklahoma. United States Geological Survey, Professional Paper No. 31, pp. 11–81.

17. ULRICH, E. O. 1911. Revision of the Paleozoic System. Bulletin of the Geological Society of America, Vol. XXII, pp. 281–680, pls. 25–29.

18. UNITED STATES GEOLOGICAL SURVEY. 1903. Nomenclature and Classification for the Geologic Atlas of the United States. 24th Annual Report.

19. WILLIAMS, HENRY S. 1895. Geological Biology. An Introduction to the Geological History of Organisms. New York. Henry Holt & Co.

19a. WILLIAMS, HENRY S. 1893. The Elements of the Geological Time Scale. Journal of Geology, Vol. I, pp. 283–295.

20. WILLIS, BAILEY. 1901. Individuals of Stratigraphic Classification. Journal of Geology, Vol. IX, pp. 557–569.

CHAPTER XXXII.

CORRELATION: ITS CRITERIA AND PRINCIPLES— PALÆOGEOGRAPHY.

CORRELATION.

"The fundamental data of geologic history are: (1) local sequences of formations, and (2) the chronologic equivalences of formations in different provinces. Through correlation all formations are referred to a general time scale, of which the units are periods. The formations made during a period are collectively designated a system." (Rule 14, Nomenclature and Classification for the Geologic Atlas of the United States.)

History of Development of Methods of Correlation.

Correlation of strata, or the establishment of an orderly relationship between the formations of separate regions, has been one of the chief aims of stratigraphers ever since the days of Werner and William Smith. Werner's correlations were based on the lithic character of the strata, but William Smith in England and Cuvier and Brogniart in France made their identifications of strata by means of the organic remains included in them. Each of these workers based his investigation upon the ascertained succession of strata in the region selected by him as typical, and thus the three fundamental criteria of correlative geology: lithic similarity, likeness of fossil content and superposition of strata, were made use of by the pioneers in stratigraphy.

The efforts of these founders of stratigraphy were directed chiefly toward establishing the identity or correspondence of strata between different localities; and, when it was recognized that strata were formed at different periods in the earth's history, the effort was further directed toward establishing the time-equivalency or synchroneity of strata. Before fossils were extensively studied, similarity of superposition and lithic identity were taken as the guides to synchroneity, a proceeding which naturally led to many erroneous correlations. Thus McClure and Eaton in their early studies of the rocks of the United States were entirely guided by superposition and lithic and structural character of the rocks, their classification being modeled upon that of Werner. Both McClure and Eaton identified the undisturbed Palæozoic formations of eastern United States with the Secondary or Mesozoic formations of England, being thus influenced in their correlation by another criterion, namely, the relative position of the strata. Lithic similarity caused Eaton to identify the Rochester shale of New York (Lower Siluric) with the Lias of England (Lower Jurassic). Lithic similarity and similarity of superposition led many of the early geologists to identify the Potsdam sandstone and the quartzose sand rock of Vermont as of the same age, though one is Upper and the other Lower Cambric. In the same manner lithic similarity led some of the earlier geologists to identify the Upper Cambric or early Ordovicic, Lake Superior sandstone with the Triassic sandstone of New Jersey and the Connecticut Valley, while the ribbon limestones of Pennsylvania and New Jersey, of Cambric and Lower Ordovicic age, and the Waterlimes of the Hudson River region—of Upper Siluric age—were not so long ago thought to be stratigraphic equivalents, on account of their great similarity in lithic characters. Superposition, sometimes erroneously inferred, similarity of lithic character, and superficial comparison of fossils led Bigsby in 1824 to identify the Rideau sandstone of Kingston, Ontario (Lower Ordovicic), with the Medina of the Niagara and Genesee gorges (Lower Siluric), and both with the Old Red Sandstone of England, on account of lithic resemblance of the two formations, and the apparent similarity of fossils in the limestones overlying them. In his later investigations Eaton, like Bigsby, made use of fossils in correlation, but the comparisons made by both were of the crudest, being chiefly by classes of organisms. Thus the Ordovicic conglomerates opposite Quebec were correlated by Bigsby with the "Carboniferous limestone" of England, because both contain remains of trilobites, "encrinites," "corallites" and other fossils. Another of the early correlations of formations by lithic characters was made in 1821 by Dr. Edwin James. He considered that the sandstone of Sault Ste. Marie (Cambric or early Ordovicic) the Triassic sandstone of the eastern foothills of the Rocky Mountains, the Catskill, Medina and Potsdam sandstones of New York and the Newark sandstone of New Jersey were of the same relative geologic age and occupied a place similar to that assigned to the "Old Red Sandstone" by Werner. Geologists, however, were not long in finding out that beds of the same lithic character are not all of the same age, but it has taken them much longer to realize that beds of the same age are not always of the same or even similar lithic character.

With the detailed study of the New York strata by the five geologists and palæontologists on the survey (Mather, Emmons, Vanuxem, Conrad and Hall), correlation by fossils became recognized as the most reliable known method. At first American species were directly identified with European types, and such identification was in many cases not far wrong. Extensive collections of fossils, however, soon showed that the rocks of this country contained an assemblage of organisms largely peculiar to themselves and specifically, if not generically, distinct from that of Europe. Correlation by similarity of faunas was then substituted for correlation by species and so the general correspondence of the strata in the two continents was established. The need of an American standard of comparison was soon felt, and such a need was supplied by the development of the "New York series" of geological formations. The succession of New York strata and the organic remains characterizing them was so thoroughly worked out that "it is and has been for decades a standard of reference for all students of the older rocks throughout the world." (Clarke–11.) Professor James Hall was one of the first in America to recognize the importance of naming formations from localities in which they were best exposed. In his report to the New York State legislature in 1839 he urges that neither lithic character nor characteristic fossils is a satisfactory source from which to derive the name of the formation, for the first may change while the second is not always ascertainable and may even be absent. He holds that it "becomes a desideratum to distinguish rocks by names which cannot be traduced, and which, when the attendant circumstances are fully understood, will never prove fallacious." Such names can be derived only from localities. It is most fortunate that this principle was recognized before the New York series of formations was fully promulgated in the final reports of the survey. As a result, the majority of formations were named from typical localities, only a relatively small number retaining the lithic or palæontologic names given them by the earlier investigators. More recently these, too, have been replaced by names derived from typical localities, of which the following is a partial list:

Calciferous............................replaced by Beekmantown.
Birdseye...............................replaced by Lowville.
Waterlime (of Buffalo)..................replaced by Bertie.
Coralline..............................replaced by Cobleskill.
Waterlimes (of the Hudson).............replaced by Rondout & Rosendale
Tentaculite limestone...................replaced by Manlius.
Lower Pentamerus......................replaced by Coeymans.
Delthyris shaly........................replaced by New Scotland.
Upper Pentamerus......................replaced by Becraft.
Upper Shaly...........................replaced by Port Ewen.
Cauda-Galli...........................replaced by Esopus.
Corniferous............................replaced by Onondaga

As the Palæozoic formations of other districts of North America were studied, it was found that the correspondence between them and the New York formations was not as close as could have been hoped. Not only did the lithic character of the strata change when traced away from the type locality, but the superposition did not, in many cases, correspond, some formations being absent altogether while others were found to be united in a single unit, often of slight thickness. Even the fossils, which had gradually come to be looked upon as the surest indicators of position in the geologic scale, appeared in horizons not known to contain them in New York. Thus the chain-coral *Halysites* was universally thought to be characteristic of the Lower Siluric (Niagaran) age, until it was discovered that this coral also occurred in the Ordovicic, in some of the localities west of New York, and in the Anticosti region, while in eastern New York it was found in an Upper Siluric horizon, the Cobleskill, which is stratigraphically many hundred feet above the Niagaran beds. In like manner *Tropidoleptus carinatus* and some of its associates, believed formerly to be restricted to the Hamilton (Mid-Devonic) formation, were found in south central New York to occur in the Ithaca (Portage) beds and, again, in the Chemung (Upper Devonic).

Recurrent faunas have also been described from the Mississipic. Weller (53) found Devonic elements in the Kinderhook fauna, and Williams and others have described such recurrence of Devonic elements in the Spergen and other Mississippic beds of central North America. Ulrich (49:296) has noted the occurrence of the trilobite *Triarthrus becki* in the Fulton shale, and in the Southgate beds 150 feet above it.

Chronological Equivalency. Contemporaneous and Homotaxial Formations. Chronological equivalency as one of the fundamental data of geologic history has repeatedly been assailed by eminent scientists. Huxley, indeed, went so far as to question the possibility of determining in any case the existence of contemporaneous strata, and he coined the term *homotaxis,* signifying similarity of order, to express the correspondence in succession rather than exact time equivalence. Geikie also held that "strict contemporaneity cannot be asserted of any strata merely on the ground of similarity or identity of fossils" (14:*608*), and H. S. Williams, among American authors, has most strenuously insisted on the impossibility of recognizing strict contemporaneity among strata of widely separated regions. Williams would refer formations not to a general time scale, but to a stratigraphic scale, of which not "periods" but systems are units. He advocates the revision of Rule 14 of the U. S. Geological Survey quoted at the beginning of this chapter so as to read (56:*138*) :

"The fundamental data of geologic history are: (1) the local sequence of formations and (2) the similarity of the fossil faunas of the formation of different provinces. Through correlation all formations are referred to a standard stratigraphic scale, of which the units are systems."

Contrary to the views of Huxley and other writers, some of whom like Edward Forbes went so far as to assert that similarity of organic content of distant formations is *prima facie* evidence, not of their similarity, but of their difference of age, most modern stratigraphers have come to believe in the possibility of essential chronological equivalency of formations characterized by the same faunas, recognizing at the same time the fact that such equivalency is not necessarily indicated by the similarity of faunas, and that a given fauna may appear earlier and continue longer in some sections than in others. The rapidity of migration shown by modern faunas indicates that, if the path is open and no barriers exist, widespread migration or dispersal may occur within such short time limits as to be considered almost homochronic.

Contemporaneity of Faunas. That several distinct faunas may exist side by side in not too widely separated districts is a well known fact. The difference of faunas north and south of Cape Cod on the Atlantic Coast may be mentioned as a modern example; also the difference between the Red Sea fauna and that of the Mediterranean, and, finally, the distinct faunas on opposite sides of the Isthmus of Panama. In all of these cases a partial or complete land barrier separated the faunas. In the case of Cape Cod, this barrier is incomplete and, although aided by cold currents from the north, it has not entirely prevented the migration around it of the faunas. The other two barriers were complete, and separated faunas of different provinces, but the transsection in 1869 of the

Suez barrier by the canal has permitted a certain commingling of faunas, a phenomenon predictable for the faunas on opposite sides of the Isthmus of Panama on the completion of the canal.

Contemporaneous faunas existed in North America at various times in its geologic history. The most noted case is that of the Upper Devonic. An indigenous fauna, the Ithaca fauna, derived largely by development from the earlier Hamilton fauna, occupied the eastern area in New York and Pennsylvania, while an immigrant fauna, the Naples fauna, occupied the region to the west of this. At first the two faunas were separated by a land barrier, but this was subsequently submerged. Nevertheless, the two faunas continued in their essential integrity through Portage time, though the area of occupancy of each varied from time to time, but within comparatively narrow limits.

Prenuncial Faunas, Colonies. Prenuncial faunas are the advance invaders of a new territory of members of a foreign host, which subsequently occupies the territory. Such have been noted in some cases, especially in that of the Styliolina limestone of the Upper Devonic of New York, which marks the first invasion of the Naples fauna into this Upper Devonic province.

The term "Colonies" was employed by Barrande to designate the appearance of a fauna normal to a later geological horizon, during a period when an earlier fauna still flourished. Though the examples cited by Barrande have proved to be mostly inadequate to establish his theory, the fact remains that faunas in their ensemble suggestive of a much later period may appear in deposits otherwise marked by the normal fauna of that period. Thus, during the Upper Siluric (Upper Monroan) time, a fauna in large measure suggestive of Middle Devonic time flourished in Michigan, Ohio, and Ontario (Anderdon fauna). In this fauna something over twenty species have exact specific, or closely similar, representatives in the Onondaga or Schoharie formation. This similarity is largely found in the coral, brachiopod, pelecypod, and trilobite elements of the fauna, while the cephalopods and gastropods are of typical Siluric species. The whole fauna is succeeded by a normal Siluric fauna, and is separated by an extensive hiatus from the overlying limestones of Middle Devonic age. The explanation of this commingling of faunas is found in the fact that two faunas, with distinctive characters, existed simultaneously, one of which furnished the faunal elements with Devonic affinities, but did not make much headway against the resident normal Siluric fauna. Continuing to modify in its own center of distribution, the more specialized fauna finally evolved into the normal Middle Devonic fauna of that region, some parts of which spread widely over the earth, and, with elements derived from other sources, constituted the local Middle Devonic faunas of eastern North America. (Grabau and Sherzer–20a.)

Standard or Type Sections. In general the first section studied is taken as the type section for the country. Often it is not the most complete nor the most perfect section, as in the case of the Devonic section of southern England (Devonshire), which is less perfect than that of the Rhine region; or the Cretacic section of Colorado and Montana, which is less complete than that of Texas and Mexico. In such cases it not infrequently happens that, by a process of natural selection, the poorer section is gradually replaced by the better, as in the case of the Rhenish Devonic, which is now more frequently used for comparison, or the Cambric of Scandinavia, which is more satisfactory than that of Wales. In America the type section for the Palæozoic formations is found in the State of New York. This not only was the first section thoroughly studied in this country, but, what is more significant, it turned out to be in many respects the most complete and most representative of all American Palæozoic sections. So truly representative is this section that, " . . . while other classifications proposed for these rocks, contemporaneously or subsequently, have fallen to the ground, it has withstood all the attacks of time." (Clarke–11.)

Not a little did the detailed palæontologic work carried on by the State Survey of New York contribute to this prominence of the New York Section. No other American region has had the organic remains of its formations so fully investigated and descriptions and illustrations of them published in such a complete manner. This thoroughness, for which in a large measure James Hall was responsible, has forever made the New York column the foundation on which all other work on Palæozoic Stratigraphy of America must be based.

In spite of this fact, however, the relationships between the various local sections of the State of New York have not yet been fully ascertained, and each year facts are discovered which demand a modification, in details, of these standard sections.

Nor is the New York column as a whole complete and without flaws. Undoubted Middle Cambric appears to be but slightly developed in the state, while the Lower and Upper Cambric also are not fully represented, so far as the sections have been studied. Hence the American type sections for these formations are obtained from other regions: that for the Lower Cambric from northwestern Vermont and that for the Middle Cambric in the Acadian provinces of Canada. In the latter region is likewise found a more complete representation of the Upper Cambric formations than has yet been ascertained to exist in the State of New York. It is on this account that the East Canadian names Bretonian, Acadian and Etcheminian (*cf.* Georgian) have been used for the Upper, Middle and Lower Cambric, respectively. (Grabau–17.)

Again, a hiatus exists in New York between the Ordovicic and Siluric, the upper part of the Ordovicic not being represented, at least not by fossiliferous formations. The lower Siluric, too, is less satisfactorily represented in New York than elsewhere, for, as currently understood, it begins with a sandstone formation, the Medina, which is a shore formation, where not of non-marine origin. For the Upper Ordovicic and Lower Siluric, then, the New York column has to be pieced out by formations developed elsewhere, the standard selected being the Cincinnati group of the south-central states for the one, and the lower Mississippi region for the other.* Even within the lower Ordovicic there is an incomplete representation of the top of the Beekmantown and of the Chazy formation, this incompleteness being measurable by thousands of feet of limestone in the Mohawk Valley, but by very much less in the Lake Champlain region. The Salina of New York, of Mid-Siluric age, also forms an unsatisfactory member of the standard series, as already pointed out, since it represents abnormal conditions of sedimentation. Aside from these, however, the New York column represents an eminently satisfactory standard of the Palæozoic formation below the Mississippic.

The standard American series for the Mississippic is that of the Mississippi Valley, though that is not itself a complete section. The standard marine sections for the Carbonic and Permic have not yet been fully worked out for this country. The former is found in Kansas, Missouri and Arkansas; the latter in Texas. No American Triassic or Jurassic standards are recognized, the fragmentary development of these formations being referred to foreign standards. The Comanchic and Cretacic, on the other hand, are well represented by formations in Mexico, Texas and the Great Plains region, which localities have furnished the standard sections. The Comanchic is well represented in the southern areas, but the sections of the typical Cretacic in the standard region (Colorado and Montana) are incomplete at the bottom and at the top, where they include non-marine formations, *i. e.*, the Dakota sandstone, and the

---

* The Anticosti section promises to be one of the most perfect North American Lower Siluric (Niagaran) sections, but it is not as yet certain in how far this section belonged to a distinct geographic province. (See Schuchert–39:532.)

Laramie formation. The standards of the North American marine Eocenic and Oligocenic are found in the Gulf States, while those of the Miocenic and Pliocenic are found on the Atlantic coast of Maryland and Virginia, the Carolinas and Florida. All these localities together, however, furnish only a partial standard of the American marine Tertiary.

A Double Standard. In some cases it has been found most practicable to have a double standard of formations: one marine, the other non-marine. This has been most fully worked out for the American Tertiary, where the continental deposits of the Great Plains region serve as a standard of comparison for similar deposits of other American regions, while the Gulf and Atlantic Coast deposits serve as our standard of marine formations. In western Europe the Carbonic is represented by the non-marine Westphalian and Stephanian, while the corresponding marine formations of eastern Europe are the Moscovian and Uralian. In America the Pocono-Mauch Chunk formations are the non-marine equivalents of the Mississippic, and the Pennsylvanic (Pottsville-Monongahela) is the non-marine standard of the Carbonic, the marine standard being still undetermined, though in part represented in the Kansas section. The Laramie, Belly River, Bear River, and Dakota formations form a nearly complete non-marine standard for the American Cretacic, and the Kootanie for the Comanchic.

Methods of Correlation.

The means by which formations of different localities are correlated may be summarized as follows:

1. Superposition.
2. Stratigraphic continuity.
3. Lithic characters.
4. Organic contents.
5. Unconformities or disconformities.
6. Regional metamorphism.
7. Diastrophism.

1. *Superposition.*

The basis of all stratigraphic work is the ascertainment of the order of superposition of the strata. No correlation of the strata in any two localities is possible until the exact superposition in each has been ascertained. The general law of superposition is: *that, of any two strata of sedimentary rocks, the one which was originally the lower is also the older.* This does not, of course, apply to intruded igneous rock, for a much later sheet of intrusive material may find its way between strata very much older and so be followed by strata older than itself. In exceptional cases, too, sedimentary rocks may not follow this rule, as in the case of deposits in caverns cut out of older rocks. Here strata may actually form beneath the surface of the lithosphere and hence below an older stratum.

Of course, in regions of faulting and strong folding, the order of the strata may be reversed, so that it becomes necessary, first of all, to demonstrate the original position of the formations.

In the ascertainment of the superposition of strata of a given region great care must be taken to note the existence of stratigraphic breaks. Disconformities of strata are often difficult to recognize, but unless ascertained are sure to introduce an element of error into the geologic columns of the region. Abrupt changes in sedimentation are a useful guide in the location of such disconformities and, in fact, where such sudden changes occur it may be taken as an indication of the possibility of the existence of such a hiatus, though this alone is not sufficient proof of its existence. A good example of a great hiatus indicated only by an abrupt change in the character of the rock is found in the case of the contact of the Black Chattanooga shale with the gray Rockwood clays in eastern Tennessee. Here there seems to be, at times, no other indication, than this sudden change in character, of the absence, between these two formations, of more than the entire Devonic system of strata. Indication of erosion surfaces, and the inclusion of the fragments of the lower in the upper beds, commonly characterize the disconformity, but give no clue as to the magnitude of the hiatus. The change from one lithic unit to another may be abrupt, without necessarily indicating a disconformity. In such cases, generally, there is some alternation of beds of the two series before the complete disappearance of the lower series.. Thus the Black Shale at the top becomes intercalated with thin bands of the overlying formation, and itself occurs at intervals in the form of thin layers for some time after the extensive development of the overlying series.

Correlation by superposition, however, is a method fraught with grave dangers. Thus a succession of formations from sandstones to shales and limestones in one part of a province is not necessarily the same as a similar series in another part of the same province, and most probably not the same as a similar series in another geologic province. Indeed, from a consideration of the phenomena accompanying marine progressive overlap, it becomes apparent that even within the same province the two series are different, unless they are situated along a line parallel to the old shore of the time when the strata accumulated.

2. Stratigraphic continuity.

When a formation can be traced, with but slight interruptions, over a wide area, the general assumption is, that it is synchronous in all its outcrops. This is true enough where the tracing of the formation is parallel to the old shore line, or source of supply, but not always true when at an angle with that line. This is especially the case when the formation in question is of terrigenous origin, formed either as a marine or as a fluviatile deposit. A basal sandstone or conglomerate, formed in a transgressing sea, rises in the scale shoreward; in a regressing sea it rises seaward (see Chapter XVIII). The Mahoning sandstone of the Lower Conemaugh of northwestern Pennsylvania had been traced almost continuously around the bituminous coal field and united with the Charleston sandstone of the Kanawha district of West Virginia. It has since been shown, however, that these sandstones are part of a series rising and overlapping northwestward, and that, whereas the Charleston end of the series lies in the Lower Allegheny, the Mahoning sandstone proper forms the westernmost part of the series, lying at the base of the Conemaugh. (Campbell.)

Limestones are, however, much more continuous, and, if traced for moderate distances, are apt to hold their own pretty well. This is especially the case with limestone beds of slight thickness interbedded with shales. Thus the Encrinal limestone has been recognized in all its outcrops, from Thedford, Ontario, to the Genesee Valley, a distance of over 200 miles, holding its own throughout in lithic character as well as fossil content, though there are other strata which have been mistaken for it farther east. It forms a prominent plane of correlation of the strata, for it seems pretty certain that this limestone in all of its occurrences represents simultaneous, or nearly simultaneous, accumulation as the result of widespread uniformity of conditions. (Shimer and Grabau–43.)

The Agoniatite limestone of the New York Marcellus has been traced from Buffalo to Schoharie, and southward to Maryland.

This limestone, intercalated between black shales, indicates a period of widespread uniform conditions, followed by a resumption of the Black Mud sedimentation. It therefore serves as an excellent horizon marker, by which the rocks above and below can be correlated. Still another example is the Cobleskill of New York, which has been traced across the State, chiefly by its fauna, and serves as a datum-plane for the strata above and below it.

3. Lithic characters.

Correlation by lithic characters is possible only in very limited areas, and where it can be used in connection with stratigraphic continuity and order of superposition. Under certain conditions, however, the lithic character becomes an important guide in correlation. An example is the St. Peter sandstone, a pure silicarenyte, which has been widely recognized by its lithic character, and its enclosure within pure limestone or dolomytes. The uniformity of grain and composition over thousands of square miles of area is its most remarkable feature. As already outlined, however (Chapter XVIII), the St. Peter, though occupying a definite position in the scale, encloses within itself a hiatus, which constantly widens northward, so that the top of the sandstone is higher in the scale and the bottom is lower in the northern region, as compared with its more southern occurrence. Moreover, there are formations, such as the Sylvania sandstone of Ohio (Upper Siluric), which are lithically identical with the St. Peter, and might be mistaken for it, if lithic character alone were considered.

An intercalated shore-derived formation between offshore formations can generally be recognized in its various outcrops by its lithic character. Such a formation represents an oscillation of the land during sedimentation, either a shoaling or a total retreat of the sea, followed by a re-advance or a deepening. Lithic character then, when taken in conjunction with superposition, may be a valuable guide in correlation. Intercalated off-shore beds among terrigenous formations may likewise serve a good purpose in correlation. Thus the Ames or Crinoidal limestone, a marine bed, has been widely recognized as an intercalated bed in the non-marine Conemaugh formation of the bituminous coal field. In this case the correlation is confirmed by the contained fauna.

Another way in which lithic character serves a useful purpose in correlation is by the occurrence of what may be called sympathetic changes in sedimentation. Thus two regions, one more distant from the shore than the other, may experience a sympathetic change in sedimentation, when simultaneously affected by an oscillatory movement. Thus, when in the near-shore region muds change upward into sands, and still higher into muds again, the corresponding change in the more distant region may be from limestones to terrigenous muds and higher still to limestones again. Such sympathetic changes seem to have taken place between the New York and Michigan Hamilton deposits.

4. *Organic contents.*

Correlation by organic contents, or Palæontologic correlation, has been found to be the most reliable method, far surpassing in importance any other single method. Nevertheless, there are many pitfalls which must be guarded against, and the sources of error must be recognized and taken into account.

(a) *Index fossils.* Index fossils have already been defined as species characteristic of definite geologic horizons, and typically occurring only in beds of that horizon (page 1094). Index fossils in order to be efficacious must be of limited vertical but wide horizontal distribution. Thus the brachiopod *Hypothyris cuboides* characterizes a certain zone in the Upper Devonic of America, Europe and Asia, while the Goniatite *Manticoceras intumescens* likewise characterizes late Devonic rocks throughout much of the northern hemisphere. Similarly, *Spirifer disjunctus* has a limited vertical range, combined with a wide horizontal one, being characteristic of the Upper Devonic of many countries. Locally, the type may transgress the normal vertical range, as in the case of the last-mentioned species, which passes up into Lower Mississippic beds in eastern North America, or, as in the case of *Tropidoleptus carinatus,* a widespread index fossil of the Mid-Devonic, but which locally passes into the Upper Devonic. The best index fossils are those which are capable of wide distribution, and remains of which' will occur in regions where the organisms may never have lived, and in sediments which may differ widely from those forming the normal facies of sea bottom for the type in question. As pointed out in an earlier chapter, epiplanktonic and pseudoplanktonic forms are most likely to produce such index fossils. The shell of Spirula, a dibranchiate cephalopod of the modern fauna, illustrates the wide distribution possible by flotation, though the animal has been found to occur only in a few localities in deep water. Epiplanktonic Hydrozoa and Bryozoa likewise suffer a wide distribution through the flotation of their host.

Among the pseudoplankton the shells of Ammonites should be especially noted as being included, at least to some extent, in sediments of varied character over wide areas.* The genera and species of ammonites as a rule were short-lived cephalopods, different species characterizing different zones. Besides having their shells widely distributed after death, by flotation, living ammonites also seem to have spread rapidly and widely, probably during a meroplanktonic stage.

Holoplanktonic organisms may also suffer a wide distribution and, if they contain parts capable of preservation, these may be entombed in sediments of widely different character. Such cases are seen in the pteropod oozes of various geologic horizons.

The wide distribution of the Ordovicic graptolites was probably due to epiplanktonic as well as holoplanktonic dispersion. Graptolite species were short-lived, hence successive zones are characterized by distinct types over a wide area. Plants whose seeds are widely distributed by winds or other agents produce good index fossils for continental deposits. Here, however, the climatic factor exercises a limiting influence, since plants will only grow where climatic conditions are favorable.

(b) *Grade of index fossil.* The grade of the index fossil commonly has a very direct relation to the magnitude of the stratigraphic divisions to be correlated. Thus, while the class of trilobites as a whole may serve for the recognition of Palæozoic rocks the world over—none having as yet been found outside of the Palæozoic—smaller subdivisions must be used for the correlation of more restricted stratigraphic divisions. Thus the family *Conocoryphidæ* among the trilobites is characteristic of the Cambric, and any member of that family will serve to determine the Cambric age of the strata in which it occurs. The family *Olenidæ* is principally restricted to the Cambric, though some members occur in the Ordovicic. The most characteristic types, nevertheless, serve to correlate the Cambric formations in all their occurrences. While any of the more characteristic genera of this family (Olenidæ) will thus serve in correlating Cambric formations as a whole, certain genera of this family serve as indices of the three principal sub-

* The pseudoplanktonic dispersal of the shells of Ammonites is strongly advocated by Walther, but questioned by Ortmann (34), Tornquist (46), J. P. Smith and others. Tornquist has urged against such interpretation the observation that in the Jurassic and Cretacic the Ammonites are distributed according to climatic zones. Examples of dispersal by flotation are, however, known, for as shown by Clarke (Naples fauna) the Goniatite fauna of the Styliolina or Genundewah limestone of western New York ("prenuncial intumescens fauna") must be regarded as derived in this manner. (See also Chapter XXIX.)

divisions. Thus *Olenellus* and *Holmia* characterize the Lower Cambric, *Paradoxides* the Middle Cambric, and *Olenus* and *Dikellocephalus* the Upper Cambric.* Again, the Middle Cambric may be subdivided into a number of zones, each characterized by a species of Paradoxides. These species are either identical or representative in the corresponding zones of the East American and West European Middle Cambric.

The dendroid graptolite *Dictyonema* may serve as an example of a genus of more extended range, some of whose species are, nevertheless, good index fossils. The genus itself begins in the transition beds from the Upper Cambric to the Lower Ordovicic, where *D. flabelliforme* is a characteristic index fossil and is of almost worldwide distribution. Other species characterize the Siluric and still others the Devonic.

(c) *Correlation by equivalent stages in development.* Among organisms characterized by community of descent corresponding stages in development are sometimes reached in different lines of evolution at about the same time period. Such homœomorphic representatives (morphological equivalents, see Chapter XXV) may thus serve as indices of a given horizon even where intercommunication has not occurred. Thus Goniatites the world over characterize the upper Palæozoic, but Goniatites are derived along different lines of descent.† The simpler types along the various lines of descent characterize the Devonic, while those with more complicated sutures,‡ greater involution, or marked ornamentation are mostly characteristic of the Mississippic and Carbonic. The Ceratite type, in which the lobes of the sutures are further modified by secondary indentations, while the saddles are entire, are typically developed along the various lines of evolution, in the Trias. Finally, the Ammonite type, in which both lobes and saddles are modified by additional indentations, appears chiefly in the Jurassic, in the various evolutional lines, and continues into the Cretacic. Owing to these facts the orginal idea prevailed that Goniatites constituted one genus, characteristic of the formations from the Devonic to the Carbonic; Ceratites formed another genus characteristic of the Trias; while Ammonites was regarded as a genus characterizing the time from the Jurassic to the Cretacic inclusive.

It is now known, however, that many exceptions to this general rule exist. Genetic series, in which acceleration of development prevailed, reached the Ceratite or even the Ammonite stage in pre-Triassic time. Thus the genus *Prodomites* from the Lower Missis-

* For illustrations see Grabau and Shimer, North American Index Fossils Vol. II.   † See Chapter XXV, p. 978.   ‡ See Chapter XXIV, p. 945.

sippic (Chouteauan) has advanced into the Ceratite stage, while *Waagenoceras* of the Permic has already true Ammonite (phylliform) sutures. Sometimes, by retardation, a type remains in a more primitive evolutional stage, one which normally characterizes a lower horizon. The case of the Triassic ammonite Trachyceras, cited by J. P. Smith (45), from the Karnic limestone of California, and referred to in Chapter XXV, belongs here. This had persisted in the more primitive Tirolites stage and so suggested correlation of the beds with those of a lower horizon. The "Pseudoceratites" of the Cretacic (Hyatt–23) form another instructive example. In these types (Protengonoceras, Engonoceras,* etc.) arrestation in development affects the later stages (the earlier stages being accelerated with reference to the corresponding stages of their Jurassic ancestors), so that the adult sutures remain in the ceratite or even goniatite stage. This is a case of heterepistasis, the cessation in development affecting only the sutures. What appears to be a good example of corresponding stages in development in distinct provinces at about the same time period, thus serving for interregional correlation, is seen in the case of Clavilithes of the Parisian Eocenic, and the corresponding morphologic equivalents of the Eocenic of the Gulf States of North America. The American series of species parallels the Parisian to such an extent that they have been regarded as varieties of the Parisian species. There is every reason for believing, however, that they represent an independent development. (Grabau–15.)

The graptolites present other examples of corresponding stages in development reached in distinct genetic series at approximately the same time. Thus, Dichograptus, Tetragraptus, Didymograptus, etc., represent stages in development rather than monophyletic genera, but, since these stages appear simultaneously in the various lines of descent, they may be used as geologic genera, eminently adapted for correlative purposes. (Ruedemann–38.)

(d) *Correlation by faunas and floras. Representative species.* When the index species themselves are not represented, correlation by means of the sum total of associated organisms must be made. Thus Paradoxides is absent from the Middle Cambric of the Appalachian and Pacific provinces of North America, nor are any of the associated species of the other genera present in these faunas. Representative species, however, occur and the sum total of the Middle Cambric faunas of the various provinces has similarity of expression, which is almost as good as absolute identity. The lower Middle Cambric of the Atlantic Coast and of western Europe

* For illustrations see North American Index Fossils, Vol. II.

has different species of Paradoxides in the different provinces, but these species are representative, so that they serve to correlate even the zones. The zones with their representative or identical species are as follows:

Eastern North America.	Western Europe.
Paradoxides forchhammeri	P. forchhammeri
P. davidis	P. davidis
P. abenacus	P. tessini
P. eteminicus	P. rugulosus
P. lamellatus	P. œlandicus

Even between provinces as close as New Brunswick and eastern Massachusetts the species are representative rather than identical. Thus *Paradoxides harlani,* the large Middle Cambric trilobite of eastern Massachusetts, is representative of *P. eteminicus* of New Brunswick, while *Acrothele gamagii* of the Massachusetts Middle Cambric is the representative of *A. matthewi* of New Brunswick. The Meekoceras beds of the Lower Trias of the Himalayas, Siberia, California, Idaho and Utah are readily correlated, though no species common to these regions are known. The genera, however, which characterize them are sufficiently short-lived and the species of the different provinces are closely representative. (Smith–45.)

5. *Correlation by unconformities and disconformities.*

Correlation by unconformities has in the past been extensively employed, and some stratigraphers have advocated the use of unconformities as a primary basis for correlation. A little reflection, however, will show that such a method, when used indiscriminately, is sure to lead to confusion and false correlation, for it is a well-ascertained fact that folding of formations was not simultaneous in different parts of a region, nor in different regions, but may be earlier in some and later in others. Thus, while there was a rather widespread period of folding in later Palæozoic time, both in Europe and North America, this folding began in the Devonic in some sections, and not until the Permic in others. Moreover, the formation next succeeding the unconformity is by no means always the same one, and grave mistakes have been made by assuming this to be the case. Thus in some cases the Triassic beds rest directly upon the folded Palæozoics, while in other cases beds of much later age, even Cretacic or Tertiary, succeed them.

In the same way the beds resting upon the truncated Ordovicic folds in New York and Pennsylvania vary considerably in age. The conglomerates succeeding the unconformity were originally all classed as basal Siluric. In reality some are of Lower and some are of Middle Siluric age, while in still other cases beds of upper Siluric or even younger age rest directly upon the truncated roots of the old folds.

Nevertheless, with due circumspection it is possible to use great and widespread unconformities for broad correlation of formations. Since there were two periods of widespread, if not universal, disturbance of the earth's crust, besides many minor ones, these at least have a considerable value in correlation. One of these occurred before the beginning of Palæozoic time, and the other came to an end before the beginning of Mesozoic time. Thus everywhere, the world over, the Archæan rocks are separated from the Palæozoic formations by great unconformities. This does not apparently hold for all pre-Cambric rocks, however, since some of the formations commonly referred to the Algonkian are separated from the Cambric only by a disconformity. It may, however, be true, as already pointed out, that the unaltered or but slightly altered rocks, like the Belt terrane, the Uinta sandstone, and others, are not necessarily pre-Palæozoic. They are known to be pre-Cambric, or better, in most cases only pre-Middle Cambric, and, since they are largely, if not entirely, of non-marine origin, they may, in part at least, represent the continental equivalents of the marine Lower Cambric beds. The unconformity between the Palæozoic and Mesozoic, though widespread, is nevertheless much more restricted than the earlier one mentioned. Moreover, it is of sufficient constancy to make possible this broad correlation, though, as before remarked, there is no guarantee that the beds next succeeding are everywhere of the same age.

Disconformities are, to a certain extent, better criteria for correlation, especially the larger and more extensive ones, which can be interpreted as due to eustatic movements of the sea. Withdrawals or transgressions of the sea, due to change in sea-level, will affect all continents more or less in the same manner, and thus serve as a primary basis for subdivision. The danger with this method lies in the difficulty of distinguishing between the local and the widespread character of the disconformity and the tendency which it induces to multiply the number of breaks in the geologic column by assuming that the minor breaks of one locality are necessarily reproduced elsewhere.

That there are widespread breaks in the geological column,

which are undoubtedly due to eustatic movements of the sea, becomes more and more apparent. The widespread mid-Jurassic transgression of the sea over Europe is well known and the disconformity (and occasional unconformity) produced by this transgression has been used for widespread correlation. The great Mid-Ordovicic hiatus first observed in North America. (Grabau–16; 18), and the similarly widespread hiatus in the Upper Ordovicic (Weller–52), are now known to be marked in North Europe as well (Bassler–5). In like manner the Mid-Siluric hiatus and disconformity so widespread in North America appear also to be present in the Baltic region of Russia and Sweden and in the Bohemian Palæozoic district. The probabilities are that in Mid-Siluric time the sea left a large part of the present land area dry. Similar widespread disconformities are recognized in the Mesozoic.

6. *Correlation by regional metamorphism.*

Regional metamorphism has already been defined as an alteration or metamorphism, which affects extensive regions and which is primarily due to tectonic disturbances. Such metamorphism may, of course, occur at any time in the history of the earth, but whenever it does occur it will affect all the formations of the region in which it takes place, though, obviously, some formations may be more strongly affected than others. This being the case, it follows that, wherever unaltered rocks overlie the metamorphosed ones, the age of the former cannot date back of the period of metamorphism, and that, hence, the lower limit of their age is fixed by this period of metamorphism. Evidently there is no guarantee here, however, that the strata of the overlying series are all of the same age, though within moderate limits this is probably true. One general rule may, perhaps, be formulated, and within certain limits applied, namely, that, of two formations in contact, the more strongly metamorphosed one is the older. Here, however, the same caution is necessary that is required in applying the rule of greater deformation to two deformed formations in contact. Some formations are more subject to metamorphism than others, just as some formations are more subject to deformation.

The method of correlation by metamorphism is, perhaps, the most applicable to the determination of the boundary line between the pre-Palæozoic and later formations, though even here it seems not always to be reliable. This would appear from the fact that extensive sedimentary formations, such as the Belt series of Montana, and its continuation into Canada, with a thickness of over 12,000 feet, and similar formations in Utah (Uinta quartzite) and in the Grand Canyon district (Unkar and Chuar series *) have suffered no appreciable metamorphism, though from their relationship to the overlying Cambric formations they are believed to be of pre-Cambric age. The Torridon sandstone of Scotland is another example of a formation underlying the Olenellus-bearing sandstones (Lower Cambric), the two being separated by a slight unconformity, while the American formations are generally separated from the Cambric only by a disconformity, or at least by an unconformity in which the deformation of the lower beds has been so slight as to appear non-existent. If these formations are really pre-Cambric, and not basal Cambric, they may well represent an earlier system, which, however, still belongs in the Palæozoic; or they may represent a pre-Palæozoic, but still post-Algonkic system, one, the formation of which succeeded the apparently world-wide metamorphism which has affected the Algonkic and earlier formations.

Finally, it must be noted that extensive metamorphism has affected rocks of Palæozoic and even of much later age. The schists and marbles of the New York City area are believed by many to be the altered Cambro-Ordovicics, which, north of the Highlands, appear unmetamorphosed. Berkey, however, holds that they belong to the pre-Cambric (6), a view strongly advocated by Crosby. A similar difference of opinion exists with reference to the metamorphic rocks of New Jersey, especially those in the region about Franklin Furnace.

On the whole, it will be seen that correlation by metamorphism, while serviceable and often very reliable within certain limits, is, nevertheless, a method likely to mislead. We need but recall that the early stratigraphers classed all metamorphic rocks as Primary, and that this included the metamorphosed Palæozoic formations of western Europe, as well as the metamorphosed Mesozoic and later formations of the Alps. Or we may compare the older and newer maps of New England and of the Appalachians, where we shall find that many of the formations formerly classed as pre-Cambric are now placed into the Palæozoic. The international map of Europe also shows many areas of pre-Cambric rock, where more recent study has led the observers to place the metamorphic formations high in the geological column.

---

* In the *Chuar* group fossils of Palæozoic character have been found, which suggests that these formations form a pre-Cambric Palæozoic system if they are not actually a part of the Lower Cambric.

7. Correlation by diastrophism.

The recognition of the widespread character of hiatuses or gaps in the sedimentary series, noted in preceding sections, suggests that the causes of these breaks are of more or less universal extent. These causes are diastrophic, or deformative of the earth's crust, for every hiatus signifies a retreat of the sea, followed by a readvance, indicating, thus, a relative rise of the land-mass, which results in the emergence of large tracts, followed by a relative depression, resulting in submergence. If these movements affect individual land blocks only, the regression and transgression are chiefly confined to this block, while, at the same time, as has been shown in Chapter I, a reverse change in relative level of sea and land may be noted on the stationary blocks, this being brought about by the readjustment of the entire sea-level, necessitated by the partial displacement of it in one region. Thus, if one land block rises independently of the others, its shores will suffer a negative or retreatal movement, and its margins will emerge. As a result of this, however, there will be a partial elevation of the sea-level as a whole, due to the displaced water, and this will affect all blocks, including the emerging one. In the latter it will tend merely to reduce somewhat the total amount of sea-retreat which the elevation of the block would bring about, but in the stationary blocks there would be a universal advance of the sea over their margins. Thus retreatal movements in one continent would be correlated with transgressive movements in the other, and, since emergence is followed by erosion, and submergence by deposition, base-leveling of one continent would go on, with deposition beyond its margins, at the same time that deposition over the submerged margins of the other continents and a reduction in the erosive activities over the unsubmerged portions of those continents would occur.

If the movement affects the suboceanic crustal block, however, a universal sinking or rising of the sea-level will result, in conformity with the lowering or elevation of this block. This will be manifested in a universal retreat and readvance of the sea along all continental margins, with the production of a widespread hiatus in the succession of formations. If the interval between the two movements is a large one, with comparative stability of the land, the base-leveling processes will tend to wear the country down to a nearly uniform level, while the resultant marginal deposits will tend further to raise the sea-level, and thus set the gravitative movement going. The shrinking of the land from invading lower temperatures will likewise tend to reduce the level of the land, and so permit the sea to transgress across it anew.

If erosion is not uniform in amount, owing to variable hardness of formations, or to other causes, the resulting hiatus will vary in magnitude from point to point. For, though the time interval between the retreat and readvance of the sea in two localities might be the same, it is obvious that the missing formations will be more extensive than can be accounted for by non-deposition, since, during the interval of exposure, erosion removes a part of the earlier deposited sediments. The amount thus removed in different sections may vary greatly, and, hence, the gap in the series will vary from place to place.

Chamberlin (9:304) has considered four stages, which must be taken cognizance of in correlation by general diastrophic movements: (1) "the stages of climacteric base-leveling and sea transgression; (2) the stages of retreat, which are the first stages of diastrophic movement after the quiescent period; (3) the stages of climacteric diastrophism and of greatest sea-retreat; and, (4) the stages of early quiescence, progressive degradation, and sea-advance."

(1) The stage where base-leveling and sea transgression have successively reached their climax is especially characterized by diminution in land, a reduction in the amount of solution, oxidation and carbonation of rocks, and, hence, in the abstraction of carbon dioxide from the atmosphere, coupled with the greatest extension of lime deposition and hence the setting free of carbon dioxide. Thus there will be a tendency toward the amelioration of the climatic conditions, and this will aid the great expansional evolution of marine life favored by the broad expansion of the littoral belt and the formation of numerous epicontinental seas. New marine faunas and floras, often of a provincial type, will come into existence, which are likely to arise through parallel evolution from closely related ancestors in the various provinces. Thus a widespread basis for faunal correlation will be inaugurated, such faunas comprising not identical, but rather closely representative, species. Pathways for extensive migration along the littoral belts of the oceans also result, and these tend to produce widespread uniformity of the littoral fauna of the oceans. Such periods of extensive transgression of the sea and corresponding expansional evolution are seen in the late Cambric and early Ordovicic, in the Middle, and early Upper Ordovicic, in the early Siluric, Middle Devonic, early

Mississippic and in the Middle and early Upper Jurassic (Callovian to Oxfordian), as well as in the early part of the Cretacic.

(2) The stages of initial diastrophism and sea-retreat are marked by the increase in deposition of the material resulting from the deep decomposition of the rock, during the period of base-leveling; the increasing deposition of terrigenous clastics, and the consequent change in the character of the fauna, a turbid water fauna taking the place of the one previously flourishing in the purer waters. The littoral belt is narrowed, the epicontinental seas disappear, and the evolution of shallow-water life and the migration of organisms are restricted.

(3) When the climax of the regression is reached the restriction in the evolution of the shallow water organisms is at its maximum. Clastic deposits predominate and they even encroach upon the continents. Climatic changes are toward a colder period, owing to the locking up of the carbon dioxide in land-vegetation, by solution of limestones, and by carbonation of silicates. Such refrigeration may go so far as to result in glaciation, at least locally, the evidences of such glaciation furnishing an additional basis for correlation. Broad land expansions would in general favor wide distribution of animals and plants, unless the severity of the climate should enter in as a deterrent factor. Should climatic factors be less in evidence, however, the wide expansion of the land might favor a wide distribution of land life. As a result, the struggle for existence would be less intense and modifications would be slower, and more of the nature of adaptations to slowly changing environment. The littoral region of the sea being, however, much reduced, the survivors of the once widespread marine littoral fauna would be forced into a more restricted area and hence a fierce struggle for existence would be sure to result. This would lead to the rapid extinction of numerous types and to the comparatively rapid modification of the survivors, and would thus produce a comparatively sudden change in the character of the fauna.

(4) The early stages of quiescence and base-leveling which follow and which initiate anew the slow transgressive movement of the sea, will again favor migration of marine faunas. Owing to the effect of the previous restrictions, however, the aspect of the fauna will have been changed to a marked degree, so that the expanding fauna will have a distinct aspect of its own. The great expansion which followed the retreat of the sea in the late Middle or early Upper Cambric time in North America brought with it the spread of a fauna widely different from that which preceded it. The Middle and early Upper Ordovicic expansional faunas (Chazy-

Trenton) differed, likewise, in a marked degree from the preceding Beekmantown faunas. The Siluric fauna of North America, also an expansional fauna, differed radically from that of the preceding Upper Ordovicic (Weller–52), which was largely exterminated by the late Ordovicic or early Siluric retreat of the sea. The comparative uniformity of expansional faunas over wide areas, such as that of the Mid-Ordovicic, the early Siluric, the Mid-Devonic, and the later Jurassic and Cretacic, shows that such periods are eminently fitted to furnish a basis for practically worldwide correlation.

Finally, it may here be noted that, if the theory of polar pendulations, as outlined in Chapter XXIII, should prove to have a sound basis in fact, we must modify our conception of movements of the water body, to the extent of recognizing the coincident rising of the sea-level in the region approaching the Equator, and the fall of the sea-level in the regions approaching the poles. Thus movements of the water body would not be uniform over the earth, but compensatory, rising in the equatorial and falling in the polar regions. For an attempt at correlation on such a basis the student is referred to Simroth's book "Die Pendulations-theorie." (44.)

PALÆOGEOGRAPHY AND PALÆOGEOGRAPHIC MAPS.

"Palæogeography," says Dacqué, "may be compared to a fire which has smoldered long under cover, but which has at last broken forth with all-consuming energy" (12). Attempts to restore the outlines of continents and seas during former geological periods were essayed by geologists and palæontologists before the middle of the nineteenth century. Since then the subject has smoldered under cover of the detailed investigations carried on in other fields by the students of the earth sciences, until, in recent years, it has burst forth with almost volcanic violence, and palæogeographic maps and palæogeographic discussions have become the order of the day.

The term *Palæogeography* is credited to Robert Etheridge, and its birth is given as in the year 1881 (Schuchert–39),* but palæogeographic maps were made much earlier. Schuchert regards those given by Dana in the first edition of his manual (1863) as the earliest; but earlier maps, though less definite in character, had been published, as, for example, those by Goodwin Austen for England

*Dacqué mentions A. Boué, who in 1875 used the terms *paläogeologische Geographie* and *geologische Paläo-Geographie.* (Sitzungsberichte K. K. Akad. Wiss. Wien. Math. Nat. Kl. Bd. 71, 1te Abt., s. 305-405.)

in 1856, by B. Crivelli for Italy in 1853 and by Gemmellaro for Sicily in 1834. (Dacqué–12:*192*.) The most elaborate recent attempt to map the conditions of land and water at different geologic periods is that of Schuchert, who, in his instructive monograph on the Palæogeography of North America, has published fifty separate maps showing the changes in outlines of North America from Cambric to Pliocenic time.

TYPES OF PALÆOGEOGRAPHIC MAPS. Palæogeographic maps may be simple or complex, special or generalized. The simple map aims to show the distribution of geographic features, of a particular period in the earth's history, over the surface of the earth, much as a modern geographic map shows this distribution for the present time; a complex map, on the other hand, attempts to show more than this. The simple map need not be confined to the depiction of the hypothetical coastline, but, if the facts available allow it, should represent the ocean currents, the mountains, the rivers, etc. As examples of maps of this type, though very incomplete, especially in so far as the land features are concerned, may be mentioned the Ordovicic map by Ruedemann (38) and those for the same time-period by Grabau (18); the older Devonic maps of Schuchert, and many others. The excellent maps by De Lapparent (31) may also be classed here, though on them the areas of continental as well as marine sedimentation are shown. The complex maps may show, in addition to the deduced geographic conditions, some of the data on which this deduction is based, especially the distribution of the geological formation in question, or of its outcrops. Such a map is in reality a combination of a palæogeographic and a geologic map, and this may prove highly useful, for the degree of detail depicted upon the map, and the extent to which the map is hypothetical, are at once apparent. Such are the maps issued by Schuchert for North America. A somewhat more complicated type is represented by the Palæogeographic maps issued by Chamberlin and Salisbury (10) where the attempt is made to represent not only the outcrop, but also the parts believed to exist beneath cover, and the areas from which the formations are believed to be removed by erosion.

The most complex and detailed maps of this type published in America are those issued by Bailey Willis (57; 59). In them the attempt is made to represent the oceanic basins, the littoral and the epicontinental waters, the areas which may have been either sea or land—separating those which were more likely sea and those which were more likely land—the lands of the time, the indeterminate areas, and the ocean currents, both polar and equatorial.

Maps of this kind are more easily read when colors instead of symbols are used. Another type of complex map is that which attempts to show changes in outline of the lands and seas during the period represented. Such are the maps of Frech (13), in which transgressions and regressions of the sea are represented by differences in color. Haug, too (21), indicates the areas of transgression upon his maps, and, furthermore, outlines the limits of the geosynclines. And, in addition, his maps are facies maps.

Special maps aim to show the outlines of lands and seas at a definite time period, as at the end of the Lower, Middle or Upper Cambric (Fig. 264 a-c), or at the beginning of a time period. Such maps may be either simple or complex. Examples of the

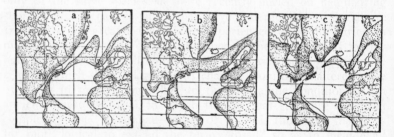

FIG. 264. Maps showing the probable distribution of land and sea around the Atlantic basin in Cambric time. *a.* At end of Lower Cambric. *b.* At end of Middle Cambric. *c.* At end of *Dictyonema flabelliforme* time. (A. W. Grabau.)

former are the maps published by Grabau (19) for the Cambric (Fig. 264), and for the various stages of the Ordovicic (18). The maps published by Schuchert, Chamberlin and Salisbury, Willis, Haug, De Lapparent, and, indeed, by most authors are general maps to cover a whole time period, though in some cases this period may be very small.

CONSTRUCTION OF PALÆOGEOGRAPHIC MAPS. In the construction of palæogeographic maps it is first of all necessary to bear in mind that modern geographic maps can at least serve only as a distorted base for such depiction. Thus the Appalachian region of North America, and the region of the Alps in southern Europe are areas where the earth's crust has been greatly foreshortened, and where, hence, localities far apart at an earlier time were brought close together. It is, of course, impossible to allow for such foreshortening, if the localities where certain formations crop out to-day are to be brought into the seas in which they were deposited. Thus, as will be seen on the maps for the Lower Cambric (Fig. 264a), the New England land barrier between the Atlantic and the Pacific extension in the Appalachian or Cumberland trough is much too narrow, while the width of that trough is also too small. The same is true for the land-barrier in North Britain, between the Atlantic and Arctic oceans. Since, however, the rocks carrying the faunas of these two seas are found so much nearer together to-day than was the case at the time of the deposition, such faulty construction seems to be unavoidable.

The overlap relations of marine strata are especially significant as aids in determining old shore-lines, for such overlap of a later over an earlier formation indicates, as a rule, that the point of overlap is also a point on the shore-line of the earlier formation. Due attention must here be given to the type of overlap (see Chapter XVIII), and the fact must be borne in mind that minor overlaps may also be developed upon an irregular sea-bottom, where wave activity or current scour is active.

Important factors that must not be overlooked in the construction of palæogeographic maps are the nature of the sediment and its source. Where coarse clastic sediments abound in the formation, a land of sufficient size must have existed to furnish this sediment. This is especially the case when the sediment consists of well-assorted material, such as quartz-sand or pebbles, when it must be remembered that such assorted material may represent only a part, perhaps less than one-fourth, of the original rock which was its source. In general, it may be said that much closer discrimination between marine and non-marine sediments than has generally been the case is necessary; and the conditions of deposition must be borne in mind, as well as the factors of marine and non-marine bionomy, and the effects of topography on currents and of both on deposition, so that we may not again fall into the error of reconstructing the area of former coral-rock formation as an arm of the sea, one-half or one-quarter of a mile in width, and less than ten fathoms in depth.

When the science of Stratigraphy has developed so that its basis is no longer purely or chiefly palæontological, and when the sciences of Lithogenesis, of Orogenesis and of Glyptogenesis, as well as of Biogenesis, are given their due share in the comprehensive investigation of the history of our earth, then we may hope that Palæogeography, the youthful daughter science of Stratigraphy, will have attained unto that stature which will make it the crowning attraction to the student of earth history.

BIBLIOGRAPHY XXXII.

1. ARLDT, TH. 1907. Die Entwicklung der Kontinente und ihrer Lebe-
    welt. Ein Beitrag zur Vergleichenden Erdgeschichte. Leipzig.
2. ARLDT, TH. 1909. Palæogeographie und Seismologie. Hettners geog-
    raphische Zeitschrift. Jahrgang 15, pp. 674–684.
3. ARLDT, TH. 1910. Methoden und Bedeutung der Palæogeographie.
    Petermanns geographische Mittheilungen, II, pp. 229–233.
4. ARLDT, TH. 1912. Palæogeographische Fragen. Geologische Rund-
    schau, Bd. III, Heft 2, pp. 93–141 (with map).
5. BASSLER, RAY S. 1911. The Early Palæozoic Bryozoa of the Baltic
    Provinces. United States National Museum, Bulletin 77.
6. BERKEY, CHARLES P. 1907. Structural and Stratigraphic Features
    of the Basal Gneisses of the Highlands. New York State Museum, Bulle-
    tin 107, pp. 361–378.
7. CAMPBELL, M. R. 1903. Variation and Equivalency of the Charleston
    Sandstone. Journal of Geology, Vol. XI, pp. 459–468.
8. CANU, F. 1895. Essai de Paléogéographie. Restauration des contours
    des mers anciennes en France et dans les pays voisins. Paris. Text
    and atlas.
9. CHAMBERLIN, THOMAS. 1910. Diastrophism as the Ultimate
    Basis of Correlation; in Outlines of Geological History, etc., by Willis and
    Salisbury, Chapter XVI, pp. 298–306.
10. CHAMBERLIN, THOMAS, and SALISBURY, ROLLIN D. 1906.
    Geology. Vols. II and III. Henry Holt & Co.
11. CLARKE, JOHN M. 1904. Nomenclature of the New York Series of
    Geologic Formations. Proceedings Eighth Annual Conference of New
    York State Science Teachers' Association. High School Bulletin 25, pp.
    495–506.
12. DACQUÉ, E. 1913. Paläogeographische Karten und die gegen sie zu
    erhebenden Einwände. Geologische Rundschau, Bd. IV, Heft 3, pp.
    186–206.
13. FRECH, FRITZ. 1897–1902. Lethæa Palæozoica. Stuttgart.
14. GEIKIE, ARCHIBALD. 1893. Text-book of Geology. 3rd edition.
    4th edition, 1903. Macmillan and Co.
15. GRABAU, A. W. 1904. The Phylogeny of Fusus and Its Allies. Smith-
    sonian Micellaneous Collections, Vol. XLIV, pp. 1–157, 18 pls., 22 figs.
16. GRABAU, A. W. 1906. Types of Sedimentary Overlap. Bulletin of the
    Geological Society of America, Vol. XVII, pp. 567–636.
17. GRABAU, A. W. 1909. A Revised Classification of the North American
    Lower Palæozoic. Science, N. S., Vol. XXIX, pp. 351–356.
18. GRABAU, A. W. 1909. Physical and Faunal Evolution of North
    America during Ordovicic, Siluric, and Early Devonic Time. Journal of
    Geology, Vol. XVII, No. 3, pp. 209–252.
19. GRABAU, A. W. 1910. Ueber die Einteilung des nord amerikanischen
    Silurs. Compte Rendu du XI: Congrès Géologique International, pp.
    979–995.
20. GRABAU, A. W. 1913. Ancient Delta Deposits. Bulletin of the Geo-
    logical Society of America, Vol. XXIV, pp. 399–528.
20a. GRABAU, A. W., and SHERZER, W. H. 1910. The Monroe Forma-
    tion, etc. Geological and Biological Survey of Michigan. Publication 2.
21. HAUG, ÉMILE, 1908–1911. Traité de Géologie, I, II, Les Périodes
    Géologiques, Paris, Armand Colin.

2. HULL. 1882. Palæo-geological and geographical maps of the British Islands. Scientific Transactions of the Royal Society of Dublin, Vol. I.

3. HYATT, ALPHEUS. 1903. Pseudoceratites of the Cretaceous. United States Geological Survey, Monograph XLIV.

4. IHERING, H. Von. 1908. Archhelenis and Archinotis. Gesammelte Beiträge zur Geschichte der neotropischen Region. Leipzig.

5. IHERING, H. Von. 1908. Die Umwandlung des amerikanischen Kontinentes während der Tertiärzeit. Neues Jahrbuch für Mineralogie, u. s. w. Beilage Band 32, pp. 134–176.

6. KARPINSKY, A. 1895. Palæogeographic Maps. (Russian title and text.) Bulletin de l'Académie Impériale de Sciences. St. Petersbourg. 5 me sér. T. I, pp. 1–19.

7. KNOWLTON, F. H. 1910. Biologic Principles of Paleogeography. The Paleontologic Record, pp. 21–23. Reprinted from Popular Science Monthly.

8. KOKEN, E. 1893. Die Vorwelt und ihre Entwicklungsgeschichte. Leipzig.

9. KOKEN, E. 1907. Indisches Perm und permische Eiszeit. Neues Jahrbuch für Mineralogie, u. s. w. Fest Band, pp. 446–546. Map.

10. KOSSMAT, F. 1908. Paläogeographie. Geologische Geschichte der Meere und Festländer. Leipzig.

11. LAPPARENT, A. DE. 1906. Traité de Géologie. First edition, Paris, 1885. Third edition, 1893. Fourth edition, 1900. Fifth edition, 1906.

12. LULL, RICHARD S. 1904. Fossil Footprints of the Jura Trias of North America. Boston Society of Natural History, Memoirs, Vol. V, pp. 461–557, 1 pl., 34 figs.

13. NEUMAYR, MELCHIOR. 1883. Ueber klimatische Zonen während der Jura—und Kreidezeit. Denkschrift der mathematisch-naturwissenschaftliche Klasse der königlich-kaiserlichen Akademie der Wissenschaften. Wien. Band XLVII, pp. 227–310.

14. ORTMANN, ARNOLD E. 1896. An Examination of the Arguments Given by Neumayr for the Existence of Climatic Zones in Jurassic Times. American Journal of Science, 4th series, Vol. I, pp. 257 et seq.

15. ORTMANN, A. E. 1902. Tertiary Invertebrates. Report of the Princeton University Expedition to Patagonia, Vol. IV, 1896–1899.

16. ORTMANN, A. E. 1902. The Geographical Distribution of Freshwater Decapods and Its Bearing upon Ancient Geography. Proceedings of the American Philosophical Society, Vol. XLI, pp. 250 et seq.

17. OSBORN, HENRY F. 1910. The Age of Mammals in Europe, Asia, and North America. New York.

18. RUEDEMANN, RUDOLF. 1904. The Graptolites of New York. Part I. New York State Museum, Memoir 7.

19. SCHUCHERT, CHARLES. 1910. Paleogeography of North America. Bulletin of the Geological Society of America, Vol. XX, pp. 427–606, pls. 46–101.

40. SCHUCHERT, C. 1910. Biologic Principles of Paleogeography. The Paleontologic Record, pp. 11–20. Reprinted from Popular Science Monthly.

41. SEMPER, M. 1896. Das paläothermale Problem, speziell die klimatischen Verhältnisse des Eocäns in Europa und im Polargebiet. Inaugural Dissertation, Munich.

42. SEMPER, M. 1908. Die Grundlagen paläogeographischer Unter suchungen. Centralblatt für Mineralogie, usw. Bd. IX, pp. 434–445.

43. SHIMER, HERVEY W., and GRABAU, A. W. 1902. Hamilton Group of Thedford, Ontario. Bulletin of the Geological Society of America, Vol. XIII, pp. 149–186.

44. SIMROTH, HEINRICH. 1907. Die Pendulations-Theorie. Leipzig.

45. SMITH, JAMES PERRIN. 1900. Principles of Paleontologic Correla-tion. Journal of Geology, Vol. VIII, pp. 673–697.

46. TORNQUIST, A. Oxford Fauna von Metam.

47. TOULA, F. 1908. Das Wandern und Schwanken der Meere. Vorträge des Vereins zur Verbeitung der naturwissenschaftlichen Kenntnisse in Wien. Jahrgang 48, Heft 11.

48. UHLIG, V. 1911. Die marinen Reiche des Jura und der Unterkreide. Mittheilungen der geologischen Gesellschaft, Bd. III, pp. 329 *et seq.*

49. ULRICH, EDWARD O. 1911. Revision of the Paleozoic Systems. Bulletin of the Geological Society of America, Vol. XXII, No. 3, pp. 281–680, 5 pls.

50. ULRICH, E. O., and SCHUCHERT, CHARLES. 1901. Paleozoic Seas and Barriers in Eastern North America. Report of the State Paleontolo-gist of New York State Museum, pp. 633–663.

51. UNITED STATES GEOLOGICAL SURVEY. 1903. Nomenclature and Classification for the Geologic Atlas of the United States. Twenty-fourth Annual Report.

52a. WALTHER, JOHANNES. 1908. Geschichte der Erde und des Lebens.

52. WELLER, STUART. 1898. The Silurian Fauna Interpreted on the Epicontinental Basis. Journal of Geology, Vol. VI, pp. 692–703.

53. WELLER, S. 1906–1909. Kinderhook Faunal Studies. IV. The Fauna of the Glen Park Limestone. St. Louis Academy of Science Transactions, Vol. XVI, No. 7, pp. 435–471, 2 pls. V. The Fauna of the Fern Glen Formation. Geological Society of America Bulletin, Vol. XX, pp. 265–332, 6 pls.

54. WELLER, S. 1907. The pre-Richmond Unconformity in the Mississippi Valley. Journal of Geology, Vol. XV, No. 6, pp. 519–525, 1 fig.

55. WHITE, D. 1907. Permocarboniferous Climatic Changes in South America. Journal of Geology, Vol. XV, pp. 619 *et seq.*

56. WILLIAMS, HENRY SHALER. 1904. Bearing of Some New Palæonto-logic Facts on Nomenclature and Classification of Sedimentary Forma-tions. Bulletin of the Geological Society of America, Vol. XVI, pp. 137–150.

57. WILLIS, BAILEY. 1909. Paleogeographic Maps of North America. Journal of Geology, Vol. XVII, pp. 203–600.

58. WILLIS, B. 1910. Principles of Paleogeography. Science, N. S., Vol. XXXI, No. 790, Feb. 18, 1910, pp. 246–249.

59. WILLIS, B., and SALISBURY, ROLLIN D. 1910. Outlines of Geologic History with Especial Reference to North America. The University of Chicago Press, Chicago.

INDEX

(This comprehensive index covers the two volumes of the book. Volume One contains pages 1 through 581 and Volume Two contains pages 582 through 1150.)

(Consult also the table of contents. Names of genera and species are, with few exceptions, omitted.)

A

CATALOG OF DOVER BOOKS

Relativity, quantum theory, nuclear physics

THE PRINCIPLE OF RELATIVITY, A. Einstein, H. Lorentz, M. Minkowski, H. Weyl. These are the 11 basic papers that founded the general and special theories of relativity, all translated into English. Two papers by Lorentz on the Michelson experiment, electromagnetic phenomena. Minkowski's SPACE & TIME, and Weyl's GRAVITATION & ELECTRICITY. 7 epochmaking papers by Einstein: ELECTROMAGNETICS OF MOVING BODIES, INFLUENCE OF GRAVITATION IN PROPAGATION OF LIGHT, COSMOLOGICAL CONSIDERATIONS, GENERAL THEORY, and 3 others. 7 diagrams. Special notes by A. Sommerfeld. 224pp. 5⅜ x 8.
S81 Paperbound **$1.75**

SPACE TIME MATTER, Hermann Weyl. "The standard treatise on the general theory of relativity," (Nature), written by a world-renowned scientist, provides a deep clear discussion of the logical coherence of the general theory, with introduction to all the mathematical tools needed: Maxwell, analytical geometry, non-Euclidean geometry, tensor calculus, etc. Basis is classical space-time, before absorption of relativity. Partial contents: Euclidean space, mathematical form, metrical continuum, relativity of time and space, general theory. 15 diagrams. Bibliography. New preface for this edition. xviii + 330pp. 5⅜ x 8.
S267 Paperbound **$1.85**

PRINCIPLES OF QUANTUM MECHANICS, W. V. Houston. Enables student with working knowledge of elementary mathematical physics to develop facility in use of quantum mechanics, understand published work in field. Formulates quantum mechanics in terms of Schroedinger's wave mechanics. Studies evidence for quantum theory, for inadequacy of classical mechanics, 2 postulates of quantum mechanics; numerous important, fruitful applications of quantum mechanics in spectroscopy, collision problems, electrons in solids; other topics. "One of the most rewarding features . . . is the interlacing of problems with text," Amer. J. of Physics. Corrected edition. 21 illus. Index. 296pp. 5⅜ x 8.
S524 Paperbound **$1.85**

PHYSICAL PRINCIPLES OF THE QUANTUM THEORY, Werner Heisenberg. A Nobel laureate discusses quantum theory; Heisenberg's own work, Compton, Schroedinger, Wilson, Einstein, many others. Written for physicists, chemists who are not specialists in quantum theory, only elementary formulae are considered in the text; there is a mathematical appendix for specialists. Profound without sacrifice of clarity. Translated by C. Eckart, F. Hoyt. 18 figures. 192pp. 5⅜ x 8.
S113 Paperbound **$1.25**

SELECTED PAPERS ON QUANTUM ELECTRODYNAMICS, edited by J. Schwinger. Facsimiles of papers which established quantum electrodynamics, from initial successes through today's position as part of the larger theory of elementary particles. First book publication in any language of these collected papers of Bethe, Bloch, Dirac, Dyson, Fermi, Feynman, Heisenberg, Kusch, Lamb, Oppenheimer, Pauli, Schwinger, Tomonoga, Weisskopf, Wigner, etc. 34 papers in all, 29 in English, 1 in French, 3 in German, 1 in Italian. Preface and historical commentary by the editor. xvii + 423pp. 6⅛ x 9¼.
S444 Paperbound **$2.45**

THE FUNDAMENTAL PRINCIPLES OF QUANTUM MECHANICS, WITH ELEMENTARY APPLICATIONS, E. C. Kemble. An inductive presentation, for the graduate student or specialist in some other branch of physics. Assumes some acquaintance with advanced math; apparatus necessary beyond differential equations and advanced calculus is developed as needed. Although a general exposition of principles, hundreds of individual problems are fully treated, with applications of theory being interwoven with development of the mathematical structure. The author is the Professor of Physics at Harvard Univ. "This excellent book would be of great value to every student . . . a rigorous and detailed mathematical discussion of all of the principal quantum-mechanical methods . . . has succeeded in keeping his presentations clear and understandable," Dr. Linus Pauling, J. of the American Chemical Society. Appendices: calculus of variations, math. notes, etc. Indexes. 611pp. 5⅜ x 8.
S472 Paperbound **$2.95**

ATOMIC SPECTRA AND ATOMIC STRUCTURE, G. Herzberg. Excellent general survey for chemists, physicists specializing in other fields. Partial contents: simplest line spectra and elements of atomic theory, building-up principle and periodic system of elements, hyperfine structure of spectral lines, some experiments and applications. Bibilography. 80 figures. Index. xii + 257pp. 5⅜ x 8.
S115 Paperbound **$1.95**

THE THEORY AND THE PROPERTIES OF METALS AND ALLOYS, N. F. Mott, H. Jones. Quantum methods used to develop mathematical models which show interrelationship of basic chemical phenomena with crystal structure, magnetic susceptibility, electrical, optical properties. Examines thermal properties of crystal lattice, electron motion in applied field, cohesion, electrical resistance, noble metals, para-, dia-, and ferromagnetism, etc. "Exposition . . . clear . . . mathematical treatment . . . simple," Nature. 138 figures. Bibliography. Index. xiii + 320pp. 5⅜ x 8.
S456 Paperbound **$1.85**

FOUNDATIONS OF NUCLEAR PHYSICS, edited by R. T. Beyer. 13 of the most important papers on nuclear physics reproduced in facsimile in the original languages of their authors: the papers most often cited in footnotes, bibliographies. Anderson, Curie, Joliot, Chadwick, Fermi, Lawrence, Cockcroft, Hahn, Yukawa. UNPARALLELED BIBLIOGRAPHY. 122 double-columned pages, over 4,000 articles, books classified. 57 figures. 288pp. 6⅛ x 9¼.
S19 Paperbound **$1.75**

MESON PHYSICS, R. E. Marshak. Traces the basic theory, and explicitly presents results of experiments with particular emphasis on theoretical significance. Phenomena involving mesons as virtual transitions are avoided, eliminating some of the least satisfactory predictions of meson theory. Includes production and study of π mesons at nonrelativistic nucleon energies, contrasts between π and μ mesons, phenomena associated with nuclear interaction of π mesons, etc. Presents early evidence for new classes of particles and indicates theoretical difficulties created by discovery of heavy mesons and hyperons. Name and subject indices. Unabridged reprint. viii + 378pp. 5⅜ x 8. S500 Paperbound **$1.95**

See also: **STRANGE STORY OF THE QUANTUM, B.** Hoffmann; **FROM EUCLID TO EDDINGTON, E.** Whittaker; **MATTER AND LIGHT, THE NEW PHYSICS, L.** de Broglie; **THE EVOLUTION OF SCIENTIFIC THOUGHT FROM NEWTON TO EINSTEIN, A.** d'Abro; **THE RISE OF THE NEW PHYSICS, A.** d'Abro; **THE THEORY OF GROUPS AND QUANTUM MECHANICS, H.** Weyl; **SUBSTANCE AND FUNCTION, & EINSTEIN'S THEORY OF RELATIVITY, E.** Cassirer; **FUNDAMENTAL FORMULAS OF PHYSICS, D. H.** Menzel.

Hydrodynamics

HYDRODYNAMICS, H. Dryden, F. Murnaghan, Harry Bateman. Published by the National Research Council in 1932 this enormous volume offers a complete coverage of classical hydrodynamics. Encyclopedic in quality. Partial contents: physics of fluids, motion, turbulent flow, compressible fluids, motion in 1, 2, 3 dimensions; viscous fluids rotating, laminar motion, resistance of motion through viscous fluid, eddy viscosity, hydraulic flow in channels of various shapes, discharge of gases, flow past obstacles, etc. Bibliography of over 2,900 items. Indexes. 23 figures. 634pp. 5⅜ x 8. S303 Paperbound **$2.75**

A TREATISE ON HYDRODYNAMICS, A. B. Basset. Favorite text on hydrodynamics for 2 generations of physicists, hydrodynamical engineers, oceanographers, ship designers, etc. Clear enough for the beginning student, and thorough source for graduate students and engineers on the work of d'Alembert, Euler, Laplace, Lagrange, Poisson, Green, Clebsch, Stokes, Cauchy, Helmholtz, J. J. Thomson, Love, Hicks, Greenhill, Besant, Lamb, etc. Great amount of documentation on entire theory of classical hydrodynamics. Vol I: theory of motion of frictionless liquids, vortex, and cyclic irrotational motion, etc. 132 exercises. Bibliography. 3 Appendixes. xii + 264pp. Vol II: motion in viscous liquids, harmonic analysis, theory of tides, etc. 112 exercises. Bibliography. 4 Appendixes. xv + 328pp. Two volume set. 5⅜ x 8.

S724 Vol I Paperbound **$1.75**
S725 Vol II Paperbound **$1.75**
The set **$3.50**

HYDRODYNAMICS, Horace Lamb. Internationally famous complete coverage of standard reference work on dynamics of liquids & gases. Fundamental theorems, equations, methods, solutions, background, for classical hydrodynamics. Chapters include Equations of Motion, Integration of Equations in Special Gases, Irrotational Motion, Motion of Liquid in 2 Dimensions, Motion of Solids through Liquid-Dynamical Theory, Vortex Motion, Tidal Waves, Surface Waves, Waves of Expansion, Viscosity, Rotating Masses of liquids. Excellently planned, arranged; clear, lucid presentation. 6th enlarged, revised edition. Index. Over 900 footnotes, mostly bibliographical. 119 figures. xv + 738pp. 6⅛ x 9¼. S256 Paperbound **$2.95**

See also: **FUNDAMENTAL FORMULAS OF PHYSICS, D. H.** Menzel; **THEORY OF FLIGHT, R.** von Mises; **FUNDAMENTALS OF HYDRO- AND AEROMECHANICS, L.** Prandtl and O. G. Tietjens; **APPLIED HYDRO- AND AEROMECHANICS, L.** Prandtl and O. G. Tietjens; **HYDRAULICS AND ITS APPLICATIONS, A. H.** Gibson; **FLUID MECHANICS FOR HYDRAULIC ENGINEERS, H.** Rouse.

Acoustics, optics, electromagnetics

ON THE SENSATIONS OF TONE, Hermann Helmholtz. This is an unmatched coordination of such fields as acoustical physics, physiology, experiment, history of music. It covers the entire gamut of musical tone. Partial contents: relation of musical science to acoustics, physical vs. physiological acoustics, composition of vibration, resonance, analysis of tones by sympathetic resonance, beats, chords, tonality, consonant chords, discords, progression of parts, etc. 33 appendixes discuss various aspects of sound, physics, acoustics, music, etc. Translated by A. J. Ellis. New introduction by Prof. Henry Margenau of Yale. 68 figures. 43 musical passages analyzed. Over 100 tables. Index. xix + 576pp. 6⅛ x 9¼.

S114 Paperbound **$2.95**

A TREATISE ON DYNAMICS OF A PARTICLE, E. J. Routh. Elementary text on dynamics for beginning mathematics or physics student. Unusually detailed treatment from elementary definitions to motion in 3 dimensions, emphasizing concrete aspects. Much unique material important in recent applications. Covers impulsive forces, rectilinear and constrained motion in 2 dimensions, harmonic and parabolic motion, degrees of freedom, closed orbits, the conical pendulum, the principle of least action, Jacobi's method, and much more. Index. 559 problems, many fully worked out, incorporated into text. xiii + 418pp. 5⅜ x 8.

S696 Paperbound **$2.25**

DYNAMICS OF A SYSTEM OF RIGID BODIES (Elementary Section), E. J. Routh. Revised 7th edition of this standard reference. This volume covers the dynamical principles of the subject, and its more elementary applications: finding moments of inertia by integration, foci of inertia, d'Alembert's principle, impulsive forces, motion in 2 and 3 dimensions, Lagrange's equations, relative indicatrix, Euler's theorem, large tautochronous motions, etc. Index. 55 figures. Scores of problems. xv + 443pp. 5⅜ x 8.

S664 Paperbound **$2.35**

DYNAMICS OF A SYSTEM OF RIGID BODIES (Advanced Section), E. J. Routh. Revised 6th edition of a classic reference aid. Much of its material remains unique. Partial contents: moving axes, relative motion, oscillations about equilibrium, motion. Motion of a body under no forces, any forces. Nature of motion given by linear equations and conditions of stability. Free, forced vibrations, constants of integration, calculus of finite differences, variations, precession and nutation, motion of the moon, motion of string, chain, membranes. 64 figures. 498pp. 5⅜ x 8.

S229 Paperbound **$2.35**

DYNAMICAL THEORY OF GASES, James Jeans. Divided into mathematical and physical chapters for the convenience of those not expert in mathematics, this volume discusses the mathematical theory of gas in a steady state, thermodynamics, Boltzmann and Maxwell, kinetic theory, quantum theory, exponentials, etc. 4th enlarged edition, with new material on quantum theory, quantum dynamics, etc. Indexes. 28 figures. 444pp. 6⅛ x 9¼.

S136 Paperbound **$2.45**

FOUNDATIONS OF POTENTIAL THEORY, O. D. Kellogg. Based on courses given at Harvard this is suitable for both advanced and beginning mathematicians. Proofs are rigorous, and much material not generally avialable elsewhere is included. Partial contents: forces of gravity, fields of force, divergence theorem, properties of Newtonian potentials at points of free space, potentials as solutions of Laplace's equations, harmonic functions, electrostatics, electric images, logarithmic potential, etc. One of Grundlehren Series. ix + 384pp. 5⅜ x 8.

S144 Paperbound **$1.98**

THERMODYNAMICS, Enrico Fermi. Unabridged reproduction of 1937 edition. Elementary in treatment; remarkable for clarity, organization. Requires no knowledge of advanced math beyond calculus, only familiarity with fundamentals of thermometry, calorimetry. Partial Contents: Thermodynamic systems; First & Second laws of thermodynamics; Entropy; Thermodynamic potentials: phase rule, reversible electric cell; Gaseous reactions: van't Hoff reaction box, principle of LeChatelier; Thermodynamics of dilute solutions: osmotic & vapor pressures, boiling & freezing points; Entropy constant. Index. 25 problems. 24 illustrations. x + 160pp. 5⅜ x 8.

S361 Paperbound **$1.75**

THE THERMODYNAMICS OF ELECTRICAL PHENOMENA IN METALS and A CONDENSED COLLECTION OF THERMODYNAMIC FORMULAS, P. W. Bridgman. Major work by the Nobel Prizewinner: stimulating conceptual introduction to aspects of the electron theory of metals, giving an intuitive understanding of fundamental relationships concealed by the formal systems of Onsager and others. Elementary mathematical formulations show clearly the fundamental thermodynamical relationships of the electric field, and a complete phenomenological theory of metals is created. This is the work in which Bridgman announced his famous "thermomotive force" and his distinction between "driving" and "working" electromotive force. We have added in this Dover edition the author's long unavailable tables of thermodynamic formulas, extremely valuable for the speed of reference they allow. Two works bound as one. Index. 33 figures. Bibliography. xviii + 256pp. 5⅜ x 8. S723 Paperbound **$1.65**

REFLECTIONS ON THE MOTIVE POWER OF FIRE, by Sadi Carnot, and other papers on the 2nd law of thermodynamics by E. Clapeyron and R. Clausius. Carnot's "Reflections" laid the groundwork of modern thermodynamics. Its non-technical, mostly verbal statements examine the relations between heat and the work done by heat in engines, establishing conditions for the economical working of these engines. The papers by Clapeyron and Clausius here reprinted added further refinements to Carnot's work, and led to its final acceptance by physicists. Selections from posthumous manuscripts of Carnot are also included. All papers in English. New introduction by E. Mendoza. 12 illustrations. xxii + 152pp. 5⅜ x 8.

S661 Paperbound **$1.50**

TREATISE ON THERMODYNAMICS, Max Planck. Based on Planck's original papers this offers a uniform point of view for the entire field and has been used as an introduction for students who have studied elementary chemistry, physics, and calculus. Rejecting the earlier approaches of Helmholtz and Maxwell, the author makes no assumptions regarding the nature of heat, but begins with a few empirical facts, and from these deduces new physical and chemical laws. 3rd English edition of this standard text by a Nobel laureate. xvi + 297pp. 5⅜ x 8.

S219 Paperbound **$1.75**

OPTICKS, Sir Isaac Newton. In its discussions of light, reflection, color, refraction, theories of wave and corpuscular theories of light, this work is packed with scores of insights and discoveries. In its precise and practical discussion of construction of optical apparatus, contemporary understandings of phenomena it is truly fascinating to modern physicists, astronomers, mathematicians. Foreword by Albert Einstein. Preface by I. B. Cohen of Harvard University. 7 pages of portraits, facsimile pages, letters, etc. cxvi + 414pp. 5⅜ x 8.
S205 Paperbound **$2.00**

OPTICS AND OPTICAL INSTRUMENTS: AN INTRODUCTION WITH SPECIAL REFERENCE TO PRACTICAL APPLICATIONS, B. K. Johnson. An invaluable guide to basic practical applications of optical principles, which shows how to set up inexpensive working models of each of the four main types of optical instruments—telescopes, microscopes, photographic lenses, optical projecting systems. Explains in detail the most important experiments for determining their accuracy, resolving power, angular field of view, amounts of aberration, all other necessary facts about the instruments. Formerly "Practical Optics." Index. 234 diagrams. Appendix. 224pp. 5⅜ x 8.
S642 Paperbound **$1.65**

PRINCIPLES OF PHYSICAL OPTICS, Ernst Mach. This classical examination of the propagation of light, color, polarization, etc. offers an historical and philosophical treatment that has never been surpassed for breadth and easy readability. Contents: Rectilinear propagation of light. Reflection, refraction. Early knowledge of vision. Dioptrics. Composition of light. Theory of color and dispersion. Periodicity. Theory of interference. Polarization. Mathematical representation of properties of light. Propagation of waves, etc. 279 illustrations, 10 portraits. Appendix. Indexes. 324pp. 5⅜ x 8.
S178 Paperbound **$1.75**

FUNDAMENTALS OF ELECTRICITY AND MAGNETISM, L. B. Loeb. For students of physics, chemistry, or engineering who want an introduction to electricity and magnetism on a higher level and in more detail than general elementary physics texts provide. Only elementary differential and integral calculus is assumed. Physical laws developed logically, from magnetism to electric currents, Ohm's law, electrolysis, and on to static electricity, induction, etc. Covers an unusual amount of material; one third of book on modern material: solution of wave equation, photoelectric and thermionic effects, etc. Complete statement of the various electrical systems of units and interrelations. 2 Indexes. 75 pages of problems with answers stated. Over 300 figures and diagrams. xix +669pp. 5⅜ x 8.
S745 Paperbound **$2.75**

THE ELECTROMAGNETIC FIELD, Max Mason & Warren Weaver. Used constantly by graduate engineers. Vector methods exclusively: detailed treatment of electrostatics, expansion methods, with tables converting any quantity into absolute electromagnetic, absolute electrostatic, practical units. Discrete charges, ponderable bodies, Maxwell field equations, etc. Introduction. Indexes. 416pp. 5⅜ x 8.
S185 Paperbound **$2.00**

ELECTRICAL THEORY ON THE GIORGI SYSTEM, P. Cornelius. A new clarification of the fundamental concepts of electricity and magnetism, advocating the convenient m.k.s. system of units that is steadily gaining followers in the sciences. Illustrating the use and effectiveness of his terminology with numerous applications to concrete technical problems, the author here expounds the famous Giorgi system of electrical physics. His lucid presentation and well-reasoned, cogent argument for the universal adoption of this system form one of the finest pieces of scientific exposition in recent years. 28 figures. Index. Conversion tables for translating earlier data into modern units. Translated from 3rd Dutch edition by L. J. Jolley. x + 187pp. 5½ x 8¾.
S909 Clothbound **$6.00**

THEORY OF ELECTRONS AND ITS APPLICATION TO THE PHENOMENA OF LIGHT AND RADIANT HEAT, H. Lorentz. Lectures delivered at Columbia University by Nobel laureate Lorentz. Unabridged, they form a historical coverage of the theory of free electrons, motion, absorption of heat, Zeeman effect, propagation of light in molecular bodies, inverse Zeeman effect, optical phenomena in moving bodies, etc. 109 pages of notes explain the more advanced sections. Index. 9 figures. 352pp. 5⅜ x 8.
S173 Paperbound **$1.85**

TREATISE ON ELECTRICITY AND MAGNETISM, James Clerk Maxwell. For more than 80 years a seemingly inexhaustible source of leads for physicists, mathematicians, engineers. Total of 1082pp. on such topics as Measurement of Quantities, Electrostatics, Elementary Mathematical Theory of Electricity, Electrical Work and Energy in a System of Conductors, General Theorems, Theory of Electrical Images, Electrolysis, Conduction, Polarization, Dielectrics, Resistance, etc. "The greatest mathematical physicist since Newton," Sir James Jeans. 3rd edition. 107 figures, 21 plates. 1082pp. 5⅜ x 8.
S636-7, 2 volume set, paperbound **$4.00**

See also: **FUNDAMENTAL FORMULAS OF PHYSICS**, D. H. Menzel; **MATHEMATICAL ANALYSIS OF ELECTRICAL & OPTICAL WAVE MOTION,** H. Bateman.

Mechanics, dynamics, thermodynamics, elasticity

MECHANICS VIA THE CALCULUS, P. W. Norris, W. S. Legge. Covers almost everything, from linear motion to vector analysis: equations determining motion, linear methods, compounding of simple harmonic motions, Newton's laws of motion, Hooke's law, the simple pendulum, motion of a particle in 1 plane, centers of gravity, virtual work, friction, kinetic energy of rotating bodies, equilibrium of strings, hydrostatics, sheering stresses, elasticity, etc. 550 problems. 3rd revised edition. xii + 367pp. 6 x 9.
S207 Clothbound **$3.95**

MECHANICS, J. P. Den Hartog. Already a classic among introductory texts, the M.I.T. professor's lively and discursive presentation is equally valuable as a beginner's text, an engineering student's refresher, or a practicing engineer's reference. Emphasis in this highly readable text is on illuminating fundamental principles and showing how they are embodied in a great number of real engineering and design problems: trusses, loaded cables, beams, jacks, hoists, etc. Provides advanced material on relative motion and gyroscopes not usual in introductory texts. "Very thoroughly recommended to all those anxious to improve their real understanding of the principles of mechanics." MECHANICAL WORLD. Index. List of equations. 334 problems, all with answers. Over 550 diagrams and drawings. ix + 462pp. 5⅜ x 8.
S754 Paperbound **$2.00**

THEORETICAL MECHANICS: AN INTRODUCTION TO MATHEMATICAL PHYSICS, J. S. Ames, F. D. Murnaghan. A mathematically rigorous development of theoretical mechanics for the advanced student, with constant practical applications. Used in hundreds of advanced courses. An unusually thorough coverage of gyroscopic and baryscopic material, detailed analyses of the Corilis acceleration, applications of Lagrange's equations, motion of the double pendulum, Hamilton-Jacobi partial differential equations, group velocity and dispersion, etc. Special relativity is also included. 159 problems. 44 figures. ix + 462pp. 5⅜ x 8.
S461 Paperbound **$2.00**

THEORETICAL MECHANICS: STATICS AND THE DYNAMICS OF A PARTICLE, W. D. MacMillan. Used for over 3 decades as a self-contained and extremely comprehensive advanced undergraduate text in mathematical physics, physics, astronomy, and deeper foundations of engineering. Early sections require only a knowledge of geometry; later, a working knowledge of calculus. Hundreds of basic problems, including projectiles to the moon, escape velocity, harmonic motion, ballistics, falling bodies, transmission of power, stress and strain, elasticity, astronomical problems. 340 practice problems plus many fully worked out examples make it possible to test and extend principles developed in the text. 200 figures. xvii + 430pp. 5⅜ x 8.
S467 Paperbound **$2.00**

THEORETICAL MECHANICS: THE THEORY OF THE POTENTIAL, W. D. MacMillan. A comprehensive, well balanced presentation of potential theory, serving both as an introduction and a reference work with regard to specific problems, for physicists and mathematicians. No prior knowledge of integral relations is assumed, and all mathematical material is developed as it becomes necessary. Includes: Attraction of Finite Bodies; Newtonian Potential Function; Vector Fields, Green and Gauss Theorems; Attractions of Surfaces and Lines; Surface Distribution of Matter; Two-Layer Surfaces; Spherical Harmonics; Ellipsoidal Harmonics; etc. "The great number of particular cases . . . should make the book valuable to geophysicists and others actively engaged in practical applications of the potential theory," Review of Scientific Instruments. Index. Bibliography. xiii + 469pp. 5⅜ x 8.
S486 Paperbound **$2.25**

THEORETICAL MECHANICS: DYNAMICS OF RIGID BODIES, W. D. MacMillan. Theory of dynamics of a rigid body is developed, using both the geometrical and analytical methods of instruction. Begins with exposition of algebra of vectors, it goes through momentum principles, motion in space, use of differential equations and infinite series to solve more sophisticated dynamics problems. Partial contents: moments of inertia, systems of free particles, motion parallel to a fixed plane, rolling motion, method of periodic solutions, much more. 82 figs. 199 problems. Bibliography. Indexes. xii + 476pp. 5⅜ x 8.
S641 Paperbound **$2.00**

MATHEMATICAL FOUNDATIONS OF STATISTICAL MECHANICS, A. I. Khinchin. Offering a precise and rigorous formulation of problems, this book supplies a thorough and up-to-date exposition. It provides analytical tools needed to replace cumbersome concepts, and furnishes for the first time a logical step-by-step introduction to the subject. Partial contents: geometry & kinematics of the phase space, ergodic problem, reduction to theory of probability, application of central limit problem, ideal monatomic gas, foundation of thermo-dynamics, dispersion and distribution of sum functions. Key to notations. Index. viii + 179pp. 5⅜ x 8.
S147 Paperbound **$1.35**

ELEMENTARY PRINCIPLES IN STATISTICAL MECHANICS, J. W. Gibbs. Last work of the great Yale mathematical physicist, still one of the most fundamental treatments available for advanced students and workers in the field. Covers the basic principle of conservation of probability of phase, theory of errors in the calculated phases of a system, the contributions of Clausius, Maxwell, Boltzmann, and Gibbs himself, and much more. Includes valuable comparison of statistical mechanics with thermodynamics: Carnot's cycle, mechanical definitions of entropy, etc. xvi + 208pp. 5⅜ x 8.
S707 Paperbound **$1.45**

THE DYNAMICS OF PARTICLES AND OF RIGID, ELASTIC, AND FLUID BODIES; BEING LECTURES ON MATHEMATICAL PHYSICS, A. G. Webster. The reissuing of this classic fills the need for a comprehensive work on dynamics. A wide range of topics is covered in unusually great depth, applying ordinary and partial differential equations. Part 1 considers laws of motion and methods applicable to systems of all sorts; oscillation, resonance, cyclic systems, etc. Part 2 is a detailed study of the dynamics of rigid bodies. Part 3 introduces the theory of potential; stress and strain, Newtonian potential functions, gyrostatics, wave and vortex motion, etc. Further contents: Kinematics of a point; Lagrange's equations; Hamilton's principle; Systems of vectors; Statics and dynamics of deformable bodies; much more, not easily found together in one volume. Unabridged reprinting of 2nd edition. 20 pages of notes on differential equations and the higher analysis. 203 illustrations. Selected bibliography. Index. xi + 588pp. 5⅜ x 8.
S522 Paperbound **$2.35**

THE THEORY OF SOUND, Lord Rayleigh. Most vibrating systems likely to be encountered in practice can be tackled successfully by the methods set forth by the great Nobel laureate, Lord Rayleigh. Complete coverage of experimental, mathematical aspects of sound theory. Partial contents: Harmonic motions, vibrating systems in general, lateral vibrations of bars, curved plates or shells, applications of Laplace's functions to acoustical problems, fluid friction, plane vortex-sheet, vibrations of solid bodies, etc. This is the first inexpensive edition of this great reference and study work. Bibliography. Historical introduction by R. B. Lindsay. Total of 1040pp. 97 figures. 5⅜ x 8.
S292, S293, Two volume set, paperbound, **$4.00**

THE DYNAMICAL THEORY OF SOUND, H. Lamb. Comprehensive mathematical treatment of the physical aspects of sound, covering the theory of vibrations, the general theory of sound, and the equations of motion of strings, bars, membranes, pipes, and resonators. Includes chapters on plane, spherical, and simple harmonic waves, and the Helmholtz Theory of Audition. Complete and self-contained development for student and specialist; all fundamental differential equations solved completely. Specific mathematical details for such important phenomena as harmonics, normal modes, vibrations of strings, theory of reed pipes, etc. Index. Bibliography. 86 diagrams. viii + 307pp. 5⅜ x 8.
S655 Paperbound **$1.50**

WAVE PROPAGATION IN PERIODIC STRUCTURES, L. Brillouin. A general method and application to different problems: pure physics, such as scattering of X-rays of crystals, thermal vibration in crystal lattices, electronic motion in metals; and also problems of electrical engineering. Partial contents: elastic waves in 1-dimensional lattices of point masses. Propagation of waves along 1-dimensional lattices. Energy flow. 2 dimensional, 3 dimensional lattices. Mathieu's equation. Matrices and propagation of waves along an electric line. Continuous electric lines. 131 illustrations. Bibliography. Index. xii + 253pp. 5⅜ x 8.
S34 Paperbound **$1.85**

THEORY OF VIBRATIONS, N. W. McLachlan. Based on an exceptionally successful graduate course given at Brown University, this discusses linear systems having 1 degree of freedom, forced vibrations of simple linear systems, vibration of flexible strings, transverse vibrations of bars and tubes, transverse vibration of circular plate, sound waves of finite amplitude, etc. Index. 99 diagrams. 160pp. 5⅜ x 8.
S190 Paperbound **$1.35**

LOUD SPEAKERS: THEORY, PERFORMANCE, TESTING AND DESIGN, N. W. McLachlan. Most comprehensive coverage of theory, practice of loud speaker design, testing; classic reference, study manual in field. First 12 chapters deal with theory, for readers mainly concerned with math. aspects; last 7 chapters will interest reader concerned with testing, design. Partial contents: principles of sound propagation, fluid pressure on vibrators, theory of moving-coil principle, transients, driving mechanisms, response curves, design of horn type moving coil speakers, electrostatic speakers, much more. Appendix. Bibliography. Index. 165 illustrations, charts. 411pp. 5⅜ x 8.
S588 Paperbound **$2.25**

MICROWAVE TRANSMISSION, J. S. Slater. First text dealing exclusively with microwaves, brings together points of view of field, circuit theory, for graduate student in physics, electrical engineering, microwave technician. Offers valuable point of view not in most later studies. Uses Maxwell's equations to study electromagnetic field, important in this area. Partial contents: infinite line with distributed parameters, impedance of terminated line, plane waves, reflections, wave guides, coaxial line, composite transmission lines, impedance matching, etc. Introduction. Index. 76 illus. 319pp. 5⅜ x 8.
S564 Paperbound **$1.50**

THE ANALYSIS OF SENSATIONS, Ernst Mach. Great study of physiology, psychology of perception, shows Mach's ability to see material freshly, his "incorruptible skepticism and independence." (Einstein). Relation of problems of psychological perception to classical physics, supposed dualism of physical and mental, principle of continuity, evolution of senses, will as organic manifestation, scores of experiments, observations in optics, acoustics, music, graphics, etc. New introduction by T. S. Szasz, M. D. 58 illus. 300-item bibliography. Index. 404pp. 5⅜ x 8.
S525 Paperbound **$1.75**

APPLIED OPTICS AND OPTICAL DESIGN, A. E. Conrady. With publication of vol. 2, standard work for designers in optics is now complete for first time. Only work of its kind in English; only detailed work for practical designer and self-taught. Requires, for bulk of work, no math above trig. Step-by-step exposition, from fundamental concepts of geometrical, physical optics, to systematic study, design, of almost all types of optical systems. Vol. 1: all ordinary ray-tracing methods; primary aberrations; necessary higher aberration for design of telescopes, low-power microscopes, photographic equipment. Vol. 2: (Completed from author's notes by R. Kingslake, Dir. Optical Design, Eastman Kodak.) Special attention to high-power microscope, anastigmatic photographic objectives. "An indispensable work," J., Optical Soc. of Amer. "As a practical guide this book has no rival," Transactions, Optical Soc. Index. Bibliography. 193 diagrams. 852pp. 6⅛ x 9¼.
Vol. 1 T611 Paperbound **$2.95**
Vol. 2 T612 Paperbound **$2.95**

THE THEORY OF OPTICS, Paul Drude. One of finest fundamental texts in physical optics, classic offers thorough coverage, complete mathematical treatment of basic ideas. Includes fullest treatment of application of thermodynamics to optics; sine law in formation of images, transparent crystals, magnetically active substances, velocity of light, apertures, effects depending upon them, polarization, optical instruments, etc. Introduction by A. A. Michelson. Index. 110 illus. 567pp. 5⅜ x 8.
S532 Paperbound **$2.45**

THE THEORY OF HEAT RADIATION, Max Planck. A pioneering work in thermodynamics, providing basis for most later work. Nobel Laureate Planck writes on Deductions from Electrodynamics and Thermodynamics, Entropy and Probability, Irreversible Radiation Processes, etc. Starts with simple experimental laws of optics, advances to problems of spectral distribution of energy and irreversibility. Bibliography. 7 illustrations, xiv + 224pp. 5⅜ x 8.
S546 Paperbound **$1.50**

A HISTORY OF THE THEORY OF ELASTICITY AND THE STRENGTH OF MATERIALS, I. Todhunter and K. Pearson. For over 60 years a basic reference, unsurpassed in scope or authority. Both a history of the mathematical theory of elasticity from Galileo, Hooke, and Mariotte to Saint Venant, Kirchhoff, Clebsch, and Lord Kelvin and a detailed presentation of every important mathematical contribution during this period. Presents proofs of thousands of theorems and laws, summarizes every relevant treatise, many unavailable elsewhere. Practically a book apiece is devoted to modern founders: Saint Venant, Lame, Boussinesq, Rankine, Lord Kelvin, F. Neumann, Kirchhoff, Clebsch. Hundreds of pages of technical and physical treatises on specific applications of elasticity to particular materials. Indispensable for the mathematician, physicist, or engineer working with elasticity. Unabridged, corrected reprint of original 3-volume 1886-1893 edition. Three volume set. Two indexes. Appendix to Vol. I. Total of 2344pp. 5⅜ x 8⅜.
S914–916 The set, Clothbound **$12.50**

THE MATHEMATICAL THEORY OF ELASTICITY, A. E. H. Love. A wealth of practical illustration combined with thorough discussion of fundamentals—theory, application, special problems and solutions. Partial Contents: Analysis of Strain & Stress, Elasticity of Solid Bodies, Elasticity of Crystals, Vibration of Spheres, Cylinders, Propagation of Waves in Elastic Solid Media, Torsion, Theory of Continuous Beams, Plates. Rigorous treatment of Volterra's theory of dislocations, 2-dimensional elastic systems, other topics of modern interest. "For years the standard treatise on elasticity," AMERICAN MATHEMATICAL MONTHLY. 4th revised edition. Index. 76 figures. xviii + 643pp. 6⅛ x 9¼.
S174 Paperbound **$2.95**

RAYLEIGH'S PRINCIPLE AND ITS APPLICATIONS TO ENGINEERING, G. Temple & W. Bickley. Rayleigh's principle developed to provide upper and lower estimates of true value of fundamental period of a vibrating system, or condition of stability of elastic systems. Illustrative examples; rigorous proofs in special chapters. Partial contents: Energy method of discussing vibrations, stability. Perturbation theory, whirling of uniform shafts. Criteria of elastic stability. Application of energy method. Vibrating systems. Proof, accuracy, successive approximations, application of Rayleigh's principle. Synthetic theorems. Numerical, graphical methods. Equilibrium configurations, Ritz's method. Bibliography. Index. 22 figures. ix + 156pp. 5⅜ x 8.
S307 Paperbound **$1.50**

INVESTIGATIONS ON THE THEORY OF THE BROWNIAN MOVEMENT, Albert Einstein. Reprints from rare European journals. 5 basic papers, including the Elementary Theory of the Brownian Movement, written at the request of Lorentz to provide a simple explanation. Translated by A. D. Cowper. Annotated, edited by R. Fürth. 33pp. of notes elucidate, give history of previous investigations. Author, subject indexes. 62 footnotes. 124pp. 5⅜ x 8.
S304 Paperbound **$1.25**

See also: FUNDAMENTAL FORMULAS OF PHYSICS, D. H. Menzel.

ENGINEERING

THEORY OF FLIGHT, Richard von Mises. Remains almost unsurpassed as balanced, well-written account of fundamental fluid dynamics, and situations in which air compressibility effects are unimportant. Stressing equally theory and practice, avoiding formidable mathematical structure, it conveys a full understanding of physical phenomena and mathematical concepts. Contains perhaps the best introduction to general theory of stability. "Outstanding," Scientific, Medical, and Technical Books. New introduction by K. H. Hohenemser. Bibliographical, historical notes. Index. 408 illustrations. xvi + 620pp. 5⅜ x 8⅜. S541 Paperbound **$2.85**

THEORY OF WING SECTIONS, I. H. Abbott, A. E. von Doenhoff. Concise compilation of subsonic aerodynamic characteristics of modern NASA wing sections, with description of their geometry, associated theory. Primarily reference work for engineers, students, it gives methods, data for using wing-section data to predict characteristics. Particularly valuable: chapters on thin wings, airfoils; complete summary of NACA's experimental observations, system of construction families of airfoils. 350pp. of tables on Basic Thickness Forms, Mean Lines, Airfoil Ordinates, Aerodynamic Characteristics of Wing Sections. Index. Bibliography. 191 illustrations. Appendix. 705pp. 5⅜ x 8. S558 Paperbound **$2.95**

SUPERSONIC AERODYNAMICS, E. R. C. Miles. Valuable theoretical introduction to the supersonic domain, with emphasis on mathematical tools and principles, for practicing aerodynamicists and advanced students in aeronautical engineering. Covers fundamental theory, divergence theorem and principles of circulation, compressible flow and Helmholtz laws, the Prandtl-Busemann graphic method for 2-dimensional flow, oblique shock waves, the Taylor-Maccoll method for cones in supersonic flow, the Chaplygin method for 2-dimensional flow, etc. Problems range from practical engineering problems to development of theoretical results. "Rendered outstanding by the unprecedented scope of its contents . . . has undoubtedly filled a vital gap," AERONAUTICAL ENGINEERING REVIEW. Index. 173 problems, answers. 106 diagrams. 7 tables. xii + 255pp. 5⅜ x 8. S214 Paperbound **$1.45**

WEIGHT-STRENGTH ANALYSIS OF AIRCRAFT STRUCTURES, F. R. Shanley. Scientifically sound methods of analyzing and predicting the structural weight of aircraft and missiles. Deals directly with forces and the distances over which they must be transmitted, making it possible to develop methods by which the minimum structural weight can be determined for any material and conditions of loading. Weight equations for wing and fuselage structures. Includes author's original papers on inelastic buckling and creep buckling. "Particularly successful in presenting his analytical methods for investigating various optimum design principles," AERONAUTICAL ENGINEERING REVIEW. Enlarged bibliography. Index. 199 figures. xiv + 404pp. 5⅝ x 8⅜.   S660 Paperbound **$2.45**

INTRODUCTION TO THE STATISTICAL DYNAMICS OF AUTOMATIC CONTROL SYSTEMS, V. V. Solodovnikov. First English publication of text-reference covering important branch of automatic control systems—random signals; in its original edition, this was the first comprehensive treatment. Examines frequency characteristics, transfer functions, stationary random processes, determination of minimum mean-squared error, of transfer function for a finite period of observation, much more. Translation edited by J. B. Thomas, L. A. Zadeh. Index. Bibliography. Appendix. xxii + 308pp. 5⅜ x 8.   S420 Paperbound **$2.25**

TENSORS FOR CIRCUITS, Gabriel Kron. A boldly original method of analysing engineering problems, at center of sharp discussion since first introduced, now definitely proved useful in such areas as electrical and structural networks on automatic computers. Encompasses a great variety of specific problems by means of a relatively few symbolic equations. "Power and flexibility . . . becoming more widely recognized," Nature. Formerly "A Short Course in Tensor Analysis." New introduction by B. Hoffmann. Index. Over 800 diagrams. xix + 250pp. 5⅜ x 8.   S534 Paperbound **$1.85**

DESIGN AND USE OF INSTRUMENTS AND ACCURATE MECHANISM, T. N. Whitehead. For the instrument designer, engineer; how to combine necessary mathematical abstractions with independent observation of actual facts. Partial contents: instruments & their parts, theory of errors, systematic errors, probability, short period errors, erratic errors, design precision, kinematic, semikinematic design, stiffness, planning of an instrument, human factor, etc. Index. 85 photos, diagrams. xii + 288pp. 5⅜ x 8.   S270 Paperbound **$1.95**

APPLIED ELASTICITY, J. Prescott. Provides the engineer with the theory of elasticity usually lacking in books on strength of materials, yet concentrates on those portions useful for immediate application. Develops every important type of elasticity problem from theoretical principles. Covers analysis of stress, relations between stress and strain, the empirical basis of elasticity, thin rods under tension or thrust, Saint Venant's theory, transverse oscillations of thin rods, stability of thin plates, cylinders with thin walls, vibrations of rotating disks, elastic bodies in contact, etc. "Excellent and important contribution to the subject, not merely in the old matter which he has presented in new and refreshing form, but also in the many original investigations here published for the first time," NATURE. Index. 3 Appendixes. vi + 672pp. 5⅜ x 8.   S726 Paperbound **$2.95**

STRENGTH OF MATERIALS, J. P. Den Hartog. Distinguished text prepared for M.I.T. course, ideal as introduction, refresher, reference, or self-study text. Full clear treatment of elementary material (tension, torsion, bending, compound stresses, deflection of beams, etc.), plus much advanced material on engineering methods of great practical value: full treatment of the Mohr circle, lucid elementary discussions of the theory of the center of shear and the "Myosotis" method of calculating beam deflections, reinforced concrete, plastic deformations, photoelasticity, etc. In all sections, both general principles and concrete applications are given. Index. 186 figures (160 others in problem section). 350 problems, all with answers. List of formulas. viii + 323pp. 5⅜ x 8.   S755 Paperbound **$1.95**

PHOTOELASTICITY: PRINCIPLES AND METHODS, H. T. Jessop, F. C. Harris. For the engineer, for specific problems of stress analysis. Latest time-saving methods of checking calculations in 2-dimensional design problems, new techniques for stresses in 3 dimensions, and lucid description of optical systems used in practical photoelasticity. Useful suggestions and hints based on on-the-job experience included. Partial contents: strained and stress-strain relations, circular disc under thrust along diameter, rectangular block with square hole under vertical thrust, simply supported rectangular beam under central concentrated load, etc. Theory held to minimum, no advanced mathematical training needed. Index. 164 illustrations. viii + 184pp. 6⅛ x 9¼.   S137 Clothbound **$3.75**

MECHANICS OF THE GYROSCOPE, THE DYNAMICS OF ROTATION, R. F. Deimel, Professor of Mechanical Engineering at Stevens Institute of Technology. Elementary general treatment of dynamics of rotation, with special application of gyroscopic phenomena. No knowledge of vectors needed. Velocity of a moving curve, acceleration to a point, general equations of motion, gyroscopic horizon, free gyro, motion of discs, the damped gyro, 103 similar topics. Exercises. 75 figures. 208pp. 5⅜ x 8.   S66 Paperbound **$1.65**
                                                                                S144 Paperbound **$1.98**

A TREATISE ON GYROSTATICS AND ROTATIONAL MOTION: THEORY AND APPLICATIONS, Andrew Gray. Most detailed, thorough book in English, generally considered definitive study. Many problems of all sorts in full detail, or step-by-step summary. Classical problems of Bour, Lottner, etc.; later ones of great physical interest. Vibrating systems of gyrostats, earth as a top, calculation of path of axis of a top by elliptic integrals, motion of unsymmetrical top, much more. Index. 160 illus. 550pp. 5⅜ x 8.   S589 Paperbound **$2.75**

FUNDAMENTALS OF HYDRO- AND AEROMECHANICS, L. Prandtl and O. G. Tietjens. The well-known standard work based upon Prandtl's lectures at Goettingen. Wherever possible hydrodynamics theory is referred to practical considerations in hydraulics, with the view of unifying theory and experience. Presentation is extremely clear and though primarily physical, mathematical proofs are rigorous and use vector analysis to a considerable extent. An Enginering Society Monograph, 1934. 186 figures. Index. xvi + 270pp. 5⅜ x 8.

S374 Paperbound **$1.85**

APPLIED HYDRO- AND AEROMECHANICS, L. Prandtl and O. G. Tietjens. Presents, for the most part, methods which will be valuable to engineers. Covers flow in pipes, boundary layers, airfoil theory, entry conditions, turbulent flow in pipes, and the boundary layer, determining drag from measurements of pressure and velocity, etc. "Will be welcomed by all students of aerodynamics," NATURE. Unabridged, unaltered. An Engineering Society Monograph, 1934. Index. 226 figures, 28 photographic plates illustrating flow patterns. xvi + 311pp. 5⅜ x 8.

S375 Paperbound **$1.85**

HYDRAULICS AND ITS APPLICATIONS, A. H. Gibson. Excellent comprehensive textbook for the student and thorough practical manual for the professional worker, a work of great stature in its area. Half the book is devoted to theory and half to applications and practical problems met in the field. Covers modes of motion of a fluid, critical velocity, viscous flow, eddy formation, Bernoulli's theorem, flow in converging passages, vortex motion, form of effluent streams, notches and weirs, skin friction, losses at valves and elbows, siphons, erosion of channels, jet propulsion, waves of oscillation, and over 100 similar topics. Final chapters (nearly 400 pages) cover more than 100 kinds of hydraulic machinery: Pelton wheel, speed regulators, the hydraulic ram, surge tanks, the scoop wheel, the Venturi meter, etc. A special chapter treats methods of testing theoretical hypotheses: scale models of rivers, tidal estuaries, siphon spillways, etc. 5th revised and enlarged (1952) edition. Index. Appendix. 427 photographs and diagrams. 95 examples, answers. xv + 813pp. 6 x 9.

S791 Clothbound **$8.00**

FLUID MECHANICS FOR HYDRAULIC ENGINEERS, H. Rouse. Standard work that gives a coherent picture of fluid mechanics from the point of view of the hydraulic engineer. Based on courses given to civil and mechanical engineering students at Columbia and the California Institute of Technology, this work covers every basic principle, method, equation, or theory of interest to the hydraulic engineer. Much of the material, diagrams, charts, etc., in this self-contained text are not duplicated elsewhere. Covers irrotational motion, conformal mapping, problems in laminar motion, fluid turbulence, flow around immersed bodies, transportation of sediment, general charcteristics of wave phenomena, gravity waves in open channels, etc. Index. Appendix of physical properties of common fluids. Frontispiece + 245 figures and photographs. xvi + 422pp. 5⅜ x 8.

S729 Paperbound **$2.25**

THE MEASUREMENT OF POWER SPECTRA FROM THE POINT OF VIEW OF COMMUNICATIONS ENGINEERING, R. B. Blackman, J. W. Tukey. This pathfinding work, reprinted from the "Bell System Technical Journal," explains various ways of getting practically useful answers in the measurement of power spectra, using results from both transmission theory and the theory of statistical estimation. Treats: Autocovariance Functions and Power Spectra; Direct Analog Computation; Distortion, Noise, Heterodyne Filtering and Pre-whitening; Aliasing; Rejection Filtering and Separation; Smoothing and Decimation Procedures; Very Low Frequencies; Transversal Filtering; much more. An appendix reviews fundamental Fourier techniques. Index of notation. Glossary of terms. 24 figures. XII tables. Bibliography. General index. 192pp. 5⅜ x 8.

S507 Paperbound **$1.85**

MICROWAVE TRANSMISSION DESIGN DATA, T. Moreno. Originally classified, now rewritten and enlarged (14 new chapters) for public release under auspices of Sperry Corp. Material of immediate value or reference use to radio engineers, systems designers, applied physicists, etc. Ordinary transmission line theory; attenuation; capacity; parameters of coaxial lines; higher modes; flexible cables; obstacles, discontinuities, and injunctions; tuneable wave guide impedance transformers; effects of temperature and humidity; much more. "Enough theoretical discussion is included to allow use of data without previous background," Electronics. 324 circuit diagrams, figures, etc. Tables of dielectrics, flexible cable, etc., data. Index. Ix + 248pp. 5⅜ x 8.

S459 Paperbound **$1.50**

GASEOUS CONDUCTORS: THEORY AND ENGINEERING APPLICATIONS, J. D. Cobine. An indispensable text and reference to gaseous conduction phenomena, with the engineering viewpoint prevailing throughout. Studies the kinetic theory of gases, ionization, emission phenomena; gas breakdown, spark characteristics, glow, and discharges; engineering applications in circuit interrupters, rectifiers, light sources, etc. Separate detailed treatment of high pressure arcs (Suits); low pressure arcs (Langmuir and Tonks). Much more. "Well organized, clear, straightforward," Tonks, Review of Scientific Instruments. Index. Bibliography. 83 practice problems. 7 appendices. Over 600 figures. 58 tables. xx + 606pp. 5⅜ x 8.

S442 Paperbound **$2.85**

See also: BRIDGES AND THEIR BUILDERS, D. Steinman, S. R. Watson; A DIDERÒT PICTORIAL ENCYCLOPEDIA OF TRADES AND INDUSTRY; MATHEMATICS IN ACTION, O. G. Sutton; THE THEORY OF SOUND, Lord Rayleigh; RAYLEIGH'S PRINCIPLE AND ITS APPLICATION TO ENGINEERING, G. Temple, W. Bickley; APPLIED OPTICS AND OPTICAL DESIGN, A. E. Conrady; HYDRODYNAMICS, Dryden, Murnaghan, Bateman; LOUD SPEAKERS, N. W. McLachlan; HISTORY OF THE THEORY OF ELASTICITY AND OF THE STRENGTH OF MATERIALS, I. Todhunter,

K. Pearson; THEORY AND OPERATION OF THE SLIDE RULE, J. P. Ellis; DIFFERENTIAL EQUA-
TIONS FOR ENGINEERS, P. Franklin; MATHEMATICAL METHODS FOR SCIENTISTS AND ENGI-
NEERS, L. P. Smith; APPLIED MATHEMATICS FOR RADIO AND COMMUNICATIONS ENGINEERS,
C. E. Smith; MATHEMATICS OF MODERN ENGINEERING, E. G. Keller, R. E. Doherty; THEORY
OF FUNCTIONS AS APPLIED TO ENGINEERING PROBLEMS, R. Rothe, F. Ollendorff, K. Pohlhausen.

CHEMISTRY AND PHYSICAL CHEMISTRY

ORGANIC CHEMISTRY, F. C. Whitmore. The entire subject of organic chemistry for the practicing chemist and the advanced student. Storehouse of facts, theories, processes found elsewhere only in specialized journals. Covers aliphatic compounds (500 pages on the properties
and synthetic preparation of hydrocarbons, halides, proteins, ketones, etc.), alicyclic compounds, aromatic compounds, heterocyclic compounds, organophosphorus and organometallic
compounds. Methods of synthetic preparation analyzed critically throughout. Includes much of
biochemical interest. "The scope of this volume is astonishing," INDUSTRIAL AND ENGINEER-
ING CHEMISTRY. 12,000-reference index. 2387-item bibliography. Total of x + 1005pp. 5⅜ x 8.
Two volume set.
S700 Vol I Paperbound **$2.00**
S701 Vol II Paperbound **$2.00**
The set **$4.00**

THE PRINCIPLES OF ELECTROCHEMISTRY, D. A. MacInnes. Basic equations for almost every
subfield of electrochemistry from first principles, referring at all times to the soundest and
most recent theories and results; unusually useful as text or as reference. Covers coulometers
and Faraday's Law, electrolytic conductance, the Debye-Hueckel method for the theoretical
calculation of activity coefficients, concentration cells, standard electrode potentials, thermodynamic ionization constants, pH, potentiometric titrations, irreversible phenomena, Planck's
equation, and much more. "Excellent treatise," AMERICAN CHEMICAL SOCIETY JOURNAL.
"Highly recommended," CHEMICAL AND METALLURGICAL ENGINEERING. 2 Indices. Appendix.
585-item bibliography. 137 figures. 94 tables. ii + 478pp. 5⅝ x 8⅜.
S52 Paperbound **$2.35**

**THE CHEMISTRY OF URANIUM: THE ELEMENT, ITS BINARY AND RELATED COMPOUNDS, J. J. Katz
and E. Rabinowitch.** Vast post-World War II collection and correlation of thousands of AEC
reports and published papers in a useful and easily accessible form, still the most complete
and up-to-date compilation. Treats "dry uranium chemistry," occurrences, preparation, properties, simple compounds, isotopic composition, extraction from ores, spectra, alloys, etc. Much
material available only here. Index. Thousands of evaluated bibliographical references. 324
tables, charts, figures. xxi + 609pp. 5⅜ x 8.
S757 Paperbound **$2.95**

KINETIC THEORY OF LIQUIDS, J. Frenkel. Regarding the kinetic theory of liquids as a gen-
eralization and extension of the theory of solid bodies, this volume covers all types of
arrangements of solids, thermal displacements of atoms, interstitial atoms and ions,
orientational and rotational motion of molecules, and transition between states of matter.
Mathematical theory is developed close to the physical subject matter. 216 bibliographical
footnotes. 55 figures. xi + 485pp. 5⅜ x 8.
S94 Clothbound **$3.95**
S95 Paperbound **$2.45**

POLAR MOLECULES, Pieter Debye. This work by Nobel laureate Debye offers a complete guide
to fundamental electrostatic field relations, polarizability, molecular structure. Partial contents: electric intensity, displacement and force, polarization by orientation, molar polarization and molar refraction, halogen-hydrides, polar liquids, ionic saturation, dielectric constant, etc. Special chapter considers quantum theory. Indexed. 172pp. 5⅜ x 8.
S64 Paperbound **$1.50**

ELASTICITY, PLASTICITY AND STRUCTURE OF MATTER, R. Houwink. Standard treatise on
rheological aspects of different technically important solids such as crystals, resins, textiles,
rubber, clay, many others. Investigates general laws for deformations; determines divergences
from these laws for certain substances. Covers general physical and mathematical aspects
of plasticity, elasticity, viscosity: Detailed examination of deformations, internal structure
of matter in relation to elastic and plastic behavior, formation of solid matter from a fluid,
conditions for elastic and plastic behavior of matter. Treats glass, asphalt, gutta percha,
balata, proteins, baker's dough, lacquers, sulphur, others. 2nd revised, enlarged edition.
Extensive revised bibliography in over 500 footnotes. Index. Table of symbols. 214 figures.
xviii + 368pp. 6 x 9¼.
S385 Paperbound **$2.45**

THE PHASE RULE AND ITS APPLICATION, Alexander Findlay. Covering chemical phenomena
of 1, 2, 3, 4, and multiple component systems, this "standard work on the subject"
(NATURE, London), has been completely revised and brought up to date by A. N. Campbell
and N. O. Smith. Brand new material has been added on such matters as binary, tertiary
liquid equilibria, solid solutions in ternary systems, quinary systems of salts and water.
Completely revised to triangular coordinates in ternary systems, clarified graphic representation, solid models, etc. 9th revised edition. Author, subject indexes. 236 figures. 505
footnotes, mostly bibliographic. xii + 494pp. 5⅜ x 8.
S91 Paperbound **$2.45**

TERNARY SYSTEMS: INTRODUCTION TO THE THEORY OF THREE COMPONENT SYSTEMS, G. Masing. Furnishes detailed discussion of representative types of 3-components systems, both in solid models (particularly metallic alloys) and isothermal models. Discusses mechanical mixture without compounds and without solid solutions; unbroken solid solution series; solid solutions with solubility breaks in two binary systems; iron-silicon-aluminum alloys; allotropic forms of iron in ternary system; other topics. Bibliography. Index. 166 illustrations. 178pp. 5⅝ x 8⅜. S631 Paperbound **$1.45**

THE STORY OF ALCHEMY AND EARLY CHEMISTRY, J. M. Stillman. An authoritative, scholarly work, highly readable, of development of chemical knowledge from 4000 B.C. to downfall of phlogiston theory in late 18th century. Every important figure, many quotations. Brings alive curious, almost incredible history of alchemical beliefs, practices, writings of Arabian Prince Oneeyade, Vincent of Beauvais, Geber, Zosimos, Paracelsus, Vitruvius, scores more. Studies work, thought of Black, Cavendish, Priestley, Van Helmont, Bergman, Lavoisier, Newton, etc. Index. Bibliography. 579pp. 5⅜ x 8. S628 Paperbound **$2.45**

See also: **ATOMIC SPECTRA AND ATOMIC STRUCTURE, G. Herzberg; INVESTIGATIONS ON THE THEORY OF THE BROWNIAN MOVEMENT, A. Einstein; TREATISE ON THERMODYNAMICS, M. Planck.**

ASTRONOMY AND ASTROPHYSICS

AN ELEMENTARY SURVEY OF CELESTIAL MECHANICS, Y. Ryabov. Elementary exposition of gravitational theory and celestial mechanics. Historical introduction and coverage of basic principles, including: the elliptic, the orbital plane, the 2- and 3-body problems, the discovery of Neptune, planetary rotation, the length of the day, the shapes of galaxies, satellites (detailed treatment of Sputnik I), etc. First American reprinting of successful Russian popular exposition. Elementary algebra and trigonometry helpful, but not necessary; presentation chiefly verbal. Appendix of theorem proofs. 58 figures. 165pp. 5⅜ x 8. T756 Paperbound **$1.25**

THE SKY AND ITS MYSTERIES, E. A. Beet. One of most lucid books on mysteries of universe; deals with astronomy from earliest observations to latest theories of expansion of universe, source of stellar energy, birth of planets, origin of moon craters, possibility of life on other planets. Discusses effects of sunspots on weather; distances, ages of several stars; master plan of universe; methods and tools of astronomers; much more. "Eminently readable book," London Times. Extensive bibliography. Over 50 diagrams. 12 full-page plates, fold-out star map. Introduction. Index, 238pp. 5¼ x 7½. T627 Clothbound **$3.00**

THE REALM OF THE NEBULAE, E. Hubble. One of the great astronomers of our time records his formulation of the concept of "island universes," and its impact on astronomy. Such topics are covered as the velocity-distance relation; classification, nature, distances, general field of nebulae; cosmological theories; nebulae in the neighborhood of the Milky Way. 39 photos of nebulae, nebulae clusters, spectra of nebulae, and velocity distance relations shown by spectrum comparison. "One of the most progressive lines of astronomical research," The Times (London). New introduction by A. Sandage. 55 illustrations. Index. iv + 201pp. 5⅜ x 8. S455 Paperbound **$1.50**

OUT OF THE SKY, H. H. Nininger. A non-technical but comprehensive introduction to "meteoritics", the young science concerned with all aspects of the arrival of matter from outer space. Written by one of the world's experts on meteorites, this work shows how, despite difficulties of observation and sparseness of data, a considerable body of knowledge has arisen. It defines meteors and meteorites; studies fireball clusters and processions, meteorite composition, size, distribution, showers, explosions, origins, craters, and much more. A true connecting link between astronomy and geology. More than 175 photos, 22 other illustrations. References. Bibliography of author's publications on meteorites. Index. viii + 336pp. 5⅜ x 8. T519 Paperbound **$1.85**

SATELLITES AND SCIENTIFIC RESEARCH, D. King-Hele. Non-technical account of the manmade satellites and the discoveries they have yielded up to the spring of 1959. Brings together information hitherto published only in hard-to-get scientific journals. Includes the life history of a typical satellite, methods of tracking, new information on the shape of the earth, zones of radiation, etc. Over 60 diagrams and 6 photographs. Mathematical appendix. Bibliography of over 100 items. Index. xii + 180pp. 5⅜ x 8½. T703 Clothbound **$4.00**

HOW TO MAKE A TELESCOPE, Jean Texereau. Enables the most inexperienced to choose, design, and build an f/6 or f/8 Newtonian type reflecting telescope, with an altazimuth Couder mounting, suitable for lunar, planetary, and stellar observation. A practical step-by-step course covering every operation and every piece of equipment. Basic principles of geometric and physical optics are discussed (though unnecessary to construction), and the merits of reflectors and refractors compared. A thorough discussion of eyepieces, finders, grinding, installation, testing, using the instrument, etc. 241 figures and 38 photos show almost every operation and tool. Potential errors are anticipated as much as possible. Foreword by A. Couder. Bibliography and sources of supply listing. Index. xiii + 191pp. 6¼ x 10. T464 Clothbound **$3.50**

AN INTRODUCTORY TREATISE ON DYNAMICAL ASTRONOMY, H. C. Plummer. Unusually wide connected and concise coverage of nearly every significant branch of dynamical astronomy, stressing basic principles throughout: determination of orbits, planetary theory, lunar theory, precession and nutation, and many of their applications. Hundreds of formulas and theorems worked out completely, important methods thoroughly explained. Covers motion under a central attraction, orbits of double stars and spectroscopic binaries, the libration of the moon, and much more. Index. 8 diagrams. xxi + 343pp. 5⅝ x 8⅜. S689 Paperbound **$2.35**

A COMPENDIUM OF SPHERICAL ASTRONOMY, S. Newcomb. Long a standard collection of basic methods and formulas most useful to the working astronomer, and clear full text for students. Includes the most important common approximations; 40 pages on the method of least squares; general theory of spherical coordinates; parallax; aberration; astronomical refraction; theory of precession; proper motion of the stars; methods of deriving positions of stars; and much more. Index. 9 Appendices of tables, formulas, etc. 36 figures. xviii + 444pp. 5⅜ x 8.
S690 Paperbound **$2.25**

AN INTRODUCTORY TREATISE ON THE LUNAR THEORY, E. W. Brown. Indispensable for all scientists and engineers interested in orbital calculation, satellites, or navigation of space. Only work in English to explain in detail 5 major mathematical approaches to the problem of 3 bodies, those of Laplace, de Pontécoulant, Hansen, Delaunay, and Hill. Covers expressions for mutual attraction, equations of motion, forms of solution, variations of the elements in disturbed motion, the constants and their interpretations, planetary and other disturbing influences, etc. Index. Bibliography. Tables. xvi + 292pp. 5⅝ x 8⅜.
S666 Paperbound **$2.00**

LES METHODES NOUVELLES DE LA MECANIQUE CELESTE, H. Poincaré. Complete text (in French) of one of Poincaré's most important works. This set revolutionized celestial mechanics: first use of integral invariants, first major application of linear differential equations, study of periodic orbits, lunar motion and Jupiter's satellites, three body problem, and many other important topics. "Started a new era . . . so extremely modern that even today few have mastered his weapons," E. T. Bell. Three volumes. Total 1282pp. 6⅛ x 9¼.
Vol. 1. S401 Paperbound **$2.75**
Vol. 2. S402 Paperbound **$2.75**
Vol. 3. S403 Paperbound **$2.75**
The set **$7.50**

SPHERICAL AND PRACTICAL ASTRONOMY, W. Chauvenet. First book in English to apply mathematical techniques to astronomical problems is still standard work. Covers almost entire field, rigorously, with over 300 examples worked out. Vol. 1, spherical astronomy, applications to nautical astronomy; determination of hour angles, parallactic angle for known stars; interpolation; parallax; laws of refraction; predicting eclipses; precession, nutation of fixed stars; etc. Vol. 2, theory, use, of instruments; telescope; measurement of arcs, angles in general; electro-chronograph; sextant, reflecting circles; zenith telescope; etc. 100-page appendix of detailed proof of Gauss' method of least squares. 5th revised edition. Index. 15 plates, 20 tables. 1340pp. 5⅜ x 8.
Vol. 1 S618 Paperbound **$2.75**
Vol. 2 S619 Paperbound **$2.75**
The set **$5.50**

THE INTERNAL CONSTITUTION OF THE STARS, Sir A. S. Eddington. Influence of this has been enormous; first detailed exposition of theory of radiative equilibrium for stellar interiors, of all available evidence for existence of diffuse matter in interstellar space. Studies quantum theory, polytropic gas spheres, mass-luminosity relations, variable stars, etc. Discussions of equations paralleled with informal exposition of intimate relationship of astrophysics with great discoveries in atomic physics, radiation. Introduction. Appendix. Index. 421pp. 5⅜ x 8.
S563 Paperbound **$2.25**

ASTRONOMY OF STELLAR ENERGY AND DECAY, Martin Johnson. Middle level treatment of astronomy as interpreted by modern atomic physics. Part One is non-technical, examines physical properties, source of energy, spectroscopy, fluctuating stars, various models and theories, etc. Part Two parallels these topics, providing their mathematical foundation. "Clear, concise, and readily understandable," American Library Assoc. Bibliography. 3 indexes. 29 illustrations. 216pp. 5⅜ x 8. S537 Paperbound **$1.50**

RADIATIVE TRANSFER, S. Chandrasekhar. Definitive work in field provides foundation for analysis of stellar atmospheres, planetary illumination, sky radiation; to physicists, a study of problems analogous to those in theory of diffusion of neutrons. Partial contents: equation of transfer, isotropic scattering, H-functions, diffuse reflection and transmission, Rayleigh scattering, X, Y functions, radiative equilibrium of stellar atmospheres. Extensive bibliography. 3 appendices. 35 tables. 35 figures. 407pp. 5⅝ x 8⅜. S599 Paperbound **$2.25**

AN INTRODUCTION TO THE STUDY OF STELLAR STRUCTURE, Subrahmanyan Chandrasekhar. Outstanding treatise on stellar dynamics by one of world's greatest astrophysicists. Uses classical & modern math methods to examine relationship between loss of energy, the mass, and radius of stars in a steady state. Discusses thermodynamic laws from Caratheodory's axiomatic standpoint; adiabatic, polytropic laws; work of Ritter, Emden, Kelvin, others; Stroemgren envelopes as starter for theory of gaseous stars; Gibbs statistical mechanics (quantum); degenerate stellar configuration & theory of white dwarfs, etc. "Highest level of scientific merit," BULLETIN, AMER. MATH. SOC. Bibliography. Appendixes. Index. 33 figures. 509pp. 5⅜ x 8. S413 Paperbound **$2.75**

PRINCIPLES OF STELLAR DYNAMICS, S. Chandrasekhar. A leading astrophysicist here presents the theory of stellar dynamics as a branch of classical dynamics, clarifying the fundamental issues and the underlying motivations of the theory. He analyzes the effects of stellar encounters in terms of the classical 2-body problem, and investigates problems centering about Liouville's theorem and the solutions of the equations of continuity. This edition also includes 4 important papers by the author published since "Stellar Dynamics," and equally indispensable for all workers in the field: "New Methods in Stellar Dynamics" and "Dynamical Friction," Parts I, II, and III. Index. 3 Appendixes. Bibliography. 50 illustrations. x + 313pp. 5⅜ x8.
S659 Paperbound **$2.00**

A SHORT HISTORY OF ASTRONOMY, A. Berry. Popular standard work for over 50 years, this thorough and accurate volume covers the science from primitive times to the end of the 19th century. After the Greeks and the Middle Ages, individual chapters analyze Copernicus, Brahe, Galileo, Kepler, and Newton, and the mixed reception of their discoveries. Post-Newtonian achievements are then discussed in unusual detail: Halley, Bradley, Lagrange, Laplace, Herschel, Bessel, etc. 2 Indexes. 104 illustrations, 9 portraits. xxxi + 440pp. 5⅜ x 8.
T210 Paperbound **$2.00**

THREE COPERNICAN TREATISES, translated with notes by Edward Rosen. 3 papers available nowhere else in English: "The Commentariolus" and "Letter against Werner" of Copernicus; the "Narratio prima" of Rheticus. The "Commentariolus" is Copernicus's most lucid exposition of his system. The "Letter against Werner" throws light on development of Copernicus's thought. The "Narratio prima" is earliest printed presentation of the new astronomy. "Educational and enjoyable," Astrophysical Journal. Corrected edition. Biographical introduction. 877-item bibliography of virtually every book, article, on Copernicus published 1939-1958. Index. 19 illustrations. 218pp. 5⅜ x 8. S585 Paperbound **$1.75**

EARTH SCIENCES

PRINCIPLES OF STRATIGRAPHY, A. W. Grabau. Classic of 20th century geology, unmatched in scope and comprehensiveness. Nearly 600 pages cover the structure and origins of every kind of sedimentary, hydrogenic, oceanic, pyroclastic, atmoclastic, hydroclastic, marine hydroclastic, and bioclastic rock; metamorphism; erosion; etc. Includes also the constitution of the atmosphere; morphology of oceans, rivers, glaciers; volcanic activities; faults and earthquakes; and fundamental principles of paleontology (nearly 200 pages). New introduction by Prof. M. Kay, Columbia U. 1277 bibliographical entries. 264 diagrams. Tables, maps, etc. Two volume set. Total of xxxii + 1185pp. 5⅜ x 8.
S686 Vol I Paperbound **$2.50**
S687 Vol II Paperbound **$2.50**
The set **$5.00**

THE GEOLOGICAL DRAMA, H. and G. Termier. Unusual work by 2 noted French geologists: not the usual survey of geological periods, but general principles; continent formation, the influence of ice-ages and earth movements in shaping the present-day land masses, the creation and advance of life, the position of man. Readable and authoritative survey for the layman; excellent supplement for the student of geology; important collection of recent European theories for the American geologist. Much material appears here for the first time in a non-technical work. Index. 30 photographs, 5 diagrams, 5 maps. 144pp. 6 x 9. T702 Clothbound **$3.95**

THE EVOLUTION OF THE IGNEOUS ROCKS, N. L. Bowen. Invaluable serious introduction applies techniques of physics and chemistry to explain igneous rock diversity in terms of chemical composition and fractional crystallization. Discusses liquid immiscibility in silicate magmas, crystal sorting, liquid lines of descent, fractional resorption of complex minerals, petrogenesis, etc. Of prime importance to geologists & mining engineers, also to physicists, chemists working with high temperatures and pressures. "Most important," TIMES, London. 3 indexes. 263 bibliographic notes. 82 figures. xviii + 334pp. 5⅜ x 8. S311 Paperbound **$1.85**

INTERNAL CONSTITUTION OF THE EARTH, edited by Beno Gutenberg. Completely revised. Brought up-to-date, reset. Prepared for the National Research Council this is a complete & thorough coverage of such topics as earth origins, continent formation, nature & behavior of the earth's core, petrology of the crust, cooling forces in the core, seismic & earthquake material, gravity, elastic constants, strain characteristics and similar topics. "One is filled with admiration . . . a high standard . . . there is no reader who will not learn something from this book," London, Edinburgh, Dublin, Philosophic Magazine. Largest bibliography in print: 1127 classified items. Indexes. Tables of constants. 43 diagrams. 439pp. 6⅛ x 9¼.
S414 Paperbound **$2.45**

HYDROLOGY, edited by Oscar E. Meinzer. Prepared for the National Research Council. Detailed complete reference library on precipitation, evaporation, snow, snow surveying, glaciers, lakes, infiltration, soil moisture, ground water, runoff, drought, physical changes produced by water, hydrology of limestone terranes, etc. Practical in application, especially valuable for engineers. 24 experts have created "the most up-to-date, most complete treatment of the subject," AM. ASSOC. of PETROLEUM GEOLOGISTS. Bibliography. Index. 165 illustrations. xi + 712pp. 6⅛ x 9¼. S191 Paperbound **$2.95**

THE BIRTH AND DEVELOPMENT OF THE GEOLOGICAL SCIENCES, F. D. Adams. Most thorough history of the earth sciences ever written. Geological thought from earliest times to the end of the 19th century, covering over 300 early thinkers & systems: fossils & their explanation, vulcanists vs. neptunists, figured stones & paleontology, generation of stones, dozens of similar topics. 91 illustrations, including medieval, renaissance woodcuts, etc. Index. 632 footnotes, mostly bibliographical. 511pp. 5⅜ x 8.   T5 Paperbound **$2.00**

DE RE METALLICA, Georgius Agricola. 400-year old classic translated, annotated by former President Herbert Hoover. The first scientific study of mineralogy and mining, for over 200 years after its appearance in 1556, it was the standard treatise. 12 books, exhaustively annotated, discuss the history of mining, selection of sites, types of deposits, making pits, shafts, ventilating, pumps, crushing machinery; assaying, smelting, refining metals; also salt, alum, nitre, glass making. Definitive edition, with all 289 16th century woodcuts of the original. Biographical, historical introductions, bibliography, survey of ancient authors. Indexes. A fascinating book for anyone interested in art, history of science, geology, etc. Deluxe edition. 289 illustrations. 672pp. 6¾ x 10¾. Library cloth.   S6 Clothbound **$10.00**

GEOGRAPHICAL ESSAYS, William Morris Davis. Modern geography & geomorphology rest on the fundamental work of this scientist. 26 famous essays presenting most important theories, field researches. Partial contents: Geographical Cycle, Plains of Marine and Subaerial Denudation, The Peneplain, Rivers and Valleys of Pennsylvania, Outline of Cape Cod, Sculpture of Mountains by Glaciers, etc. "Long the leader & guide," ECONOMIC GEOGRAPHY. "Part of the very texture of geography . . . models of clear thought," GEOGRAPHIC REVIEW. Index. 130 figures. vi + 777pp. 5⅜ x 8.   S383 Paperbound **$2.95**

A HISTORY OF ANCIENT GEOGRAPHY, E. H. Bunbury. Standard study, in English, of ancient geography; never equalled for scope, detail. First full account of history of geography from Greeks' first world picture based on mariners, through Ptolemy. Discusses every important map, discovery, figure, travel, expedition, war, conjecture, narrative, bearing on subject. Chapters on Homeric geography, Herodotus, Alexander expedition, Strabo, Pliny, Ptolemy, would stand alone as exhaustive monographs. Includes minor geographers, men not usually regarded in this context: Hecataeus, Pythea, Hipparchus, Artemidorus, Marinus of Tyre, etc. Uses information gleaned from military campaigns such as Punic wars, Hannibal's passage of Alps, campaigns of Lucullus, Pompey, Caesar's wars, the Trojan war. New introduction by W. H. Stahl, Brooklyn College. Bibliography. Index. 20 maps. 1426pp. 5⅜ x 8.
T570-1, clothbound, 2 volume set **$12.50**

URANIUM PROSPECTING, H. L. Barnes. For immediate practical use, professional geologist considers uranium ores, geological occurrences, field conditions, all aspects of highly profitable occupation. Index. Bibliography. x + 117pp. 5⅜ x 8.   T309 Paperbound **$1.00**

BIOLOGICAL SCIENCES

THE ORIGIN OF LIFE, A. I. Oparin. A classic of biology. This is the first modern statement of the theory of gradual evolution of life from nitrocarbon compounds. A brand-new evaluation of Oparin's theory in light of later research, by Dr. S. Morgulis, University of Nebraska. xxv +270pp. 5⅜ x8.   S213 Paperbound **$1.75**

HEREDITY AND YOUR LIFE, A. M. Winchester. Authoritative, concise explanation of human genetics, in non-technical terms. What factors determine characteristics of future generations, how they may be altered; history of genetics, application of knowledge to control health, intelligence, number of entire populations. Physiology of reproduction, chromosomes, genes, blood types, Rh factor, dominant, recessive traits, birth by proxy, sexual abnormalities, radiation, much more. Index. 75 illus. 345pp. 5⅜ x 8.   T598 Paperbound **$1.45**

MATHEMATICAL BIOPHYSICS: PHYSICO-MATHEMATICAL FOUNDATIONS OF BIOLOGY, N. Rashevsky. One of most important books in modern biology, now revised, expanded with new chapters, to include most significant recent contributions. Vol. 1: Diffusion phenomena, particularly diffusion drag forces, their effects. Old theory of cell division based on diffusion drag forces, other theoretical approaches, more exhaustively treated than ever. Theories of excitation, conduction in nerves, with formal theories plus physico-chemical theory. Vol. 2: Mathematical theories of various phenomena in central nervous system. New chapters on theory of color vision, of random nets. Principle of optimal design, extended from earlier edition. Principle of relational mapping of organisms, numerous applications. Introduces into mathematical biology such branches of math as topology, theory of sets. Index. 236 illustrations. Total of 988pp. 5⅜ x 8.   S574 Vol. 1 (Books 1, 2) Paperbound **$2.50**
S575 Vol. 2 (Books 3, 4) Paperbound **$2.50**
2 vol. set **$5.00**

ELEMENTS OF MATHEMATICAL BIOLOGY, A. J. Lotka. A pioneer classic, the first major attempt to apply modern mathematical techniques on a large scale to phenomena of biology, biochemistry, psychology, ecology, similar life sciences. Partial Contents: Statistical meaning of irreversibility; Evolution as redistribution; Equations of kinetics of evolving systems; Chemical, inter-species equilibrium; parameters of state; Energy transformers of nature, etc. Can be read with profit even by those having no advanced math; unsurpassed as study-reference. Formerly titled ELEMENTS OF PHYSICAL BIOLOGY. 72 figures. xxx + 460pp. 5⅜ x 8. S346 Paperbound **$2.45**

FRESHWATER MICROSCOPY, W. J. Garnett. Non-technical, practical book for the layman and student. Contains only information directly confirmed by the distinguished British scientist's personal observation. Tells how to collect and examine specimens, describes equipment and accessories, mounting, staining, correct illumination, measuring, the microprojector, etc. Describes hundreds of different plant and animal species, over 200 illustrated by micro-photos. Many valuable suggestions on the work amateurs can do to throw new light on the field. Index. 51 full-page plates. 50 diagrams. Bibliography. 2 Appendices. Glossary of scientific terms. xii + 300pp. 6 x 9. S790 Clothbound **$5.95**

CULTURE METHODS FOR INVERTEBRATE ANIMALS, P. S. Galtsoff, F. E. Lutz, P. S. Welch, J. G. Needham, eds. A compendium of practical experience of hundreds of scientists and technicians, covering invertebrates from protozoa to chordata, in 313 articles on 17 phyla. Explains in great detail food, protection, environment, reproduction conditions, rearing methods, embryology, breeding seasons, schedule of development, much more. Includes at least one species of each considerable group. Half the articles are on class insecta. Introduction. 97 illustrations. Bibliography. Index. xxix + 590pp. 5⅜ x 8. S526 Paperbound **$2.75**

THE BIOLOGY OF THE LABORATORY MOUSE, edited by G. D. Snell. 1st prepared in 1941 by the staff of the Roscoe B. Jackson Memorial Laboratory, this is still the standard treatise on the mouse, assembling an enormous amount of material for which otherwise you spend hours of research. Embryology, reproduction, histology, spontaneous tumor formation, genetics of tumor transplantation, endocrine secretion & tumor formation, milk, influence & tumor formation, inbred, hybrid animals, parasites, infectious diseases, care & recording. Classified bibliography of 1122 items. 172 figures, including 128 photos. ix + 497pp. 6⅛ x 9¼. S248 Clothbound **$6.00**

THE BIOLOGY OF THE AMPHIBIA, G. K. Noble, Late Curator of Herpetology at the Am. Mus. of Nat. Hist. Probably the most used text on amphibia, unmatched in comprehensiveness, clarity, detail. 19 chapters plus 85-page supplement cover development; heredity; life history; speciation; adaptation; sex, integument, respiratory, circulatory, digestive, muscular, nervous systems; instinct, intelligence, habits, environment, economic value, relationships, classification, etc. "Nothing comparable to it," C. H. Pope, Curator of Amphibia, Chicago Mus. of Nat. Hist. 1047 bibliographic references. 174 illustrations. 600pp. 5⅜ x 8. S206 Paperbound **$2.98**

STUDIES ON THE STRUCTURE AND DEVELOPMENT OF VERTEBRATES, E. S. Goodrich. A definitive study by the greatest modern comparative anatomist. Exceptional in its accounts of the ossicles of the ear, the separate divisions of the coelem and mammalian diaphragm, and the 5 chapters devoted to the head region. Also exhaustive morphological and phylogenetic expositions of skeleton, fins and limbs, skeletal visceral arches and labial cartilages, visceral clefts and gills, vascular, respiratory, excretory, and periphal nervous systems, etc., from fish to the higher mammals. 754 illustrations. 69 page biographical study by C. C. Hardy. Bibliography of 1186 references. "What an undertaking . . . to write a textbook which will summarize adequately and succinctly all that has been done in the realm of Vertebrate Morphology these recent years," Journal of Anatomy. Index. Two volumes. Total 906pp. 5⅜ x 8. Two vol. set S449-50 Paperbound **$5.00**

THE GENETICAL THEORY OF NATURAL SELECTION, R. A. Fisher. 2nd revised edition of a vital reviewing of Darwin's Selection Theory in terms of particulate inheritance, by one of the great authorities on experimental and theoretical genetics. Theory is stated in mathematical form. Special features of particulate inheritance are examined: evolution of dominance, maintenance of specific variability, mimicry and sexual selection, etc. 5 chapters on man and his special circumstances as a social animal. 16 photographs. Bibliography. Index. x + 310pp. 5⅜ x 8. S466 Paperbound **$1.85**

THE AUTOBIOGRAPHY OF CHARLES DARWIN, AND SELECTED LETTERS, edited by Francis Darwin. Darwin's own record of his early life; the historic voyage aboard the "Beagle"; the furor surrounding evolution, and his replies; reminiscences of his son. Letters to Henslow, Lyell, Hooker, Huxley, Wallace, Kingsley, etc., and thoughts on religion and vivisection. We see how he revolutionized geology with his concept of ocean subsidence; how his great books on variation of plants and animals, primitive man, the expression of emotion among primates, plant fertilization, carnivorous plants, protective coloration, etc., came into being. Appendix. Index. 365pp. 5⅜ x 8. T479 Paperbound **$1.65**

THE LIFE OF PASTEUR, R. Vallery-Radot. 13th edition of this definitive biography, cited in Encyclopaedia Britannica. Authoritative, scholarly, well-documented with contemporary quotes, observations; gives complete picture of Pasteur's personal life; especially thorough presentation of scientific activities with silkworms, fermentation, hydrophobia, innoculation, etc. Introduction by Sir William Osler. Index. 505pp. 5⅜ x 8. T633 Paperbound **$2.00**

ANTONY VAN LEEUWENHOEK AND HIS "LITTLE ANIMALS," edited by Clifford Dobell. First book to treat extensively, accurately, life and works (relating to protozoology, bacteriology) of first microbiologist, bacteriologist, micrologist. Includes founding papers of protozoology, bacteriology; history of Leeuwenhoek's life; discussions of his microscopes, methods, language. His writing conveys sense of an enthusiastic, naive genius, as he looks at rainwater, pepper water, vinegar, frog's skin, rotifers, etc. Extremely readable, even for nonspecialists. "One of the most interesting and enlightening books I have ever read," Dr. C. C. Bass, former Dean, Tulane U. School of Medicine. Only authorized edition. 400-item bibliography. Index. 32 illust. 442pp. 5⅜ x 8.　　　　　　　　　　　S594 Paperbound **$2.25**

MICROGRAPHIA, Robert Hooke. Hooke, 17th century British universal scientific genius, was a major pioneer in celestial mechanics, optics, gravity, and many other fields, but his greatest contribution was this book, now reprinted entirely from the original 1665 edition, which gave microscopy its first great impetus. With all the freshness of discovery, he describes fully his microscope, and his observations of cork, the edge of a razor, insects' eyes, fabrics, and dozens of other different objects. 38 plates, full-size or larger, contain all the original illustrations. This book is also a fundamental classic in the fields of combustion and heat theory, light and color theory, botany and zoology, hygrometry, and many other fields. It contains such farsighted predictions as the famous anticipation of artificial silk. The final section is concerned with Hooke's observations on the moon and stars. 323pp. 5⅜ x 8.
Paperbound **$2.00**

CONDITIONED REFLEXES: AN INVESTIGATION OF THE PHYSIOLOGICAL ACTIVITIES OF THE CEREBRAL CORTEX, I. P. Pavlov. Full, authorized translation of Pavlov's own survey of his work in experimental psychology reviews entire course of experiments, summarizes conclusions, outlines psychological system based on famous "conditioned reflex" concept. Details of technical means used in experiments, observations on formation of conditioned reflexes, function of cerebral hemispheres, results of damage, nature of sleep, typology of nervous system, significance of experiments for human psychology. Trans. by Dr. G. V. Anrep, Cambridge Univ. 235-item bibliography. 18 figures. 445pp. 5⅜ x 8.　　S614 Paperbound **$2.25**

THE PRINCIPLES OF PSYCHOLOGY, William James. The full long course, unabridged, of one of the great classics of Western science. Wonderfully lucid descriptions of human mental activity, consciousness, emotions, reason, abnormal phenomena, and similar topics. Examines motor zones, sensory aphasia, phosphorus and thought, cerebral thermometry, neural process in perception, ideo-motor action—in short, the entire spectrum of human mental activity. "Standard reading . . . a classic of interpretation," PSYCHIATRIC QUARTERLY. 94 illustrations. Two volume set. Total of 1408pp. 5⅜ x 8.　　　　　　T381 Vol I Paperbound **$2.50**
T382 Vol II Paperbound **$2.50**
The set **$5.00**

THE TRAVELS OF WILLIAM BARTRAM, edited by Mark Van Doren. This famous source-book of American anthropology, natural history, geography is the record kept by Bartram in the 1770's, on travels through the wilderness of Florida, Georgia, the Carolinas. Containing accurate and beautiful descriptions of Indians, settlers, fauna, flora, it is one of the finest pieces of Americana ever written. Introduction by Mark Van Doren. 13 original illustrations. Index. 448pp. 5⅜ x 8.　　　　　　　　　　　　　　　T13 Paperbound **$2.00**

FRUIT KEY AND TWIG KEY TO TREES AND SHRUBS (FRUIT KEY TO NORTHEASTERN TREES, TWIG TREE TO DECIDUOUS WOODY PLANTS OF EASTERN NORTH AMERICA), W. M. Harlow. The only guides with photographs of every twig and fruit described—especially valuable to the novice. The fruit key (both deciduous trees and evergreens) has an introduction explaining seeding, organs involved, fruit types and habits. The twig key introduction treats growth and morphology. In the keys proper, identification is easy and almost automatic. This exceptional work, widely used in university courses, is especially useful for identification in winter, or from the fruit or seed only. Over 350 photos, up to 3 times natural size. Bibliography, glossary, index of common and scientific names, in each key. xvii + 125pp. 5⅜ x 8⅜.　　　　　　　　　　　　　　　　　　　　　　T511 Paperbound **$1.25**

TREES OF THE EASTERN AND CENTRAL UNITED STATES AND CANADA, W. M. Harlow, Professor of Wood Technology, College of Forestry, State University of N. Y., Syracuse, N. Y. This middle-level text is a serious work covering more than 140 native trees and important escapes, with information on general appearance, growth habit, leaf forms, flowers, fruit, bark, and other features. Commercial use, distribution, habitat, and woodlore are also given. Keys within the text enable you to locate various species with ease. With this book you can identify at sight almost any tree you are likely to encounter; you will know which trees have edible fruit, which are suitable for house planting, and much other useful and interesting information. More than 600 photographs and figures. xiii + 288pp. 4⅝ x 6½.
T395 Paperbound **$1.35**

HOW TO KNOW THE FERNS, F. T. Parsons. Ferns, among our most lovely native plants, are all too little known. This modern classic of nature lore will enable the layman to identify any American fern he is likely to come across. After an introduction on the structure and life of ferns, the 57 most important ferns are fully pictured and described (arranged upon a simple identification key). Index of Latin and English names. 61 illustrations and 42 full-page plates. xiv + 215pp. 5⅜ x 8.　　　　　　　　　　　T740 Paperbound **$1.25**

INSECT LIFE AND INSECT NATURAL HISTORY, S. W. Frost. Unusual for emphasizing habits, social life, and ecological relations of insects, rather than more academic aspects of classification and morphology. Prof. Frost's enthusiasm and knowledge are everywhere evident as he discusses insect associations, and specialized habits like leaf-mining, leaf-rolling, and casemaking, the gall insects, the boring insects, aquatic insects, etc. He examines all sorts of matters not usually covered in general works, such as: insects as human food; insect music and musicians; insect response to electric and radio waves; use of insects in art and literature. The admirably executed purpose of this book, which covers the middle ground between elementary treatment and scholarly monographs, is to excite the reader to observe for himself. Over 700 illustrations. Extensive bibliography. x + 524pp. 5⅜ x 8.

T517 Paperbound **$2.25**

COMMON SPIDERS OF THE UNITED STATES, J. H. Emerton. Only non-technical, but thorough, reliable guide to spiders for the layman. Over 200 spiders from all parts of the country, arranged by scientific classification, are identified by shape and color, number of eyes, habitat and range, habits, etc. Full text, 501 line drawings and photographs, and valuable introduction explain webs, poisons, threads, capturing and preserving spiders, etc. Index. New synoptic key by S. W. Frost. xxiv + 225pp. 5⅜ x 8.

T223 Paperbound **$1.35**

BEHAVIOR AND SOCIAL LIFE OF THE HONEYBEE, Ronald Ribbands. Outstanding scientific study; a compendium of practically everything known about social life of the honeybee. Stresses behavior of individual bees in field, hive. Extends Frisch's experiments on communication among bees. Covers perception of temperature, gravity, distance, vibration; sound production; glands; structural differences; wax production; temperature regulation; recognition, communication; drifting, mating behavior, other highly interesting topics. Bibliography of 690 references. Indexes. 127 diagrams, graphs, sections of bee anatomy, fine photographs. 352pp. 5½ x 8½.

S410 Clothbound **$4.50**

ANIMALS IN MOTION, Eadweard Muybridge. Largest, most comprehensive selection of Muybridge's famous action photos of animals, from his ANIMAL LOCOMOTION. 3919 high-speed shots of 34 different animals and birds in 123 different types of action: horses, mules, oxen, pigs, goats, camels, elephants, dogs, cats, guanacos, sloths, lions, tigers, jaguars, raccoons, baboons, deer, elk, gnus, kangaroos, many others, in different actions — walking, running, flying, leaping. Horse alone shown in more than 40 different ways. Photos taken against ruled backgrounds; most actions taken from 3 angles at once: 90°, 60°, rear. Most plates original size. Of considerable interest to scientists as a classic of biology, as a record of actual facts of natural history and physiology. "A really marvellous series of plates," NATURE (London). "A monumental work," Waldemar Kaempffert. Photographed by E. Muybridge. Edited by L. S. Brown, American Museum of Natural History. 74-page introduction on mechanics of motion. 340 pages of plates, 3919 photographs. 416pp. Deluxe binding, paper. (Weight 4½ lbs.) 7⅞ x 10⅝.

T203 Clothbound **$10.00**

THE HUMAN FIGURE IN MOTION. Eadweard Muybridge. This new edition of a great classic in the history of science and photography is the largest selection ever made from the original Muybridge photos of human action: 4789 photographs, illustrating 163 types of motion: walking, running, lifting, etc. in time-exposure sequence photos of speeds up to 1/6000th of a second. Men, women, children, mostly undraped, showing bone and muscle positions against ruled backgrounds, mostly taken at 3 angles at once. Not only was this a great work of photography, acclaimed by contemporary critics as a work of genius, it was also a great 19th century landmark in biological research. Historical introduction by Prof. Robert Taft, U. of Kansas. Plates original size, full detail. Over 500 action strips. 407pp. 7¾ x 10⅝. Deluxe edition.

T204 Clothbound **$10.00**

See also: ANALYSIS OF SENSATIONS, E. Mach; ON THE SENSATIONS OF TONE, H. Helmholtz; FROM MAGIC TO SCIENCE, C. Singer; A SHORT HISTORY OF ANATOMY AND PHYSIOLOGY FROM THE GREEKS TO HARVEY, C. Singer; ELEMENTARY STATISTICS, WITH APPLICATIONS IN MEDICINE AND THE BIOLOGICAL SCIENCES, F. E. Croxton.

MEDICINE

CLASSICS OF CARDIOLOGY, F. A. Willius and T. E. Keys. Monumental collection of 52 papers by 51 great researchers and physicians on the anatomy, physiology, and pathology of the heart and the circulation, and the diagnosis and therapy of their diseases. These are the original writings of Harvey, Sénac, Auenbrugger, Withering, Stokes, Einthoven, Osler, and 44 others from 1628 to 1912. 27 of the papers are complete, the rest in major excerpts; all are in English. The biographical notes and introductory essays make this a full history of cardiology —with exclusively first-hand material. 103 portraits, diagrams, and facsimiles of title pages. Chronological table. Total of xx + 858pp. 5⅝ x 8⅜. Two volume set.

T912 Vol I Paperbound **$2.00**
T913 Vol II Paperbound **$2.00**
The set **$4.00**

SOURCE BOOK OF MEDICAL HISTORY, compiled, annotated by Logan Clendening, M.D. Unequalled collection of 139 greatest papers in medical history, by 120 authors, covers almost every area: pathology, asepsis, preventive medicine, bacteriology, physiology, etc. Hippocrates, Gain, Vesalius, Malpighi, Morgagni, Boerhave, Pasteur, Walter Reed, Florence Nightingale, Lavoisier, Claude Bernard, 109 others, give view of medicine unequalled for immediacy. Careful selections give heart of each paper, save you reading time. Selections from non-medical literature show lay-views of medicine: Aristophanes, Plato, Arabian Nights, Chaucer, Molière, Dickens, Thackeray, others. "Notable . . . useful to teacher and student alike," Amer. Historical Review. Bibliography. Index. 699pp. 5⅜ x 8.   T621 Paperbound **$2.75**

CLASSICS OF MEDICINE AND SURGERY, edited by C. N. B. Camac. 12 greatest papers in medical history, 11 in full: Lister's "Antiseptic Principle;" Harvey's "Motion in the Heart and Blood;" Auenbrugger's "Percussion of the Chest;" Laënnec's "Auscultation and the Stethoscope;" Jenner's "Inquiry into Smallpox Vaccine," 2 related papers; Morton's "Administering Sulphuric Ether," letters to Warren, "Physiology of Ether;" Simpson's "A New Anaesthetic Agent;" Holmes' "Puerperal Fever." Biographies, portraits of authors, bibliographies. Formerly "Epoch-making Contributions to Medicine, Surgery, and the Allied Sciences." Introduction. 14 illus. 445pp. 5⅜ x 8.   S539 Paperbound **$2.25**

FREE! All you do is ask for it!

A WAY OF LIFE, Sir William Osler. The complete essay, stating his philosophy of life, as given at Yale University by this great physician and teacher. 30 pages. Copies limited, no more than 1 to a customer.

EXPERIMENTS AND OBSERVATIONS ON THE GASTRIC JUICE AND THE PHYSIOLOGY OF DIGESTION, William Beaumont. A gunshot wound which left a man with a 2½ inch hole through his abdomen into his stomach (1822) enabled Beaumont to perform the remarkable experiments set down here. The first comprehensive, thorough study of motions and processes of the stomach, "his work remains a model of patient, persevering investigation. . . . Beaumont is the pioneer physiologist of this country." (Sir William Osler, in his introduction.) 4 illustrations. xi + 280pp. 5⅜ x 8.   S527 Paperbound **$1.50**

AN INTRODUCTION TO THE STUDY OF EXPERIMENTAL MEDICINE, Claude Bernard. 90-year-old classic of medical science, only major work of Bernard available in English, records his efforts to transform physiology into exact science. Principles of scientific research illustrated by specific case histories from his work; roles of chance, error, preliminary false conclusions, in leading eventually to scientific truth; use of hypothesis. Much of modern application of mathematics to biology rests on the foundation set down here. New foreword by Professor I. B. Cohen, Harvard Univ. xxv + 266pp. 5⅜ x 8.   T400 Paperbound **$1.50**

A WAY OF LIFE, AND OTHER SELECTED WRITINGS, Sir William Osler, Physician and humanist, Osler discourses brilliantly in thought provoking essays and on the history of medicine. He discusses Thomas Browne, Gui Patin, Robert Burton, Michael Servetus, William Beaumont, Laënnec. Includes such favorite writings as the title essay, "The Old Humanities and the New Science," "Creators, Transmitters, and Transmuters," "Books and Men," "The Student Life," and five more of his best discussions of philosophy, religion and literature. 5 photographs. Introduction by G. L. Keynes, M.D., F.R.C.S. Index. xx + 278pp. 5⅜ x 8.
T488 Paperbound **$1.50**

LANGUAGE AND TRAVEL AIDS FOR SCIENTISTS

Trubner foreign language manuals

These unusual books are members of the famous Trubner series of colloquial manuals. They have been written to provide adults with a sound colloquial knowledge of a foreign language, and are suited for either class use or self-study. Each book is a complete course in itself, with progressive, easy to follow lessons. Phonetics, grammar, and syntax are covered, while hundreds of phrases and idioms, reading texts, exercises, and vocabulary are included. These books are unusual in being neither skimpy nor overdetailed in grammatical matters, and in presenting up-to-date, colloquial, and practical phrase material. Bilingual presentation is stressed, to make thorough self-study easier for the reader.

COLLOQUIAL HINDUSTANI, A. H. Harley, formerly Nizam's Reader in Urdu, U. of London. 30 pages on phonetics and scripts (devanagari & Arabic-Persian) are followed by 29 lessons, including material on English and Arabic-Persian influences. Key to all exercises. Vocabulary. 5 x 7½. 147pp.   Clothbound **$1.75**

COLLOQUIAL GERMAN, P. F. Doring. Intensive thorough coverage of grammar in easily-followed form. Excellent for brush-up, with hundreds of colloquial phrases. 34 pages of bilingual texts. 224pp. 5 x 7½.   Clothbound **$1.75**

COLLOQUIAL ARABIC. DeLacy O'Leary. Foremost Islamic scholar covers language of Egypt, Syria, Palestine, & Northern Arabia. Extremely clear coverage of complex Arabic verbs & noun plurals; also cultural aspects of language. Vocabulary. xviii + 192pp. 5 x 7½.
Clothbound **$1.75**

COLLOQUIAL PERSIAN, L. P. Elwell-Sutton. Best introduction to modern Persian, with 90 page grammatical section followed by conversations, 35 page vocabulary. 139pp. Clothbound **$1.75**

COLLOQUIAL SPANISH, W. R. Patterson. Castilian grammar and colloquial language, loaded with bilingual phrases and colloquialisms. Excellent for review or self-study. 164pp. 5 x 7½.
Clothbound **$1.75**

COLLOQUIAL RUMANIAN, G. Nandris, Professor of University of London. Extremely thorough coverage of phonetics, grammar, syntax; also included 70 page reader, and 70 page vocabulary. Probably the best grammar for this increasingly important language. 340pp. 5 x 7½.
Clothbound **$2.50**

COLLOQUIAL FRENCH, W. R. Patterson. 16th revised edition of this extremely popular manual. Grammar explained with model clarity, and hundreds of useful expressions and phrases; exercises, reading texts, etc. Appendixes of new useful words and phrases. 223pp. 5 x 7½.
Clothbound **$1.75**

COLLOQUIAL CZECH, J. Schwarz, former headmaster of Lingua Institute, Prague. Full easily followed coverage of grammar, hundreds of immediately useable phrases, texts. Perhaps the best Czech grammar in print. "An absolutely successful textbook," JOURNAL OF CZECHO-SLOVAK FORCES IN GREAT BRITAIN. 252pp. 5 x 7½. Clothbound **$3.00**

COLLOQUIAL ITALIAN, A. L. Hayward. Excellent self-study course in grammar, vocabulary, idioms, and reading. Easy progressive lessons will give a good working knowledge of Italian in the shortest possible time. 5 x 7½. Clothbound **$1.75**

AN ENGLISH-FRENCH-GERMAN-SPANISH WORD FREQUENCY DICTIONARY, H. S. Eaton. An indispensable language study aid, this is a semantic frequency list of the 6000 most frequently used words in 4 languages—24,000 words in all. The lists, based on concepts rather than words alone, and containing all modern, exact, and idomatic vocabulary, are arranged side by side to form a unique 4-language dictionary. A simple key indicates the importance of the individual words within each language. Over 200 pages of separate indexes for each language enable you to locate individual words at a glance. Formerly "Semantic Frequency List." 2 Appendixes. xxi + 441pp. 6 x 9. T738 Paperbound **$2.45**

NEW RUSSIAN-ENGLISH AND ENGLISH-RUSSIAN DICTIONARY, M. A. O'Brien. Unusually comprehensive guide to reading, speaking, writing of Russian for both advanced and beginning students. Over 70,000 entries provided in new orthography, with full information on accentuation, grammatical classification. Shades of meaning, idiomatic uses, colloquialisms; tables of irregular verbs for both languages. Individual entries indicate stems, transitiveness, perfective and imperfective aspects, conjugation, regular and irregular sound changes, shift of accent, etc. Includes pronunciation instruction. Used at Harvard, Yale, Cornell, etc. 738pp. 4¼ x 6½. T208 Paperbound **$2.00**

PHRASE AND SENTENCE DICTIONARY OF SPOKEN RUSSIAN. English-Russian, Russian-English. Based on phrases and complete sentences, rather than isolated words; recognized as one of the best methods of learning the idiomatic speech of a country. Over 11,500 entries, indexed by single words, with more than 32,000 English and Russian sentences and phrases, in immediately useable form. Probably the largest list ever published. Shows accent changes in conjugation and declension; irregular forms listed in both alphabetical place and under main form of word. 15,000 word introduction covering Russian sounds, writing, grammer, syntax. 15 page appendix of geographical names, money, important signs, given names, foods, special Soviet terms, etc. Travellers, businessmen, students, government employees have found this their best source for Russian expressions. Originally published as U.S. Government Technical Manual TM 30-944. iv + 573pp. 5⅝ x 8⅜. T496 Paperbound **$2.75**

PHRASE AND SENTENCE DICTIONARY OF SPOKEN SPANISH, Spanish-English, English-Spanish. Cómpiled from spoken Spanish, emphasizing idiom and colloquial usage in both Castilian and Latin-American. More than 16,000 entries containing over 25,000 idioms—the largest list of idiomatic constructions ever published. Complete sentences given, indexed under single words —language in immediately useable form, for travellers, businessmen, students, etc. 25 page introduction provides rapid survey of sounds, grammar, syntax, with full consideration of irregular verbs. Especially apt in modern treatment of phrases and structure. 17 page glossary gives translations of geographical names, money values, numbers, national holidays, important street signs, useful expressions of high frequency, plus unique 7 page glossary of Spanish and Spanish-American foods and dishes. Originally published as U.S. Government Technical Manual TM 30-900. iv + 513pp. 5⅜ x 8. T495 Paperbound **$1.75**

MONEY CONVERTER AND TIPPING GUIDE FOR EUROPEAN TRAVEL, Charles Vomacka. A convenient purse-size handbook crammed with information about currency regulations and tipping for every European country. Newly added sections cover Israel, Turkey, Czechoslovakia, Rumania, Egypt, Russia, Poland. Telephone, cablegram, postal rates; duty-free imports, passports, visas, health certificates; foreign clothing sizes; weather tables. What and when to tip in every conceivable travel situation. 6th year of publication. 128pp. 5½ x 5¼. Sturdy paper binding. T260 Paperbound **60¢**

Listen and Learn

LISTEN & LEARN is the only language record course designed especially to meet your travel and everyday needs. It is available in separate sets for FRENCH, SPANISH, GERMAN, PORTUGUESE, MODERN GREEK, ITALIAN, RUSSIAN, or JAPANESE, and each set contains three 33⅓ rpm long-playing records—1½ hours of recorded speech by eminent native speakers who are professors at Columbia, New York University, Queens College.

Check the following special features found only in LISTEN & LEARN.

Dual-language recording. 812 selected phrases and sentences, over 3200 words, spoken first in English, then in their foreign language equivalents. A suitable pause follows each foreign phrase, allowing you time to repeat the expression. You learn by unconscious assimilation.

128- to 206-page manual contains everything on the records, plus a simple phonetic pronounciation guide.

Indexed for convenience. The only set on the market that is completely indexed. No more puzzling over where to find the phrase you need. Just look in the rear of the manual.

Practical. No time wasted on material you can find in any grammar. LISTEN & LEARN covers central core material with phrase approach. Ideal for the person with limited learning time.

Living, modern expressions, not found in other courses. Hygienic products, modern equipment, shopping—expressions used every day, like "nylon" and "air-conditioned."

Limited objective. Everything you learn, no matter where you stop, is immediately useful. You have to finish other courses, wade through grammar and vocabulary drill, before they help you.

High-fidelity recording. LISTEN & LEARN records equal in clarity and surface-silence any record on the market costing up to $6 per record.

"Excellent . . . the spoken records . . . impress me as being among the very best on the market," **Prof. Mario Pei,** Dept. of Romance Languages, Columbia University." "Inexpensive and well-done . . . it would make an ideal present," CHICAGO SUNDAY TRIBUNE. "More genuinely helpful than anything of its kind which I have previously encountered," **Sidney Clark,** well-known author of "ALL THE BEST" travel books.

UNCONDITIONAL GUARANTEE. Try LISTEN & LEARN, then return it within 10 days for full refund, if you are not satisfied. It is guaranteed after you actually use it.

LISTEN & LEARN comes in 6 useful modern languages—FRENCH, SPANISH, GERMAN, ITALIAN, PORTUGUESE, MODERN GREEK, RUSSIAN or JAPANESE—one language to each set of three 33⅓ rpm records. 128- to 206-page manual. Album.

Spanish	the set **$5.95**	**German**	the set **$5.95**	**Japanese**	the set **$5.95**
French	the set **$5.95**	**Italian**	the set **$5.95**	**Russian**	the set **$5.95**
Modern Greek	the set **$5.95**	**Portuguese**	the set **$5.95**		

Dover publishes books on art, music, philosophy, literature, languages, history, social sciences, psychology, handcrafts, orientalia, puzzles and entertainments, chess, pets and gardens, books explaining science, intermediate and higher mathematics mathematical physics, engineering, biological sciences, earth sciences, classics of science, etc. Write to:

Dept. catrr.
Dover Publications, Inc.
180 Varick Street, N. Y. 14, N. Y.